TABLE OF CONTENTS

(For Alphabetical Index, See Pages IV through XV. For Index of Tables, See Page XVI.)

HANDY REPAIR

COMMON SPECIFICATIONS FOR

1. Spark plug gap: .030 All Models
2. Condenser capacity: .18 to .24 MFD. All Models
3. Contact point gap: .020 All Models

	BASIC MODEL SERIES	IDLE SPEED	ARMATURE AIR GAP		VALVE CLEARANCE		VALVE GUIDE REJECT GAGE	TORQUE SPECIFICATIONS		
			TWO LEG	THREE LEG	INTAKE	EXHAUST		FLYWHEEL NUT FT. LBS.	CYLINDER HEAD IN. LBS.	CONN. ROD IN. LBS.
ALUMINUM	60000*	1750	.006 .010	.012 .016	.005 .007	.007 .009	19122	55	140	100
ALUMINUM	80000, 81000, 82000	1750	.006 .010	.012 .016	.005 .007	.007 .009	19122	55	140	100
ALUMINUM	90000, 92000, 93000, 94000, 95000	1750	.006 .010		.005 .007	.007 .009	19122	55	140	100
ALUMINUM	100200, 100900	1750	.010 .014	.012 .016	.005 .007	.007 .009	19122	60	140	100
ALUMINUM	100700	1750	.006 .010		.005 .007	.007 .009	19122	55	140	100
ALUMINUM	110000	1750	.006 .010		.005 .007	.007 .009	19122	55	140	100
ALUMINUM	120000	1750	.006 .010		.005 .007	.007 .009	19122	55	140	100
ALUMINUM	130000	1750	.010 .014		.005 .007	.009 .011	19122	60	140	100
ALUMINUM	170000, 171700●	1750◆	.010 .014		.005 .007	.009 .011	19151	65	165	165
ALUMINUM	190000, 191700● 192700, 193700●	1750◆	.010 .014		.005 .007	.009 .011	19151	65	165	185
ALUMINUM	220000, 250000	1750◆	.010 .014		.005 .007	.009 .011	19151	65	165	185
ALUMINUM	280000	1750◆	.010 .014		.005 .007	.009 .011	19151	65	165	185
CAST IRON	230000	1200◆	.010 .014	.022 .026	.007 .009	.017 .019	19151	145	190	190
CAST IRON	240000	1200◆	.010 .014		.007 .009	.017 .019	19151	145	190	190
CAST IRON	300000	1200◆	.010 .014		.007 .009	.017 .019	19151	145	190	190
CAST IRON	320000	1200◆	.010 .014		.007 .009	.017 .019	19151	145	190	190

CHECK CHART

ALL POPULAR ENGINE MODELS

4. **Top governed speed: See Briggs & Stratton Service Bulletin No. 467 or Engine Replacement Data**
5. **Crankshaft End Play: .002-.008 except Model Series 100700 and 120000**

   NOTE: On Model Series 100700 and 120000 Crankshaft End Play is .002-.030".

CRANKSHAFT REJECT SIZE			MAIN BEARING REJECT GAGE	CYLINDER BORE STD. ▲
MAG JOURNAL	CRANKPIN JOURNAL	PTO JOURNAL		
.873	.870	.873	19166	2.375* 2.374
.873	.996	.873	19166	2.375 2.374
.873	.996	.873	19166	2.5625 2.5615
.873	.996	.998	19166 Mag. 19178 PTO	2.500 2.499
.873	.996	1.060	19166 Mag.	2.5625 2.5615
.873	.996	.873	19166	2.7812 2.7802
.873	.996	1.060	19166 Mag. 19375 PTO	2.6885 2.6875
.873	.996	.998	19166 Mag. 19178 PTO	2.5625 2.5615
.997 1.179•	1.090	1.179	19178	3.000 2.999
.997 1.179•	1.122	1.179	19178	3.000 2.999
1.376	1.247	1.376	19219	3.4375 3.4365
1.376	1.247	1.376	19219	3.4375 3.4365
1.3769	1.1844	1.3769	19117	3.000 2.999
Ball	1.3094	Ball	Ball	3.0625 3.0615
Ball	1.3094	Ball	Ball	3.4375 3.4365
Ball	1.3094	Ball	Ball	3.5625 3.5615

INITIAL CARBURETOR ADJUSTMENT ALL MODELS TURNS OPEN FROM SEAT

Needle Valve	Idle Valve
1-1/2	1-1/4

CYLINDER RESIZING

▲Resize if .003 or more wear or .0015 out of round on C.I. bore cylinders, .0025 out of round on aluminum bore cylinders.

Resize to .010, .020, or .030 over standard bore.

*Early Model Series 60000 and 61000 engines have cylinder bore of 2.3125-2.3115.

RING GAP REJECT SIZES

MODEL	COMP. RINGS	OIL RING
Aluminum Cylinder Models	.035"	.045"
Cast Iron Cylinder Models	.030"	.035"

♦GOVERNED IDLE

For Adjustment Procedures, See "Service and Repair Instructions."

• Synchro-Balance.

INDEX

INDEX (Continued)

INDEX (Continued)

INDEX (Continued)

INDEX (Continued)

INDEX (Continued)

INDEX (Continued)

INDEX (Continued)

INDEX (Continued)

INDEX OF TABLES

Repair Instructions IV (MS-4750)

Section 1
GENERAL INFORMATION

Briggs & Stratton single cylinder engines are of the same basic 4-stroke cycle design used in automobiles, aircraft, trucks and tractors. As the name indicates, there are four strokes to one complete power cycle:

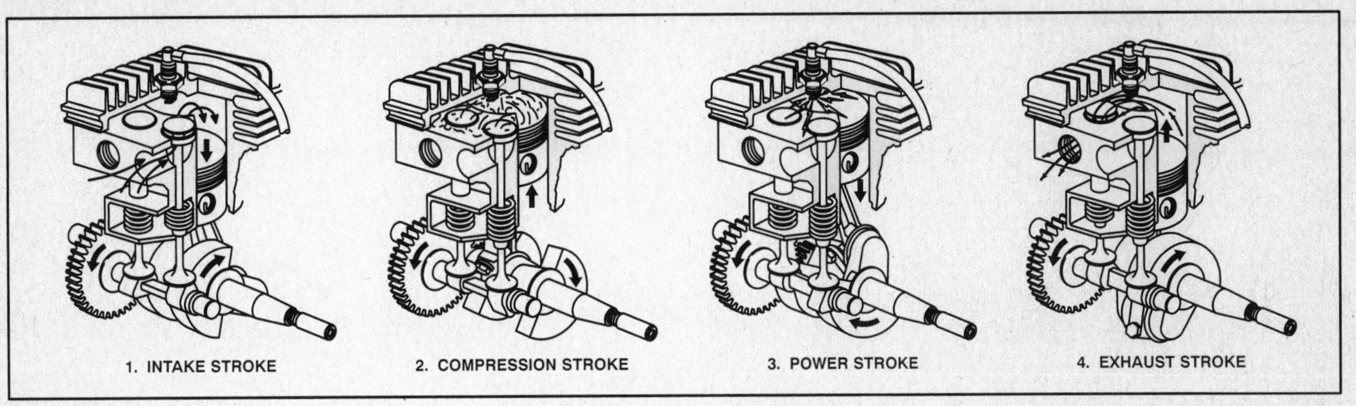

Fig. 1 – The 4-Stroke Cycle

1. INTAKE STROKE: As piston moves down, a vacuum occurs in the cylinder. The intake valve has been opened by the cam gear. Atmospheric pressure pushes the air/fuel mixture through the open intake valve into the cylinder above the piston. At the bottom of the stroke the intake valve closes. The exhaust valve stays closed.
2. COMPRESSION STROKE: As the piston moves up with both valves closed, the air/fuel mixture becomes highly compressed in the space left between the top of the piston and the cylinder head.
3. POWER STROKE: Just before the compression stroke ends, the magneto produces a high voltage arc across the spark plug gap igniting the air/fuel mixture. The rapidly burning mixture produces very high pressure to push the piston down.
4. EXHAUST STROKE: As the piston begins to go up, the cam gear opens the exhaust valve and the piston pushes out the burned gases completing the fourth cycle and begins the first stroke again.

WARNING

Exhaust gases contain CARBON MONOXIDE which is an odorless and deadly poison. Proper care must be taken to provide adequate ventilation when running an engine indoors.

Do not fill the fuel tank while the engine is running. Allow engine to cool for two minutes before refueling. Avoid spilling gasoline on a hot engine. This can cause an explosion and serious injury.

CAUTION

Fill the crankcase with proper oil before starting engine. See that oil level is maintained at the proper level.

IN THE INTEREST OF SAFETY

THIS SYMBOL MEANS WARNING OR CAUTION. PERSONAL INJURY AND/OR PROPERTY DAMAGE MAY OCCUR UNLESS INSTRUCTIONS ARE FOLLOWED CAREFULLY.

WARNING:

DO NOT run engine in an enclosed area. Exhaust gases contain carbon monoxide, an odorless and deadly poison.

DO NOT check for spark with spark plug or spark plug wire removed. Use an approved tester.

DO NOT crank engine with spark plug removed. If engine is flooded, place throttle in FAST position and crank until engine starts.

DO NOT crank engine more than 15 seconds without allowing starter motor to cool for two minutes.

DO NOT smoke when filling fuel tank.

DO NOT FILL FUEL TANK while engine is running. Allow engine to cool for two minutes before refueling.

DO NOT operate engine when an odor of gasoline is present or other explosive conditions exist.

DO NOT operate engine if gasoline is spilled. Move machine away from the spill and avoid creating any ignition until the gasoline has evaporated.

DO NOT STORE, SPILL OR USE GASOLINE NEAR AN OPEN FLAME, or devices such as a stove, furnace, or water heater which utilize a pilot light or devices which can create a spark.

DO NOT refuel indoors where area is not well ventilated. Outdoor refueling is preferred.

DO NOT OPERATE ENGINE WITHOUT A MUFFLER. Inspect periodically and replace if defective.

DO NOT operate engine with an accumulation of grass, leaves, dirt or other combustible material in the muffler area.

DO NOT use this engine on any forest covered, brush covered, or grass covered unimproved land unless a spark arrested is installed on the muffler.

DO NOT run engine with air cleaner or cover, directly over the carburetor air intake, removed.

CAUTION:

DO NOT RUN ENGINE AT EXCESSIVE SPEEDS, AS THIS MAY RESULT IN INJURY.

DO NOT tamper with governor springs, governor links or other parts which may increase the governed engine speed.

DO NOT tamper with the engine speed selected by the original equipment manufacturer.

DO NOT touch hot mufflers, cylinders, or fins as contact may cause burns.

DO NOT place hands or feet near moving or rotating parts.

DO keep cylinder fins and governor parts free of grass and other debris as this can affect engine speed.

DO pull starter cord slowly until resistance is felt. Then pull cord rapidly to avoid kickback and prevent hand or arm injury.

DO use fresh gasoline. Stale fuel can cause leakage.

TO PREVENT ACCIDENTAL STARTING when servicing the engine or equipment, always remove the spark plug or wire from the spark plug. Disconnect negative wire from battery terminal if equipped with a 12 volt starting system.

FUEL AND OIL RECOMMENDATIONS
GASOLINE

FUEL RECOMMENDATIONS

This engine is certified to operate on unleaded gasoline. Use clean, fresh, unleaded gasoline with a minimum of 85 octane. Do not mix oil with gasoline. Purchase fuel in quantity that can be used within 30 days to assure fuel freshness. We recommend the use of Briggs & Stratton Gasoline Additive. (See your Authorized Briggs & Stratton Service Dealer for Part No. 5041 or the single-use pouch.)

In countries other than U.S.A., leaded gasoline may be used if it is commercially available and unleaded is unavailable.

Note: Some fuels, called oxygenated or reformulated gasolines, are gasoline blended with alcohols or ethers. Excessive amounts of these blends can damage the fuel system or cause performance problems. Do not use gasoline which contains Methanol. If any undesirable operating symptoms occur, use gasoline with a lower percentage of alcohol or ether.

ENGINE OIL
SAE VISCOSITY GRADES

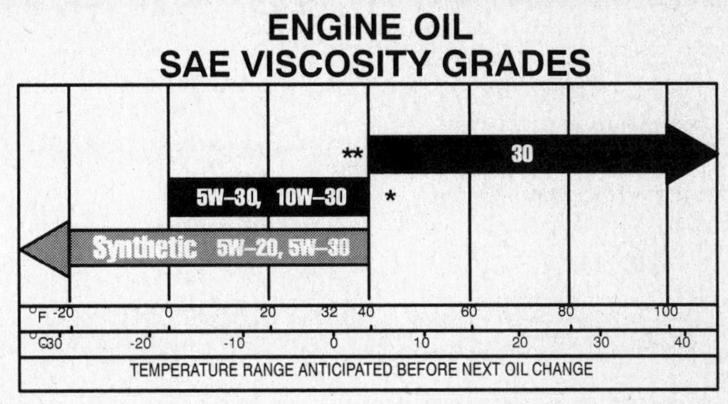

We recommend the use of a high quality detergent oil classified "For Service SE, SF, SG," such as Briggs & Stratton 30 weight oil, Part No. 100005 or 1000028. Detergent oils keep the engine cleaner and retard the formation of gum and varnish deposits. No special additives should be used with recommended oils.

* Air cooled engines run hotter than automotive engines. Use of multi-viscosity oils (10W-30, etc.) above 40° F (4° C) will result in high oil consumption and possible engine damage. Check oil level more frequently if using these types of oils.

** SAE 30 oil, if used below 40° F (4° C), will result in hard starting and possible engine bore damage due to inadequate lubrication.

CHANGE OIL after first 5 hours of operation. Thereafter, change oil monthly or every 50 hours of operation. Change oil more often if engine is operated under heavy load, or in high ambient air temperatures.

During normal operation, small particles of metal from the cylinder walls, pistons, bearings and combustion deposits will gradually contaminate the oil. Dust particles from the air also contaminate the oil. If oil is not changed regularly, these foreign particles can cause increased friction and a grinding action which shortens the life of the engine. Fresh oil also assists in cooling. Old oil gradually becomes thick and loses its cooling ability as well as its lubricating qualities.

CLEAN COOLING SYSTEM

Grass particles, chaff or dirt can clog the air cooling system, especially after prolonged service in cutting dry grass or very dirty air. Continued operation with a clogged cooling system can cause severe overheating and possible engine damage. The figure shows the blower housing removed and areas to be cleaned. This should be a regular maintenance operation, performed yearly or every 100 hours, whichever comes first. Clean more often under dusty conditions or when airborne debris is present.

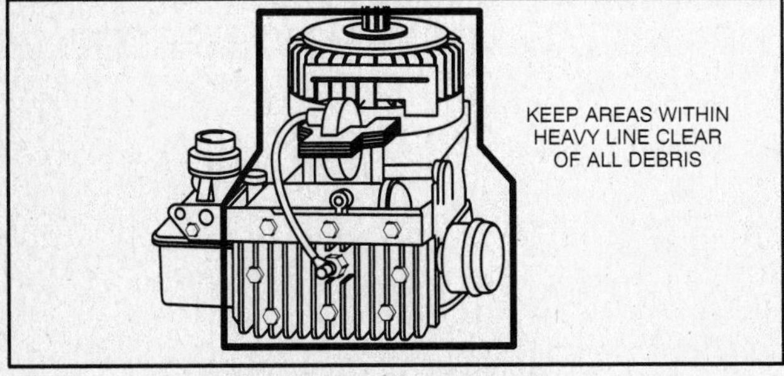

Vertical Crankshaft

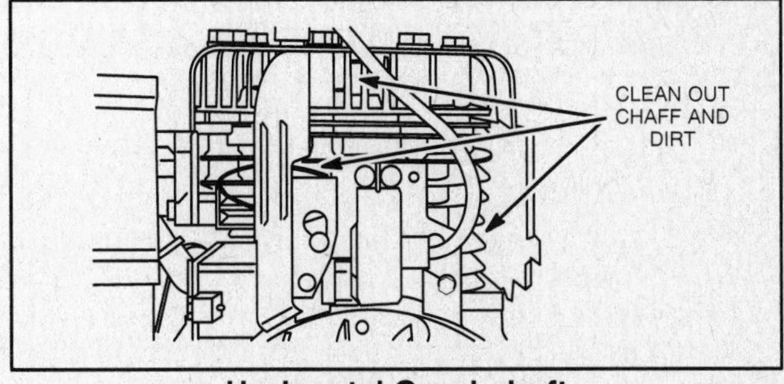

Horizontal Crankshaft

TUNE-UP PROCEDURE

A "Tune-Up," in the steps listed below, would normally be performed on relatively new engines brought in for minor difficulties. By performing these steps you will either be sure that the engine is functioning properly or will know what major repairs should be made.

The steps are also covered in the Overhaul Procedure and will normally be performed as a part of the complete overhaul.

STEP NO.	
1.	Remove air cleaner, check for proper servicing.
2.	Check oil level and drain. (Clean fuel tank and lines if separate from carburetor.)
3.	Remove blower housing, inspect rope and rewind assembly and starter clutch if equipped.
4.	Clean cooling fins and entire engine. Rock flywheel counterclockwise to check compression.
5.	Remove carburetor, disassemble and inspect for wear or damage. Wash in solvent, replace parts as necessary and assemble. Set initial adjustment.
6.	Inspect crossover tube or intake elbow for damaged gaskets.
7.	Check governor blade, linkage and spring for damage or wear. If mechanical, also check static adjustment.
8.	Remove flywheel, check for oil seal leakage, both flywheel and PTO sides. Check flywheel key.
9.	Remove breaker cover and check for proper sealing, if equipped.

STEP NO.	
10.	Inspect breaker points and condenser, if equipped. Replace or clean and adjust. Check plunger.
11.	Check armature, inspect all wires for breaks, damaged insulation. Be sure lead wires do not touch flywheel. Check stop switch and lead.
12.	Replace breaker cover. Use sealer where wires enter.
13.	Install flywheel. Time engine if necessary. Set air gap. Check for spark with #19051 or 19368 tester.
14.	Remove cylinder head, check gasket, remove spark plug, and clean carbon. Inspect valves for seating.
15.	Replace cylinder head. Torque to specified torque, set spark plug gap or replace plugs if necessary.
16.	Replace oil and fuel, check muffler for restrictions or damage.
17.	Adjust remote control linkage and cable if used, for correct operation.
18.	Service air cleaner. Check gaskets and element for damage.
19.	Run and adjust mixture and top speed.

OVERHAUL PROCEDURE

The Overhaul Procedure which follows is intended to help you to become accustomed to a systematic method of repairing Briggs & Stratton engines. Naturally these steps could be rearranged in different order but efficiency is obtained when the repair operations are performed in the same sequence every time. The exact procedure will vary according to the engine model being repaired.

The Overhaul Procedure can also be used as an index. For information on how to perform most operations listed, refer to the section number or operation. Be careful to locate the instructions covering the specific model being repaired.

DISASSEMBLY

SECTION	
8	Change oil
3	Air cleaner and stud
3	Fuel pipe and tank assembly
3	Air cleaner elbow or pipe
3	Carburetor and linkage
3	Carburetor intake elbow
	Muffler
3	Check space between upper and lower carburetor body or carburetor to tank fit.
3	Check throttle shaft and bushings for wear. Disassemble carburetor.
7B	Electric starter (110 V) (12 V)
	Blower housing
6	Spin flywheel counterclockwise to check compression
2	Spark plug-adjust gap (.030") clean and wash.
3	Fuel tank and bracket assembly or carburetor
7A	Rope starter cup, if equipped
2	Check air gap – armature to flywheel
5	Governor blade
8	Breather or valve cover
6	Cylinder head and shield
6	Check tappet clearance
6	Valves and springs
7A	Rope starter pulley or recoil starter clutch
2	Flywheel

SECTION	
2	Breaker point cover, if so equipped
2	Check breaker point gap, if so equipped
2	Check breaker point plunger hole, if so equipped
2	Test condenser and remove if necessary, if so equipped
2	Test coil and remove if necessary
2	Breaker arm assembly and condenser, if so equipped
2	Breaker box, if so equipped
2	Breaker shaft, if so equipped
10	Check end play
10	Remove burrs from crankshaft extension
10	Crankcase cover, base or sump
10	Auxiliary drive
11	Damaged oil seals
5	Mechanical governor parts
8	Inspect oil slinger
10	Cam gear
6	Tappets
9	Connecting rod and piston
10	Crankshaft – inspect and check
10	Check cam gear
11	Cylinder – check bore, main bearing, valve guides and seats
9	Disassemble connecting rod and piston
9	Check piston, rings, connecting rod, piston pin

1

REPAIRS

SECTION	
	Clean parts
11	Resize cylinder bore to next oversize
6	Replace valve guide – intake or exhaust
6	Reface valves and seats and lap
6	Replace valve seat insert
11	Replace main bearings
11	Replace oil seal
2	Install breaker point plunger bushing and plunger in cylinder (Internal breaker), if so equipped
2	Install breaker point plunger bushing and plunger in cylinder (External breaker), if so equipped
3	Replace throttle shaft bushing
3	Repair carburetor
7A	Replace rewind starter spring and rope
7A	Starter clutch
11	Remove ball bearing and reassemble to crankshaft

REASSEMBLE

SECTION	
10	Tappets, cam gear, camshaft
10	Crankshaft and bearing support
10	Crankshaft, bearing plate – adjust crankshaft end play
9	Piston, piston pin, connecting rod, rings, and dipper, if equipped
8	Oil slinger
5	Mechanical governor
10	Sump or crankcase cover – adjust crankshaft end play
6	Adjust valve tappet clearance
6	Valves, springs, retainer
2	Armature, governor blade

REASSEMBLE (cont'd.)

SECTION	
2	Breaker points (Internal system), if so equipped
2	Condenser (Internal system), if so equipped
2	Adjust armature timing
2	Condenser, if so equipped
2	Adjust and clean breaker points (External), if so equipped
2	Breaker point cover, if so equipped
2	Coil and armature assembly
2	Breaker box cover, if so equipped
2	Flywheel and starter pulley or clutch
7B	Electric starter (110 V) (12 V)
2	Adjust air gap – armature to flywheel
2	Check spark
8	Breather or valve cover
6	Cylinder head and shield
2	Spark plug
	Muffler
3	Intake elbow or carburetor and tank
4	Carburetor, linkage and governor controls
5	Check air vane governor
5	Check and adjust mechanical governor
	Blower housing
3	Fuel filter parts, tank & line
3	Air cleaner elbow or pipe
8	Change oil (crankcase)
1	Start engine (fill with gas)
6	Retighten cylinder head screws
3	Adjust carburetor
5	Set governor to obtain correct engine speed (remote controls)
3	Clean, fill, assemble air cleaner
	Spray engine and apply decals

CHECK-UP

Most complaints concerning engine operation can be classified as one or a combination of the following:

1. Will not start
2. Hard starting
3. Kicks back when starting
4. Lack of power
5. Vibration
6. Erratic operation
7. Overheating
8. High oil consumption

When the cause of malfunction is not readily apparent, perform a check of the compression, ignition, and carburetion systems. This check-up, performed in a systematic manner, can usually be done in a matter of minutes. It is the quickest and surest method of determining the cause of failure. This check-up will point out possible cause of future failures, which can be corrected at the time. The basic check-up procedure is the same for all engine models, while any variation, by model, will be shown under the subject heading.

NOTE: What appears to be an engine malfunction may be a fault of the powered equipment rather than the engine. If equipment is suspect, see "Equipment – Affecting Engine Operation."

Check Compression

Spin flywheel in reverse rotation (counterclockwise) to obtain accurate compression check. The flywheel should rebound sharply, indicating satisfactory compression.

If compression is poor, look for:

1. Loose spark plug
2. Loose cylinder head bolts
3. Blown head gasket
4. Burned valves, valve seats
5. Insufficient tappet clearance
6. Warped cylinder head
7. Warped valve stems
8. Worn bore and/or rings
9. Broken connecting rods

Check Ignition

WARNING: DO NOT REMOVE SPARK PLUG WHEN CHECKING IGNITION.

Connect spark plug wire to long terminal of tester, Tool #19051 or #19368 and ground tester to engine with alligator clip. Operate starter and observe spark gap in tester. If spark jumps tester gap, you can assume ignition is good. Try a new spark plug.

If spark does not occur, look for:

1. Incorrect armature air gap
2. Worn bearings and/or shaft on flywheel side only
3. Sheared flywheel key
4. Incorrect breaker point gap, if so equipped
5. Dirty or burned breaker points, if so equipped
6. Breaker plunger stuck or worn, if so equipped
7. Shorted ground wire (when so equipped)
8. Shorted stop switch (when so equipped)
9. Condenser failure, if so equipped
10. Armature failure
11. Improperly operating interlock system

NOTE: If engine runs but misses during operation, a quick check to determine if ignition is or is not at fault can be made by inserting the 19051 or 19368 tester between the ignition cable and the spark plug. A spark miss will be readily apparent. While conducting this test on Magnamatic equipped engine, Models 9, 14, 19 and 23 use a new spark plug with gap set to .060" in place of old plug.

Check Carburetion

Before making a carburetion check, be sure the fuel tank has an ample supply of fresh, clean gasoline, On gravity feed (Flo-Jet) models, see that the shut-off valve is open and fuel flows freely through the fuel line. On all models, inspect and adjust the needle valves. Check to see that the choke closes completely. If engine will not start, remove and inspect the spark plug. If plug is wet, look for:

1. Overchoking
2. Excessively rich fuel mixture
3. Water in fuel
4. Inlet valve stuck open (Flo-Jet carburetor)

If plug is dry, look for:

1. Leaking carburetor mounting gaskets
2. Gummy or dirty screen or check valve (Pulsa-Jet and Vacu-Jet carburetors)
3. Inlet valve stuck shut (Flo-Jet carburetors)
4. Inoperative pump (Pulsa-Jet carburetors)
5. Plugged fuel filter.
6. Closed fuel tank valve.

A simple check to determine if the fuel is getting to the combustion chamber through the carburetor is to remove the spark plug and pour a small quantity of gasoline through the spark plug hole. Replace the plug. If the engine fires a few times and then quits, look for the same condition as for a dry plug.

Equipment-Affecting Engine Operation

Frequently, what appears to be a problem with engine operation, such as hard starting, vibration, etc., may be the fault of the equipment powered rather than the engine itself. Since many varied types of equipment are powered by Briggs & Stratton engines, it is not possible to list all of the various conditions that may exist. Listed are the most common effects of equipment problems, and what to look for as the most common cause.

Hard Starting, Kickback, or Will Not Start

1. Loose blade – blade must be tight to shaft or adaptor. Check for partially sheared flywheel key. Damaged blade and hub.
2. Loose belt – a loose belt like a loose blade can cause a back-lash effect, which will counteract engine cranking effort.
3. Starting under load – See if the unit is disengaged when engine is started; or if engaged, does not have a heavy starting load.
4. Check remote Choke-A-Matic® or speed control assembly for proper adjustment.
5. Check interlock system for shorted wires, loose or corroded connections, or defective modules or switches.

Vibration

1. Cutter blade bent or out of balance – Remove and balance. Check for partially sheared flywheel key.
2. Crankshaft bent – Replace.
3. Worn blade coupling – Replace if coupling allows blade to shift, causing unbalance.
4. Mounting bolts loose – Tighten.
5. Mounting deck or plate cracked – Repair or replace.

Power Loss

1. Bind or drag in unit – If possible, disengage engine and operate unit manually to feel for any binding action.
2. Grass cuttings build-up under deck.
3. No lubrication in transmission or gear box.
4. Excessive drive belt tension may cause seizure.

Noise

1. Cutter blade coupling or pulley – an oversize or worn coupling can result in knocking, usually under acceleration. Check for fit, or tightness.
2. No lubricant in transmission or gear box.

HOW TO READ BRIGGS & STRATTON MODEL, TYPE AND CODE NUMBERS

MODEL	TYPE	CODE
92902	1234-01	90012201

This chart explains how to read Briggs & Stratton's numerical model designation system. It makes it possible to determine the more important mechanical features of the engine by knowing the model number.

A. The first one or two digits indicate the approximate CUBIC INCH DISPLACEMENT.

B. The first digit after the displacement indicates the BASIC DESIGN SERIES, relating to cylinder construction, ignition, or other major differences.

C. The second digit after the displacement indicates POSITION OF CRANKSHAFT, TYPE OF CARBURETOR, and sometimes GOVERNOR.

D. The third digit after the displacement indicates TYPE OF BEARING and whether or not the engine is equipped with REDUCTION GEARS, AUXILIARY PTO, or PRESSURE LUBRICATION.

E. The last digit indicates the TYPE STARTER or CHARGING SYSTEM.

BRIGGS & STRATTON MODEL NUMBER SYSTEM

A	B	C	D	E
	FIRST DIGIT AFTER DISPLACEMENT	SECOND DIGIT AFTER DISPLACEMENT	THIRD DIGIT AFTER DISPLACEMENT	FOURTH DIGIT AFTER DISPLACEMENT
CUBIC INCH DISPLACEMENT	BASIC DESIGN SERIES	CRANKSHAFT, CARBURETOR, GOVERNOR	PTO BEARING, REDUCTION GEAR, AUXILIARY DRIVE, LUBRICATION	TYPE OF STARTER
6	0	0 - Horizontal Shaft Diaphragm Carburetor Pneumatic Governor	0 - Plain Bearing/DU Non-Flange Mount	0 - Without Starter
8	1	1 - Horizontal Shaft Vacu-Jet Carburetor Pneumatic Governor	1 - Plain Bearing Flange Mounting	1 - Rope Starter
9	2	2 - Horizontal Shaft Pulsa-Jet Carburetor Pneumatic or Mechanical Governor	2 - Sleeve Bearing Flange Mounting Splash Lube	2 - Rewind Starter
10	3	3 - Horizontal Shaft Flo-Jet Carburetor Pneumatic Governor	3 - Ball Bearing Flange Mounting Splash Lube	3 - Electric Starter Only 120 Volt Gear Drive
11	4	4 - Horizontal Shaft Flo-Jet Carburetor Mechanical Governor	4 - Ball Bearing Flange Mounting Pressure Lubrication on Horizontal Shaft	4 - Electric Starter/Generator 12 Volt Belt Drive
12	5	5 - Vertical Shaft Vacu-Jet Carburetor Pneumatic or Mechanical Governor	5 - Plain Bearing Gear Reduction (6 to 1) CW Rotation Flange Mounting	5 - Electric Starter Only 12 Volt Gear Drive
13	6	6 - Vertical Shaft	6 - Plain Bearing Gear Reduction (6 to 1) CCW Rotation	6 - Alternator Only
16	7	7 - Vertical Shaft Flo-Jet Carburetor Pneumatic or Mechanical Governor	7 - Plain Bearing Pressure Lubrication on Vertical Shaft	7 - Electric Starter 12 Volt Gear Drive With Alternator
17	8	8 - Vertical Shaft Flo-Jet Carburetor Mechanical Governor	8 - Plain Bearing Auxiliary Drive (PTO) Perpendicular to Crankshaft	8 - Vertical Pull Starter or Side Pull Starter
18	9	9 - Vertical Shaft Pulsa-Jet Carburetor Pneumatic or Mechanical Governor	9 - Plain Bearing Auxiliary Drive Parallel to Crankshaft	
19	A to Z			
22				
23				
24				
25				
26				
28				
29				
30				
32				
35				
40				
42				

Example: **MODEL** 92902

9	2	9	0	2
9 Cubic Inch	Design Series 2	Vertical Crankshaft Pulsa-Jet Carburetor Pneumatic Governor	Plain Bearing/DU Non-Flange Mount	Rewind Starter

TYPE 1234-01, The type number identifies the engines mechanical parts, color of paint, decals, Governed Speed, and Original Equipment Manufacturer.

CODE 90012201, The code is the manufacturing date and is read as follows:

YEAR	MONTH	DAY	ASSEMBLY LINE AND MANUFACTURING PLANT
90	01	22	01

Section 2
IGNITION

2

SECTION INDEX

NOTE: METRIC EQUIVALENTS ARE LISTED ON PAGE 25 OF THIS SECTION.

SECTION INDEX, (Cont'd.)

IGNITION, (CONT'D)

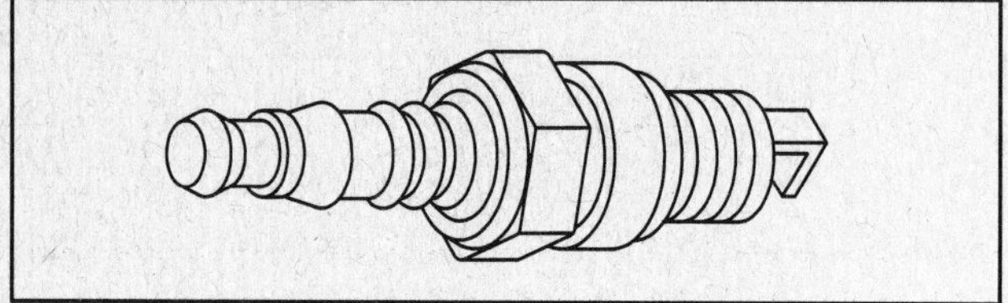

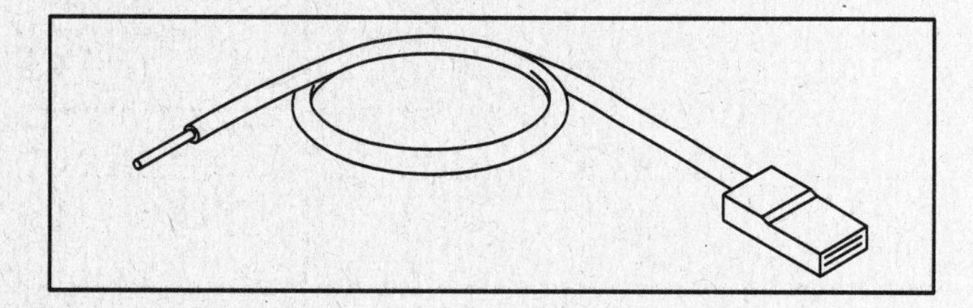

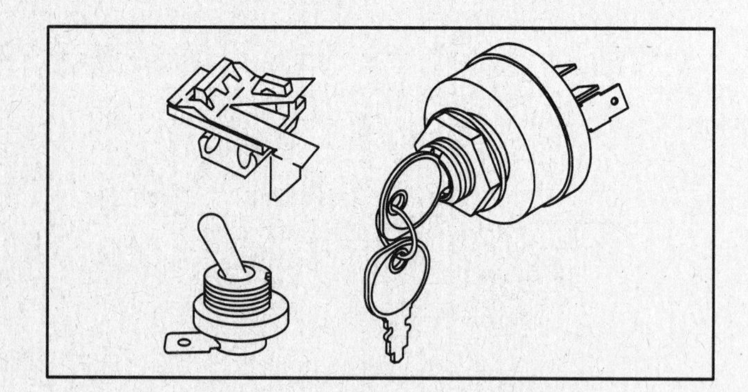

Three basic types of ignition systems are described:

1. Magnetron® ignition, a self-contained transistor module, ignition armature and flywheel, Fig. 2. **For service information see page 7.**

2. Magnavac ignition, using magnetically operated sealed points, ignition armature and flywheel, Fig. 1. **For service information see page 9**

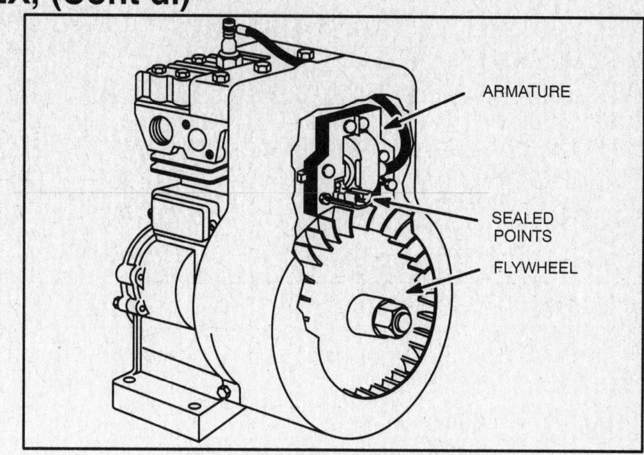

Fig. 1 – Magnavac Ignition

3. Flywheel magneto ignition, using either internal or external breaker points, ignition armature and flywheel, Fig. 3. **For service information see page 9 for flywheel magneto ignition with internal breaker points or page 14, flywheel magneto ignition with external breaker points.**

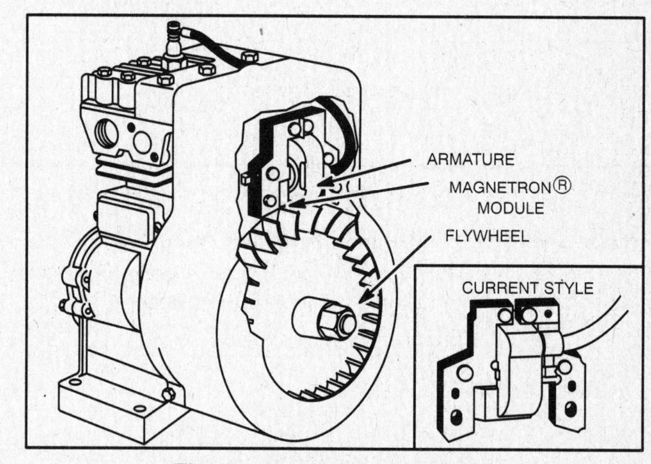

Fig. 2 – Magnetron® Ignition

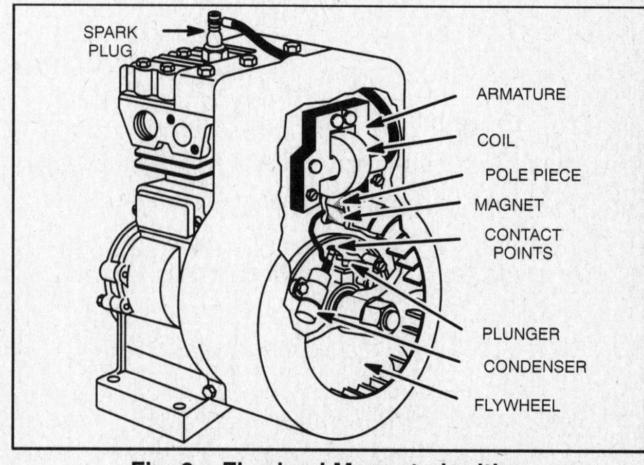

Fig. 3 – Flywheel Magneto Ignition

NOTE: METRIC EQUIVALENTS ARE LISTED ON PAGE 25 OF THIS SECTION.

TABLE NO. 1
SPECIFICATIONS FOR ALL POPULAR ENGINE MODELS

1. **Spark plug gap: .030 "**
2. **Condenser capacity: .18 to .24 M.F.D.**
3. **Breaker point gap: .020"**

BASIC MODEL SERIES	ARMATURE TWO-LEG AIR GAP Inches	ARMATURE THREE-LEG AIR GAP Inches	FLYWHEEL PULLER TOOL NO.	FLYWHEEL HOLDER TOOL NO.	FLYWHEEL TORQUE Ft. Lbs.
ALUMINUM CYLINDERS					
60000, 80000	.006-.010	.012-.016	19069	19167 or 19372	55♦
90000, 110000, 120000	.006-.010		19069	19167 or 19372	55♦
100700	.006-.010		19069	19310 or 19372	55♦
100200, 100900, 130000	.010-.014	.012-.016	none	19372	65♦
170000, 190000	.010-.014	.012-.016	19165	19372	65♦
220000, 250000*	.010-.014		19203●*	19372	65♦
280000	.010-.014		19203	19321 or 19372	65♦
CAST IRON CYLINDERS					
233400	.010-.014	.022-.026	19068 or 19203	19372	145♦
240000, 300000, 320000	.010-.014		19068 or 19203	19372	145♦

♦ Use 19244 starter clutch wrench on rewind starter engines.
● Use 19203, Flywheel Puller, on Model Series 250000 built after 1975 and all Model Series 220000.
* Use 19165, Flywheel Puller, on Model Series 250000 built 1975 and before.

CHECK IGNITION

WARNING: DO NOT REMOVE SPARK PLUG WHEN CHECKING IGNITION. A fire or explosion may occur.

1. Connect spark plug wire to long terminal of Tool #19051 or #19368, Spark Tester, and ground tester to engine with alligator clip, Fig. 4.

2. Operate starter and observe spark gap in tester.

3. If spark jumps tester gap, you can assume ignition is good.

NOTE: Flywheel must rotate at 350 RPM minimum on engines equipped with Magnetron® ignition.

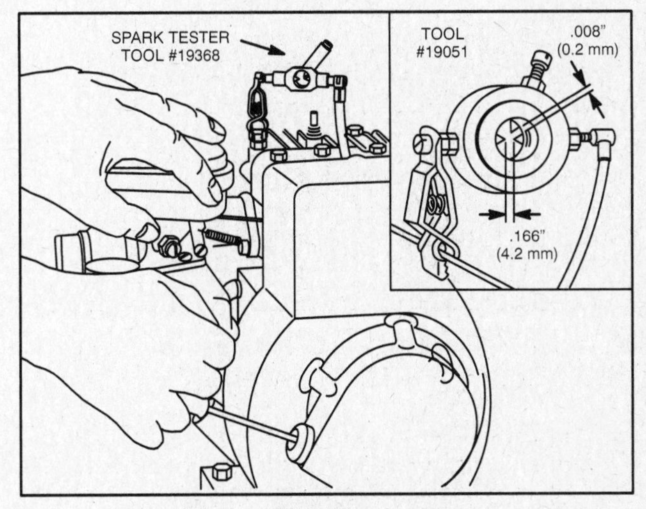

Fig. 4 - Checking Ignition

NOTE: If engine runs but misses during operation, a quick check can determine if the miss is ignition or not.

NOTE: METRIC EQUIVALENTS ARE LISTED ON PAGE 25 OF THIS SECTION.

Check For Spark Miss

1. Place Tool #19051 or 19368, Spark Tester, in series with engine's spark plug and spark plug wire, Fig. 5.

2. An ignition miss will be readily apparent when the engine is started and run.

3. If there is no ignition miss, check compression and fuel system.

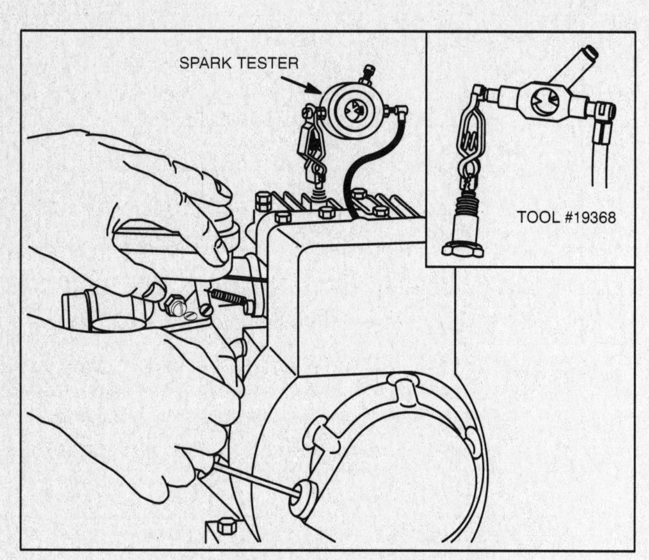

Fig. 5 – Checking for Spark Miss

SPARK PLUGS

Spark plugs recommended by Briggs & Stratton are as follows:

PART NUMBER		
1-1/2" Plug	**2" Plug**	
298323●	29693●	
492167●*	-	
293918	392588●	
802592●*	-	
–	496018	
Part #293918 is 3/4" hex	All spark plugs in this column are13/16" hex except 496018 which is 5/8" hex	Spark Plug Wrench (deep socket) Part #89838 (3/4" – 13/16") or Part #19374 (5/8' – 13/16")

● Uses 13/16" spark plug wrench.

*Spark plugs marked by an asterisk can be used in place of standard plugs if short plug life is experienced or repeated fouling occurs.

NOTE: In some areas, local law requires the use of a resistor spark plug to suppress ignition signals. If an engine was originally equipped with a resistor spark plug, be sure to use the same type of spark plug for replacement.

Spark Plug Service

Gap spark plug to .030" gap, Fig. 6. Replace spark plug if electrodes are burned away or porcelain is cracked. DO NOT USE ABRASIVE CLEANING MACHINES.

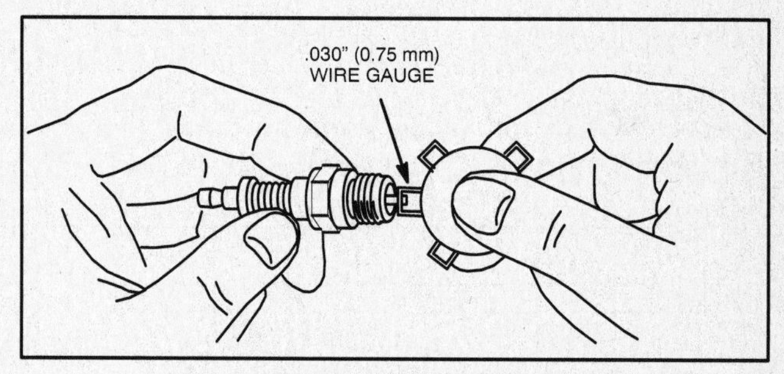

Fig. 6 – Adjusting Spark Plug Gap

ARMATURE (COIL) AND CONDENSER TESTING

All Models

Use an approved tester to test coils and condensers. Specifications are supplied by the tester manufacturer or refer to MS-7862, Testing Briggs & Stratton Ignition Coils.

REMOVE FLYWHEEL

All Model Series except those listed in NOTE below

NOTE: Aluminum Series 80000 (with cast iron flywheel) 100700, 100200, 100900, 130000, and 280000 flywheels are removed using different procedures. These Model Series will be described separately.

NOTE: METRIC EQUIVALENTS ARE LISTED ON PAGE 25 OF THIS SECTION.

Remove Flywheel Nut or Rewind Starter Clutch

1. On flywheels 6-3/4 inches in diameter or less, use Tool #19167 or #19372, Flywheel Holder, to hold flywheel from turning, Fig. 7.
2. Use Tool #19244, Starter Clutch Wrench, to remove rewind starter clutch.

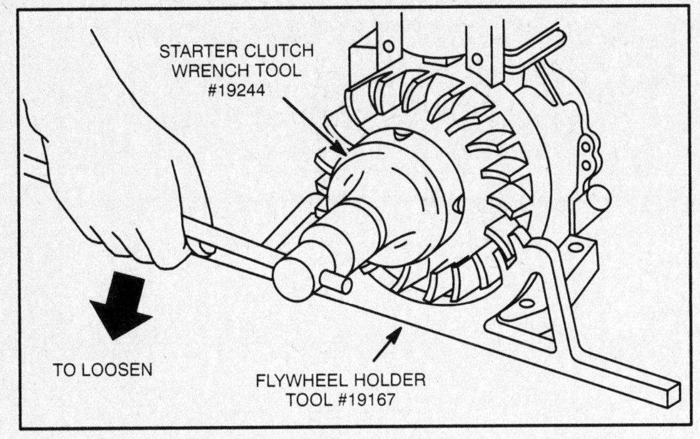

Fig. 7 - Removing Rewind Starter Clutch

For flywheels larger than 6-3/4 inches in diameter, use Tool #19372, Flywheel Holder, Fig. 8.

NOTE: DO NOT use fins on magnet insert to prevent flywheel from turning.

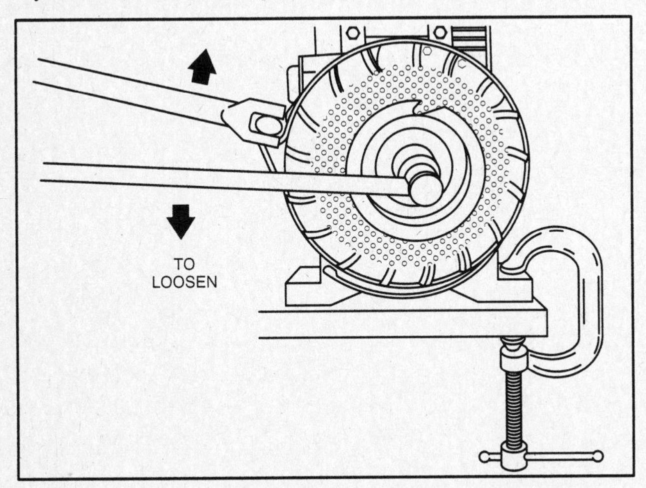

Fig. 8 - Removing Flywheel Nut, Large Flywheels

Remove Flywheel

1. Refer to Table No. 1 for correct flywheel puller by Model Series.
2. Use flywheel nut to protect crankshaft threads and for puller to bear against, Fig. 9.
3. Thread flywheel nut onto crankshaft until top of nut is flush with crankshaft threads or slightly above end of threads.
4. See Fig. 9 for pulling procedure.

NOTE: Care is required not to damage flywheel fins, magnets or ring gear, Fig. 9.

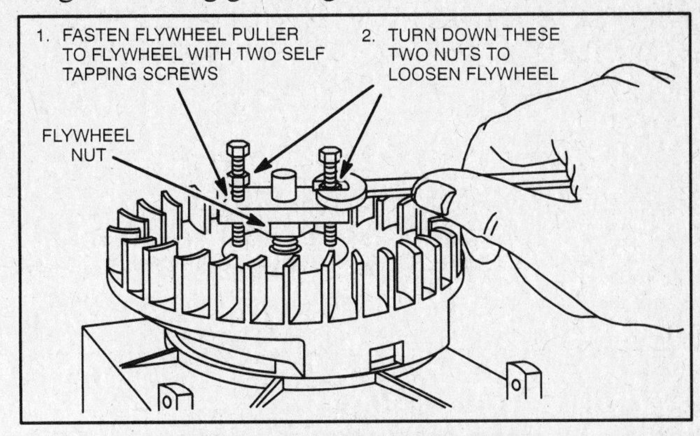

Fig. 9 - Removing Flywheel

Cast Iron Flywheel, Model Series 80000, 100200, 100900, 110000, 130000

1. Support flywheel with a gloved hand or a shop rag while exerting an upward pull.
2. Strike outside rim of flywheel with a rawhide hammer using a sharp blow.
3. Several blows may be required on a tight or rusted flywheel.

DO NOT STRIKE MAGNETS OR FINS.

Model Series 100700

Remove Flywheel Nut

1. Remove flywheel cover and rotating screen.
2. Place Tool #19310, Flywheel Holder, with tangs of holder in pockets of flywheel, Fig. 10, or use Tool #19372, Flywheel Holder, Fig. 8.
3. Loosen flywheel nut with socket and wrench. Remove nut, washer and flywheel fan.

Fig. 10 - Removing Flywheel Nut

4. Refer to Table No. 1 for correct flywheel puller by Model Series.

NOTE: METRIC EQUIVALENTS ARE LISTED ON PAGE 25 OF THIS SECTION.

5. Use flywheel nut to protect crankshaft threads and for puller to bear against, Fig. 9.

6. Thread flywheel nut onto crankshaft until top of nut is flush with crankshaft threads or slightly above end of threads.

7. See Fig. 9 for pulling procedure.

Model Series 280000

1. Remove blower housing and rotating screen, when so equipped.

2. Place Tool #19321, Flywheel Holder, on fan retainer with lugs of flywheel holder engaging the slots of the fan retainer, or use Tool #19372, Flywheel Holder.

3. Loosen flywheel nut or rewind starter clutch with socket and wrench or Tool #19244, Starter Clutch Wrench, and wrench, Fig. 11.

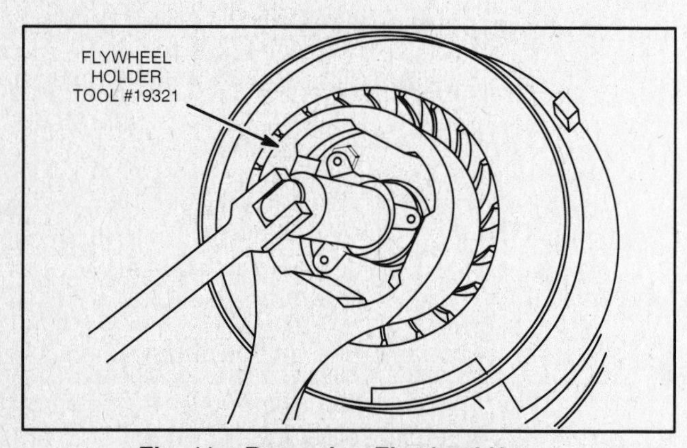

Fig. 11 – Removing Flywheel Nut or Rewind Starter Clutch

4. Remove two screws and fan retainer. Refer to Table No. 1 for correct flywheel puller by Model Series.

5. Use flywheel nut to protect crankshaft threads and for puller to bear on, Fig. 12.

6. Tighten both puller screws equally until flywheel is loose.

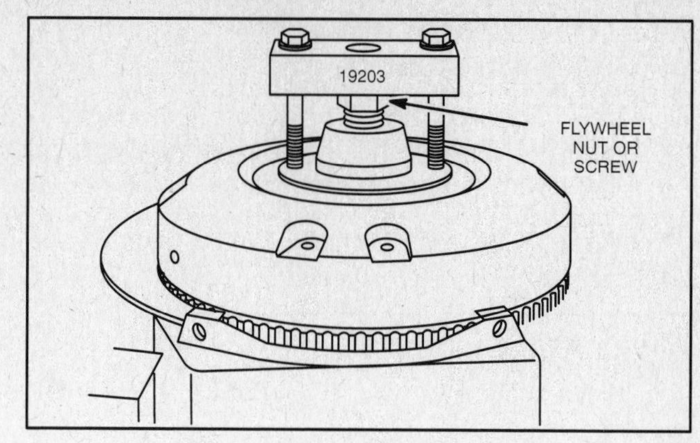

Fig. 12 – Removing Flywheel

NOTE: If puller screws on Tool #19203, Flywheel Puller, are too short, use two head bolts from Model Series 280000, Part #93723.

INSPECT FLYWHEEL KEY, KEYWAYS, FLYWHEEL AND CRANKSHAFT

Inspect flywheel key for partial or complete shearing. If sheared, replace, Fig. 13. Inspect flywheel and crankshaft keyways for damage. If damaged, replace with new parts.

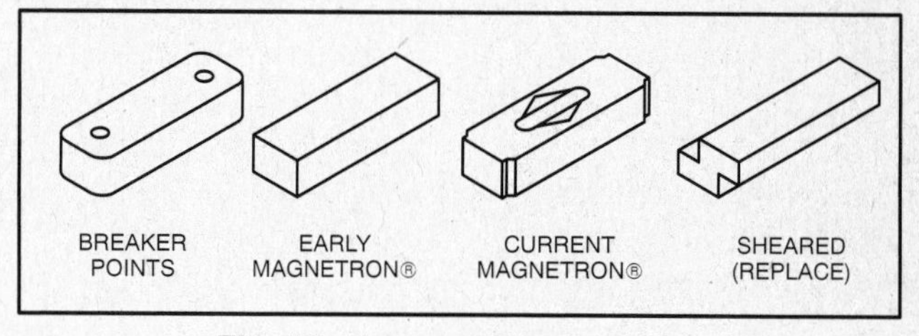

Fig. 13 – Inspect Flywheel Key

INSTALL FLYWHEEL

All Model Series

1. Clean flywheel taper and crankshaft taper of all grease, oil and dirt.

2. Slide flywheel onto crankshaft and line up both keyways.

3. Insert flywheel key into keyways.

Install Flywheel Nut or Rewind Starter Clutch

1. Install fan retainer or rotating screen cup (when used), then flat or Belleville washer, and flywheel nut or rewind starter clutch.

2. When installing Belleville washer have hollow side towards flywheel.

NOTE: METRIC EQUIVALENTS ARE LISTED ON PAGE 25 OF THIS SECTION.

3. Use tools as listed in Table No. 1 or clamp engine to work surface and torque nut or rewind starter clutch to specifications listed in Table No. 1.

NOTE: Use only the ORIGINAL FLYWHEEL KEYS SUPPLIED WITH THE ENGINE. DO NOT use a steel key under any circumstances.

MAGNETRON® IGNITION

Identification

Magnetron® has been produced in two versions, composite (Type I, Type II) and replaceable module, Fig. 14.

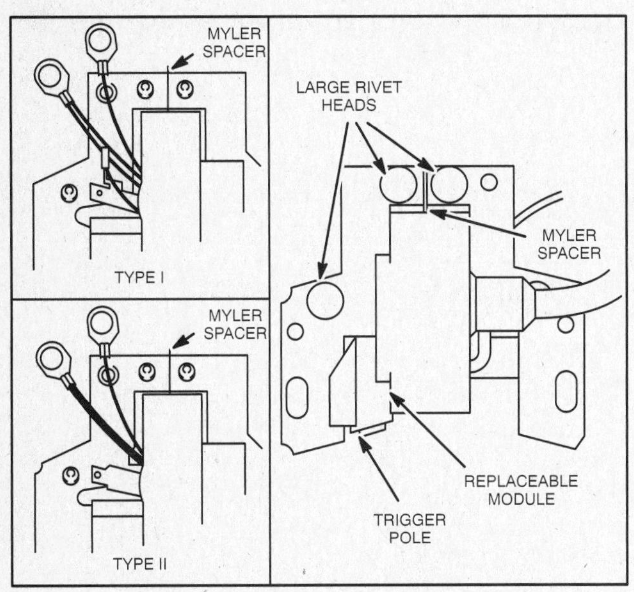

Fig. 14 - Identifying Magnetron®

NOTE: Magnetron® armatures used on Model Series 120000, 280000 do not have a visible trigger pole and do not have a Mylar spacer, Fig. 15.

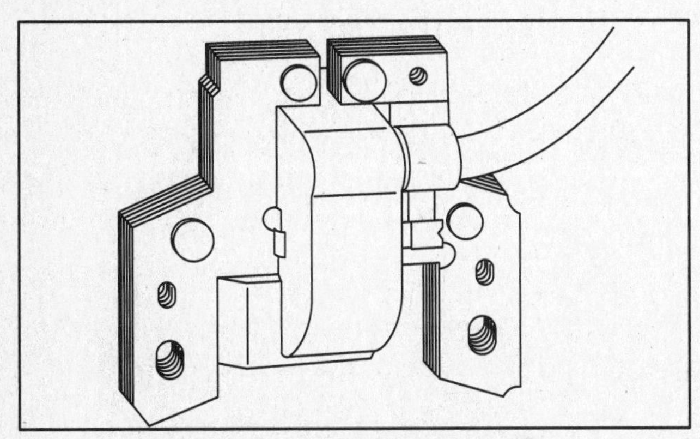

Fig. 15 - Armature without Trigger Pole or Mylar Spacer

Magnetron® Armature Testing

Use an approved tester to test armature. Specifications are supplied by the tester manufacturer or refer to MS-7862, Testing Briggs & Stratton Coils.

Remove Magnetron® Armatures

Removal of the flywheel is not required to remove Magnetron® armatures except to inspect flywheel key and keyways on crankshaft and flywheel.

1. Remove armature mounting screws and lift off armature.
2. Disconnect stop switch wire at spade terminal on composite armatures.
3. On armatures with replaceable Magnetron® modules, use breaker point condenser from Part #294628 point set or a 3/16 inch diameter pin punch to release wires from module, Fig. 16.
4. Unsolder stop switch wire from module wire and armature primary wire.

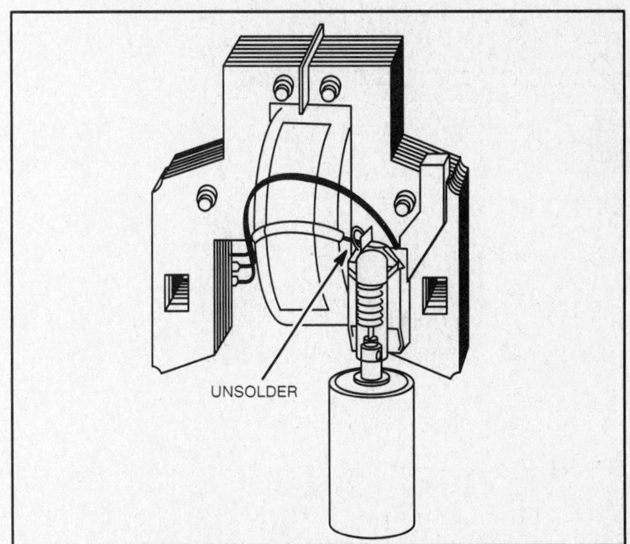

Fig. 16 - Disconnecting Stop Switch Wire

Remove Magnetron® Module

1. Remove sealant and/or tape holding armature wires to armature.
2. Unsolder and separate remaining wires.

   NOTE: On some armatures, the module ground wire is soldered to the armature ground wire. Unsolder and disconnect.
3. Move all wires so module will clear armature and laminations.
4. Pull module retainer away from laminations and push module off laminations, Fig. 17.

NOTE: METRIC EQUIVALENTS ARE LISTED ON PAGE 25 OF THIS SECTION.

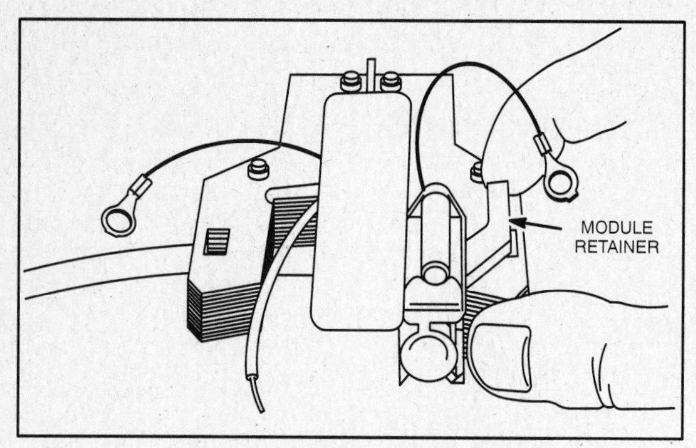

Fig. 17 - Removing Module

Install Module on Armature

The armature has a front side identified by large rivet heads, Fig. 14. The module is installed with the retainer on the back side, Fig. 18, small rivet ends.

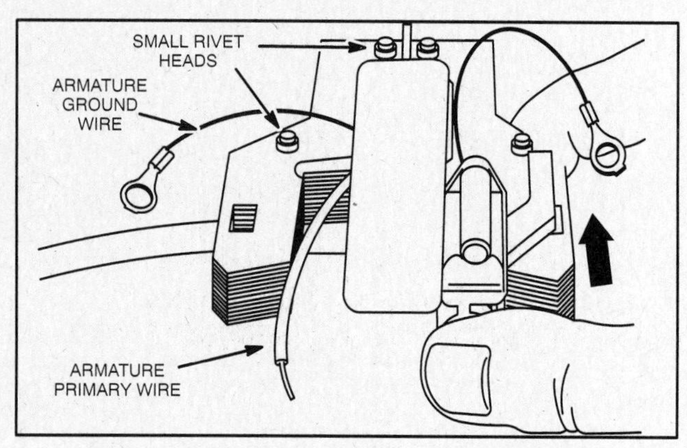

Fig. 18 - Installing Module on Armature

Install Stop Switch and Armature Primary Wire

1. Be sure all insulating material is removed from wires to ensure good contact.

2. Use a 3/16 inch diameter pin punch or a condenser from point set Part #294628 to compress wire retainer spring and insert stop switch and armature primary wire under hook of wire retainer, Fig. 19.

3. Twist wires together and solder twisted section with 60/40 rosin core solder. Take care not to damage module case.

4. Install wires in module retainer.

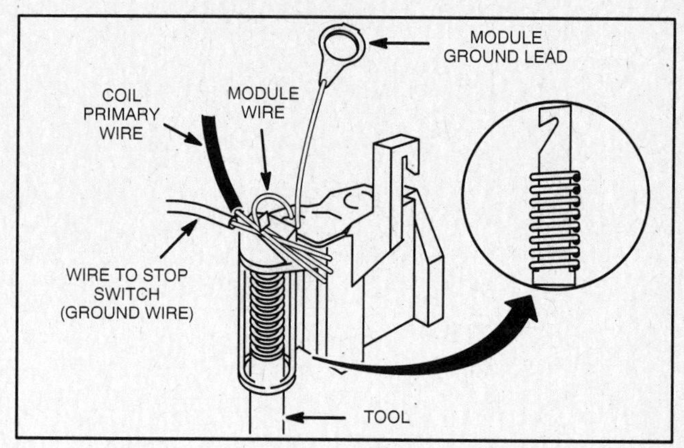

Fig. 19 - Installing Wires on Module

5. Seal wires to armature with Permatex® No. 2 or similar sealer to prevent wires from vibrating and breaking, Fig. 20.

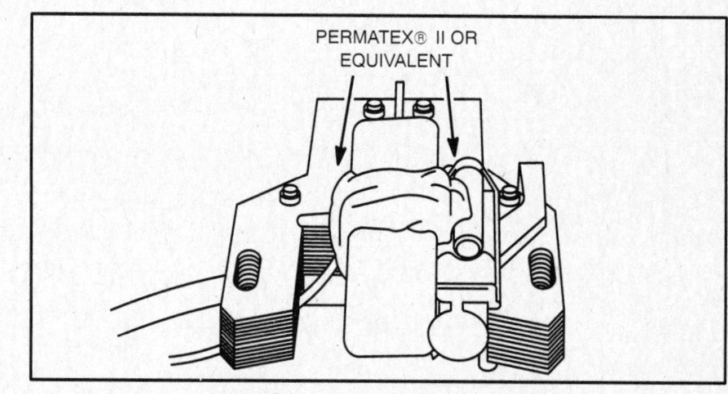

Fig. 20 - Cementing Wires

Timing Magnetron® Ignition

Timing of Magnetron® ignition is controlled by the flywheel key on all Model Series except 230000, 240000 and 320000.

Timing Magnetron® Armature, Gasoline Model Series 230000, 240000, 320000

Position armature bracket so mounting screws are centered in armature bracket slots and tighten screws, Fig. 21.

NOTE: METRIC EQUIVALENTS ARE LISTED ON PAGE 25 OF THIS SECTION.

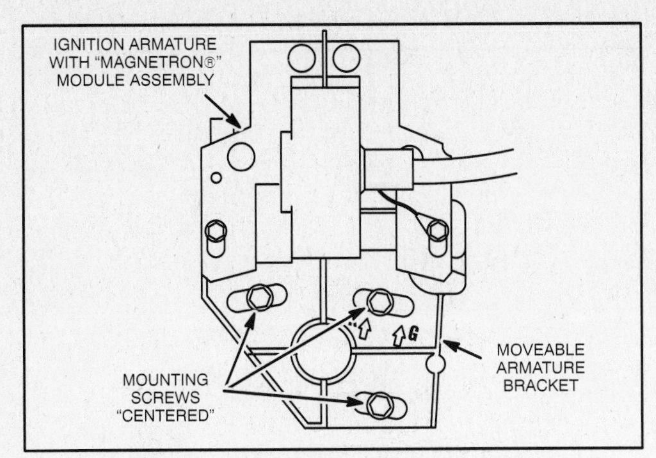

Fig. 21 – Timing Armature, Gasoline

Timing Magnetron® Armature, Kerosene Model Series 230000, 240000, 320000

Position armature bracket to the right, as far as it will go and tighten screws, Fig. 22.

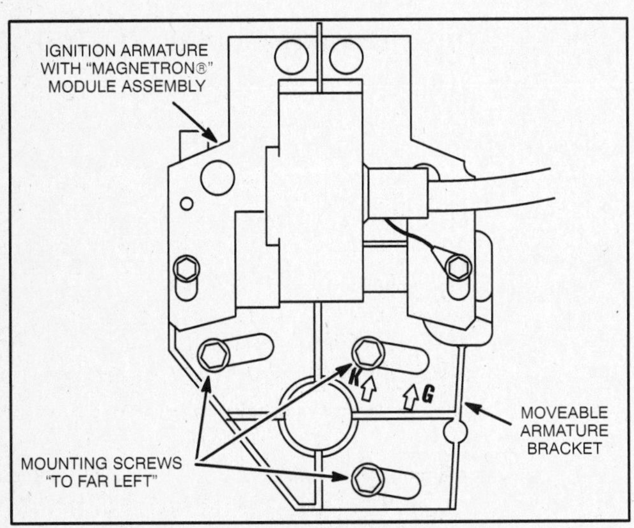

Fig. 22 – Timing Armature, Kerosene

MAGNAVAC IGNITION

Magnavac Armature Testing

Use an approved tester to test armature. Specifications are supplied by the tester manufacturer or refer to MS-7862, Testing Briggs & Stratton Coils.

Remove Magnavac Armatures

Removal of the flywheel is not required to remove Magnavac armatures except to inspect flywheel key and keyways on crankshaft and flywheel. Remove armature mounting screws and lift off armature. Disconnect stop switch wire by using a 5/32 inch diameter pin punch to depress spring and retainer, Fig. 23.

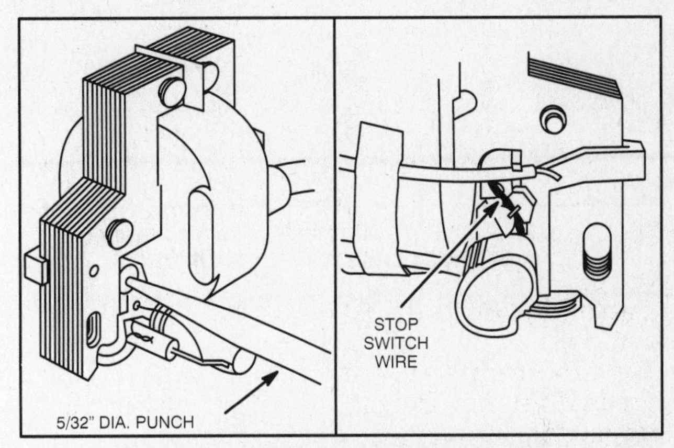

Fig. 23 – Removing Stop Switch Wire

FLYWHEEL MAGNETO IGNITION BREAKER POINTS – INTERNAL

Remove Breaker Cover

Care should be taken when removing breaker cover, to avoid damaging cover. If cover is bent or damaged, it should be replaced to ensure a proper dust seal.

Breaker Points

Breaker point gap is .020 inches on all models. Breaker points should be checked for contact and for signs of burning or pitting. Points gapped too wide will advance spark timing and may cause kickback when starting. Points gapped too close will retard spark timing and decrease engine power.

Breaker Point Identification

Three styles of internal breaker points are described for engines covered by this manual, Fig's. 24, 25, and 26.

NOTE: METRIC EQUIVALENTS ARE LISTED ON PAGE 25 OF THIS SECTION.

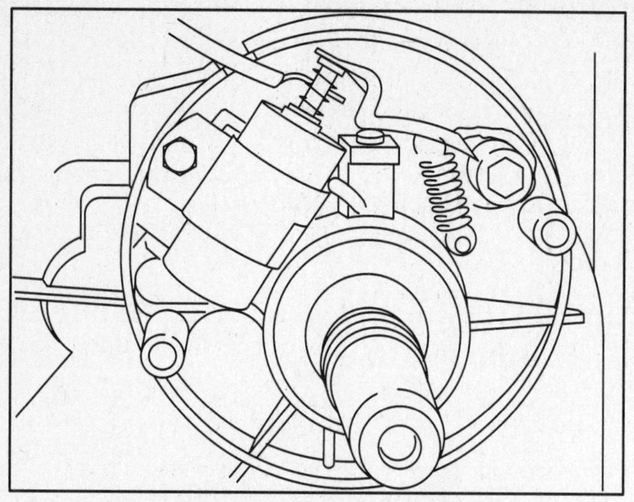

Fig. 24 - Style I - Aluminum Model Series Except Those Listed for Styles II and III

Remove Style I Breaker Points .... Page 10

Install Style I Breaker Points .... Page 12

Adjust Style I Breaker Points .... Page 13

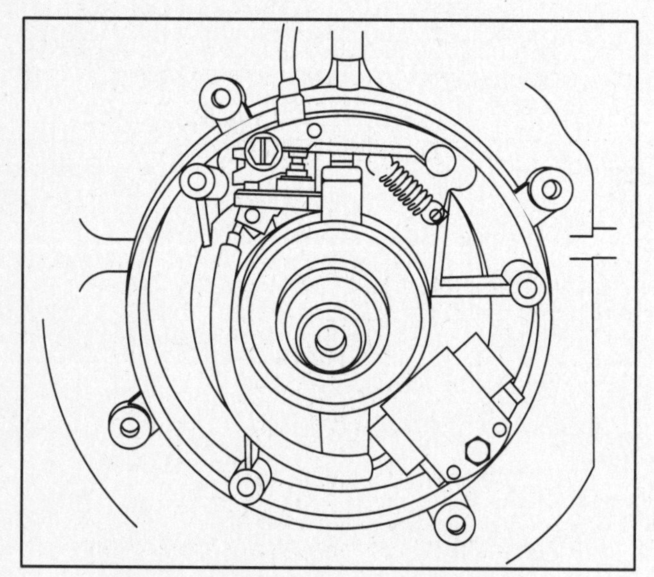

Fig. 25 - Style II - Model Series 250000

Remove Style II Breaker Points .... Page 11

Install Style II Breaker Points .... Page 12

Adjust Styles II Breaker Points .... Page 13

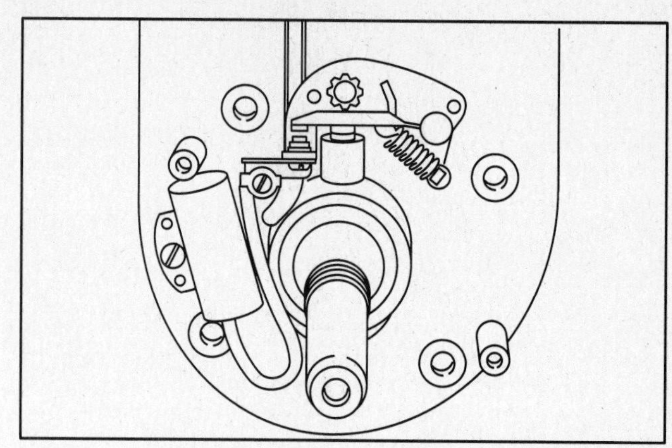

Fig. 26 - Style III - Aluminum Model Series 170400, Type Nos. 0010 Through 0271, 170700 Before Code No. 6906251

Remove Style III Breaker Points .... Page 11

Install Style III Breaker Points .... Page 13

Adjust Style III Breaker Points .... Page 13

Remove Style I Breaker Points

1. Remove condenser clamp screw and clamp, Fig. 27.

2. Lift condenser and wires away from cylinder. Compress condenser spring to remove stop switch wire and armature primary wire, Fig. 28. The tip of the condenser is one-half of the breaker points.

3. Remove post mounting screw to remove post, breaker spring and moveable point, Fig. 27.

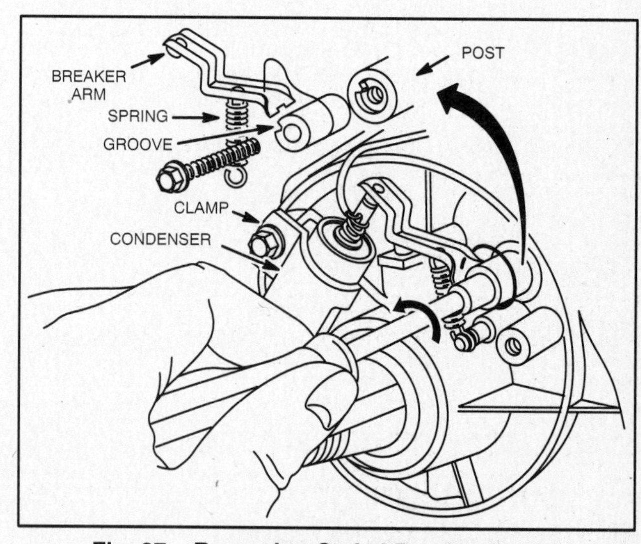

Fig. 27 - Removing Style I Breaker Points

NOTE: Early style condensers had a threaded condenser post. Remove nut and washer.

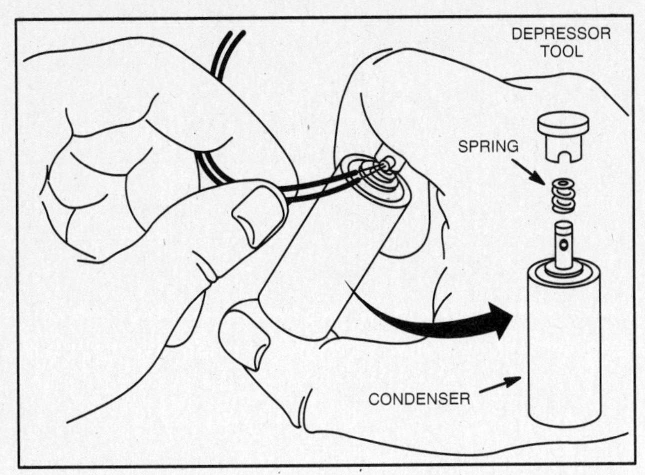

Fig. 28 - Removing or Installing Wires on Condenser

Remove Style II Breaker Points

1. Remove screw holding breaker assembly to cylinder block, Fig. 29.
2. Turn breaker points over and loosen screw holding armature primary wire and condenser wire.
3. Remove wires.

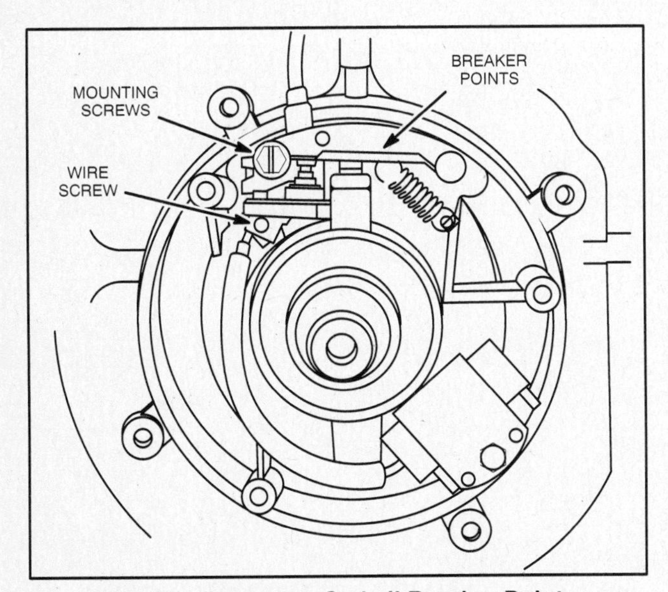

Fig. 29 - Removing Style II Breaker Points

Remove Style III Breaker Points

1. Loosen screw on breaker point assembly and remove armature primary wire and condenser wire, Fig. 30.
2. Remove screw holding breaker point to armature plate and remove points.

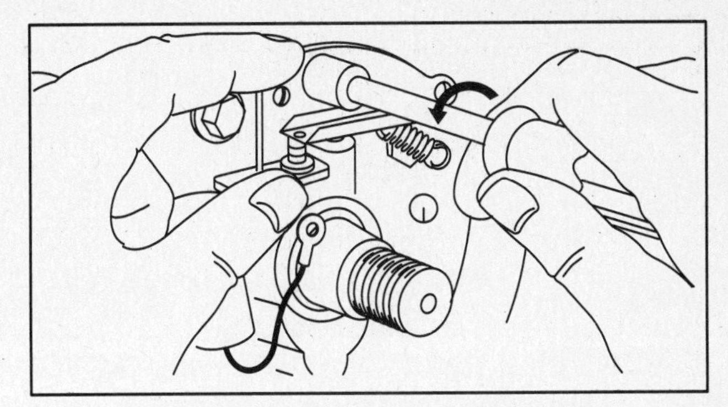

Fig. 30 - Removing Style III Breaker Points

Check Breaker Point Plunger Hole

A worn breaker point plunger hole can cause oil to leak past the plunger and contaminate the breaker points causing the points to burn.

1. To check for plunger hole wear, remove breaker points and plunger.
2. If flat end of Tool #19055, Plug Gauge, will enter plunger hole for a distance of 1/4 inch or more, the hole should be rebushed, Fig. 31.

NOTE: When breaker point plunger hole is worn beyond reject, installing Magnetron® on two leg armatures can be done on aluminum cylinder engines equipped with two (2) legged armatures instead of rebushing breaker point plunger hole. However, if breaker points and plunger are removed, plunger hole must be plugged using P/N 231143 which can be ordered through your normal source of supply.

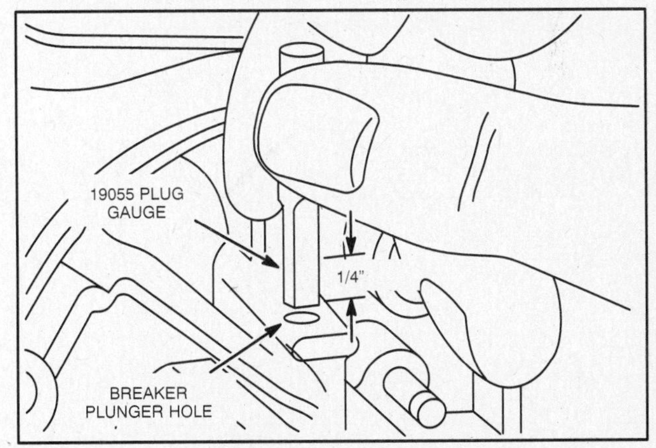

Fig. 31 - Checking Breaker Point Plunger Hole

Rebush Breaker Point Plunger Hole

1. Remove breaker points, armature, crankshaft, and breaker point plunger.
2. Use Tool #19056, Counterbore Reamer, to hand ream worn plunger hole, Fig. 32.
3. Keep reamer in alignment with plunger hole.

NOTE: METRIC EQUIVALENTS ARE LISTED ON PAGE 25 OF THIS SECTION.

NOTE: Crankshaft must be removed.

4. Drive service bushing, Part No. 23513, with Tool #19057, Bushing Driver, until upper end of bushing is flush with the top of the boss, Fig. 32.
5. Use Tool #19058, Finish Reamer, to hand ream the new bushing.
6. Keep reamer in alignment with bushing and plunger hole.
7. Remove all reaming chips and dirt.

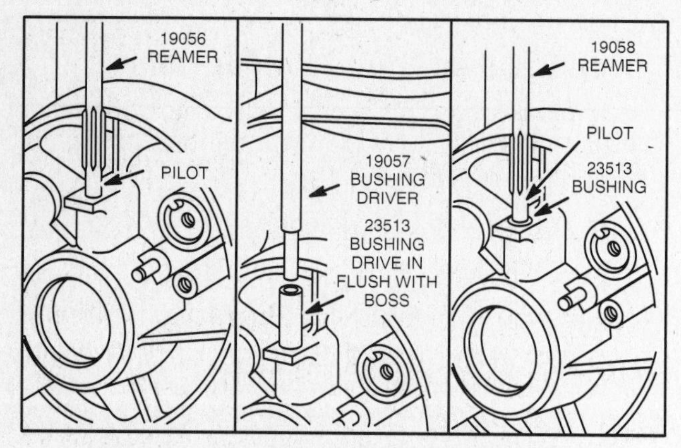

Fig. 32 – Installing Breaker Point Bushing

Check Breaker Point Plunger

Replace breaker point plunger if worn to .870 inches or less. Insert plunger with groove towards breaker points or oil will enter breaker point box, Fig. 33.

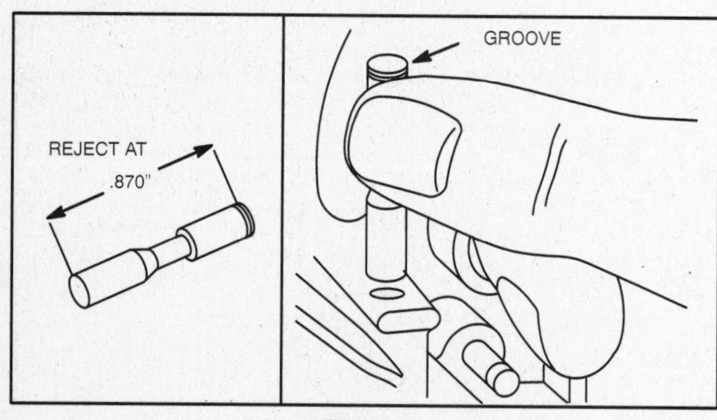

Fig. 33

INSTALL BREAKER POINTS

Install Style I Breaker Points

1. Install breaker point plunger, Fig. 33.
2. Install post into recess of cylinder with groove of post in notch of recess, Fig. 34. Note position of braided wire.
3. Tighten mounting screw securely.
4. Hook open loop of breaker spring into two holes of breaker arm, Fig. 34, and then hook closed loop of spring over spring post and into groove of post.
5. Push flat of breaker arm toward groove in mounting post until flat engages groove.
6. Compress spring on condenser and slip armature primary wire (and stop switch wire, if used) into hole of condenser post.
7. Release spring to clamp wire(s). Lay condenser into cylinder recess and install clamp and screw securely, Fig. 34.

NOTE: On early style threaded post condensers install wire(s), eyelet(s), washer and nut.

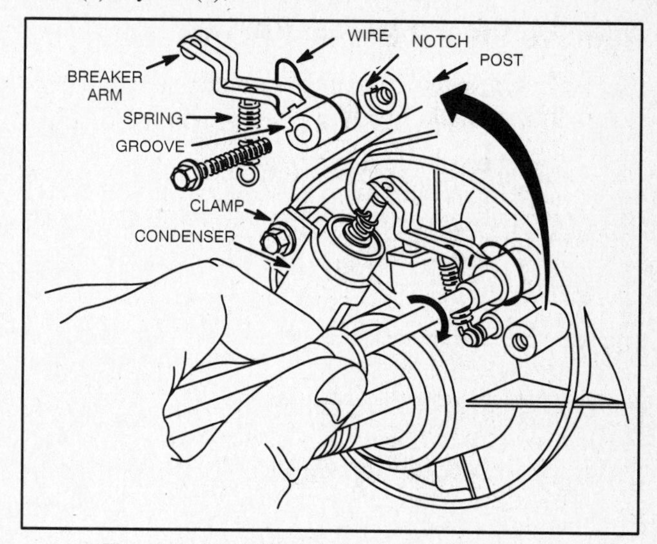

Fig. 34 – Installing Style I Breaker Points

Install Style II Breaker Points

1. Install armature primary wire in slot of insulation with end of wire under clamp and wire from condenser under clamp on breaker point set, Fig. 35. Note position of wires.
2. Place screw through eyelet of stop switch wire and install screw and eyelet on breaker point set terminal. Note position of eyelet.
3. Tighten screw while holding wires in correct position.
4. Install breaker point plunger in plunger hole, Fig. 33.
5. Place breaker set on cylinder with pin in hole of breaker set, Fig. 35.
6. Tighten screw finger tight.

NOTE: METRIC EQUIVALENTS ARE LISTED ON PAGE 25 OF THIS SECTION.

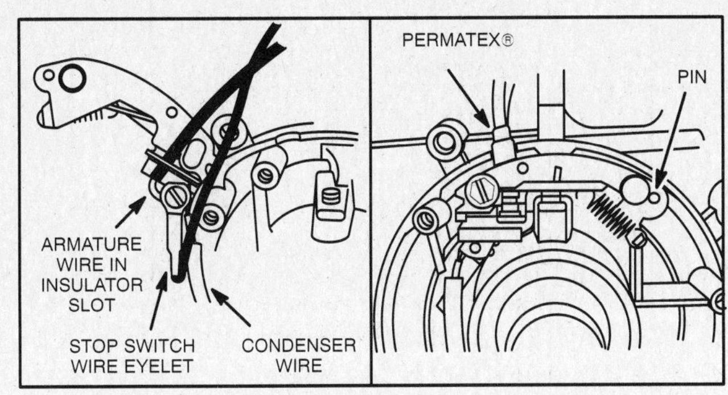

Fig. 35 - Installing Style II Breaker Points

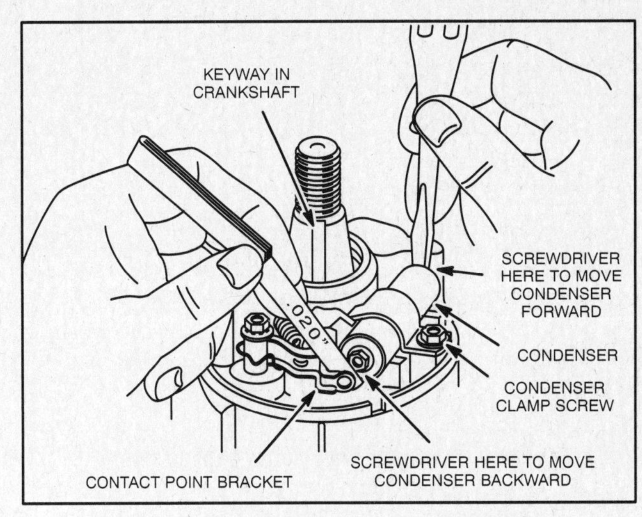

Fig. 37 - Adjusting Style I Breaker Points

Install Style III Breaker Points

1. Place armature wire and condenser wire under wire terminal, Fig. 36. Note position of wires.

2. Install breaker point set on engine with cast boss in plate entering hole in point set, Fig. 36.

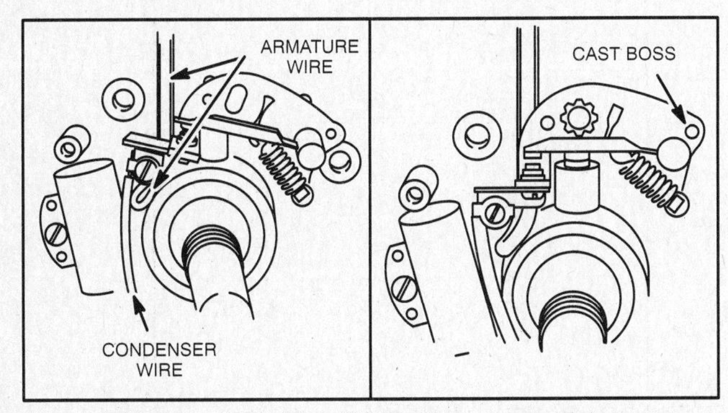

Fig. 36 - Installing Style III Breaker Points

Adjust Breaker Point Gap

Turn crankshaft until breaker points open to their widest gap.

Adjust Style I Breaker Points

With a screwdriver, move condenser back and forth until breaker points are gapped .020 inches wide, Fig. 37.

Adjust Styles II Breaker Points

1. Mounting screw should be finger tight.

2. With a screwdriver in the adjusting slot, move point bracket until breaker points are gapped .020 inches wide, Fig. 38.

3. Tighten mounting screw and recheck gap.

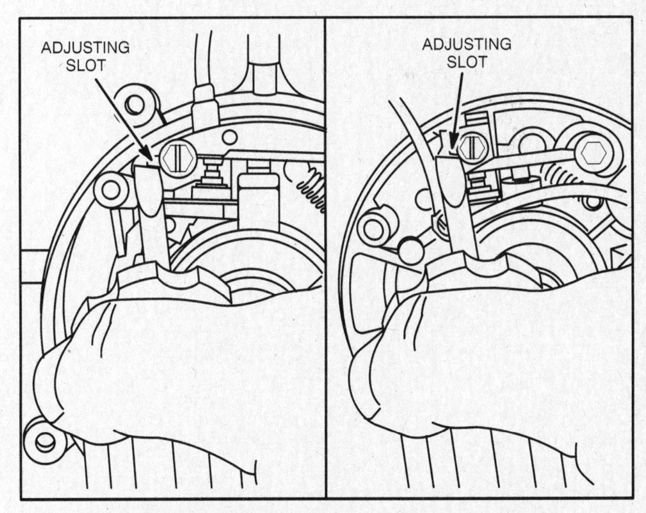

Fig. 38 - Adjusting Style II Breaker Points

Adjust Style III Breaker Points

1. With mounting screw finger tight, move point bracket until breaker points are gapped .020 inches wide, Fig. 39.

2. Tighten mounting screw and recheck point gap.

NOTE: METRIC EQUIVALENTS ARE LISTED ON PAGE 25 OF THIS SECTION.

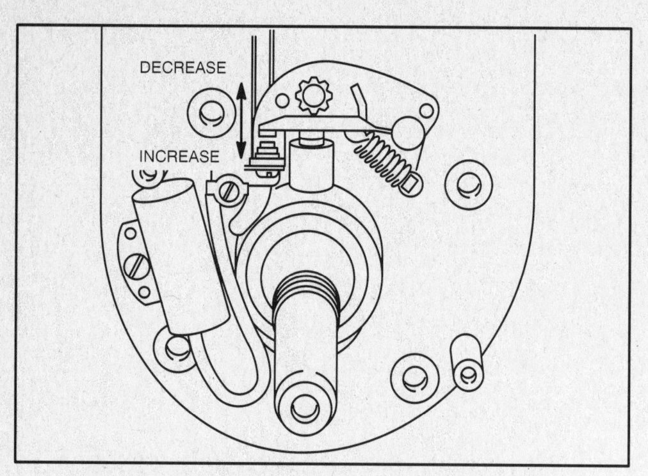

Fig. 39 - Adjusting Style III Breaker Points

NOTE: Always clean breaker points after adjustment.

1. Open breaker points and insert a piece of lint-free paper between points.
2. Rotate paper using breaker points as a pivot.
3. Open breaker points to remove paper so it will not tear or leave dirt on breaker points.
4. Continue to clean breaker points until paper comes out clean.

Breaker Point Cover

The breaker point cover protects the breaker points from dirt and moisture. The opening for the armature primary wire (and stop switch wire, when used) should be sealed with Permatex® or similar sealant to prevent dirt and moisture from entering breaker box, Fig. 40. Distorted covers will not seal around the outer edge and should be replaced.

NOTE: Engines used in winter applications use vented breaker covers. Refer to "Illustrated Parts List" for part numbers.

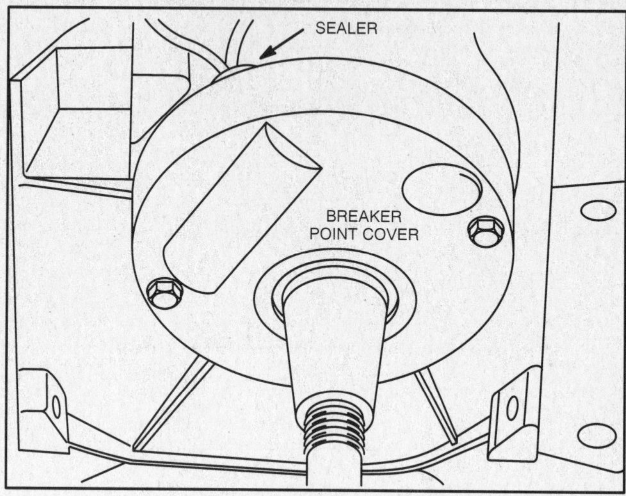

Fig. 40 - Installing and Sealing Breaker Cover (Typical)

FLYWHEEL MAGNETO IGNITION BREAKER POINTS - EXTERNAL

Remove Breaker Points Model Series 233000, 243000, 300000, 320000

1. Remove breaker cover.
2. For ease of assembly and point adjustment, if crankshaft was not removed, turn crankshaft until breaker points are at their widest gap.
3. Remove condenser, upper, and lower mounting screws.
4. Loosen lock nut and turn point adjustment screw counterclockwise to remove breaker points, Fig. 41.

BREAKER TERMINAL SCREW
UPPER MOUNTING SCREW
LOWER MOUNTING SCREW
CONDENSER
TURN BREAKER POINT SCREW CLOCKWISE TO INCREASE GAP
LOCK NUT
.020" GAP

Fig. 41 - Removing Breaker Points

NOTE: METRIC EQUIVALENTS ARE LISTED ON PAGE 25 OF THIS SECTION.

Breaker Point Plunger Seal

A seal, eyelet, and retainer were used on later production engines to prevent oil leakage past the breaker point plunger. If points were contaminated with oil on engines without these parts, add these parts to stop contamination, Fig. 42.

EXTREME CARE SHOULD BE TAKEN WHEN INSTALLING SEAL ON PLUNGER TO PREVENT FRACTURING SEAL.

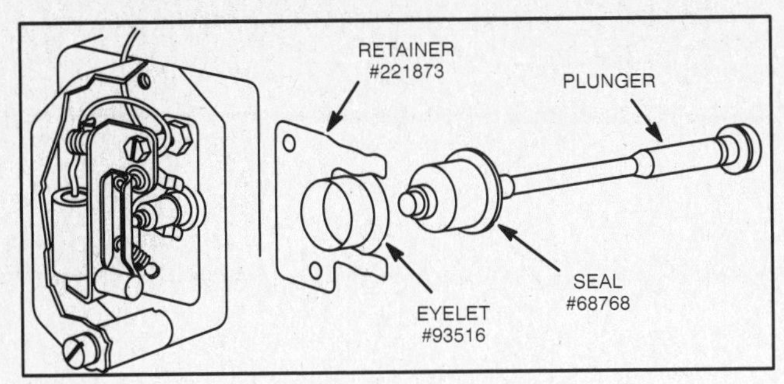

Fig. 42 - Seal Assembly

Replace Point Plunger or Plunger Bushing

Two styles of plunger bushings have been used. Removal and installation is as follows:

Remove Style I Plunger Bushing

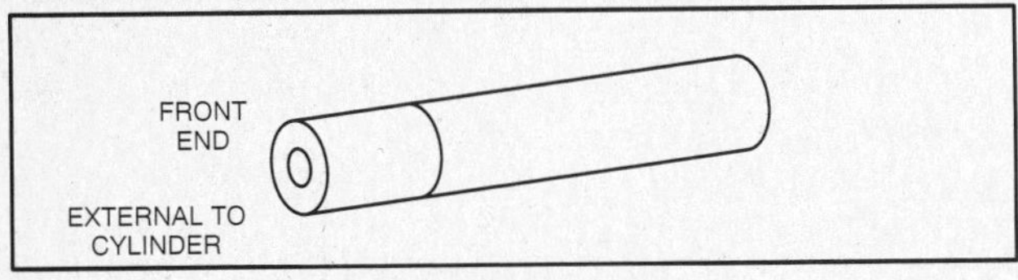

Fig. 43 - Style I Bushing

1. Remove breaker box cover, condenser, and breaker assembly, Fig. 41.
2. Pull breaker plunger out as far as possible.
3. Use a pair of pliers to break plunger off as close to bushing as possible, Fig. 44, Illus. "A."
4. Tap plunger bushing with a 1/4-20 tap or self-tapping screw, Part #93029 1/2 to 5/8 inches to deep, Fig. 44, Illus. "B."
5. Use a 1/4-20 x 1/2 inch long hex head screw and two spacer washers, Fig. 44, Illus. "C," to pull bushing out of the cylinder. The bushing will be free when it has been pulled 5/16 inches.
6. CAREFULLY remove the bushing and plunger and broken plunger.
7. DO NOT allow the plunger or chips to fall into the crankcase.

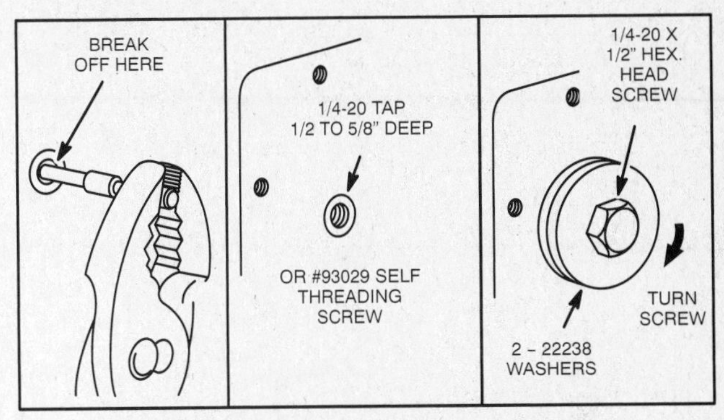

Fig. 44 - Removing Bushing and Plunger

Install Style I Bushing and Plunger

1. Insert plunger in new bushing, Fig. 45.

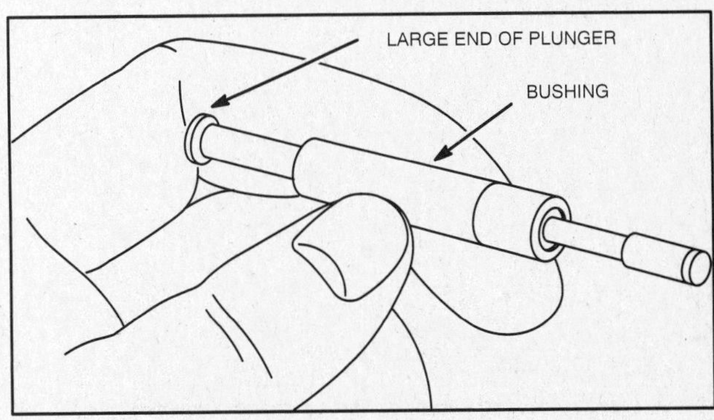

Fig. 45 - Inserting New Plunger in Bushing

2. Insert plunger and bushing into cylinder.
3. Use a hammer and the old bushing to drive new bushing into cylinder until bushing is flush with the face of the cylinder, Fig. 46.
4. Check for freedom of movement of the plunger.

NOTE: METRIC EQUIVALENTS ARE LISTED ON PAGE 25 OF THIS SECTION.

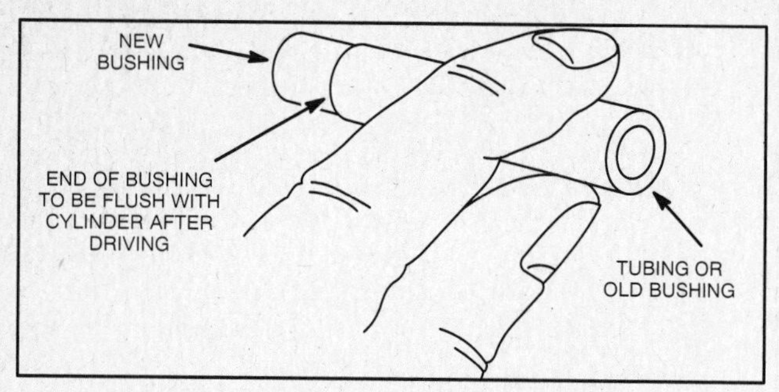

Fig. 46 - Installing Bushing and Plunger

Remove Style II Bushing

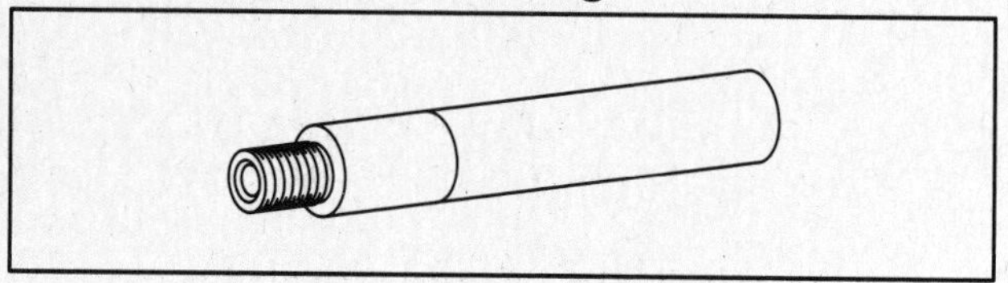

Fig. 47 - Style II Bushing

1. Remove breaker box cover, condenser, and breaker assembly, Fig. 41.
2. Place a thick 3/8 inch inside diameter washer, such as Part #22238, over the end of bushing and screw on a 3/8-24 nut, Fig. 48, Illus. "A."
3. Tighten nut to pull bushing.
4. After the bushing has moved about 1/8 inch, remove the nut and put on a second washer, Fig. 48, Illus. "B."
5. Reinstall nut and continue to turn nut until bushing is free.

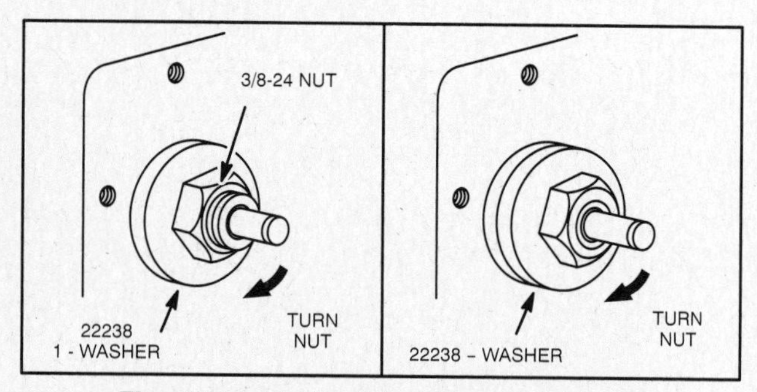

Fig. 48 - Installing Bushing and Plunger

Install Style II Bushing and Plunger

1. Insert new plunger into bushing with large end of plunger opposite threads on bushing.
2. Screw 3/8-24 nut onto threaded end of bushing to protect threads, Fig. 49.

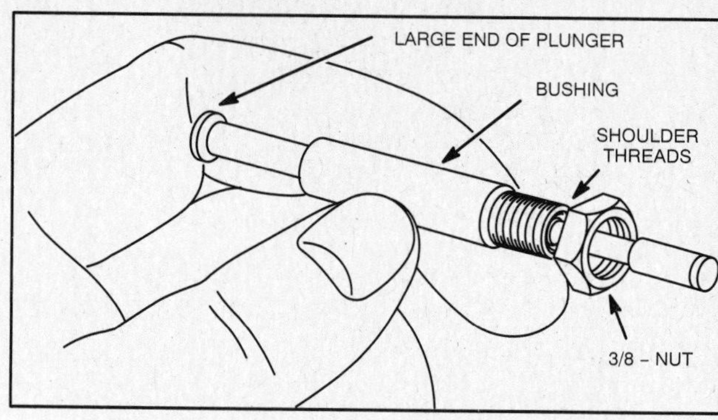

Fig. 49 - Inserting Plunger into Bushing

3. Insert bushing and plunger into cylinder.
4. Use a piece of metal tubing or Part #295840 piston pin to drive bushing into cylinder.
5. Drive bushing until square shoulder of bushing is flush with the face of cylinder, Fig. 50.
6. Check to be sure that plunger moves freely.

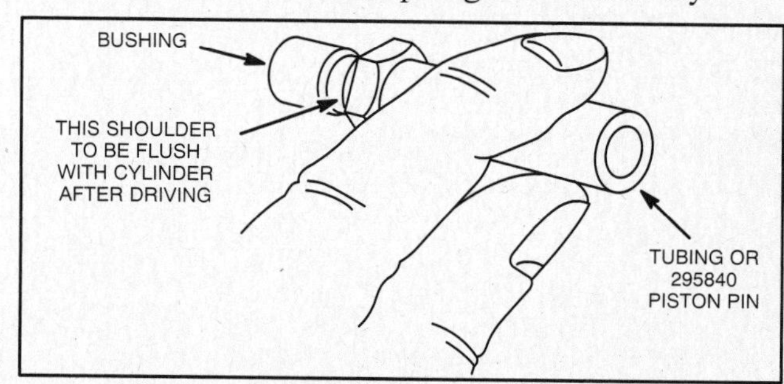

Fig. 50 - Installing Plunger and Bushing

Assembly Condenser and Breaker Points

1. Install armature primary wire and condenser lead under terminal clamp and tighten screw. Note position of armature primary and condenser lead, Fig. 51.

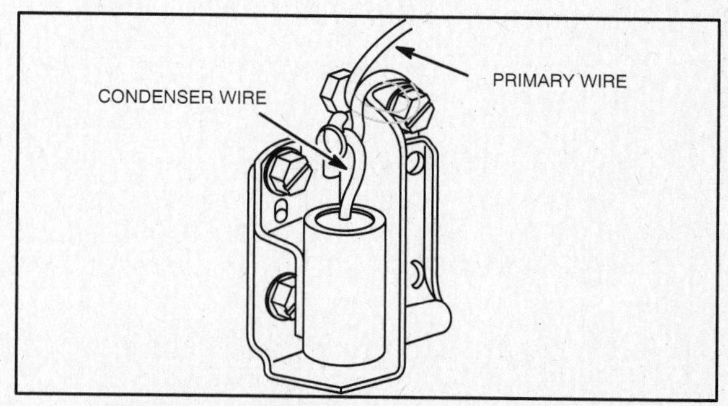

Fig. 51 - Installing Wire and Condenser

2. Apply sealer, such as Permatex® or similar sealant, to adjusting screw and two mounting screws. Sealant prevents engine oil from leaking into breaker cover and onto points.

NOTE: METRIC EQUIVALENTS ARE LISTED ON PAGE 25 OF THIS SECTION.

3. On new breaker points, turn lock nut back until it contacts ferrule on breaker point bracket.

   NOTE: On breaker points that are being reused, turn lock nut back until it contacts ferrule on breaker point bracket.

4. While holding adjusting screw, tighten nut against ferrule. This secures the adjustment screw to the breaker point bracket.

Install Breaker Point and Condenser Assembly

1. Place breaker assembly on engine and start adjustment screw.
2. Install lower mounting screw through bracket and lower hole of seal retainer.
3. Start upper mounting screw and then tighten lower mounting screw.
4. Now tighten the upper mounting screw, Fig. 52.

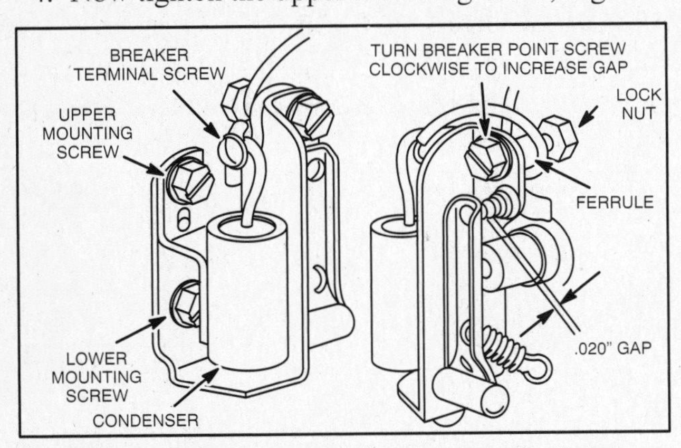

Fig. 52 - Installing and Adjusting Breaker Points

Adjust Breaker Points

1. Turn crankshaft until breaker points are at their widest gap.
2. Turn adjusting screw until point gap is .020 inches.
3. Tighten lock nut while holding adjustment screw, Fig. 52.
4. Recheck point gap after tightening lock nut.
5. Readjust as required.

Clean Breaker Points

1. Turn crankshaft until breaker points are closed.
2. Open breaker points and insert a piece of lint-free paper and close points.
3. Rotate paper using breaker points as a pivot point.
4. Open breaker points and withdraw paper from breaker points. Removing paper with breaker points closed can tear paper and will leave dirt on the breaker points.
5. Continue to clean breaker points until paper comes out clean.

Install Breaker Cover

Apply sealer such as Permatex® No. 2 at the opening on the breaker cover for the armature primary wire. This sealant is to prevent entry of dirt and moisture, Fig. 53.

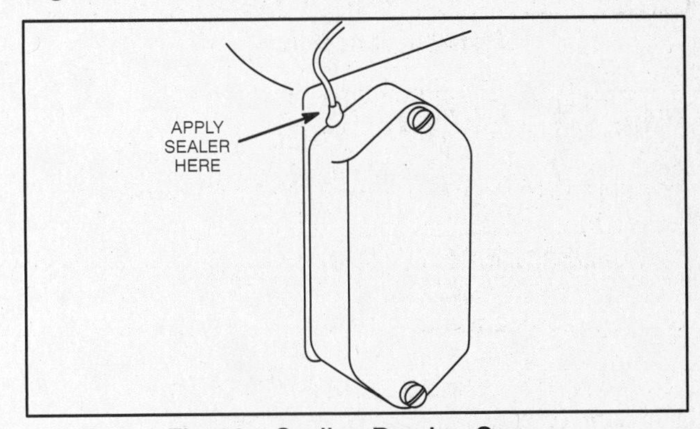

Fig. 53 - Sealing Breaker Cover

INSTALL ARMATURES

Install Armatures, Air Vane Governor

1. Install armature and air vane, when used. The mounting holes of the armature are slotted.
2. Push armature away from flywheel as far as possible and tighten one mounting screw, Fig. 54.

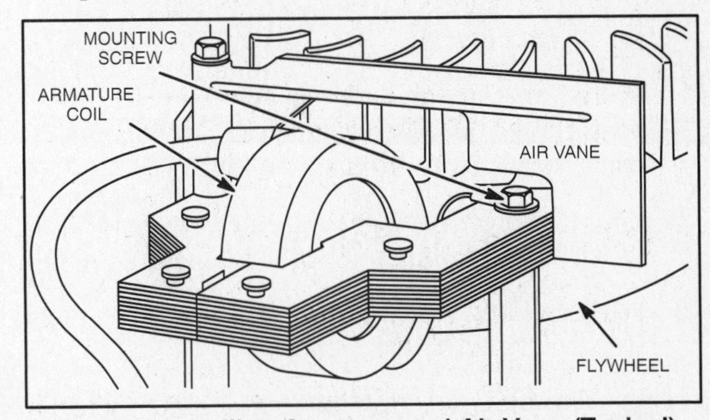

Fig. 54 - Installing Armature and Air Vane (Typical)

NOTE: METRIC EQUIVALENTS ARE LISTED ON PAGE 25 OF THIS SECTION.

Install Armatures, Mechanical Governors

1. Install armature and air guide. The mounting holes of the armature are slotted.
2. Push armature away from flywheel and tighten one screw, Fig. 55.

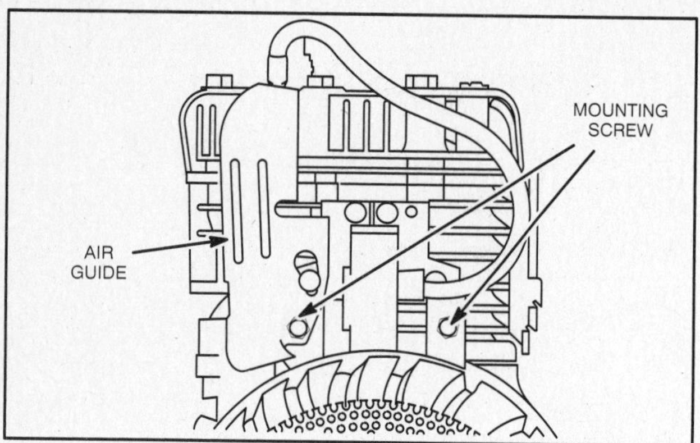

Fig. 55 - Installing Armature and Air Guide

Adjust Armature Air Gap

Two styles of armatures have been used. Style I is the three leg style and Style II is the two leg style, Fig. 56.

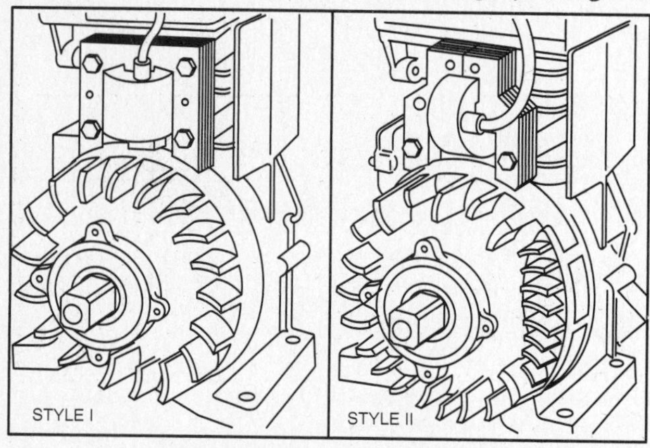

Fig. 56 - Types of Armatures

Adjust Armature Air Gap

1. Armature air gaps are found in Table No. 1, page 2 for Styles I and II.
2. With armature away from flywheel as far as possible and one screw tightened, turn flywheel so magnets are away from armature.
3. Place the proper thickness gauge between rim of flywheel and laminations of the armature.
4. While holding gauge, turn flywheel until magnets are directly under laminations.
5. Loosen the one screw holding armature and let magnets pull armature down against flywheel.
6. Tighten both mounting screws.
7. Rotate flywheel until gauge is free, Fig. 57.

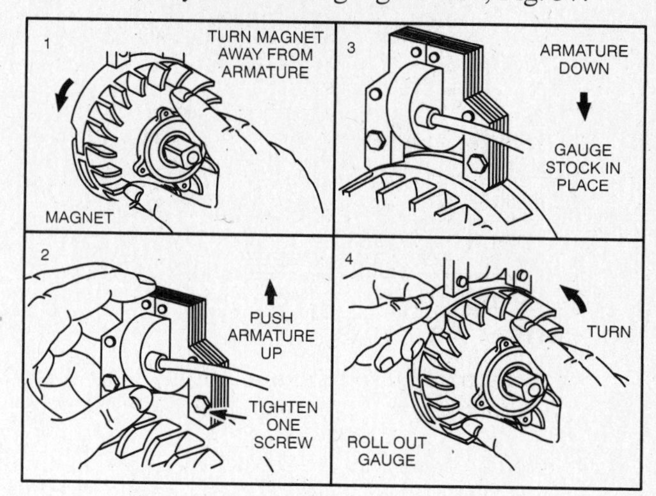

Fig. 57 - Adjusting Armature Air Gap

Adjust Armature Timing External Breaker Points, Model Series 230000, 243400, 300000, 320000

NOTE: Before armature can be timed, flywheel must be removed and breaker points must be adjusted to .020 inches.

1. Slide flywheel onto crankshaft taper.
2. Slip flywheel key into place.
3. Install flywheel nut finger tight.
4. Using Tool #19357, Digital Multimeter, or Tool #19236, VOA Meter, Fig. 58, set meter to ohms (Ω) zeroing meter if required, and connect one test lead to breaker point primary lead.
5. Connect second test lead to breaker point mounting bracket.

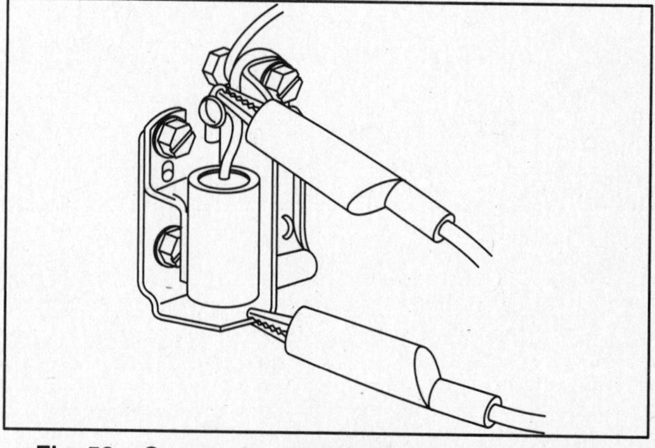

Fig. 58 - Connecting Digital Multimeter #19357 or VOA Meter #19236

NOTE: METRIC EQUIVALENTS ARE LISTED ON PAGE 25 OF THIS SECTION.

6. Disconnect armature ground wire from armature laminations and pull wire away from laminations, Fig. 59.
7. Turn flywheel clockwise until meter shows points are closed (low ohms reading).
8. Turn flywheel slowly clockwise until points open (high ohms reading).
9. Arrow on flywheel should be in line with arrow on armature bracket when points just open, Fig. 59.

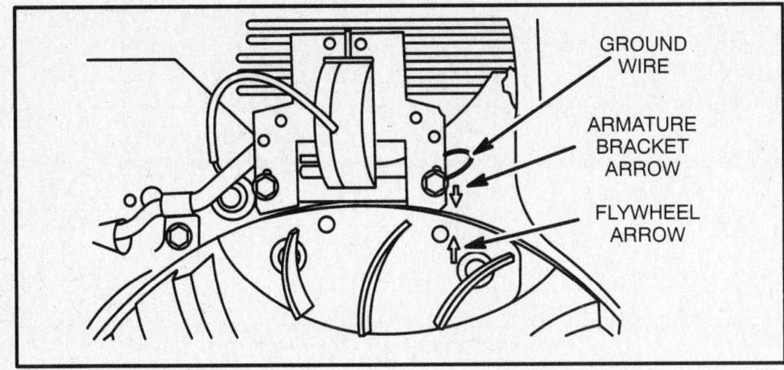

Fig. 59 – Timing Armature

10. If arrows do not line up, remove flywheel without moving crankshaft.
11. Loosen screws holding armature bracket until bracket can be moved with a slight drag.
12. Slip flywheel back on crankshaft without moving crankshaft.
13. Insert flywheel key. Install flywheel key and nut finger tight.
14. Move armature bracket assembly until arrows line up, Fig. 59.
15. Remove flywheel and tighten armature bracket screws.
16. Torque flywheel and adjust armature air gap to specifications listed in Table No. 1, page 2.

STOP SWITCH IDENTIFICATION

Stationary, rotary, toggle, and key stop switches are used to meet various equipment needs, Fig. 60.

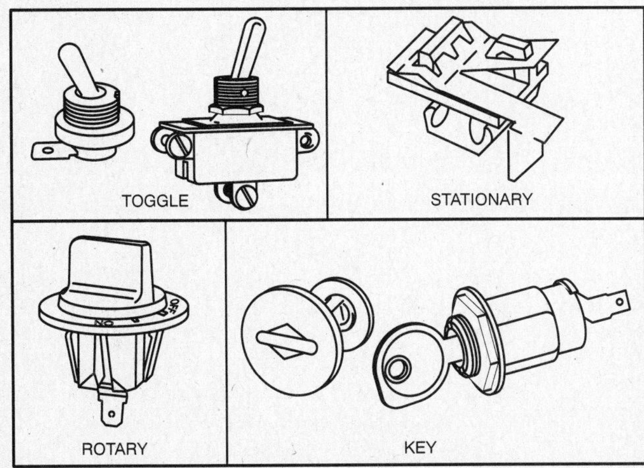

Fig. 60 – Types of Stop Switches

TOGGLE SWITCHES

KEY SWITCHES

Stationary Stop Switch

Stationary stop switches are located on fuel tank brackets, governor control brackets, cylinder head brackets, System 2® and System 4® band brake control brackets, and brake shoe on Model Series 100700, 120000.

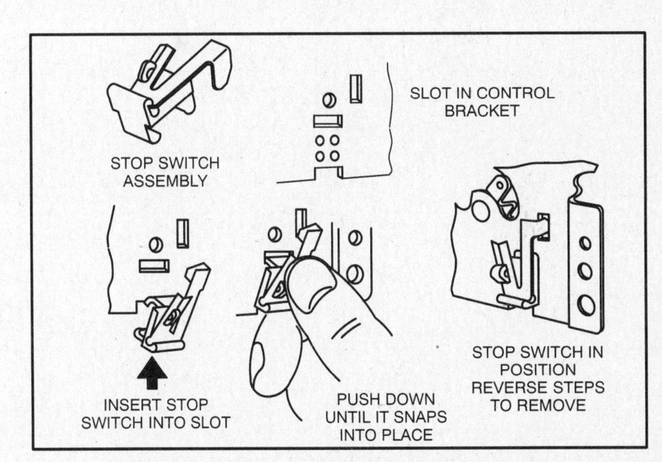

Fig. 61 – Typical Stop Switch Installation

Stationary Stop Switch, Mechanical Check

1. Move control lever away from stop switch, Fig. 62, using safety control shown in Fig. 66 or by moving control lever at engine, in direction shown in Fig. 62.

2. Then release control completely. Control lever at engine must contact stop switch at tang shown in Fig. 63.

NOTE: METRIC EQUIVALENTS ARE LISTED ON PAGE 25 OF THIS SECTION.

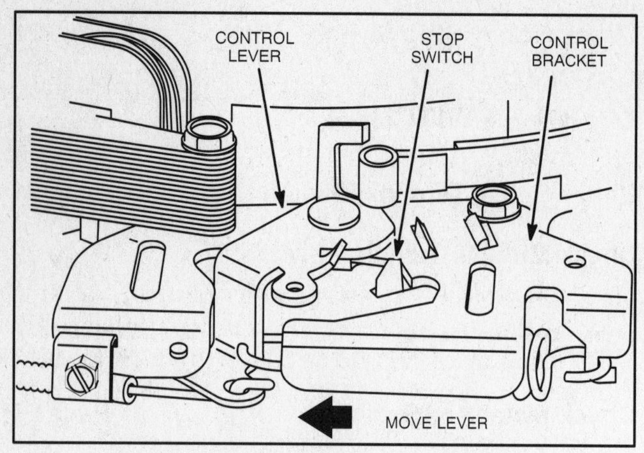

Fig. 62 - Control Lever, RUN Position

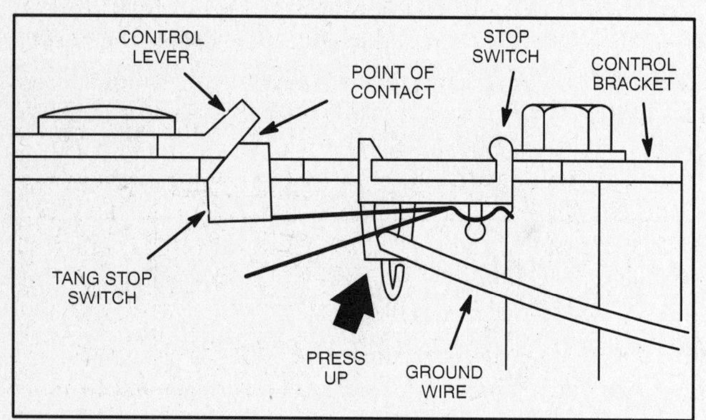

Fig. 63 - Control Lever - STOP Position

Fig. 64 - System 2® Engine

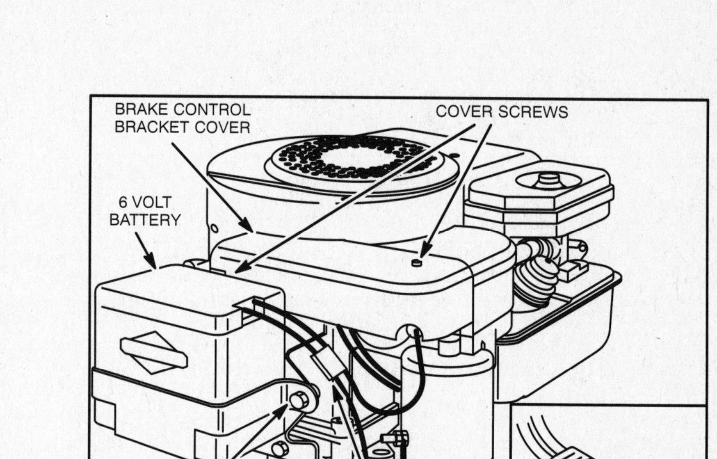

Fig. 65 - System 3® & System 4® Engine

DISCONNECT THE BATTERY TO PREVENT ACCIDENTAL STARTER OPERATION.

Stationary Stop Switch, Electrical Check

1. Push down on wire retainer and remove stop switch wire. On System 2® and System 4® the band brake control cover must be removed, Fig's. 64 and 65.

NOTE: On System 3® & System 4® engines with battery mounted on the engine, the battery must be removed from the battery holder before the cover can be removed.

NOTE: On Model Series 100700 engines the flywheel must be removed before the stop switch can be tested.

2. Using Tool #19357, Digital Multimeter, or Tool #19326, VOA Meter, set meter to ohms (Ω) zeroing meter if required, and connect test leads to engine ground and other test lead to wire retainer. Move control lever to run position.

NOTE: On System 2® and System 4® engines operate safety control (operator presence control) to move control lever away from stop switch, Fig's. 66, 67, and 68.

NOTE: METRIC EQUIVALENTS ARE LISTED ON PAGE 25 OF THIS SECTION.

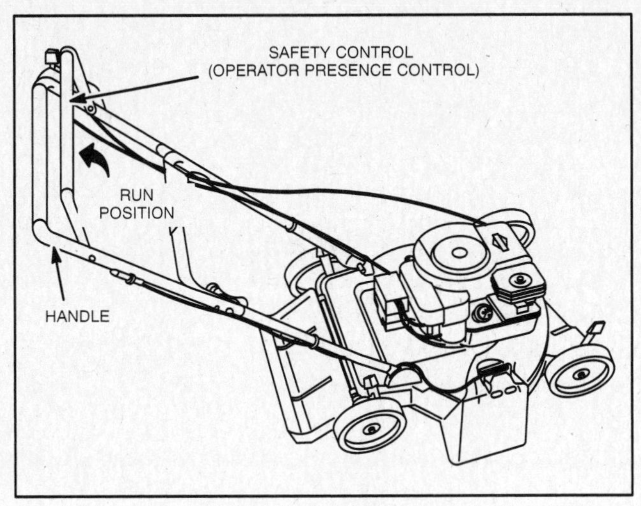

Fig. 66 - Typical Control

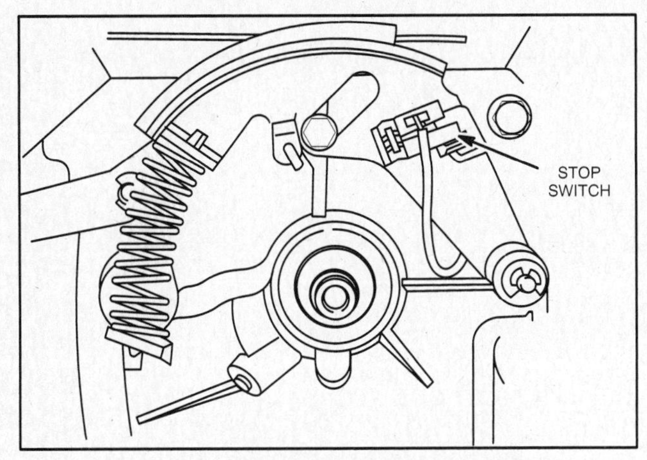

Fig. 67 - Brake Shoe Stop Switch, Model Series 100700

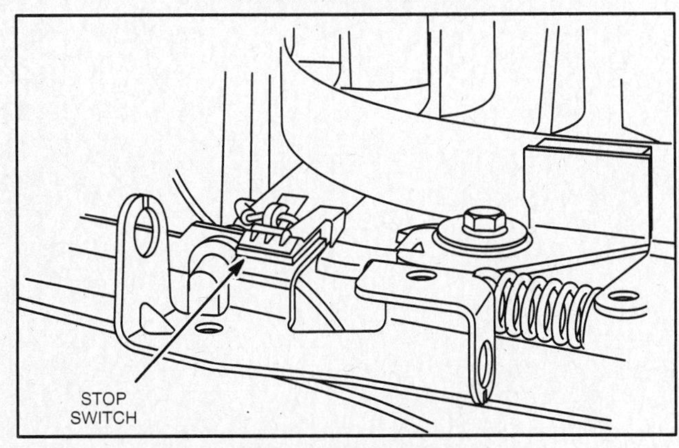

Fig. 68 - Brake Shoe Stop Switch, Model Series 120000

3. With control lever in run position, VOA meter should show no continuity (high ohms reading).

4. Move control lever to stop position or release safety control (operator presence control) to move control lever.

5. Meter should show continuity (low ohms reading).

6. If switch shows continuity in both run and stop positions or no continuity in both positions, replace stop switch and check stop switch wire for damage.

Check Rotary Stop Switch

1. Remove blower housing from engine and disconnect stop switch wire from switch.

2. Using Tool #19357, Digital Multimeter, or Tool #19236, VOA Meter, set meter to ohms (Ω) zeroing meter if required, and connect test leads to blower housing and to stop switch terminal, Fig. 69.

3. With switch in "OFF" position there should be continuity (low ohms reading).

4. Turn switch to "ON" position and there should be no continuity (high ohms reading).

5. Replace switch if there is no continuity in both "ON" and "OFF" positions or there is continuity in both positions and check stop switch wire for damage.

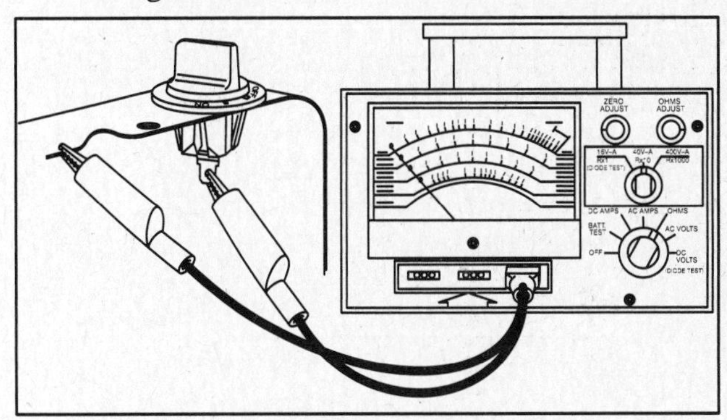

Fig. 69 - Checking Rotary Stop Switch

Toggle Switches

Two styles of toggle switches have been used, single terminal and multiple terminals.

Check Single Terminal Switch

1. Disconnect stop switch wire from spade terminal.

2. Using Tool #19357, Digital Multimeter, or Tool #19236, VOA Meter, set meter to ohms (Ω) zeroing meter if required, and connect test leads to spade terminal and to switch mounting surface.

   NOTE: Mounting surface must be free of paint, rust or dirt.

3. With switch in "OFF" position there should be continuity (low ohms reading).

NOTE: METRIC EQUIVALENTS ARE LISTED ON PAGE 25 OF THIS SECTION.

4. Move switch to "ON" position. There should be no continuity (high ohms reading), Fig. 70.

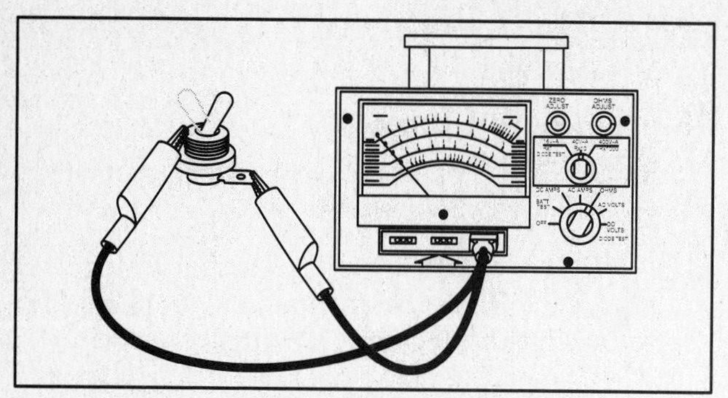

Fig. 70 - Checking Toggle Stop Switch

Check Multiple Terminal Switch

1. Disconnect all wires from switch marking each wire for correct reinstallation.

2. Using Tool #19357, Digital Multimeter, or Tool #19236, VOA Meter, set meter to ohms (Ω) zeroing meter if required, and connect test leads to either center terminal and a terminal on either end of switch on the same side as the center terminal.

3. If meter shows continuity (low ohms reading) move switch to other position and the reading should not show continuity (high ohms reading), Fig. 71.

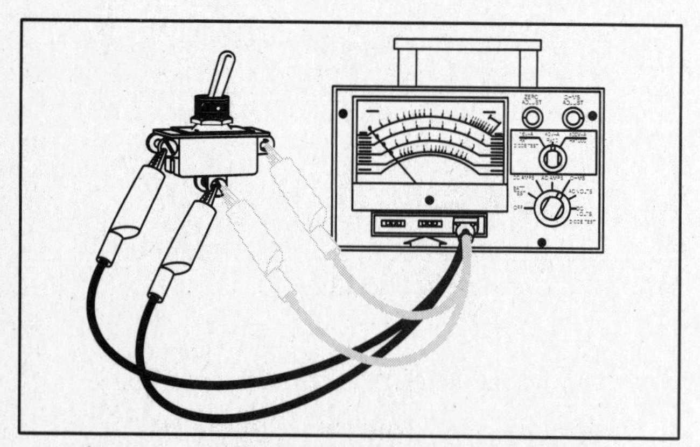

Fig. 71 - Checking Multiple Terminal Switch

4. Move tests lead from end terminal to other end terminal and repeat tests. Test results should be the opposite of first tests, Fig. 71.

5. Repeat tests for terminals on other side of switch. If there is continuity in both switch positions or no continuity in either switch position, replace switch and check stop switch wire for damage.

Key Switches

Two styles of key switches have been used, metal key and plastic key.

Check Metal Key Switch

1. Disconnect stop switch wire from spade terminal. Using Tool #19357, Digital Multimeter, or Tool #19236, VOA Meter, set meter to ohms (Ω) zeroing meter if required, and connect test leads to spade terminal and to switch mounting surface.

   NOTE: Surface must be free of paint, rust and dirt.

2. With key in "OFF" position there should be continuity (low ohms reading).

3. Turn key to "ON" position. There should not be continuity (high ohms reading), Fig. 72.

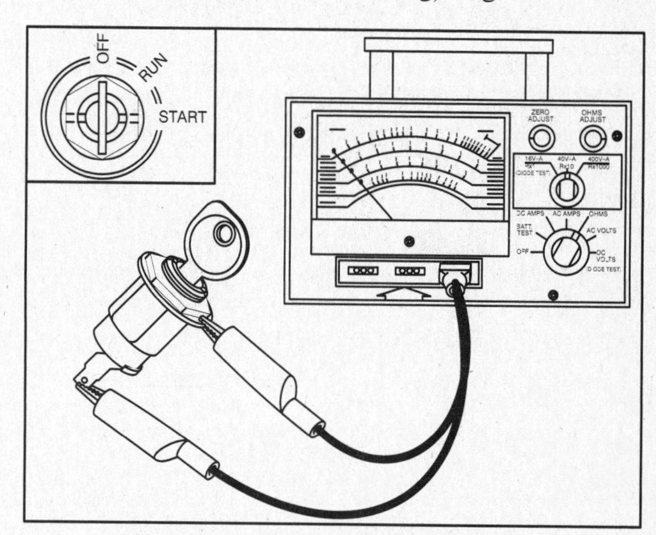

Fig. 72 - Checking Metal Key Switch

Check Switch with Plastic Key

1. Disconnect stop switch wire from spade terminal. Using Tool #19357, Digital Multimeter, or Tool #19236, VOA Meter, set meter to ohms (Ω) zeroing meter if required, and connect test leads to spade terminal and to switch mounting surface.

   NOTE: Mounting surface must be free of paint, rust and dirt.

2. With key pushed all the way in there should be no continuity (high ohms reading).

3. Pull key out and there should be continuity (low ohms reading), Fig. 73.

NOTE: METRIC EQUIVALENTS ARE LISTED ON PAGE 25 OF THIS SECTION.

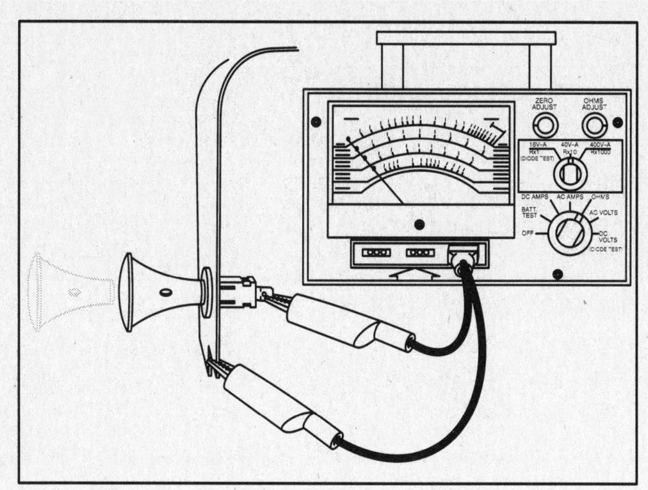

Fig. 73 - Checking Switch with Plastic Key

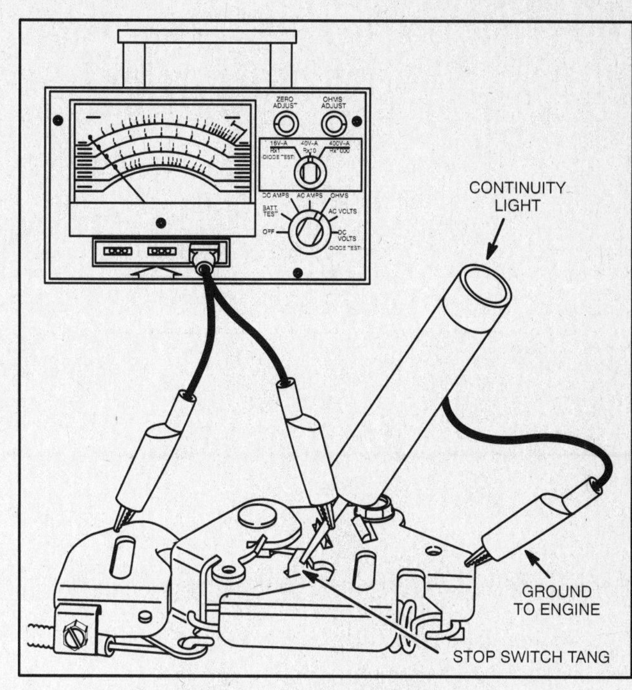

Fig. 74 - Testing Continuity

STOP SWITCH WIRE, ALL MODELS

Check Stop Switch Wire

1. Using Tool #19357, Digital Multimeter, or Tool #19236, VOA Meter, set meter to ohms (Ω) zeroing meter if required, and connect one test lead to end of stop switch wire.

2. Connect other test lead to engine ground. There should be continuity (low ohms reading).

3. Move wire back and forth and up and down.

4. If readings change, repair or replace damaged wire.

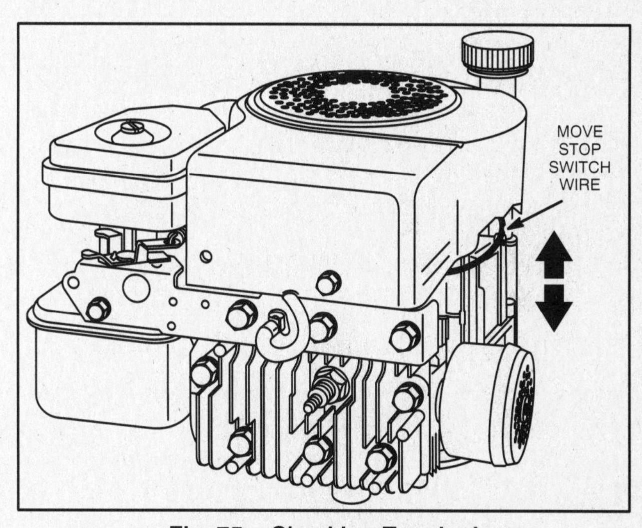

Fig. 75 - Checking Terminal

Stop Switch Wire Continuity Test

To test, place control lever, Fig. 62, and safety control, if engine is mounted on equipment, in run position.

1. Use a continuity light, Tool #19357, Digital Multimeter, or Tool #19236, VOA Meter, set meter to ohms (Ω) zeroing meter, and connect one test lead to ground (unpainted bracket or engine surface).

2. Hold other test lead against stop switch tang, Fig. 74, while moving stop switch wire up and down, Fig. 75. **CAUTION:** Do not pull on stop switch wire.

3. Continuity light should remain ON or meter should read less than 1 ohm or more than 0.3 ohms during stop switch wire movement.

4. If test is positive, reassemble any parts that were removed to perform test.

5. If light goes out or meter reads open circuit, check for proper contact at stop switch tang and engine ground.

6. Retest.

NOTE: METRIC EQUIVALENTS ARE LISTED ON PAGE 25 OF THIS SECTION.

7. Poor or no continuity requires replacing stop switch wire and/or soldering stop switch wire to armature primary wire at replaceable MAGNETRON® module terminal, Fig. 76.

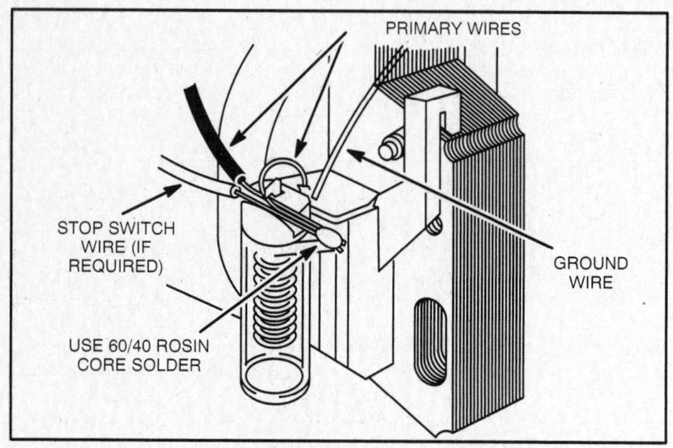

Fig. 76 – Check Magnetron® Module Terminal

Typical Stop Switch Wire Routings

To prevent stop switch wire damage, route as shown in figures below which show the engine system used on equipment, Fig's. 77, 78, 79, and 80.

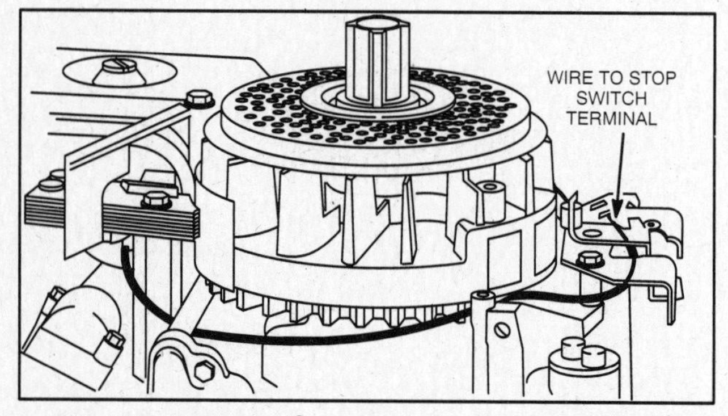

Fig. 77 – System 2®, except Model Series 120000

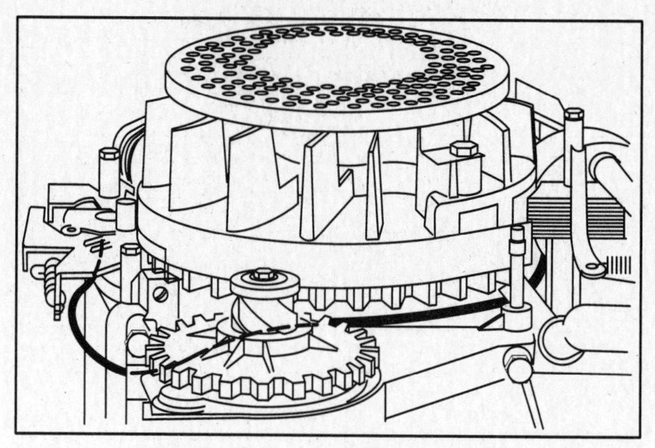

Fig. 78 – System 3®, System 4®, except Model Series 120000

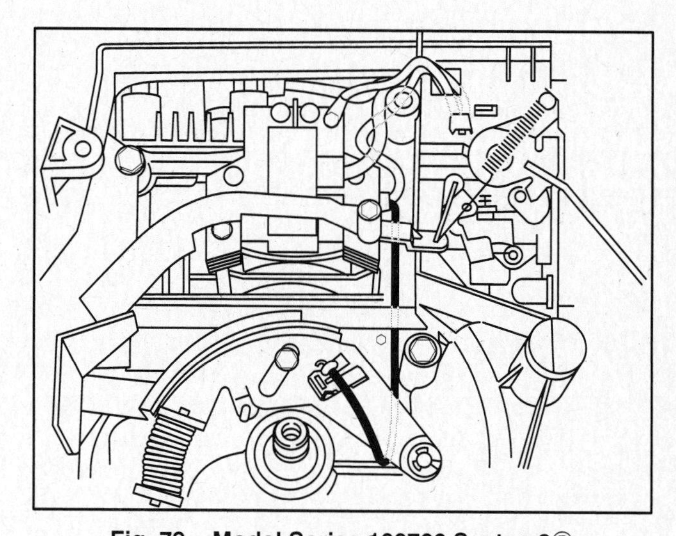

Fig. 79 – Model Series 100700 System2®

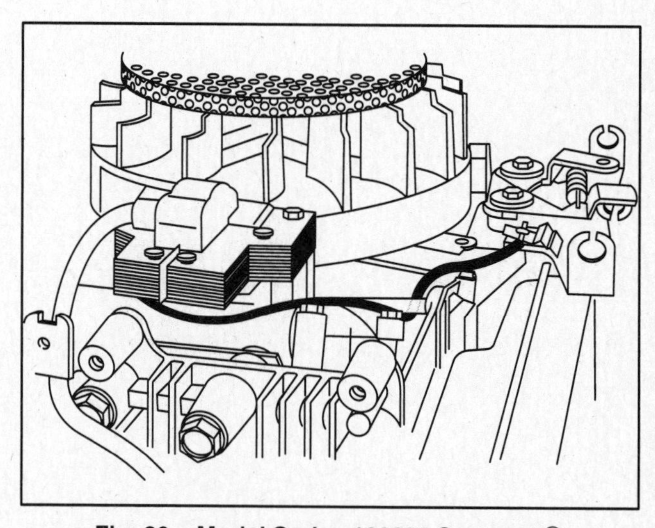

Fig. 80 – Model Series 120000 System 2®

NOTE: METRIC EQUIVALENTS ARE LISTED ON PAGE 25 OF THIS SECTION.

METRIC EQUIVALENTS

DIMENSIONS, FRACTIONAL	
Inches	**Millimeters**
1/8	3.2
1/4	6.4
5/32	3.9
3/16	4.7
5/16	7.9
1/2	12.7
5/8	15.9
3/4	19.0
13/16	20.6
1-1/2	38.1
2	50.8
6-3/4	171.00

DIMENSIONS, DECIMAL	
.006	.15
.008	.20
.010	.25
.012	.30
.014	.36
.016	.41
.020	.50
.022	.56
.026	.66
.030	.76
.166	4.22
.870	22.10

TORQUE		
Ft. Lbs.	**Kpm**	**Nm**
55	7.6	74.6
65	9.0	88.1
145	20.0	196.6

NOTE: METRIC EQUIVALENTS ARE LISTED ON PAGE 25 OF THIS SECTION.

Section 3
CARBURETION

AIR CLEANER IDENTIFICATION, see page 4

CARBURETOR IDENTIFICATION

Three styles of carburetors are used on Briggs & Stratton engines. Compare carburetor to be repaired with illustrations below and on following pages to determine style of carburetor you have and refer to pages listed for service and repair information.

Before removing any carburetor for repair, look for signs of air leakage, or mounting gaskets that are loose, have deteriorated, or are otherwise damaged.

Note position of governor springs, governor link, remote control or other attachments to facilitate reassembly. Do not bend links or stretch springs. (Section 4, Governor Controls & Carburetor Linkages, illustrates popular engine models.)

FLO-JET CARBURETORS

SMALL B&S/WALBRO

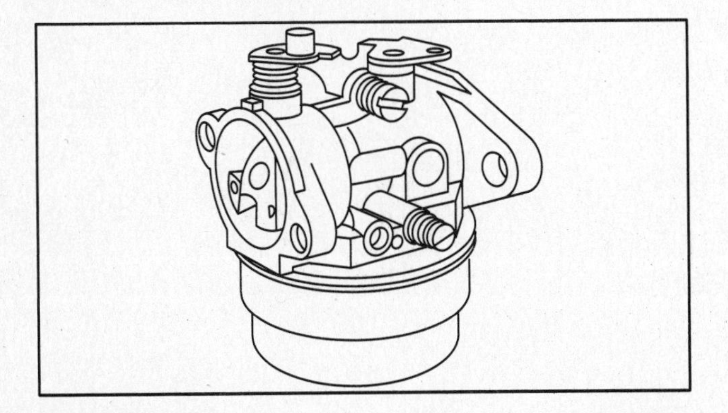

LARGE B&S/WALBRO

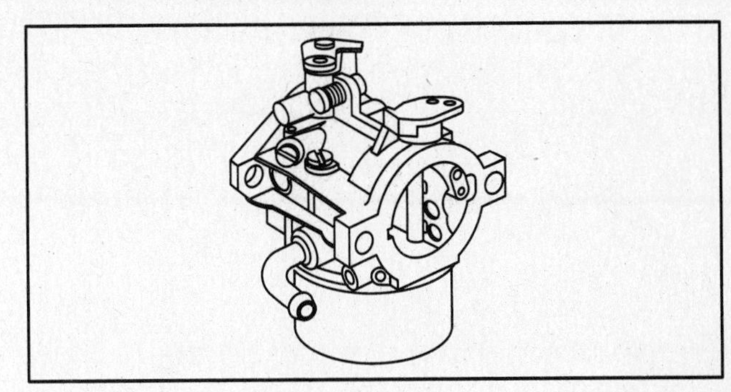

ONE PIECE

TWO PIECE

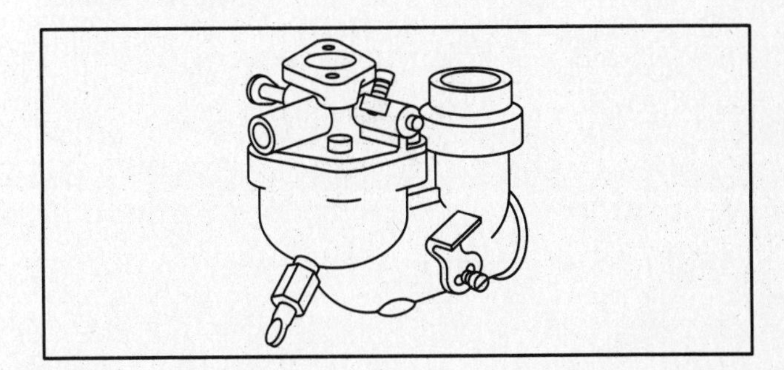

NOTE: METRIC EQUIVALENTS ARE LISTED ON PAGE 68 OF THIS SECTION.

FLO-JET CARBURETORS, CONT'D.

CROSS-OVER

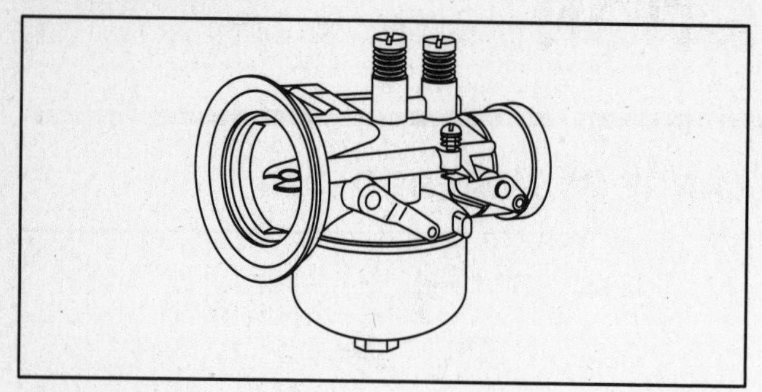

PULSA-JET CARBURETORS

PULSA-PRIME

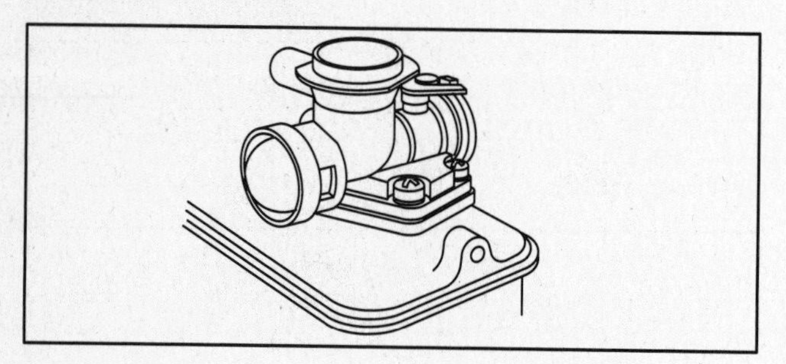

FIXED JET

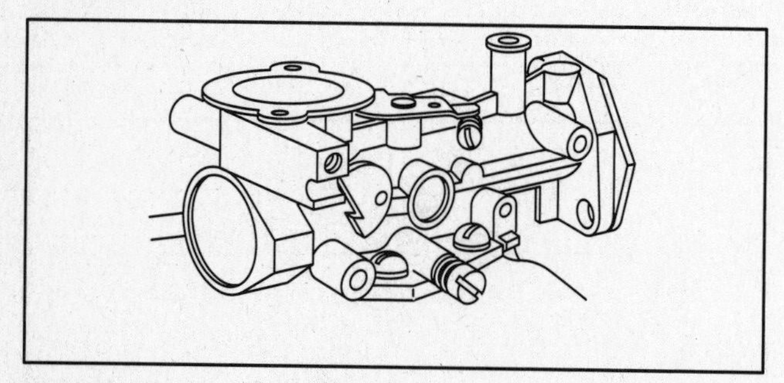

ALL TEMPERATURE/AUTOMATIC CHOKE

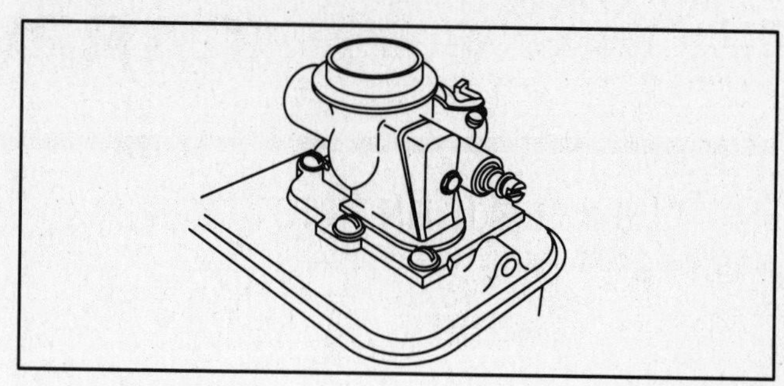

AUTOMATIC CHOKE

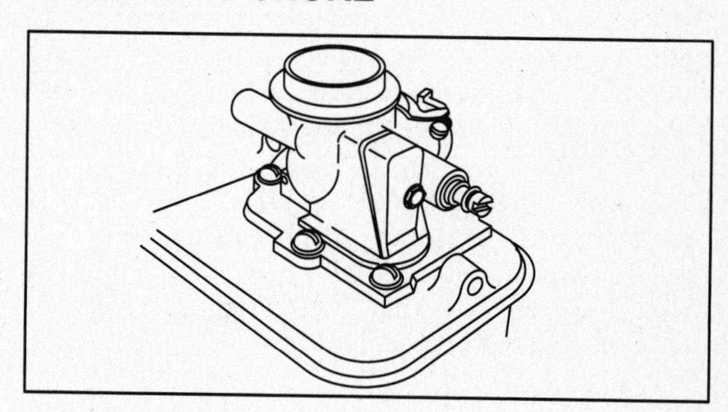

ROTARY CHOKE

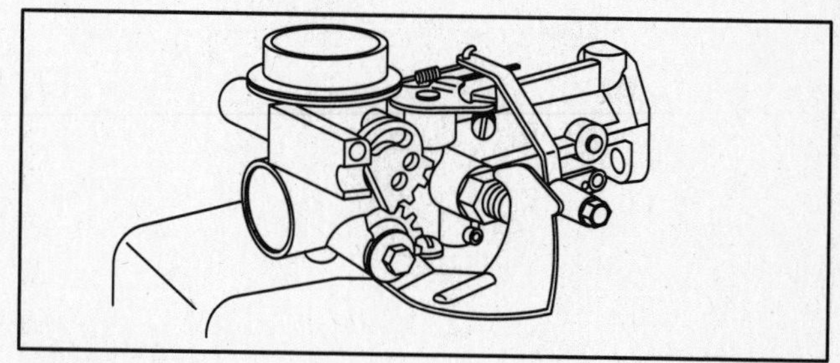

NOTE: METRIC EQUIVALENTS ARE LISTED ON PAGE 68 OF THIS SECTION.

PULSA-JET CARBURETORS, CONT'D.

SLIDE CHOKE

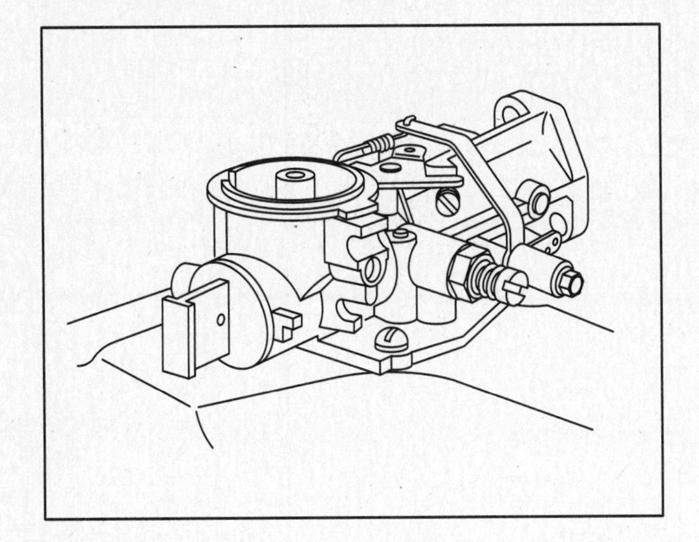

CHOKE-A-MATIC®

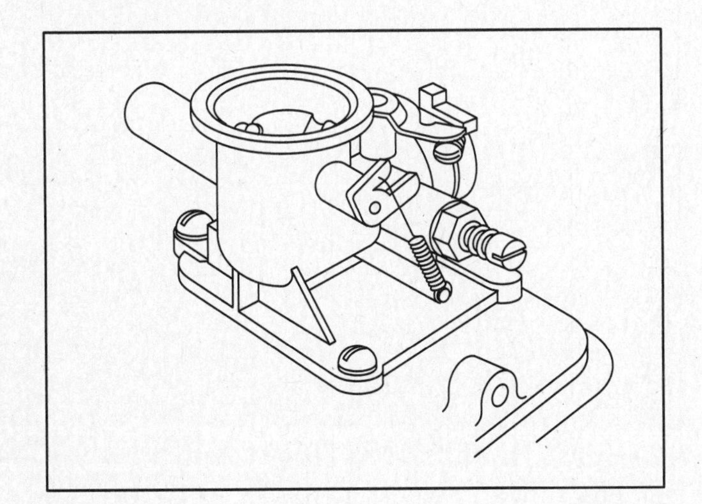

VACU-JET CARBURETORS

ALL TEMPERATURE/AUTOMATIC CHOKE

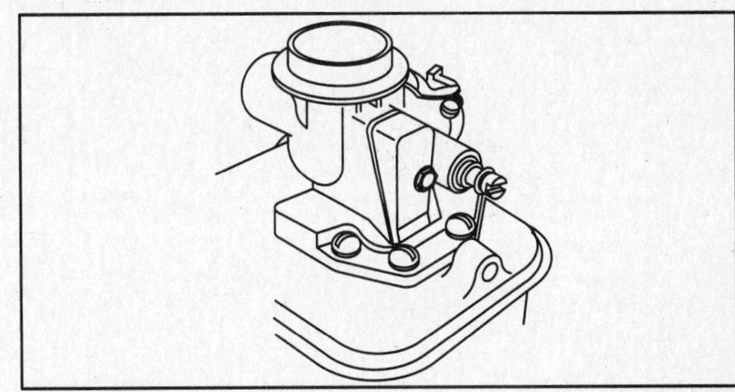

AUTOMATIC CHOKE

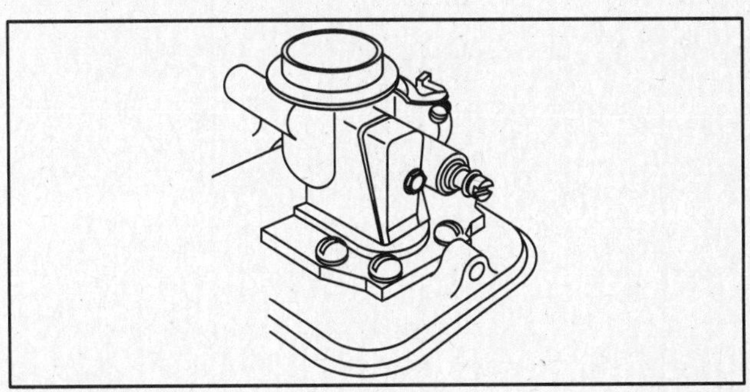

CHOKE-A-MATIC®

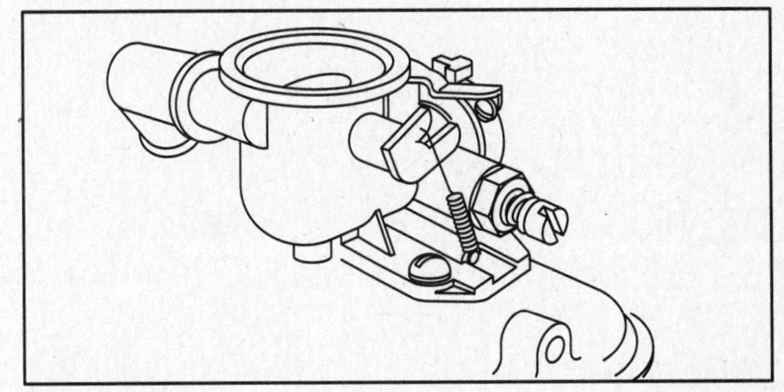

NOTE: METRIC EQUIVALENTS ARE LISTED ON PAGE 68 OF THIS SECTION.

AIR CLEANERS

A properly serviced air cleaner protects internal parts of engine from dust particles in the air. If air cleaner instructions are not carefully followed, dirt and dust which should be collected in cleaner, will be drawn into engine. It will become a part of oil film and is very detrimental to engine life; dirt in oil forms an abrasive mixture which wears moving parts, instead of protecting them.

No engine can stand up under the grinding action which takes place when this occurs. The air cleaner on every engine brought in for a check up or repair should be examined and serviced. If cleaner shows signs of neglect, show it to customer before cleaning, and instruct him on proper care to ensure long engine life.

NOTE: Air cleaner element and/or cartridge should be replaced if damaged or restricted. Replace air cleaner gaskets and mounting gaskets that are worn or damaged to prevent dirt and dust entering engine through improper sealing. Straighten or replace bent mounting studs.

AIR CLEANER IDENTIFICATION

Refer to Fig's. 1 through 18 to determine type air cleaner being used and service procedures to use.

CARTRIDGE TYPE

(with or without Oil Foam®
pre-cleaner or non-oiled pre-cleaner)

Remove and Install

1. Remove wing nut and cover.
2. Carefully remove cartridge to prevent dirt entry into carburetor.
3. Replace grommet, if torn or damaged.
4. Clean cartridge, as described on page 9.

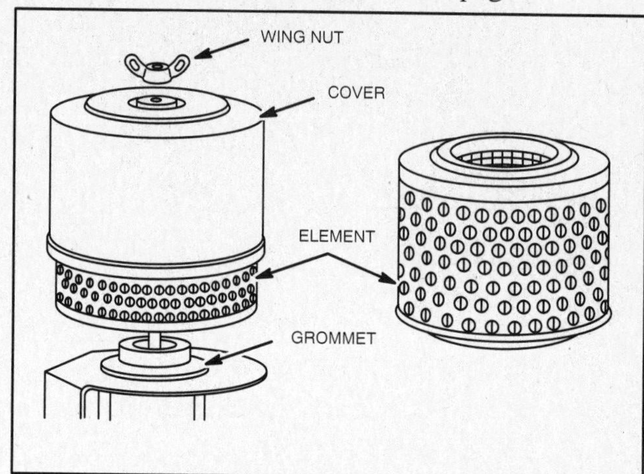

Fig. 1 – Cartridge Air Cleaner

Remove and Install

1. Remove air cleaner stud, cover screw, cover and gasket. Replace gasket if damaged.
2. Remove plate screw, washer and plate.
3. Remove cartridge and clean air cleaner body carefully to prevent dirt from entering carburetor. Brush dirt from body through holes into duct.
4. Clean cartridge, as described on page 9.
5. Re-assemble air cleaner as shown in Fig. 2.

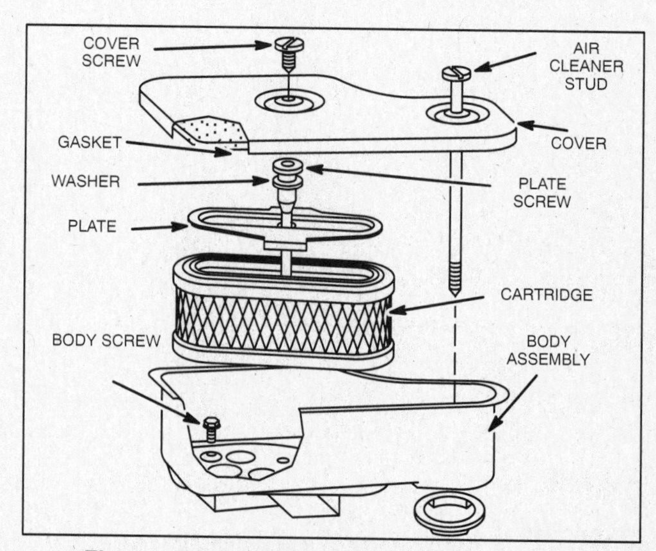

Fig. 2 – Reverse Flow Cartridge Air Cleaner, Vertical Crankshaft

NOTE: METRIC EQUIVALENTS ARE LISTED ON PAGE 68 OF THIS SECTION.

Remove and Install

1. Loosen screw and tilt cover as illustrated in Fig's. 3 and 4.

2. Carefully remove cartridge and foam pre-cleaner when so equipped.

3. Clean cartridge, as described on page 9 and pre-cleaner (optional), as described on page 9.

4. Reassemble air cleaner as shown in Fig's. 3 and 4. Refer to Fig's. 4 and 4A, if pre-cleaner has lip, for proper installation.

5. Install cartridge and foam pre-cleaner, when so equipped.

6. Then close cover and fasten screw securely. Tabs in cover must be in slots of back plate, Fig. 3.

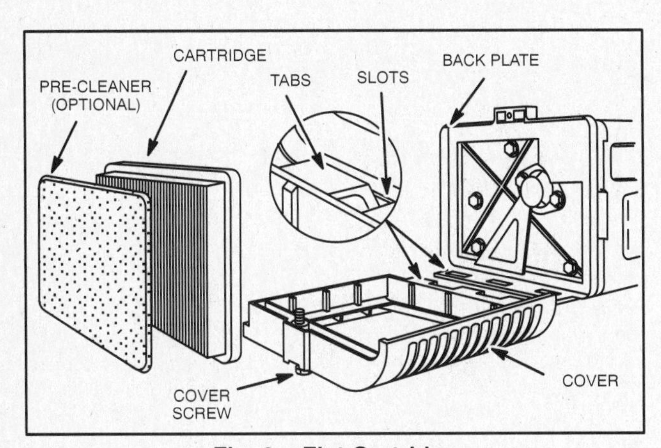

Fig. 3 - Flat Cartridge

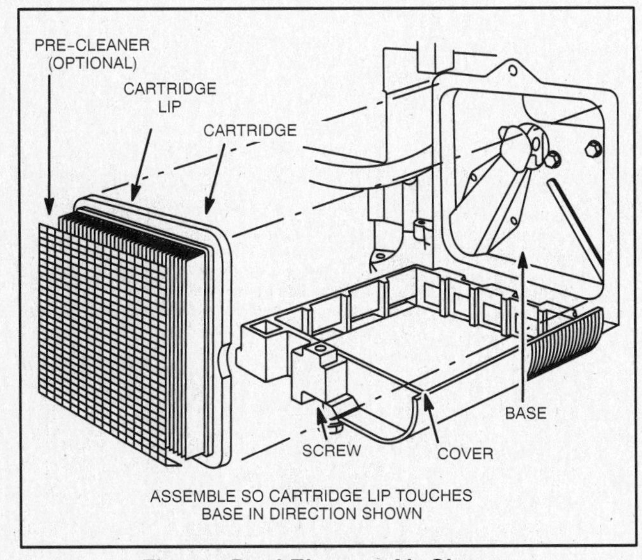

Fig. 4 - Dual Element Air Cleaner

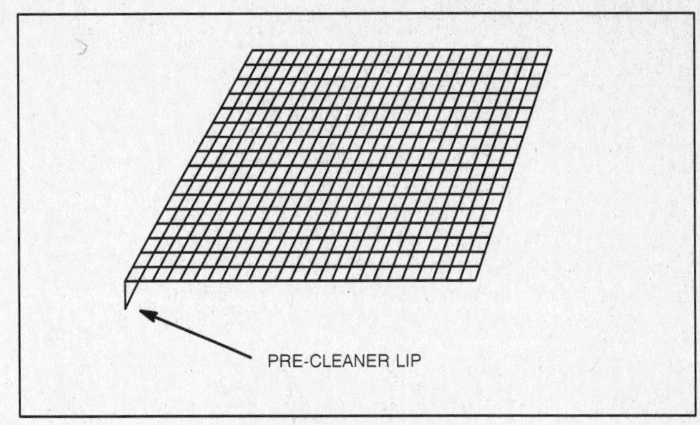

Fig. 4A - Pre-cleaner

Remove and Install

1. Loosen screws and remove cover, Fig. 5.

2. Carefully remove pre-cleaner (when so equipped) and cartridge.

3. Clean cartridge, as described on page 9 and pre-cleaner (optional), as described on page 9.

4. Install cartridge and pre-cleaner (optional).

5. Reinstall air cleaner cover and tighten screws as shown in Fig. 5.

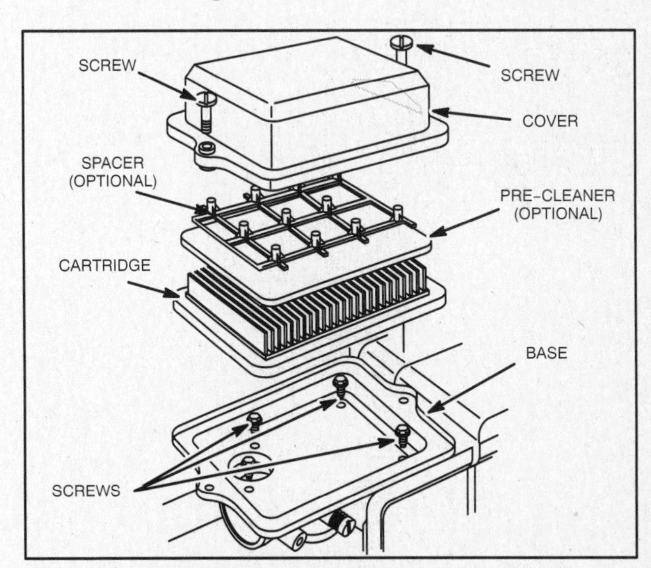

Fig. 5 - Flat Cartridge, Horizontal Crankshaft

Remove and Install

1. Unclamp air cleaner cover from bottom of air cleaner base and remove, Fig. 6.

2. Clean cartridge as described on page 9.

3. Clean any dirt from inside of cover.

4. Reinstall cartridge in cover with mesh side out.

5. Place slots in cover on tabs of air cleaner back and push in on bottom of cover until cover clamps on to air cleaner base, Fig. 6.

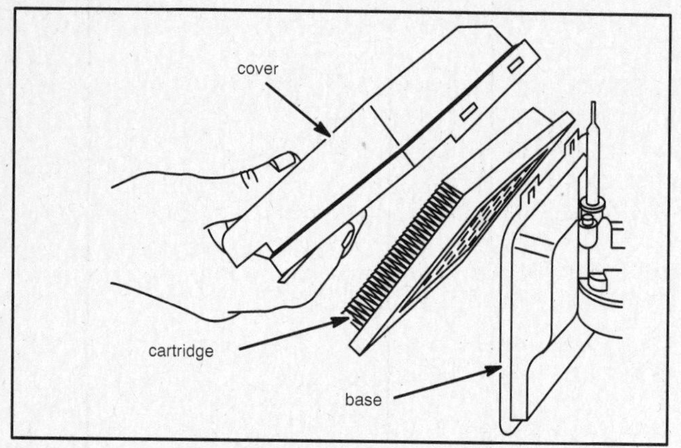

Fig. 6 - Flat Cartridge, Horizontal Crankshaft

DUAL ELEMENT AIR CLEANERS
Remove and Install

1. Remove knob or wing nut and cover.

2. If servicing pre-cleaner, slide pre-cleaner off cartridge and clean as described on page 9. If servicing both pre-cleaner and cartridge, remove wing nut (when so equipped), washer (when so equipped) and pre-cleaner with cartridge together. Clean cartridge as described on page 9.

3. Reassemble air cleaner as shown in Fig's. 7 and 8.

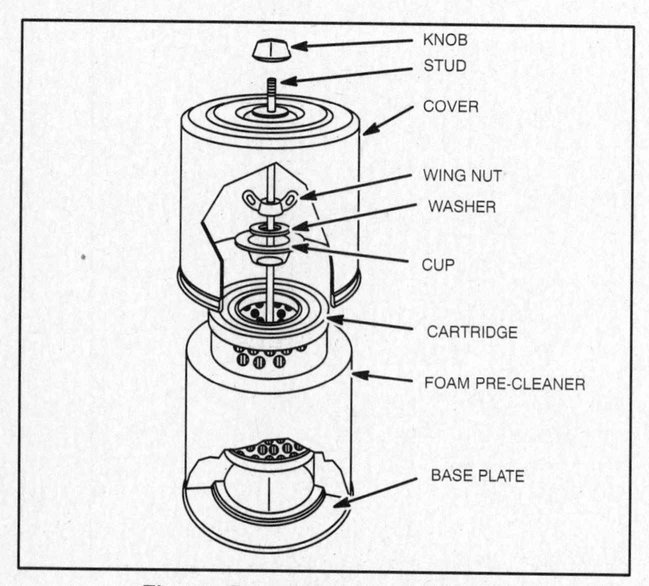

Fig. 7 - Dual Element, Horizontal and Vertical Crankshaft

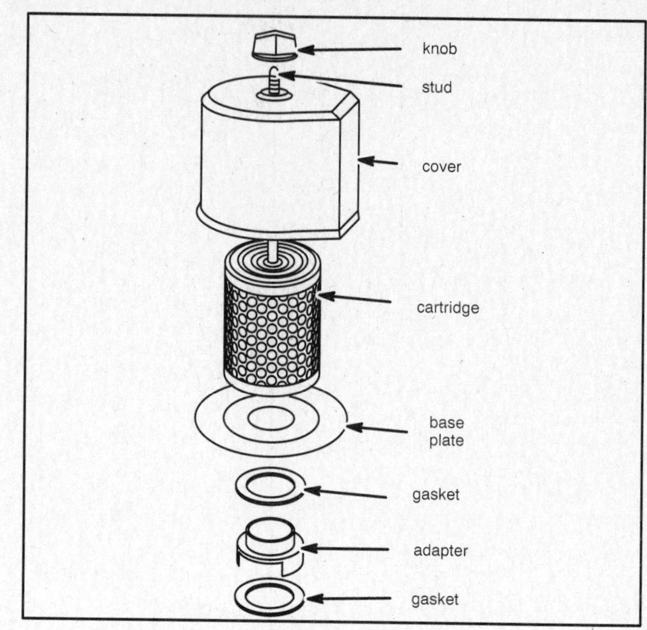

Fig. 8 - Dual Element Air, Horizontal and Vertical Crankshaft

Remove and Install

1. Loosen cover screws. Remove cover and air cleaner assembly from air cleaner base.

2. Remove air cleaner assembly from inside air cleaner cover and disassemble.

3. To clean pre-cleaner, see page 9, Clean Oil Foam® element or pre-cleaner. To clean cartridge, see page 9, Clean Cartridge.

4. Reassemble retainer on pre-cleaner (screen side of pre-cleaner toward pleats on cartridge). Install assembly in air cleaner cover.

5. Insert tabs of cover in slots of air cleaner base and tighten cover screws securely, Fig's. 9 and 10.

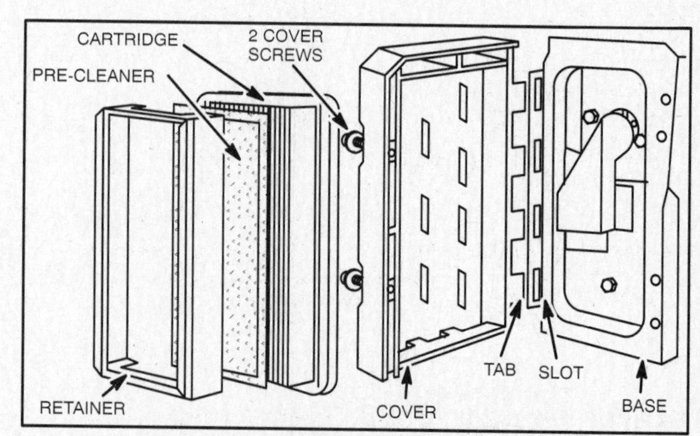

Fig. 9 - Dual Element Air Cleaner, Horizontal Crankshaft

NOTE: METRIC EQUIVALENTS ARE LISTED ON PAGE 68 OF THIS SECTION.

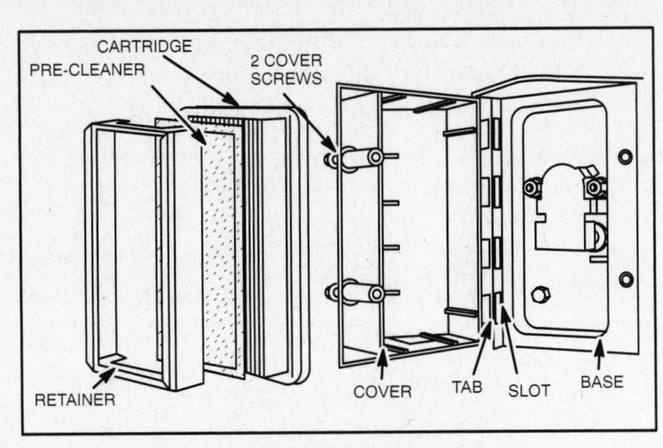

Fig. 10 - Dual Element Air Cleaner, Horizontal Crankshaft

Remove and Install

1. Remove two (2) knobs and air cleaner cover.
2. If servicing pre-cleaner, slide pre-cleaner off cartridge and clean as described on page 9. If servicing both pre-cleaner and cartridge, remove wing nuts and pre-cleaner with cartridge together. Clean cartridge as described on page 9.
3. Slide pre-cleaner on cartridge and install assembly on air cleaner base.
4. Install two (2) wing nuts and tighten securely.
5. Install air cleaner cover and two (2) knobs securely, Fig. 11.

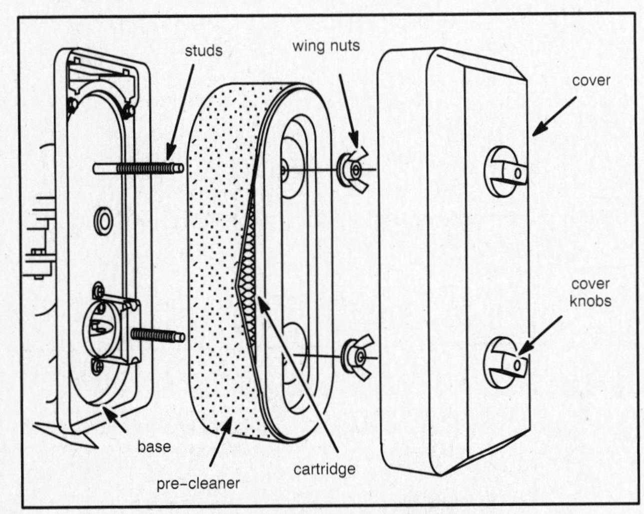

Fig. 11 - Front Mount Dual Element Air Cleaner, Horizontal Crankshaft

Remove and Install

1. Remove cover knob(s) and cover.
2. If servicing pre-cleaner, slide pre-cleaner off cartridge and clean as described on page 9. If servicing both pre-cleaner and cartridge, remove cartridge knob(s) and pre-cleaner with cartridge together. Clean cartridge as described on page 9.
3. Slide pre-cleaner onto cartridge.
4. Install cartridge (if removed) and cover.
5. Install cartridge knob(s) (if removed) securely.
6. Install cover and cover knobs, Fig's. 12 and 13.

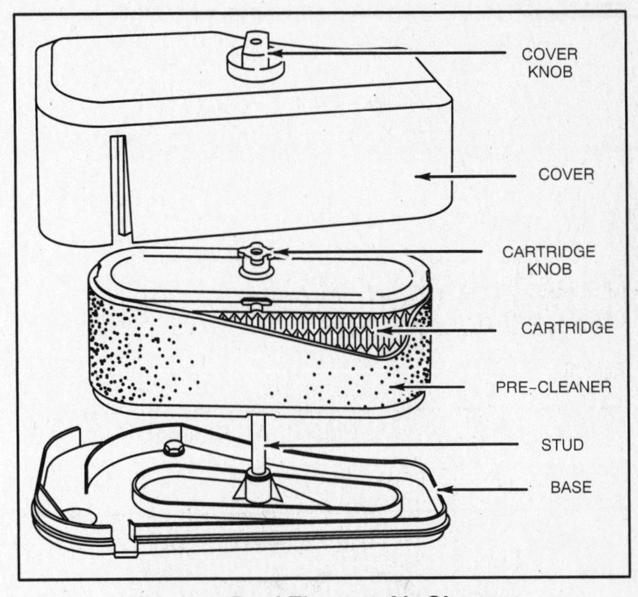

Fig. 12 - Dual Element Air Cleaner, Vertical Crankshaft, Single Stud

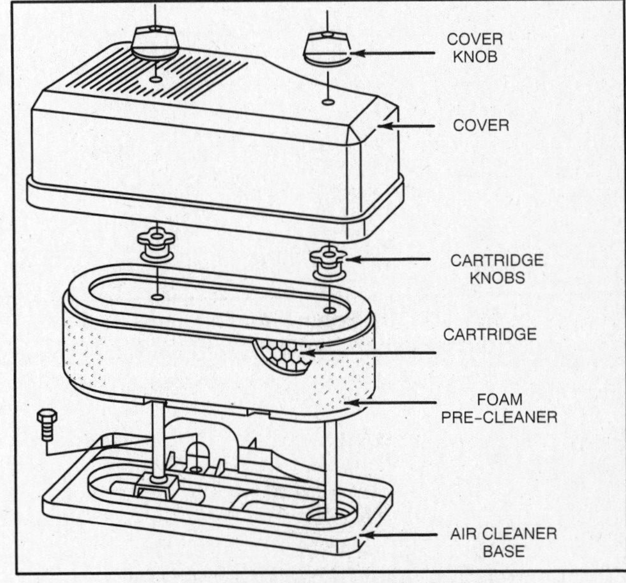

Fig. 13 - Dual Element Air Cleaner, Vertical Crankshaft, Dual Studs

NOTE: METRIC EQUIVALENTS ARE LISTED ON PAGE 68 OF THIS SECTION.

OIL-FOAM® AIR CLEANER

Remove and Install

1. Remove screw or wing nut.
2. Remove air cleaner carefully to prevent dirt from entering carburetor.
3. Disassemble air cleaner.
4. Clean Oil Foam® element, as described on page 9.
5. Reassemble air cleaner as shown in Fig's. 14 or 15.

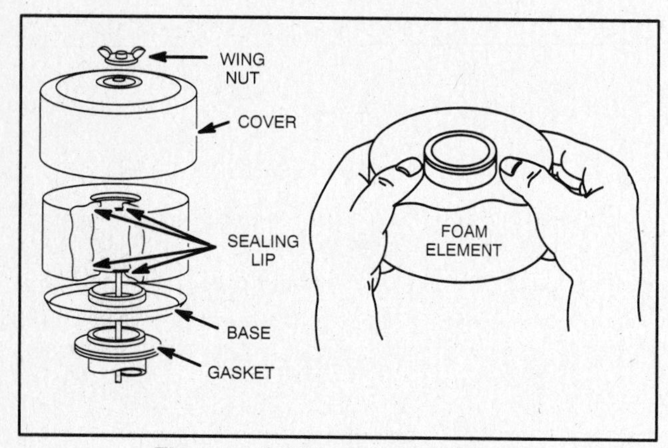

Fig. 14 - Oil-Foam® Air Cleaner

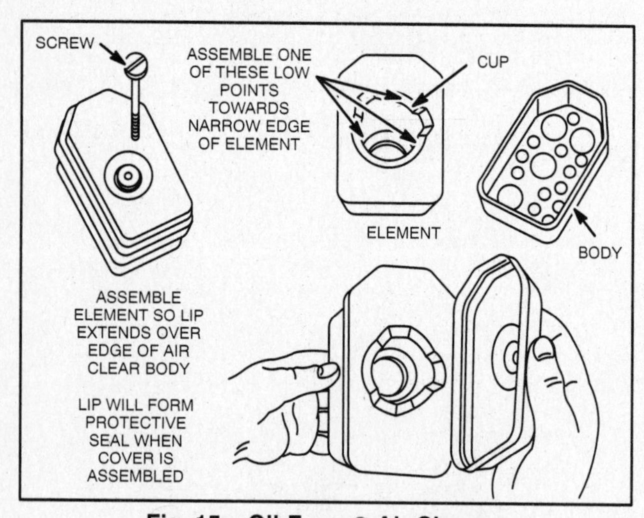

Fig. 15 - Oil-Foam® Air Cleaner, Horizontal and Vertical Crankshaft

Remove and Install

1. Lift latch on narrow end of air cleaner cover and remove cover.
2. Remove Oil Foam® from air cleaner body.
3. Clean as described on page 9.
4. Place Oil Foam® element in air cleaner body making sure lip of element extends over all edges of air cleaner body to form a seal.
5. Insert slot on cover into tabs on air cleaner body and press down on cover until cover latch snaps into place, Fig. 16.

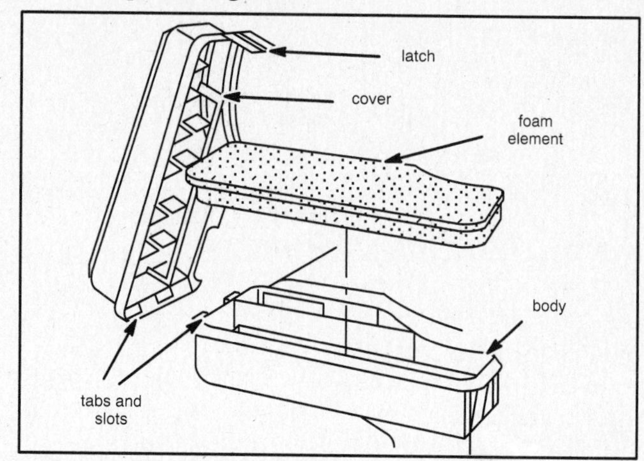

Fig. 16 - Oil Foam® Air Cleaner, Vertical Crankshaft

Remove and Install

1. Remove two (2) screws and lift off complete air cleaner.
2. Disassemble air cleaner.
3. Clean spacers, element support, screen, cup, body and cover.
4. Clean Oil Foam® element as described on page 9.
5. Insert element support into body (when used, Fig. 18) and then place Oil Foam® element into body. Make sure that lip of Oil Foam® element extends over edge of body all the way around to assure a protective seal.
6. Install spacer(s), screen and cup, Fig's. 17 and 18.
7. Place cover on air cleaner assembly with two (2) screws, Fig. 18.
8. Install air cleaner assembly on carburetor, Fig. 18.

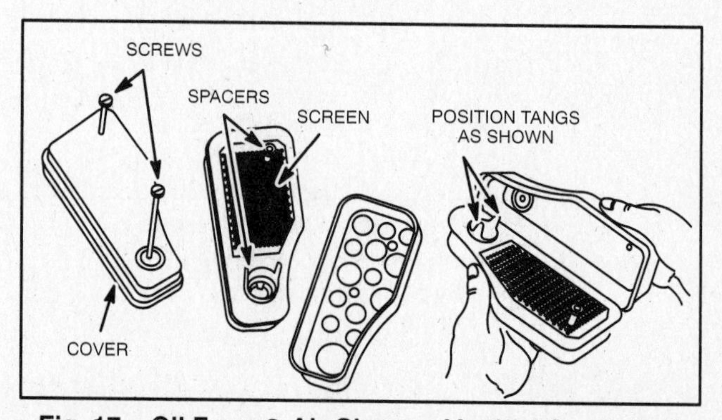

Fig. 17 - Oil Foam® Air Cleaner, Vertical Crankshaft

NOTE: METRIC EQUIVALENTS ARE LISTED ON PAGE 68 OF THIS SECTION.

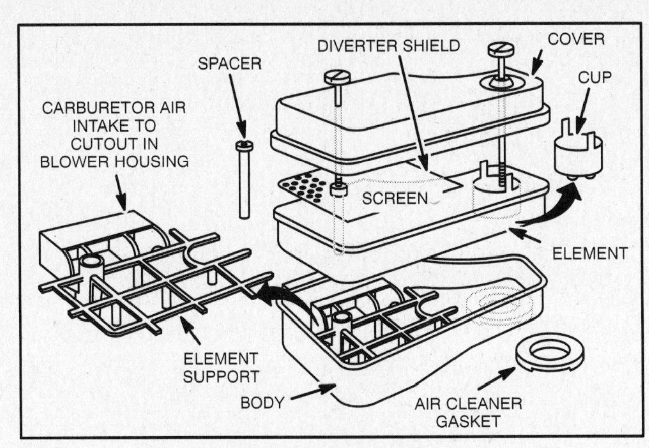

Fig. 18 – Ducted Oil Foam® Air Cleaner, Vertical Crankshaft

CLEANING AIR CLEANERS

When to Clean

CARTRIDGE only, Clean every 25 hours or once a season, whichever comes first. More often in dusty conditions.

CARTRIDGE with dry pre-cleaner, pre-cleaner every 25 hours and cartridge every 100 hours. More often in dusty conditions.

CARTRIDGE with oiled pre-cleaner, pre-cleaner every 25 hours and cartridge every 100 hours. More often in dusty conditions.

OIL-FOAM®, every 25 hours. More often in dusty conditions.

Clean Cartridge

1. Clean cartridge by tapping gently on flat surface.
   a. If very dirty, replace cartridge or wash in a low or non-sudsing detergent and warm water solution.
   b. Rinse thoroughly with flowing water from inside out until water is clear, all cartridges except **REVERSE FLOW.**
   c. Rinse thoroughly from OUTSIDE IN until water is clear, **REVERSE FLOW only.**
   d. Cartridge must be allowed to stand and air dry thoroughly before using.
2. Reassemble as described on previous pages, based on type of air cleaner.

CAUTION: Petroleum solvents, such as kerosene, are not to be used to clean cartridge. They may cause deterioration of cartridge. DO NOT OIL CARTRIDGE. DO NOT USE PRESSURIZED AIR TO CLEAN OR DRY CARTRIDGE.

Clean and re-oil air cleaner element every 25 hours or at three month intervals under normal conditions. Capacity of "Oil-Foam®" air cleaner is adequate for a full season's use, without cleaning, in average home-owner's lawn mower service. (Clean every few hours under extremely dusty conditions.) See Fig. 19.

Clean Oil Foam® Element or Pre-cleaner

1. WASH foam element in kerosene or liquid detergent and water to remove dirt, Fig. 19A.
2. Wrap foam in cloth and squeeze dry, Fig. 19B.
3. Saturate foam with engine oil. Squeeze to remove excess oil, Fig's. 19C and D. **DO NOT OIL pre-cleaners THAT ARE IMPRINTED "DO NOT OIL."**
4. Reassemble as described on previous pages, based on type of air cleaner.

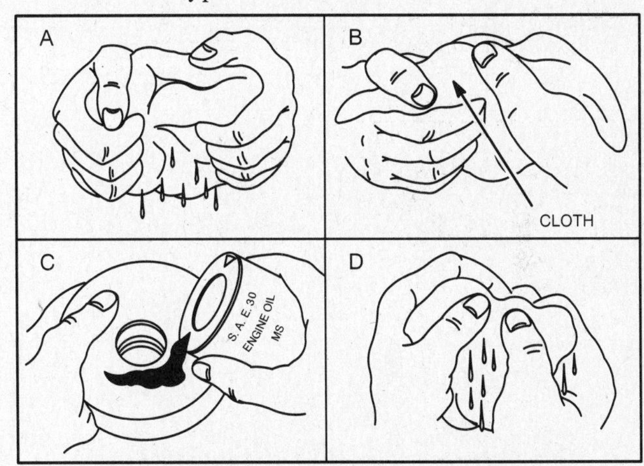

Fig. 19 – Cleaning Oil-Foam® Air Cleaner

PULSA-PRIME CARBURETORS, MODEL SERIES 93900, 95900, 96900, VERTICAL CRANKSHAFT

Pulsa-Prime Operation

Pulsa-Prime carburetors consist of a reinforced nylon body, carburetor to tank gasket, fuel pump diaphragm, throttle shaft and valve, fuel pipe with check valve, jet screen, diaphragm spring, primer check valve seat, ball, and spring, and prime bulb and retainer. The carburetor does not have a choke valve or idle system.

NOTE: METRIC EQUIVALENTS ARE LISTED ON PAGE 68 OF THIS SECTION.

Pressing on primer bulb compresses air inside the carburetor body seating the check valve in the fuel pipe. Air is pushed pass the primer check valve. When the primer bulb is released, a vacuum now exists inside the primer fuel pipe.

Air pressure inside fuel tank pushes fuel past fuel pipe check valve up fuel pipe, past check valve to begin filling fuel pump cavity. Fuel also moves through primer passages to primer bulb. Pushing primer bulb only once on a dry fuel system will not fill all passages.

On the third push, fuel will fill fuel pump, pushing fuel past outlet valve into fuel well in tank top, through jet screen and up through fixed jet. Also pass primer check valve into throat of carburetor for starting.

Remove Carburetor and Tank

1. Remove carburetor and fuel tank assembly mounting bolts, Fig. 20.

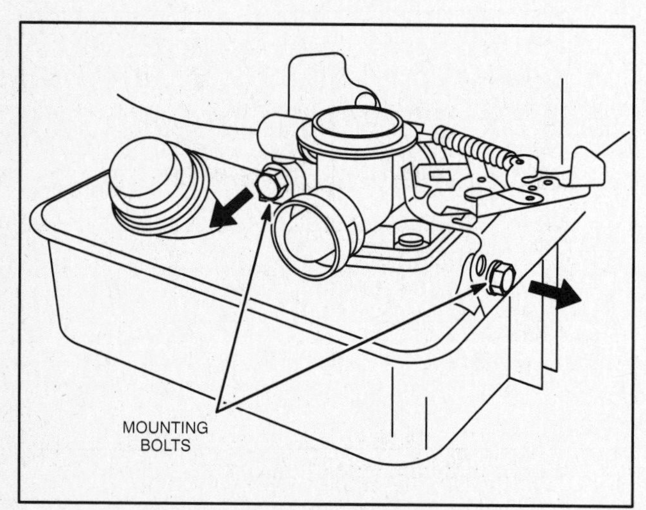

Fig. 20 - Removing Mounting Bolts

2. Slip carburetor and fuel tank assembly off end of fuel intake tube.
3. Turn assembly to free throttle link from throttle lever.
4. This will leave governor link and governor spring connected to governor blade and control lever, Fig. 21.

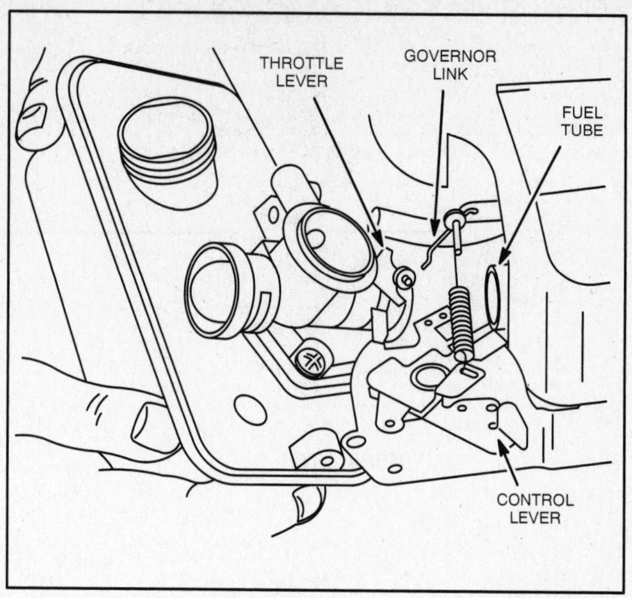

Fig. 21 - Removing Carburetor and Tank Assembly

Remove Carburetor from Fuel Tank

1. Remove five screws holding carburetor to tank.
2. Remove carburetor from tank and remove diaphragm and gasket from tank, Fig. 22.

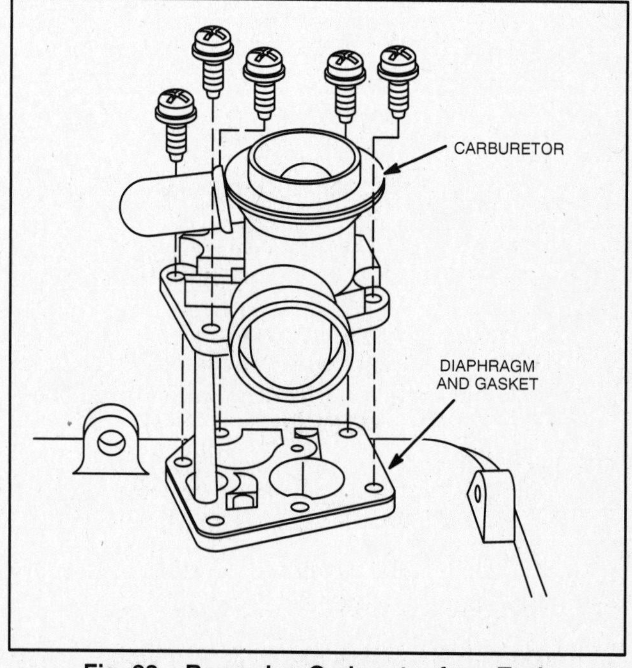

Fig. 22 - Removing Carburetor from Tank

NOTE: METRIC EQUIVALENTS ARE LISTED ON PAGE 68 OF THIS SECTION.

DISASSEMBLE CARBURETOR

1. Slide jet screen off carburetor body. Fixed main jet is not a service part.
2. Press in from both sides of primer bulb cavity to release retainer tabs.
3. Pry retainer out and remove primer bulb.
4. Remove primer seat using a crochet hook or other type of hook. Ball and spring will fall out, Fig. 25.
5. Remove intake tube "O" ring from carburetor.

NOTE: Do not stretch, bend or compress primer spring.

Remove Throttle Valve and Shaft

1. Rotate throttle shaft lever to wide open throttle position, Fig. 21.
2. With a pair of needle nose pliers grasp center of throttle valve and pull out of throttle shaft, making sure that throttle valve is not bent during removal.
3. Remove throttle shaft and foam dust seal.

Remove Fuel Pipe

- Fuel pipe on Pulsa-Prime carburetor is the snap-in design. Pipe requires considerable force to snap out, Fig. 23.

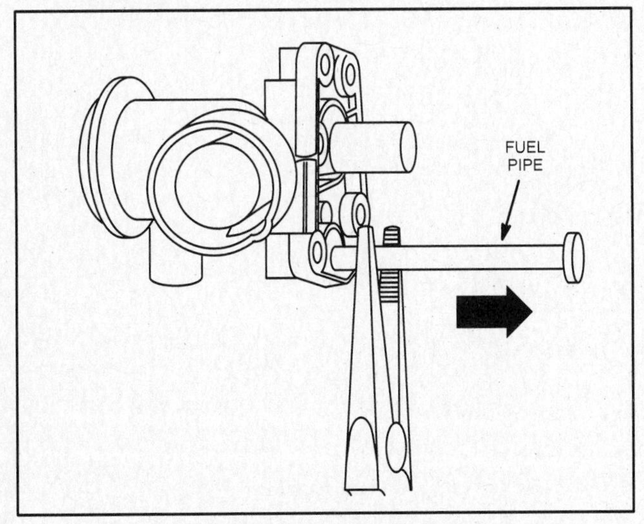

Fig. 23 - Removing Fuel Pipe, Reinforced Nylon Carburetor

Clean Fuel System

Gummy or dirty fuel tanks, lines and carburetors should be cleaned in a carburetor cleaner, such as Bendix. Do not soak diaphragms, rubber, or nylon parts in cleaner.

NOTE: Commercial carburetor cleaners will soften or dissolve reinforced nylon bodies, if left in for long periods of time. DO NOT EXCEED 15 MINUTES.

INSPECTION

Inspect jet screen for clogging, varnish deposits, and damage to screen. Replace if any of these conditions exist. Inspect throttle shaft and throttle shaft bearing for wear. Replace either or both if worn. Inspect diaphragm for holes, tears or curled fuel valves. Replace if any of these conditions exist.

ASSEMBLE CARBURETOR

High Altitude Compensation

NOTE: When carburetor is used at high altitudes, and performance is poor, remove main jet air bleed, Fig. 24.

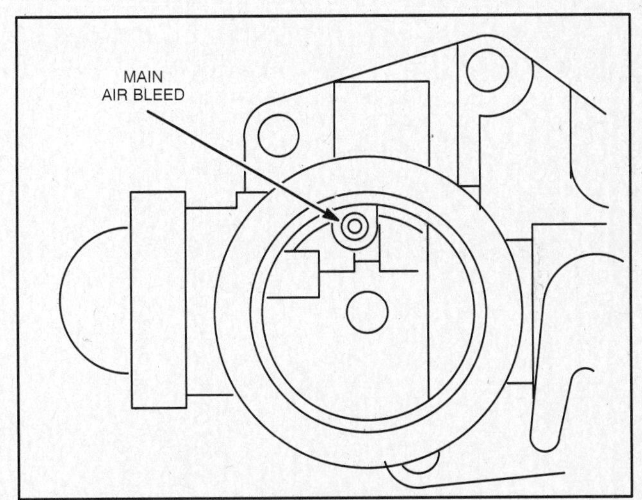

Fig. 24 - Removing Main Air Bleed

1. Place primer spring and ball in primer valve bore.
2. Press primer seat into bore with groove on seat facing out, Fig. 25.
3. Insert primer bulb into retainer and moisten inside diameter of primer bulb.
4. Press into primer cavity lining up locking tabs with locking slot in cavity.
5. Press until both tabs are seated in locking slots, Fig. 25.

NOTE: METRIC EQUIVALENTS ARE LISTED ON PAGE 68 OF THIS SECTION.

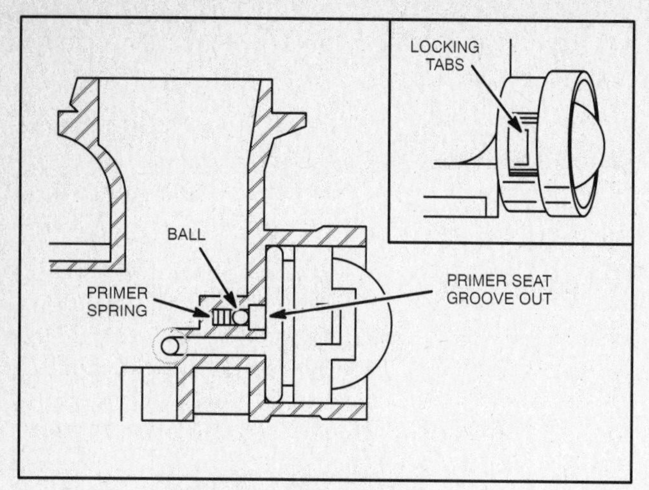

Fig. 25 – Installing Primer

Install Fuel Pipe

- Insert fuel pipe in carburetor body and place fuel pipe on a hard surface with the fuel pipe and body square to the hard surface. Fuel pipe may snap into place with considerable force, Fig. 26.

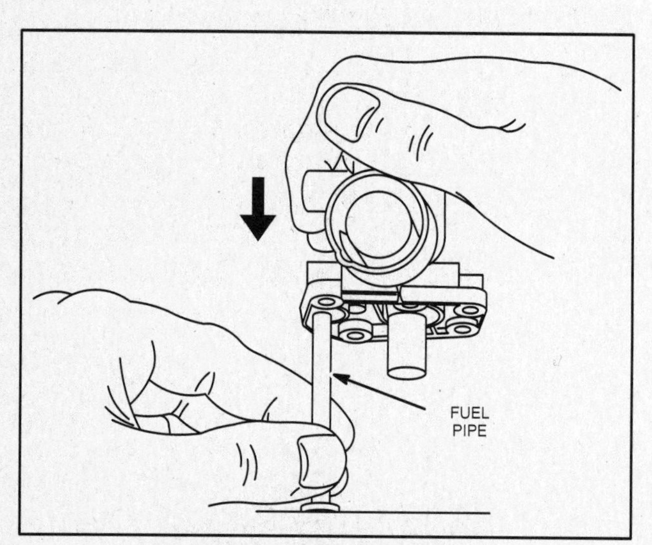

Fig. 26 – Installing Fuel Pipe, Reinforced Nylon Carburetor

Install Throttle Shaft and Valve

1. Insert throttle shaft and new foam dust seal into carburetor body.
2. Insert throttle valve into throttle shaft with single dimple in first, Fig. 27. Push until two dimples contact throttle shaft, Fig. 27.
3. Rotate shaft and valve to check for freedom of movement and to center throttle valve in throttle shaft.

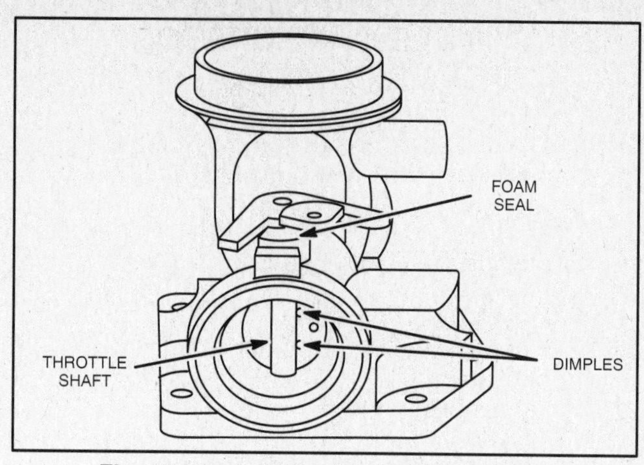

Fig. 27 – Install Throttle Shaft and Valve

4. Slide jet screen onto main jet tube and place fuel pump spring on spring boss, Fig. 28.

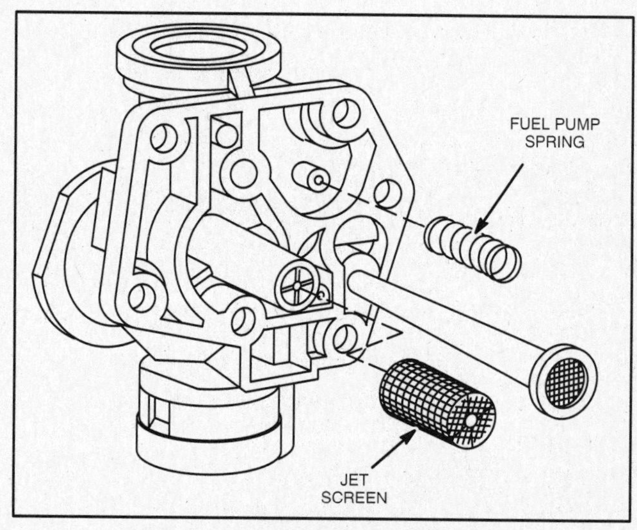

Fig. 28 – Installing Jet Screen and Fuel Pump Spring

Assemble Carburetor to Fuel Tank

1. Place new diaphragm on tank top and then place new gasket on top of diaphragm.
2. Lower carburetor assembly down onto gasket and diaphragm.
3. Install five screws and tighten screws evenly, Fig. 29.

NOTE: METRIC EQUIVALENTS ARE LISTED ON PAGE 68 OF THIS SECTION.

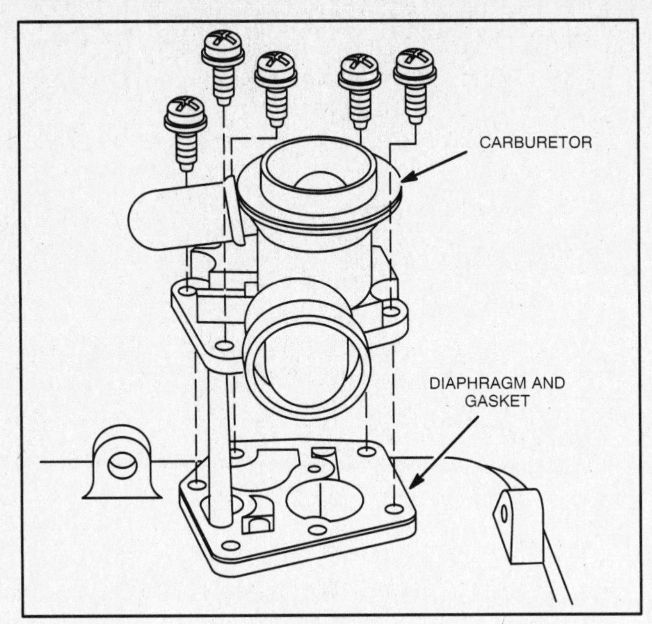

Fig. 29 - Installing Carburetor on Fuel Tank

Assemble Carburetor and Fuel Tank to Engine

1. Insert throttle link into throttle lever and rotate carburetor and fuel tank assembly.
2. Install "O" ring in carbretor intake opening and oil "O" ring.
3. Slide carburetor onto intake tube until fuel tank mounting boss are lined up. Breather tube should be inserted into breather grommet.
4. Install and tighten mounting screws securely, Fig. 30.

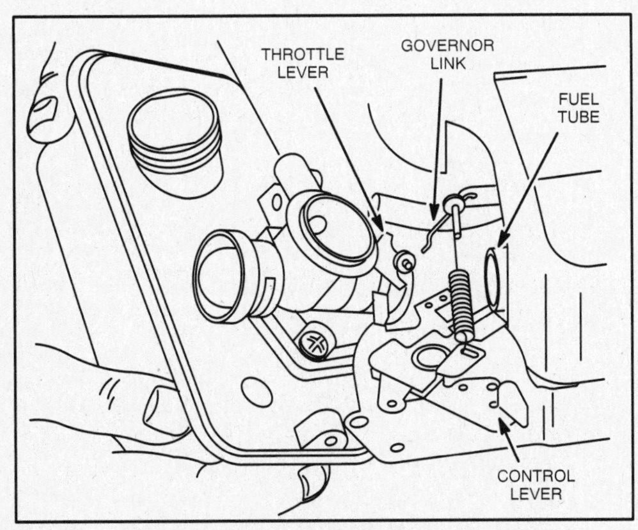

Fig. 30 - Installing Carburetor and Fuel Tank on Engine

PULSA-JET CARBURETORS WITH FIXED JET MODEL SERIES 80200, 82200, 90200, 91200, 112200, 130200, 132200, 135200, HORIZONTAL CRANKSHAFT

Fixed jet Pulsa-Jet carburetors have been made in three versions. Current version is small well, bottom fixed jet, C. (Low emission carburetors have a filter screen surrounding the small well); second version is small well, fixed side jet, B.; and first version is large well, fixed side jet, A., Fig. 31.

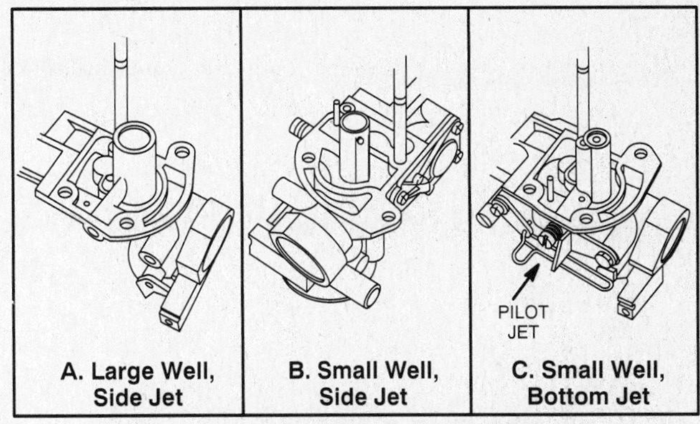

Fig. 31 - Pulsa-Jet Carburetor, Fixed Jet

Remove Control Panel

1. Remove air cleaner assembly.
2. Disconnect choke link from control panel lever, when used.
3. Remove two screws holding control panel and remove control panel, Fig. 32.
4. Disconnect stop switch wire from stop switch and set control panel aside.

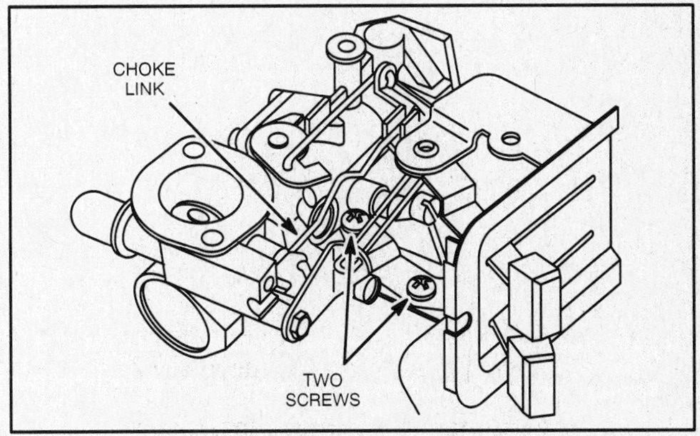

Fig. 32 - Removing Control Panel

Remove Carburetor and Tank Assembly

1. Using Tool #19305, Offset Screwdriver, Tool #19391, Torx® Wrench, or open end wrench, remove two screws holding carburetor to cylinder and remove screw holding fuel tank bracket, Fig. 33.

NOTE: METRIC EQUIVALENTS ARE LISTED ON PAGE 68 OF THIS SECTION.

2. Remove assembly while disconnecting throttle linkage or governor rods.

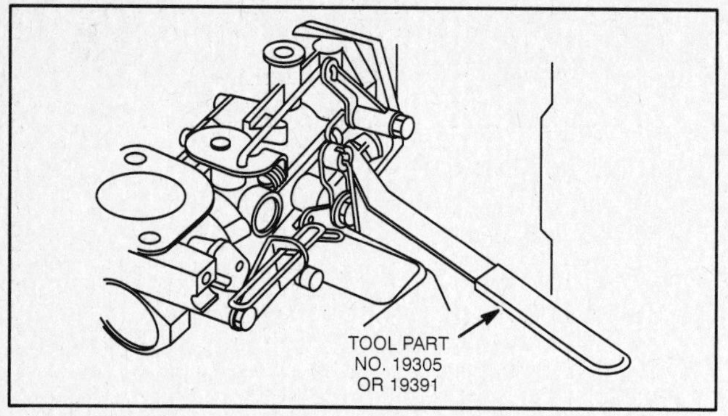

Fig. 33 – Removing Carburetor and Tank Assembly

Disassemble Carburetor

1. Remove remaining screws from carburetor and separate carburetor from fuel tank.
2. Remove old carburetor mounting gasket.
3. Back off idle speed screw until throttle shaft stops moving.
4. Remove throttle valve screw and valve.
5. Remove throttle shaft and foam seal. Remove throttle shaft rubber seal.
6. Remove idle mixture needle and spring.

   NOTE: Low emissions carburetors use a pilot jet instead of an idle mixture needle and spring. Remove pilot jet.

7. Snap out choke valve and remove choke shaft.
8. Remove filter screen from well, when used.
9. With a modified 5/32 inch pin punch, remove welch plug(s) from carburetor body, Fig. 34. DO NOT remove fixed jet.

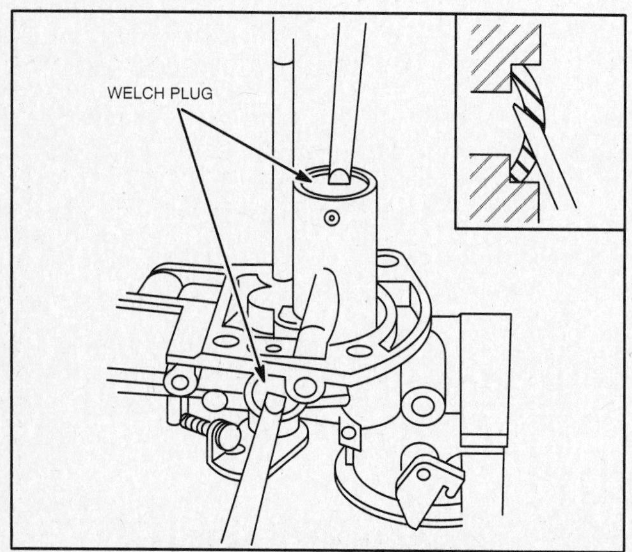

Fig. 34 – Removing Welch Plug(s)

10. To remove screen housing or nylon pipe from brass pipe, slide retaining clip up onto brass pickup tube.
11. Cut end of nylon tube where tube connects to brass tube and remove tube.
12. Slide off old retaining clip and discard, Fig. 35.

NOTE: DO NOT remove brass pipe.

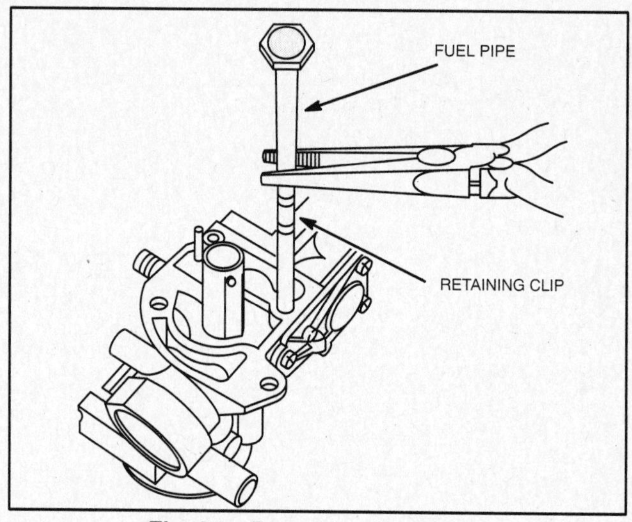

Fig. 35 – Removing Fuel Pipe

Disassemble Fuel Pump

1. Remove fuel pump cover, diaphragm, spring and cup, Fig. 36.
2. Inspect diaphragm for punctures, cracks and fatigue. Replace if damaged. Inspect all sealing surfaces for nicks or damages and repair or replace as required.

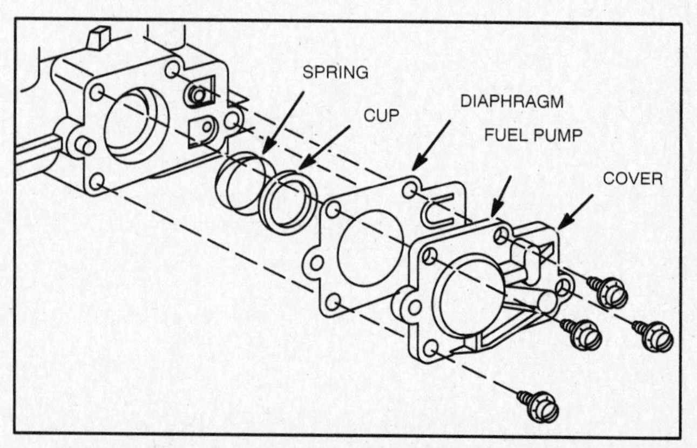

Fig. 36 – Pulsa-Jet Carburetor Fuel Pump

NOTE: METRIC EQUIVALENTS ARE LISTED ON PAGE 68 OF THIS SECTION.

INSPECT CARBURETOR

After cleaning, inspect for wear, damage, cracks, or plugged openings. Replace body if any of above conditions exist. Use only compressed air to clear plugged openings. Inspect idle mixture needle for bent needle point or a groove in tip of needle. Replace if bent or grooved. On low emission carburetors, inspect pilot jet for dirt and sealing in seat area. Do not use drills or wire when checking pilot jet.

ASSEMBLE CARBURETOR

High Altitude Compensation

NOTE: When carburetor is used at high altitudes, and performance is poor, remove main jet air bleed, Fig. 37.

NOTE: For Low emission carburetors use the following procedure.

1. Remove end welch plug.
2. Using a #3–48 UNC tap, tap into main air jet, Fig. 37.
3. Clamp square end of tap in vise and turn carburetor body clockwise to pull air jet.
4. Press high altitude air jet in until flush with boss,

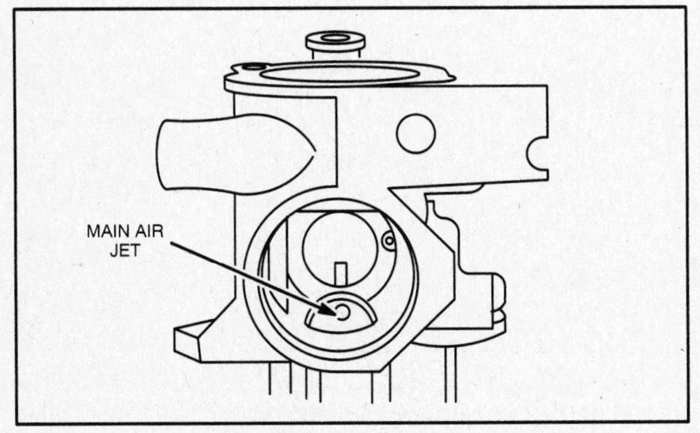

Fig. 37 – Removing Main Air Jet

Install Welch Plug(s)

1. Place a small amount of non-hardening sealant such as Permatex® II or nail polish around outside edge of welch plug(s) and place plug in metering or bottom well.
2. With a 1/4" dia., or larger, pin punch, set welch plug with pin punch in center of plug. Do not collapse plug, Fig. 38.

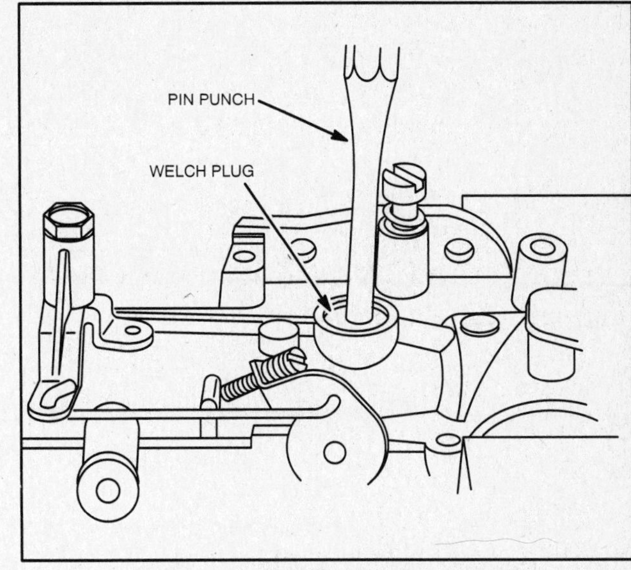

Fig. 38 – Installing Welch Plugs

Install Fuel Pipe

Slide new retainer clip onto brass pipe. Heat small end of new nylon tube in hot water and push onto brass tube. Slide retaining clip down onto nylon tube over groove on brass pipe, Fig. 39.

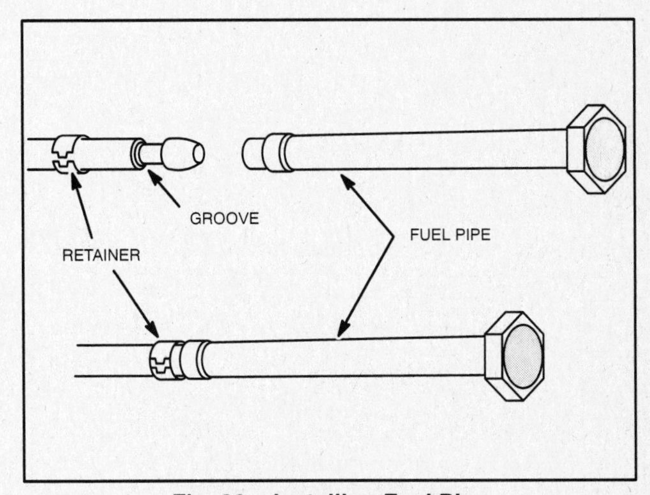

Fig. 39 – Installing Fuel Pipe

NOTE: METRIC EQUIVALENTS ARE LISTED ON PAGE 68 OF THIS SECTION.

Install Throttle Shaft and Valve

1. Press in new rubber throttle shaft seal with sealing lip down until seal bottoms.
2. Place new foam seal on throttle and insert shaft in carburetor body. Throttle valve is chamfered and has an identification letter stamped on one side of valve.
3. Place valve in carburetor with stamped letter to right and install throttle valve screw, Fig. 40.

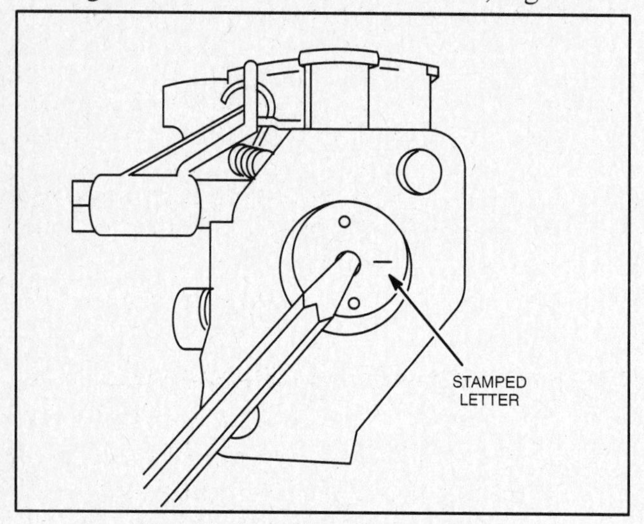

Fig. 40 – Installing Throttle Valve

Install Choke Shaft and Valve

1. Place metal washer next to choke lever and then foam washer.
2. Insert shaft assembly in carburetor body with stop against remote control boss.
3. Insert choke valve in shaft with hole up and indentations towards large welch plug, Fig. 41.

NOTE: On Choke-A-Matic® carburetors, be sure that both ends of choke spring are engaged before sliding shaft all the way into carburetor, Fig. 41.

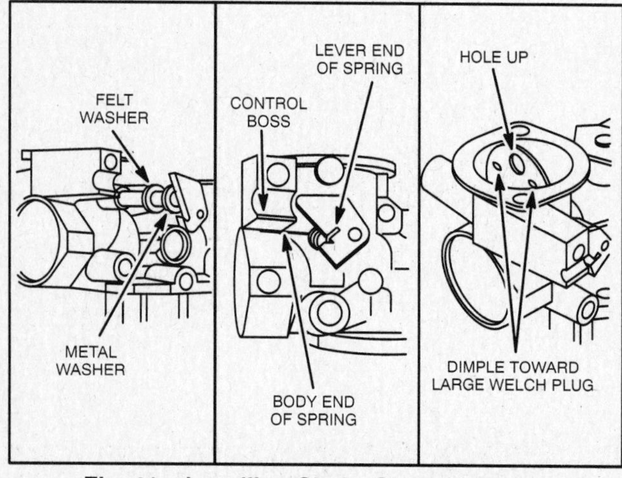

Fig. 41 – Installing Choke Shaft and Valve

NOTE: On low emission carburetors, install choke shaft as shown in Fig. 42.

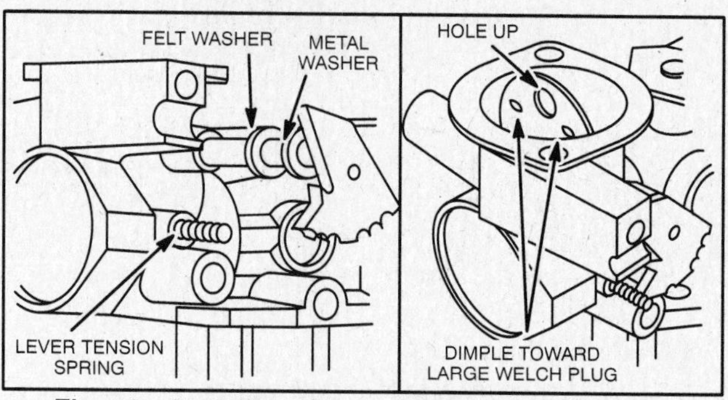

Fig. 42 – Installing Choke Shaft and Valve, Low Emissions Carburetors

Assemble Carburetor to Fuel Tank

1. Place new tank gasket on fuel tank.
2. Lower carburetor into fuel tank and install two screws next to choke valve, Fig. 43.

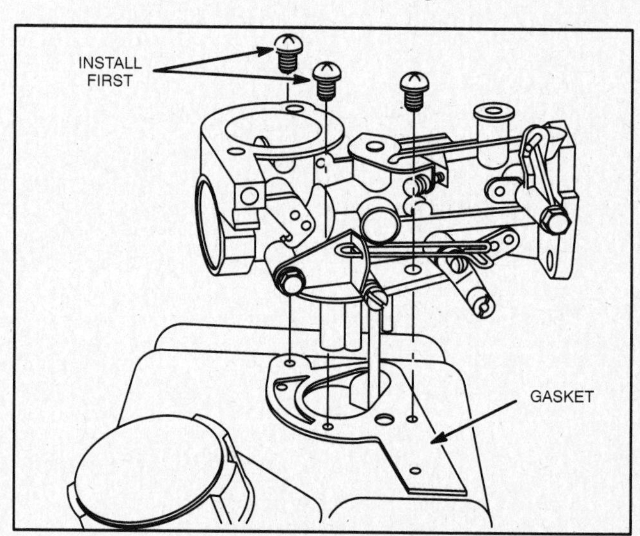

Fig. 43 – Installing Carburetor on Fuel Tank

Install Carburetor and Fuel Tank on Engine

1. Connect governor linkage to carburetor linkage and using Tool #19305, Offset Screwdriver, Tool #19391, Torx® Wrench, or open end wrench, install two screws holding carburetor to engine, Fig. 44.

NOTE: On low emissions carburetors, install pilot jet until it seats firmly, Fig 31.

2. Install screw to bottom of fuel tank bracket.

NOTE: METRIC EQUIVALENTS ARE LISTED ON PAGE 68 OF THIS SECTION.

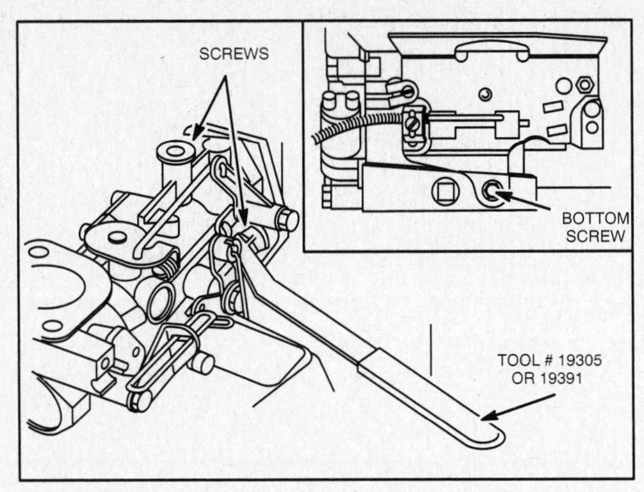

Fig. 44 - Install Carburetor and Fuel Tank on Engine

Install Control Panel

1. Connect control linkage to control panel, when used and place control panel on fuel tank and carburetor.
2. Install and tighten two screws securely.

CARBURETOR ADJUSTMENT

NOTE: On low emission carburetors, the only adjustment to be made is idle RPM.

Initial Adjustment

1. Install idle mixture valve and spring. Turn mixture valve clockwise until valve just touches valve seat.
2. Back out valve 1-1/2 turns counterclockwise. This is the preliminary adjustment.
3. Install carburetor on engine and connect stop switch wire and governor controls.
4. Install complete air cleaner assembly.
5. Start and run engine for five minutes to warm up engine before making final adjustments.

Final Adjustment, except Low Emissions Carburetors

1. Place equipment control lever in "SLOW" position.
2. Turn needle valve in until engine slows (clockwise - lean mixture).
3. Then turn it out past smooth operating point until engine runs unevenly (rich mixture).
4. Now turn needle valve to midpoint between rich and lean so engine runs smoothly.
5. Next, adjust idle RPM. Rotate throttle counterclockwise and hold against stop while adjusting idle speed adjusting screw to obtain 1750 RPM.
6. While holding throttle closed, move speed control to fast position.
7. Release throttle. Engine should accelerate without hesitation or sputtering.
8. If engine does not accelerate smoothly, carburetor should be readjusted, usually to a slightly richer mixture.

Final Adjustment, Low Emissions Carburetors

1. Start and run engine for five minutes to warm up engine before making final adjustments.
2. Place speed control in slow position.
3. Next, adjust idle RPM. Rotate throttle counterclockwise and hold against stop while adjusting idle speed adjusting screw to obtain 1500 RPM.
4. Release throttle and bend governed idle bracket to obtain 1750 RPM, Fig. 45.

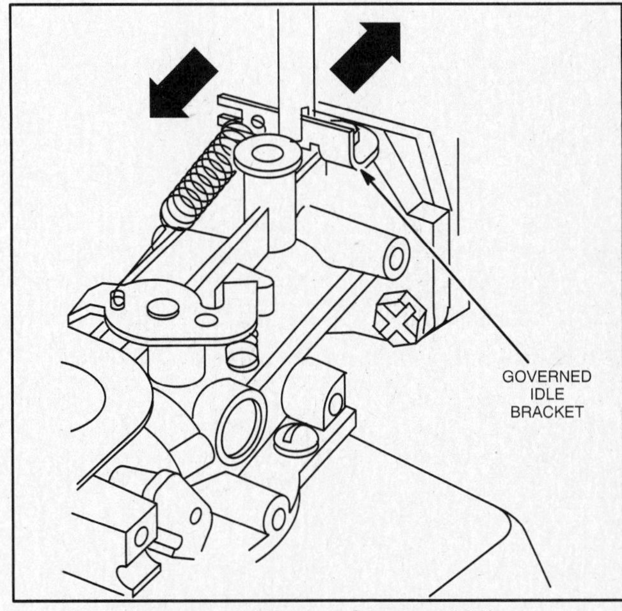

Fig. 45 - Adjusting Governed Idle

NOTE: METRIC EQUIVALENTS ARE LISTED ON PAGE 68 OF THIS SECTION.

ALL-TEMPERATURE/AUTOMATIC CHOKE PULSA-JET & VACU-JET CARBURETORS, MODEL SERIES 92500, 92900, 93500, 94500, 94900, 110900, 112900, 113900, 114900, VERTICAL CRANKSHAFT

The all-temperature carburetor is equipped with a bimetal spring which compensates for temperature and better regulates automatic choke action. The bimetal spring reacts to crankcase air temperature via breather tube, Fig. 46. This feature is found on some current vertical crankshaft Pulsa-Jet and Vacu-Jet carburetors.

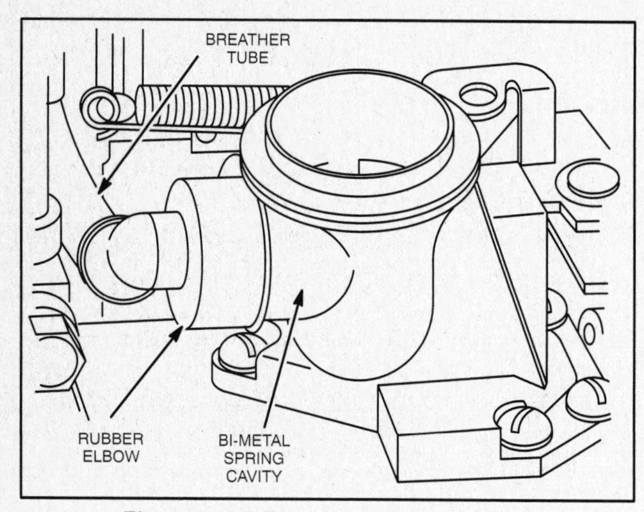

Fig. 46 – All-Temperature Carburetor

AUTOMATIC CHOKE CARBURETORS, MODEL SERIES 92000, 93000, 94000, 95000, 110900, 111900, 112900, 113900 (EXCEPT TYPE #2999), 114900, VERTICAL CRANKSHAFT

NOTE: For Model Series 113900, Type Number 2999 service procedures, see page 30.

A diaphragm under carburetor is connected to choke shaft by a link, Fig. 47. A calibrated spring under diaphragm holds choke valve closed when engine is not running.

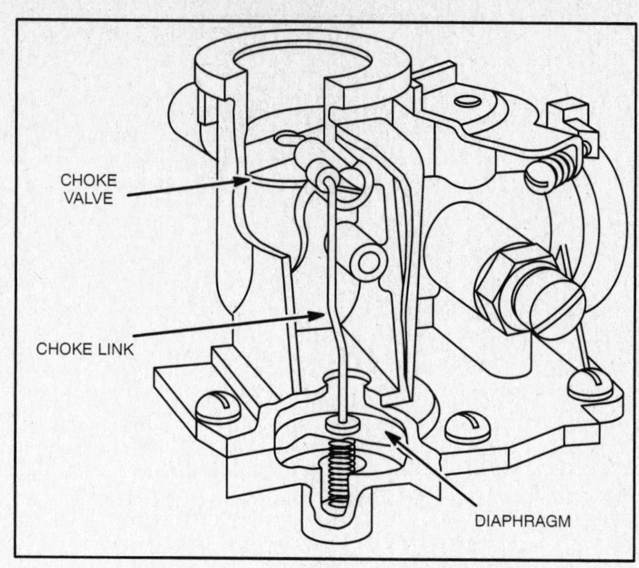

Fig. 47 – Automatic Choke System

Upon starting, vacuum created during intake stroke is routed to bottom of diaphragm, through a calibrated passage, thereby opening choke against spring pressure.

This system also has the ability to respond similar to an acceleration pump. As speed decreases during heavy loads, choke valve partially closes enriching mixture, thereby improving low speed performance and lugging power.

Check Automatic Choke Operation All-Temperature/Automatic Choke and Automatic Choke

The automatic choke can easily be checked to determine if it is or is not functioning properly.

1. Remove air cleaner and replace stud. Observe position of choke valve; it should be fully closed.
2. Move speed control to stop position; governor spring should be holding throttle in a closed position. Pull starter rope rapidly. Choke valve should alternately open and close.
3. If engine can be started, run for two or three minutes, at a normal operating speed. Check to be sure fuel tank is 1/4 full of fuel. Close needle valve to be sure mixture can be made too lean. Adjust needle valve 3/8 turn open from lean position.

Allow engine to run at idle speed for three to five minutes. Again, close needle valve; mixture should become so lean engine will stop. If engine continues to run at idle with needle valve closed, a fuel leak is occurring in one of the following areas: Check items 2D, 2H, 2I, 2J and 2K.

If choke valve does not react as stated in Steps 1, 2, and 3, carburetor will have to be disassembled to determine problem. (See Repair Procedure below.)

The following list is given to aid you in checking performance of All-Temperature/Automatic Choke and automatic choke carburetion systems.

1. Engine Appears to be Under-Choked –
   - A. Carburetor adjusted too lean
   - B. Fuel pipe check valve inoperative (Vacu-Jet only)
   - C. Bent air cleaner stud
   - D. Sticking choke shaft due to dirt, etc.
   - E. Choke spring damaged or too short (See Repair Procedure)
   - F. Diaphragm not pre-loaded (See Repair Procedure)
2. Engine Appears to be Over-Choked –
   - A. Carburetor adjusted too rich
   - B. Bent air cleaner stud
   - C. Sticking choke shaft due to dirt, etc.
   - D. Ruptured diaphragm
   - E. Vacuum passage restricted
   - F. Choke spring distorted, stretched, etc.
   - G. Gasoline or oil in vacuum chamber
   - H. Leak between link and diaphragm
   - I. Diaphragm folded during assembly, causing vacuum leak
   - J. Machined surface on tank top not flat (See Repair Procedure)
   - K. Needle valve seat loose

If engine on a mower with a high-inertia disc type cutter blade becomes hard starting when engine is warm, a leaner carburetor mixture may be required. See following note:

NOTE: A heavy, high-inertia disc type cutter blade rotates for a longer period of time, after governor control is placed in "STOP" position. During this "coasting" period, engine continues to induct fuel-air mixture, even when choke is open.

If carburetor mixture is too rich, warm engine may flood and become hard starting. If original carburetor adjustment has not been changed, turn needle valve clockwise (leaner) approximately 1/8 turn. If original carburetor adjustment has been changed, check previous list, this page, paragraph No. 2-A, B and C, then adjust 1/8 turn leaner.

DISASSEMBLE CARBURETOR

Disassemble Pulsa-Jet and Vacu-Jet All-Temperature Automatic Choke and Automatic Choke as follows:

Remove Carburetor and Fuel Tank (Air Vane Governor)

1. Remove carburetor and fuel tank assembly mounting bolts, Fig. 48.

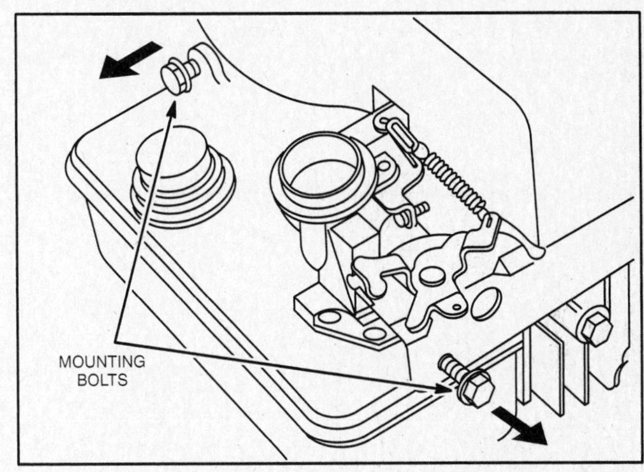

Fig. 48 – Removing Mounting Bolts

2. Slip carburetor and fuel tank assembly off end of fuel intake tube and turn assembly to free throttle link from throttle lever.

3. This will leave governor link and governor spring connected to governor blade and control lever, Fig. 49.

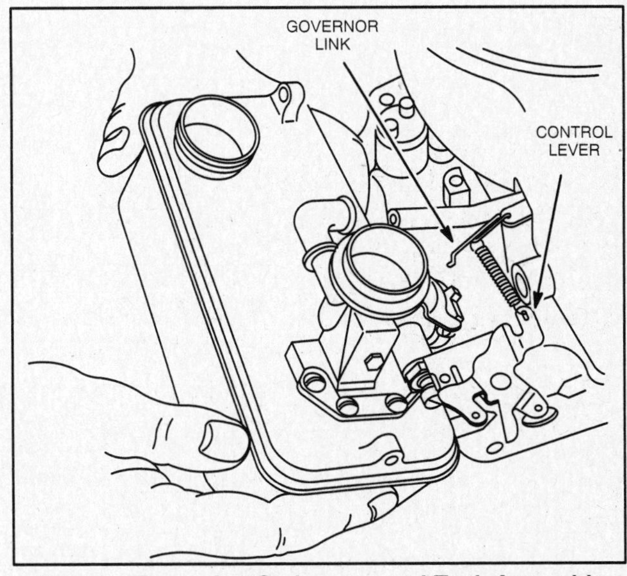

Fig. 49 – Removing Carburetor and Tank Assembly

NOTE: METRIC EQUIVALENTS ARE LISTED ON PAGE 68 OF THIS SECTION.

Remove Carburetor and Tank, Model Series (Mechanical Governor) 92900, 94000, 95000, 112900, 113900 (Except Type Number 2999), and 114900, Vertical Crankshaft

NOTE: For Model Series 113900, Type Number 2999 service procedures, see page 30.

1. Disconnect governor spring from control lever.
2. Slide carburetor and fuel tank assembly off end of fuel intake tube and turn assembly to disconnect governor link from bell crank lever.
3. This will leave governor spring and bell crank assembly on carburetor and fuel tank assembly, Fig. 50.

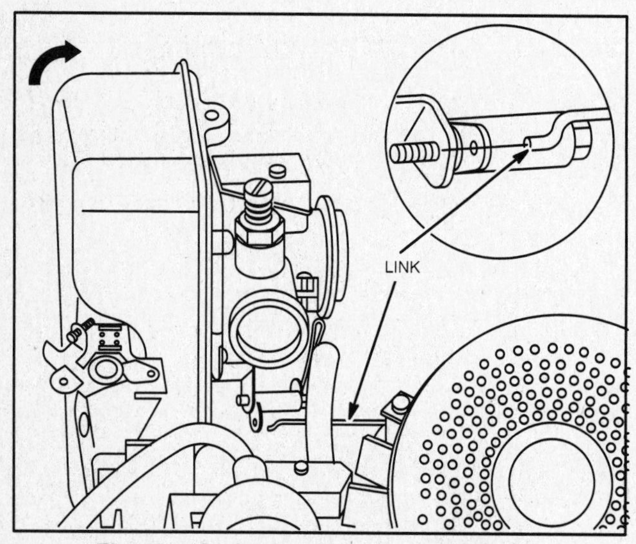

Fig. 50 – Removing Fuel Tank Assembly

Remove Carburetor, Model Series 92000, 93000, 94000, 95000, 96000, 110900, 111900, 112900, 113900 (Except Type Number 2999), and 114900 Automatic Choke, Vertical Crankshaft

NOTE: For Model Series 113900, Type Number 2999 service procedures, see page 30.

1. Remove screws holding carburetor on tank body.

   NOTE: On Model Series 110900, 111900, 113900, and 114900 a mounting screw may be located under choke valve. To gain access to screw, open choke valve completely. Use a #2 Phillips head screwdriver to remove screw, Fig. 51.

2. Then lift carburetor straight up.
3. Remove pump spring, spring cup (when used) and diaphragm.

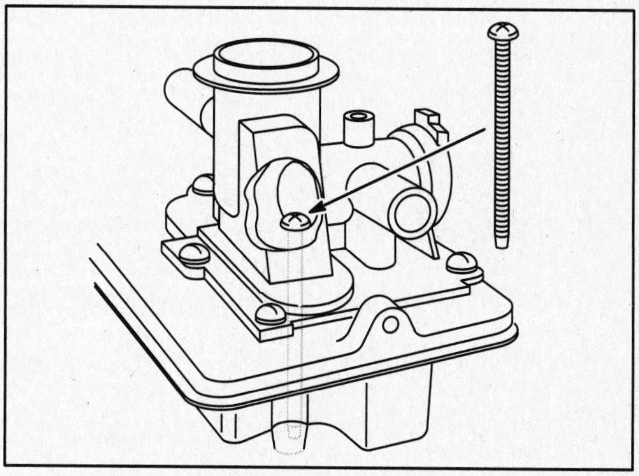

Fig. 51 – Screw Under Choke Valve

DISASSEMBLE CARBURETOR – PULSA-JET, VACU-JET

Always remove all nylon and rubber parts if carburetor is to be soaked in solvent or carburetor cleaner.

All-Temperature/Automatic Choke, Automatic Choke

Inspect automatic choke for freeness of operation. Any sticking problems should be corrected, as proper choke operation depends on freedom of choke to travel as controlled by engine vacuum and/or crankcase air temperature.

Remove All-Temperature/Automatic Choke Carburetor

Remove rubber elbow which connects breather tube to carburetor and inspect for leaks or damage. Inspect bimetal spring assembly cavity. Clean if required, Fig. 52.

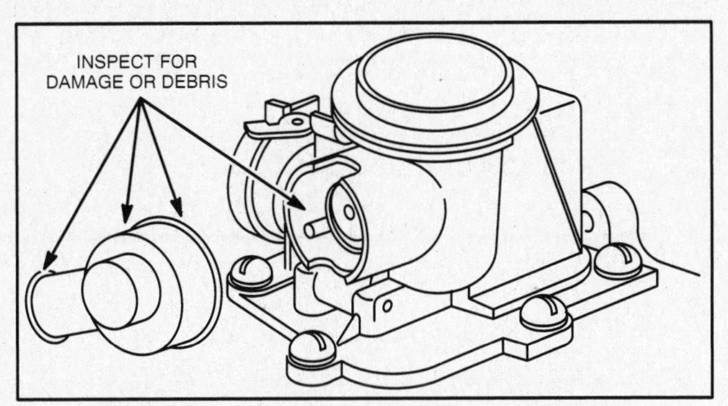

Fig. 52 - Inspecting Bimetal Spring Cavity

Remove Bimetal Spring Assembly

1. The bimetal spring and shaft assembly may be removed for cleaning or replacement.
2. Remove air cleaner assembly and rubber elbow and bimetal spring and shaft assembly may be disassembled.
3. Apply pressure on end of shaft to loosen as shown in Fig. 53.
4. Remove spring from post. Assembly may now be removed.

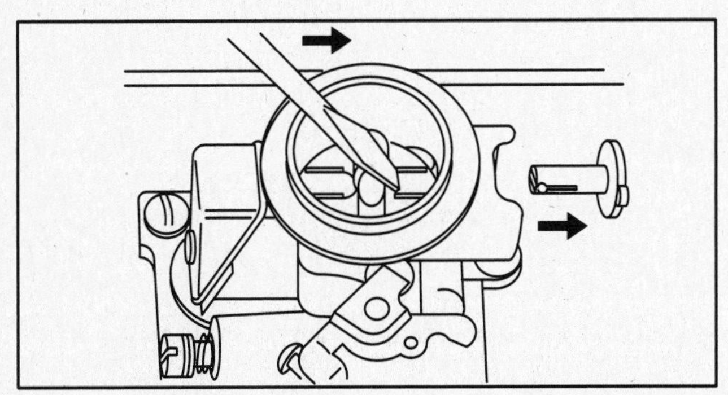

Fig. 53 - Removing Bimetal Spring and Shaft Assemble

NOTE: Spring anchor posts on early Minlon™ carburetors were flared over to better retain bimetal spring loop, Fig. 54. Scrape off flared portion before removing bimetal spring and shaft assembly on these models.

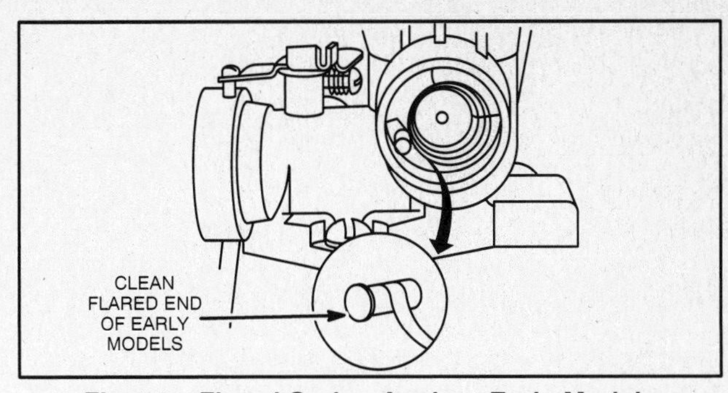

Fig. 54 - Flared Spring Anchor, Early Models

A replacement bimetal spring and shaft assembly may be obtained from your Briggs & Stratton source of supply using part number from Illustrated Parts List which describes your engine model and type number.

Remove Needle Valve Assembly - Zinc Carburetor Body

1. Remove and discard "O" ring.
2. Remove and inspect needle valve, packing and seat.
3. Metering holes in carburetor body should be cleaned with solvent and compressed air only.
4. DO NOT ALTER SIZE OF HOLES, Fig. 55.

NOTE: Some zinc carburetors use Minlon™ needle valve assembly, Fig. 81. See next paragraph "MINLON™ CARBURETOR BODY."

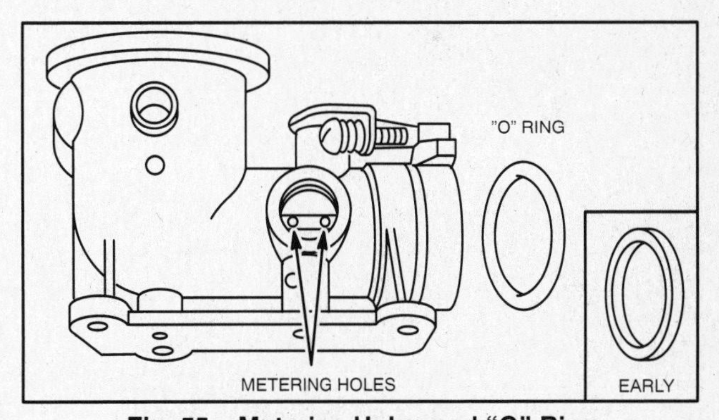

Fig. 55 - Metering Holes and "O" Ring

Remove Needle Valve Assembly - Minlon™ Carburetor Body

1. Remove and discard "O" ring.
2. Remove needle and seat assembly by backing out mixture adjusting needle about four to five turns counterclockwise.
3. Then pull needle and seat assembly out.
4. Remove inner "O" ring, Fig. 56.

NOTE: METRIC EQUIVALENTS ARE LISTED ON PAGE 68 OF THIS SECTION.

5. Metering holes in carburetor body should be cleaned with solvent and compressed air only.

6. DO NOT ALTER SIZE OF METERING HOLES, Fig. 57.

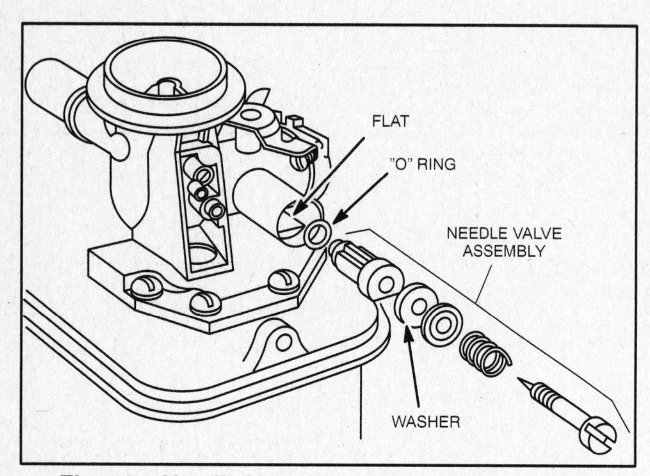

Fig. 56 - Needle Valve Assembly, Minlon™ Body

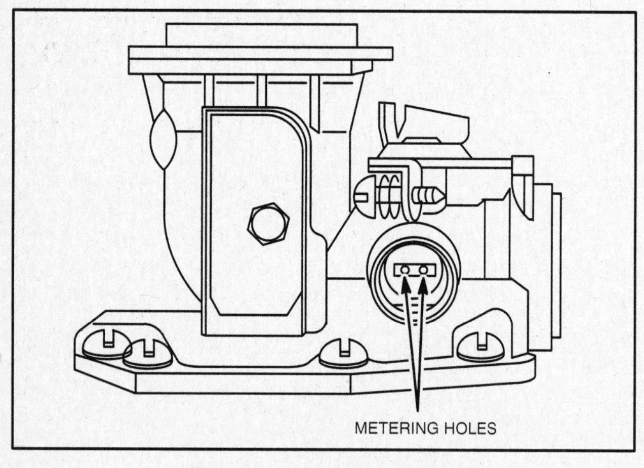

Fig. 57 - Metering Holes

Remove Throttle

- Throttle, Fig. 58, is removed by backing out idle speed adjusting screw and using a Phillips screwdriver to remove throttle valve screw. After removal of valve, throttle may be lifted out, Fig. 59.

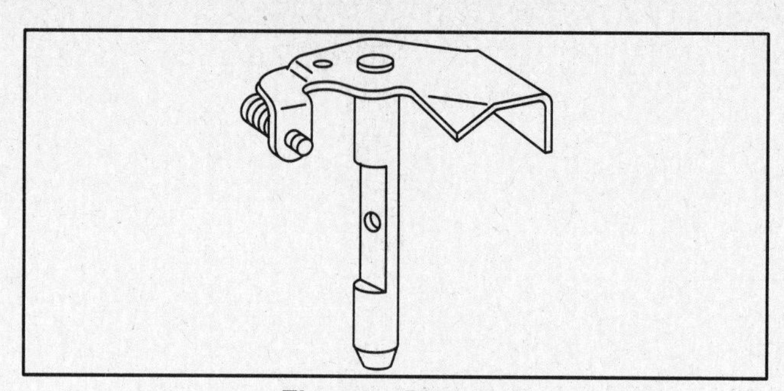

Fig. 58 - Throttle

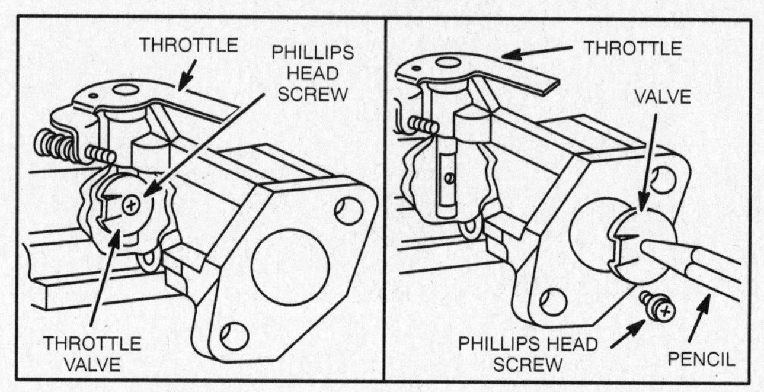

Fig. 59 - Removing Stamped Throttle

Remove Automatic Choke

1. To remove choke parts, first remove automatic choke link cover.

2. Then slide choke link out choke shaft lever. Pull shaft out of valve, Fig. 60.

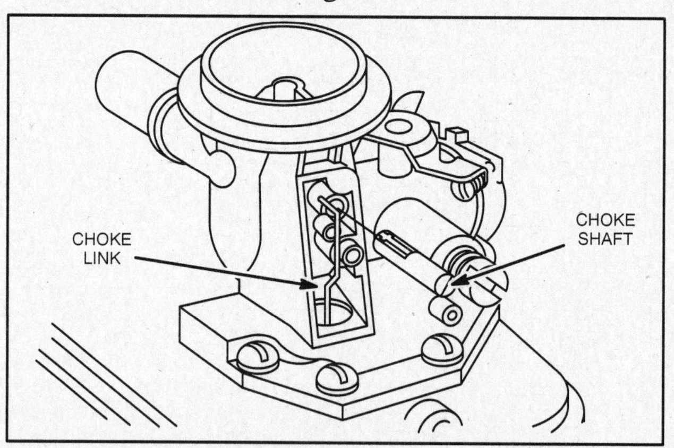

Fig. 60 - Removing Automatic Choke

Remove Fuel Pipes, Zinc Carburetors Model Series 92000, 110900, 111900, 112900, 113900 (Except Type Number 2999), and 114900, Vertical Crankshaft

- Nylon fuel pipe is threaded into carburetor body. To remove, use socket as shown in Fig. 61.

NOTE: For Model Series 113900, Type Number 2999 service procedures, see page 30.

NOTE: METRIC EQUIVALENTS ARE LISTED ON PAGE 68 OF THIS SECTION.

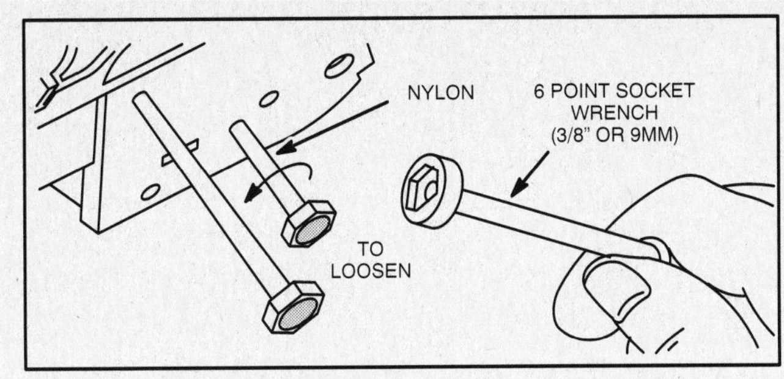

Fig. 61 - Removing Nylon Fuel Pipes, Zinc Carburetor

Remove Fuel Pipe, Minlon™ Carburetor Model Series 92500, 93500, 94500, and 95500, Vertical Crankshaft

- Fuel pipe on Minlon™ carburetors is the snap-in design. Pipe may snap out with considerable force. Fig. 62.

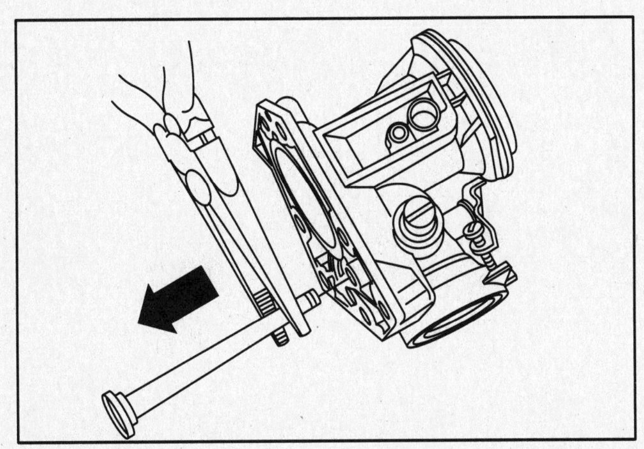

Fig. 62 - Removing Fuel Pipe, Minlon™ Carburetor

Breather and Intake Manifold

- Intake manifold is bolted to cylinder on Model Series 92000, 93000, 94000, 95000, 110900, 111900, 112900, 113900, and 114900, Fig. 63. Check for good fit or damaged gaskets to prevent air leaks or entry of dirt.

NOTE: When installing reinforced plastic or metal intake manifold and new gasket, torque screws to 30 in. lbs.

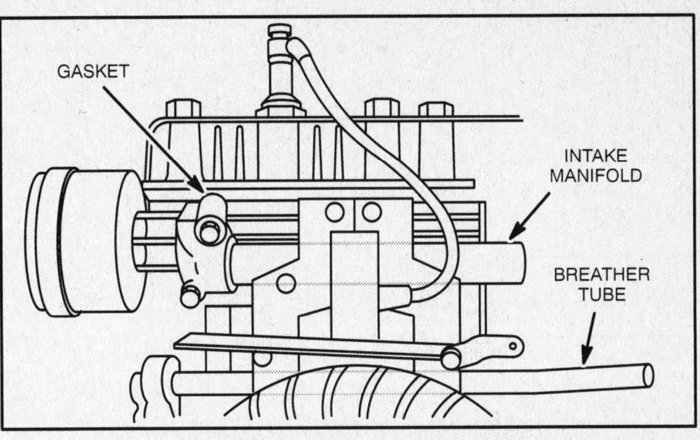

Fig. 63 - Breather and Intake Manifold

Place "O" ring in groove in throttle bore, Fig. 64.

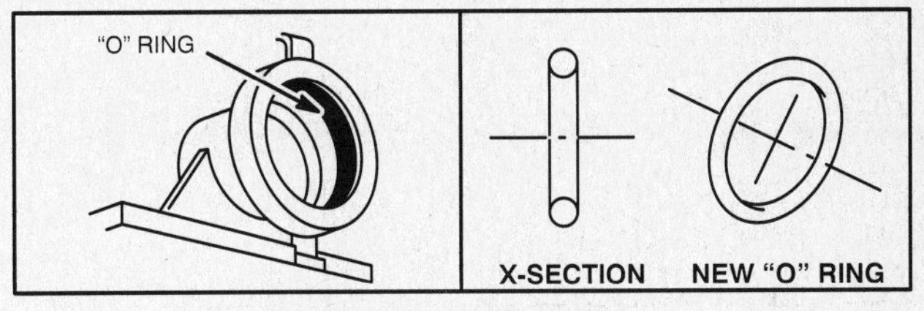

Fig. 64 - "O" Ring

INSPECTION AND REPAIR

Check all parts for wear and replace as needed. Examine fuel pipe screens for gum deposits and dirt. Replace if dirty. Replace diaphragm if worn, torn, punctured or stiff. Inspect mixture adjustment needle, Fig. 65, and replace if damaged.

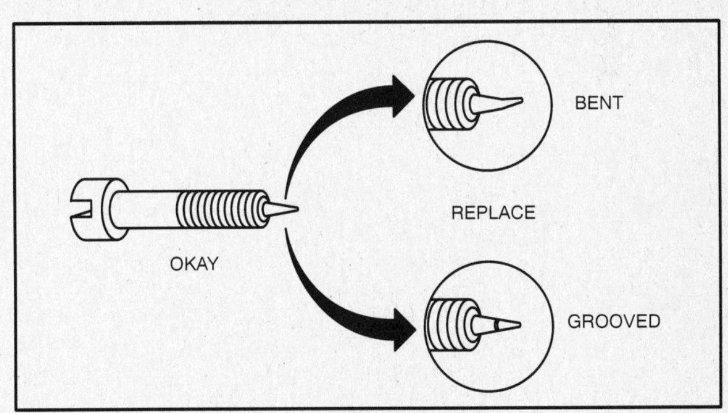

Fig. 65 - Mixture Needle

Inspect Tank

After removal of carburetor from fuel tank, inspect tank for presence of water and deposits of dirt, rust, gum, and/or varnish.

NOTE: On Vacu-Jet carburetors there is a check ball in fuel pickup tube. To function properly, screen must be clean and check ball free. Replace pipe if screen is clogged or check ball is not free to move.

NOTE: METRIC EQUIVALENTS ARE LISTED ON PAGE 68 OF THIS SECTION.

3

Clean Fuel System

Gummy or dirty fuel tanks, lines and carburetors should be cleaned in a carburetor cleaner, such as Bendix. Do not soak diaphragms or nylon parts in cleaner.

NOTE: Commercial carburetor cleaners will soften or dissolve Minlon™ bodies, if left in for long periods of time. DO NOT EXCEED 15 MINUTES.

Check Diaphragm and Spring

The diaphragm is suitable for further use, provided it has not developed wear spots, become stiff, or has punctures. (On Pulsa-Jet models check to ensure fuel pump valves are not damaged.)

Also check choke spring length, Table No. 1.

TABLE NO. 1

DIAPHRAGM SPRING LENGTH

Color	Minimum Length	Maximum Length
None	15/16"	1"
Red	1-1/8"	1-7/32"
Blue	1-5/16"	1-3/8"
Green	1-7/64"	1-3/8"

If spring length is shorter or longer than specified, replace diaphragm and spring.

Check Tank Top

Machine surface on top of fuel tank must be flat in order for diaphragm to provide an adequate seal between carburetor and tank. If machined surface on tank is not flat, it is possible for gasoline to enter vacuum chamber by passing between machined surface and diaphragm. Once fuel has entered vacuum chamber, it can move through vacuum passage and into carburetor.

Flatness of machined surface on tank top can be checked by straight edge and feeler gauge, as shown in Fig. 66. A .002" feeler gauge should not enter between straight edge and machined surface, when checking at shaded areas shown, Fig. 66. Replace tank if gauge enters.

NOTE: STRAIGHT EDGE MUST BE ACCURATE. DO NOT FILE TANK TOP TO RESTORE FLATNESS, THIS WILL CAUSE CARBURETOR TO RUN EVEN RICHER.

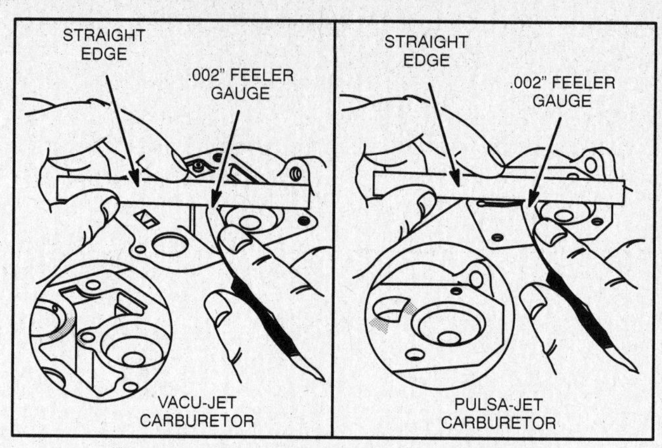

Fig. 66 - Checking Tank Top Flatness

Repair kit #391413 may be used to repair Pulsa-Jet fuel tanks which are not flat. Install roll pin and Teflon washer as shown in Fig. 67.

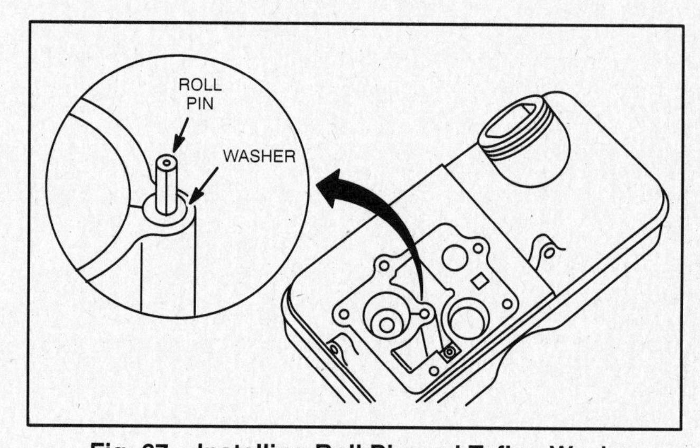

Fig. 67 - Installing Roll Pin and Teflon Washer

NOTE: This kit cannot be used on **All-Temperature/ Automatic Choke** carburetors.

Assemble Carburetor
Install Fuel Pipes, Zinc Bodies

- Thread fuel pipe(s) into carburetor body using either a 3/8" or 9/16" wrench or socket, Fig. 68. No sealant is required on threads of fuel pipes.

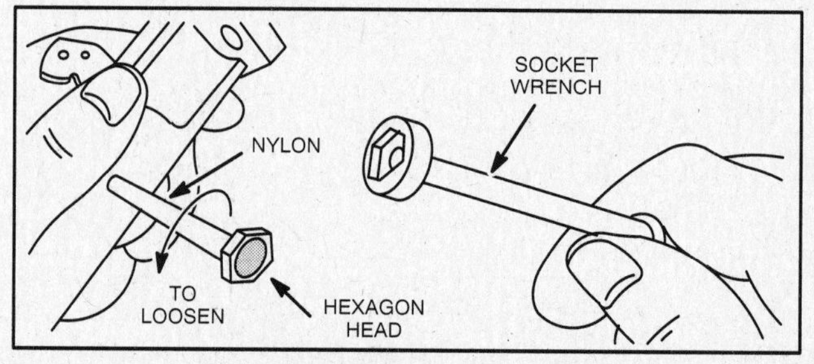

Fig. 68 - Installing Fuel Pipe

NOTE: METRIC EQUIVALENTS ARE LISTED ON PAGE 68 OF THIS SECTION.

Install Fuel Pipe, Minlon™ Carburetor Body

- Insert fuel pipe in carburetor body and place fuel pipe on a hard surface with the fuel pipe and body square to the hard surface. Fuel pipe may snap into place with some force, Fig. 69.

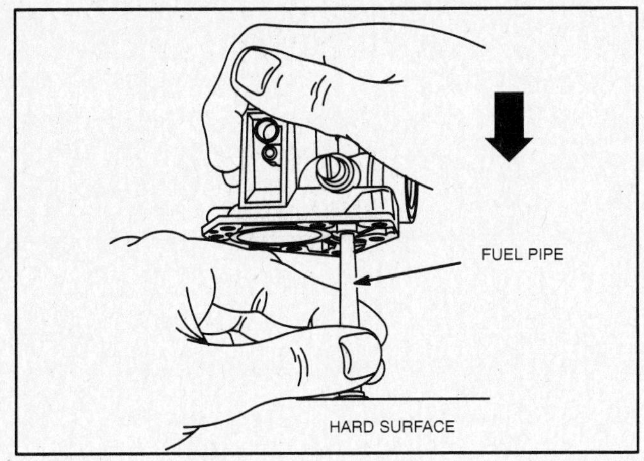

Fig. 69 - Installing Fuel Pipe, Minlon™ Carburetor

Install Throttle

- Throttle, Fig. 70, is installed by using a Phillips or straight blade screwdriver to install throttle valve screw, Fig. 71.

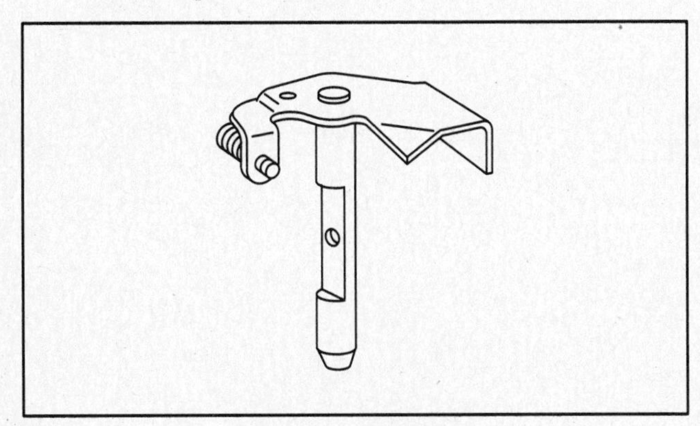

Fig. 70 - Throttle

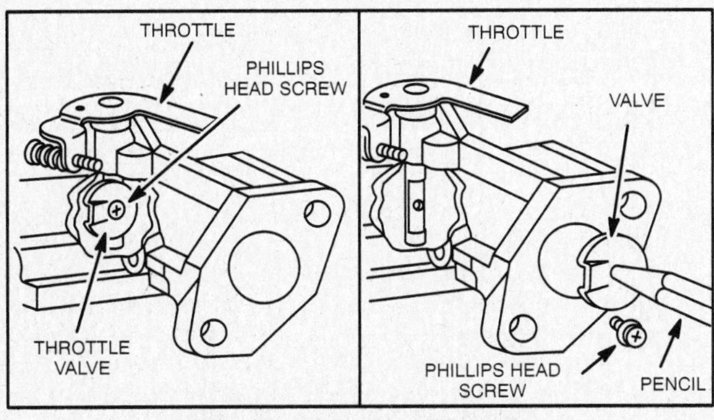

Fig. 71 - Installing Throttle

Assemble Automatic Choke

1. Place choke valve in throat of carburetor placing short shaft in hole next to breather inlet.

2. Insert choke shaft into choke shaft bore with automatic choke link hole positioned as shown in Fig. 72.

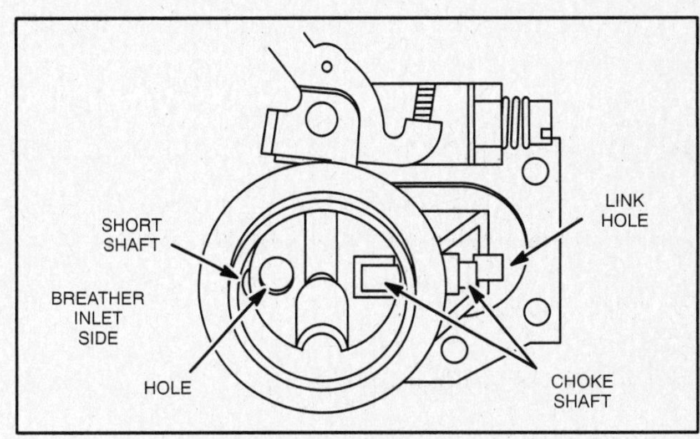

Fig. 72 - Assembling Automatic Choke

Assemble Choke Valve (With Poppet Valve)

- Do not reseal parts on assembly. When replacing choke valve and shaft, install choke valve so poppet valve spring is visible when valve is in full choke position on carburetors using poppet valve, Fig. 73.

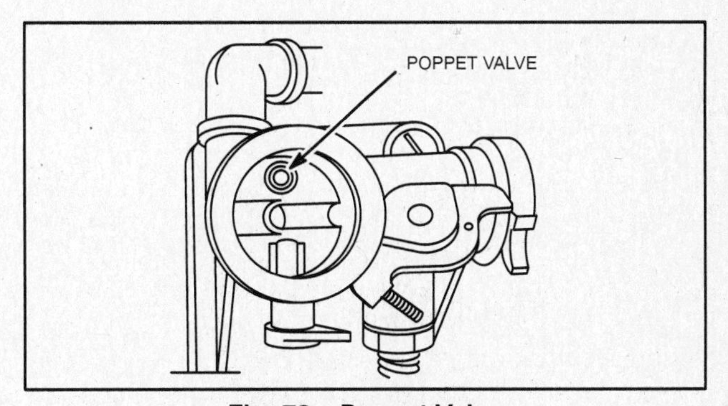

Fig. 73 - Poppet Valve

NOTE: All-Temperature Automatic choke valves are supported by the bimetal spring assembly on the breather tube side of the carburetor. See next paragraph for installation.

Assemble Bimetal Spring

After cleaning, repairing and assembly of other carburetor parts, bimetal spring and shaft assembly may be installed.

1. Place choke plate in choke (closed) position.

NOTE: METRIC EQUIVALENTS ARE LISTED ON PAGE 68 OF THIS SECTION.

2. Position notch of shaft assembly so that free end of spring loop will be within shaded area of cavity, Fig. 74.

3. Insert shaft into carburetor until notch JUST slides on choke plate. (With shaft on choke plate and spring loop off anchor post-"free"-loop position will vary within shaded area due to different ambient temperatures.)

4. Place spring loop on anchor post.

5. Slide shaft on choke plate until it locks in position.

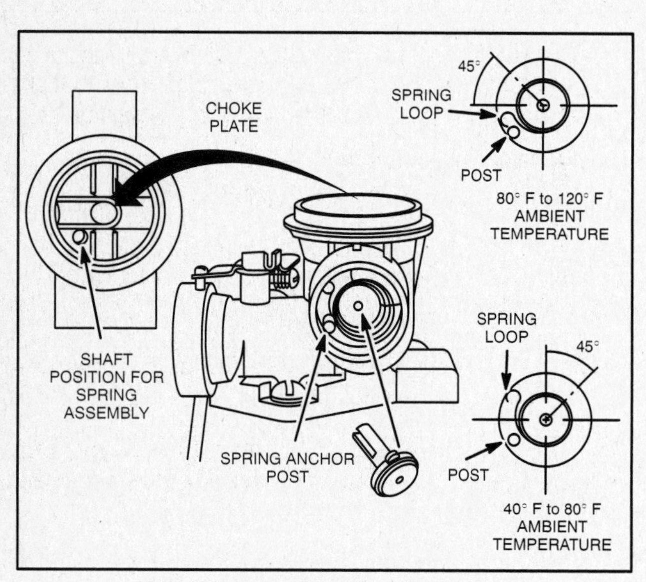

Fig. 74 – Installing Choke Spring

NOTE: Minlon™ carburetors with short spring posts must be flared on end to retain spring. Slightly flare with a WARM soldering gun.

6. If a new diaphragm is being installed, assemble choke spring to diaphragm, as shown in Fig. 75. See Table No. 2 for correct spring usage. Be careful not to bend or distort spring.

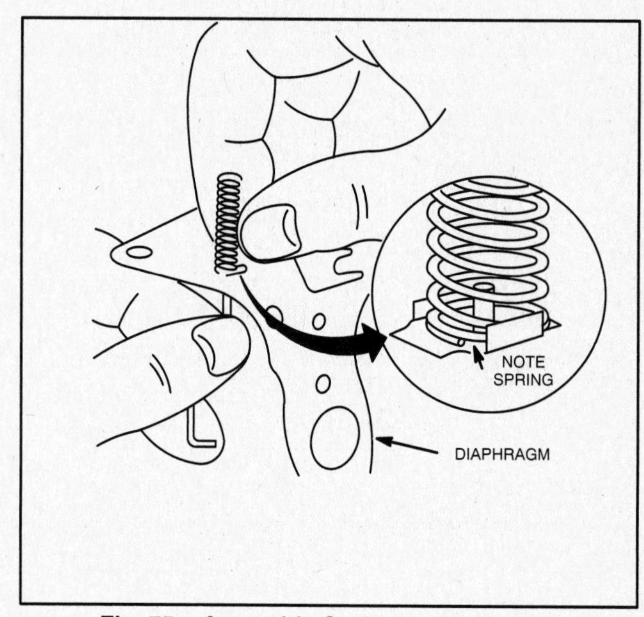

Fig. 75 – Assemble Spring to Diaphragm

TABLE NO. 2		
DIAPHRAGM SPRINGS WHERE USED BY COLOR		
	Model Series	
Carburetor Type	**90000**	**110000**
Vacu-Jet Automatic Choke	Not Colored, Standard GREEN, See Service Bulletin #533	
Vacu-Jet All Temperature Automatic Choke	Not Colored, Standard GREEN, See Service Bulletin #533	
Pulsa-Jet Automatic Choke	RED, Standard GREEN, See Service Bulletin #533	BLUE, Standard GREEN, See Service Bulletin #533
Pulsa-Jet All Temperature Automatic Choke	BLUE, Standard GREEN, See Service Bulletin #533	BLUE, Standard GREEN, See Service Bulletin #533

NOTE: METRIC EQUIVALENTS ARE LISTED ON PAGE 68 OF THIS SECTION.

NOTE: Service Bulletin #533 covered installation of choke valve and choke spring (GREEN) (part #396227) to eliminate problems with hot starting.

7. Holding carburetor body upside down, place diaphragm on body while guiding choke link thru hole for link. On Pulsa-Jet carburetor, have pump spring and cap in fuel pump well, Fig. 76.

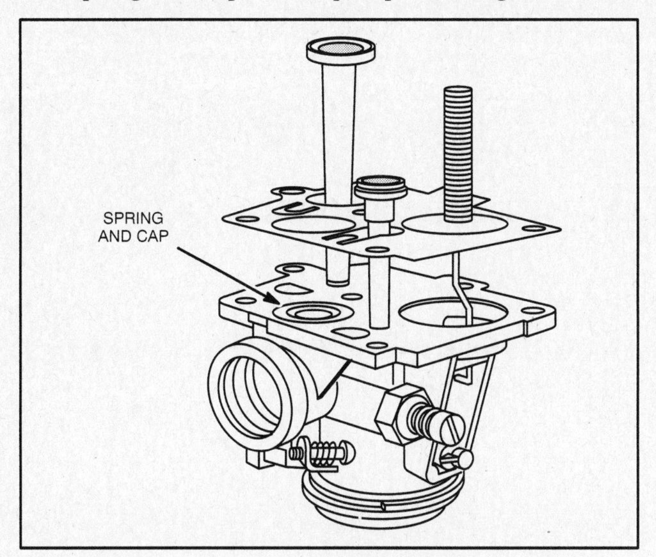

Fig. 76 - Locating Diaphragm on Carburetor

8. Lower tank down onto carburetor, while guiding choke spring into spring well, Fig. 77.

9. While holding carburetor and body together, turn assembly right side up.

10. Thread carburetor mounting screws into tank top about two turns. DO NOT TIGHTEN.

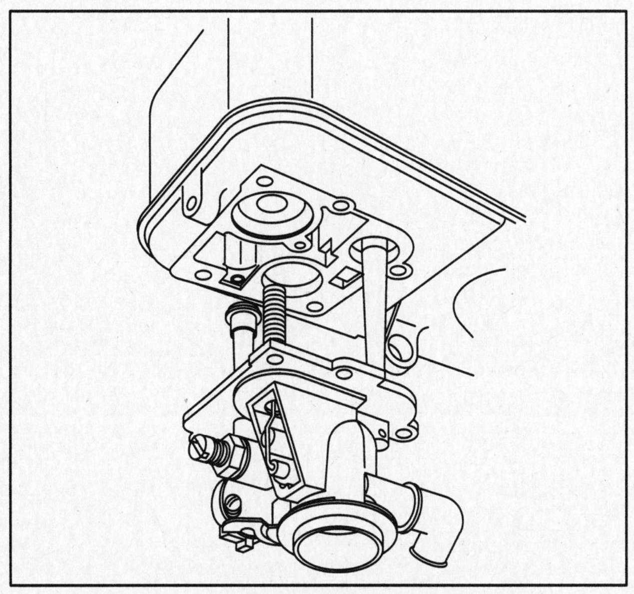

Fig. 77 - Assembling Tank to Carburetor

11. Close choke valve. Insert choke link into choke shaft as shown, Fig. 78.

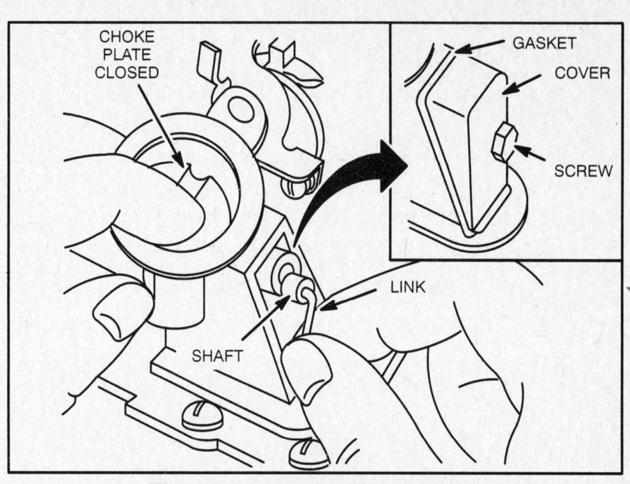

Fig. 78 - Inserting Choke Link

12. Install rubber elbow and assemble carburetor to fuel tank including pre-loading automatic choke (diaphragm), as described in next paragraph.

Pre-Load Diaphragm

1. Move choke plate to an over center position as shown in Fig. 79.

2. Hold choke while tightening carburetor mounting screws in a staggered sequence.

NOTE: Opening choke to an over center position places diaphragm in a pre-loaded condition.

3. Move choke plate to normal closed position. Choke plate should now remain fully closed, Fig. 78.

4. If choke valve is not fully closed, check to be sure choke spring is properly assembled to diaphragm, and also properly inserted in its pocket in tank top.

5. Install choke link cover and gasket.

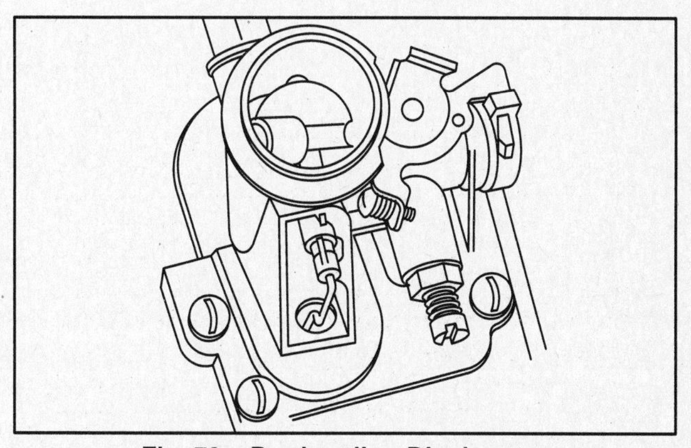

Fig. 79 - Pre-Loading Diaphragm

Install Needle Valve Assembly, Zinc Body

1. Install needle valve seat being sure not to cause burrs in slot.

2. Then install needle valve assembly, Fig. 80.

NOTE: METRIC EQUIVALENTS ARE LISTED ON PAGE 68 OF THIS SECTION.

NOTE: On zinc carburetor bodies that use Minlon™ needle valve assembly, see next two paragraphs and Fig's. 81 and 82.

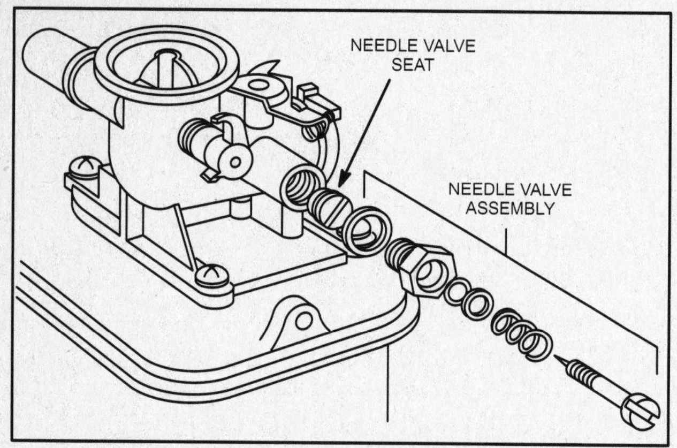

Fig. 80 - Needle Valve Assembly, Zinc Body

Install Needle Valve Assembly, Minlon™ Body

1. To install Minlon™ needle valve assembly, place "O" ring on shoulder of needle seat.
2. Then turn needle in until large seal washer just touches needle seat, Fig. 81.

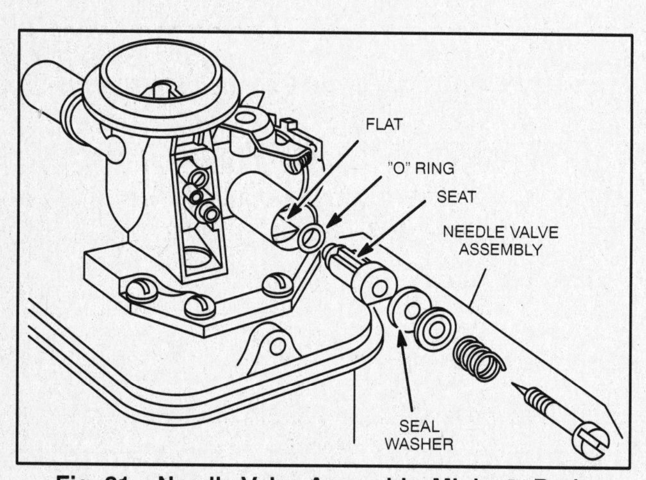

Fig. 81 - Needle Valve Assembly, Minlon™ Body

3. Assemble needle valve assembly and turn screw until it just touches spring.
4. Install needle valve as an assembly being sure flat on valve seat lines up with flat in carburetor body, Fig. 81.

NOTE: On later carburetors, a slot was added to top of needle valve assembly bore to line up with rib on needle valve assembly, Fig. 82.

5. Oil fill tube, Part #280131 will help firmly seat valve assembly, Fig. 82.

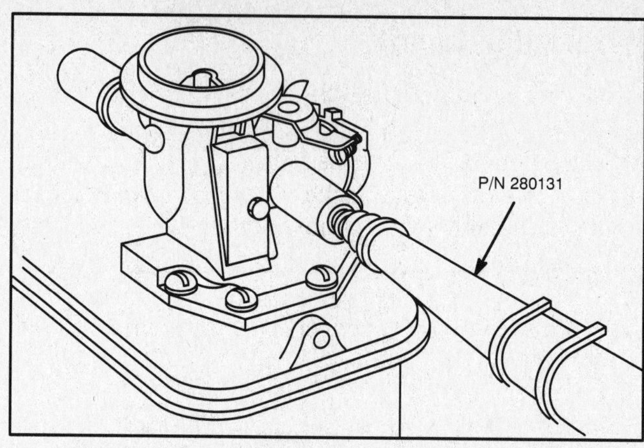

Fig. 82 - Assembling Valve in Minlon™ Body

Assemble Carburetor to Tank, Automatic Choke, Model Series 92000, 93500, 94000, 95000, 110900, 111900, Vertical Crankshaft

- Assemble carburetor to tank as outlined on page 27 of this section.

Install Carburetor and Tank Assembly, Automatic Choke, Model Series 92000, 110900, 111900, Vertical Crankshaft

1. Apply light film of oil to "O" ring in throttle bore. Then hook governor link to governor blade.
2. Align carburetor with intake tube and breather tube grommet.
3. Be sure "O" ring does not distort when fitting carburetor to intake tube. Install governor spring as shown in Section 4, page 8.

Install Carburetor and Tank Assembly Automatic Choke, Model Series 94000, 95000, Vertical Crankshaft

1. Apply light film of oil "O" ring in throttle bore.
2. Then hook bell crank into governor lever rod.
3. Align carburetor with intake tube and breather grommet.
4. Be sure "O" ring does not distort when fitting carburetor to intake tube.
5. Install governor spring as shown in Section 4, page 8.

CARBURETOR ADJUSTMENT

NOTE: When making carburetor adjustments on Vacu-Jet and Pulsa-Jet carburetors, air cleaner and stud must be installed on carburetor.

Model Series 92500, 93500, 94500, and 95500 engines should be adjusted with fuel tank one-quarter (1/4) full of gasoline.

Initial Adjustment

1. Turn needle valve clockwise to just close it.
2. Then open 1-1/2 turns. This initial adjustment will permit engine to be started and warmed up before making final adjustment.

Final Adjustment

1. Place governor speed control lever in "FAST" position.
2. Turn needle valve in until engine misses (clockwise – lean mixture) then turn needle valve out (counterclockwise) 3/8 turn.
3. Next, adjust idle RPM.
4. Rotate throttle counterclockwise and hold against stop.
5. Adjust idle speed adjusting screw to obtain 1750 RPM.
6. Release throttle – engine should accelerate without hesitation or sputtering.
7. If engine does not accelerate properly, carburetor should be re-adjusted, usually to a slightly richer mixture.

NOTE: If carburetor is out of adjustment so that it will not start, close needle valve by turning it clockwise. Then open needle valve 1-1/2 turns counterclockwise using Tool #19263, Carburetor Adjusting Screwdriver, Fig. 83.

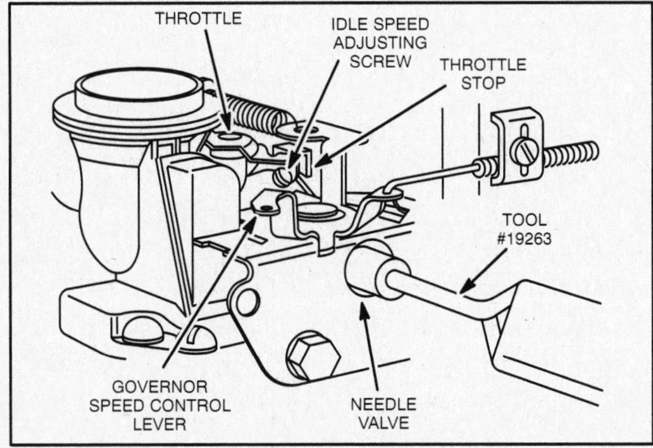

Fig. 83 – Adjusting Carburetor

NOTE: Flooding can occur if engine is tipped at an angle for a prolonged period of time, if engine is cranked repeatedly when spark plug wire is disconnected, or if carburetor mixture is adjusted too rich.

In case of flooding, move governor control to "STOP" position and pull starter rope at least six times. (Crank electric starter models for at least 5 seconds.)

Then move control to "FAST" position and start engine. If engine continues to flood, lean carburetor needle valve – 1/8 to 1/4 turn clockwise or see page 19, paragraph 2-A, B, and C.

When control is placed in "STOP" position governor spring holds throttle in a closed (idle) position. Cranking engine with a closed throttle creates a higher vacuum which opens choke rapidly, permitting engine to clear itself of excess fuel.

ADJUSTABLE PULSA-JET AND VACU-JET CARBURETORS WITH CHOKE-A-MATIC®, MANUAL, AND REMOTE CHOKE, MODEL SERIES 60000, 80000, 90000, 100000, 110000, 130000, HORIZONTAL AND VERTICAL CRANKSHAFTS

PULSA-JET CARBURETORS

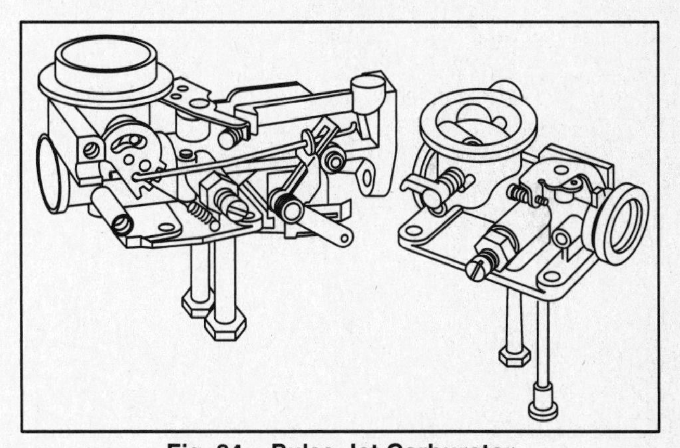

Fig. 84 – Pulsa-Jet Carburetor

VACU-JET CARBURETORS

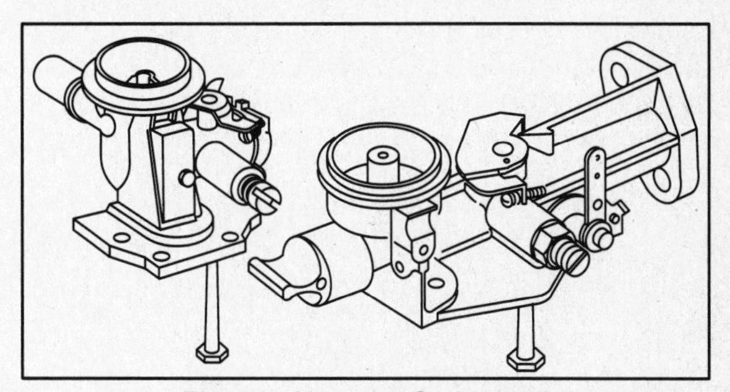

Fig. 85 – Vacu-Jet Carburetor

NOTE: METRIC EQUIVALENTS ARE LISTED ON PAGE 68 OF THIS SECTION.

Remove Carburetor and Tank Assembly (Except Model Series 100900, 113900 Type #2999, 130900, 131900 and 132900)

1. Remove carburetor and fuel tank as a unit, being careful not to bend governor linkage.

2. On models equipped with a stop switch, remove stop switch wire, Fig. 86.

NOTE: On some horizontal crankshaft Pulsa-Jet carburetors, Tool #19305, Offset Screwdriver, or Tool # 19391, Torx® Wrench, or open end wrench can be used.

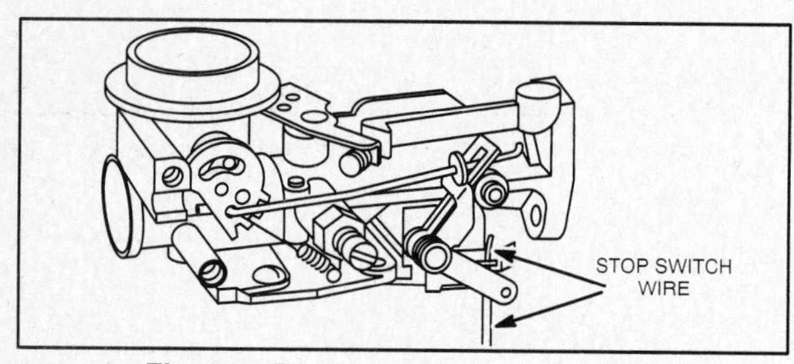

Fig. 86 – Removing Stop Switch Wire

Remove Carburetor, Model Series 92000 Choke-A-Matic®, Vertical Crankshaft

1. Remove screws holding carburetor onto tank body.

2. Then lift carburetor straight up. Remove pump spring, spring cup and diaphragm.

Remove Carburetor and Tank, Model 100900, 113900 Type #2999, 130900, 131900, and 132900, Vertical Crankshaft

1. Disconnect stop switch wire and governor spring.

2. Remove two cylinder head bolts or studs and rear tank mounting screw.

   NOTE: Model Series 113900 Type #2999 has a stud and a mounting screw.

3. Slip carburetor over notch in cylinder shield and away from intake tube, Fig. 87. Rotate carburetor and tank assembly to disconnect governor link from throttle lever.

NOTE: On some models, it may be necessary to remove blower housing.

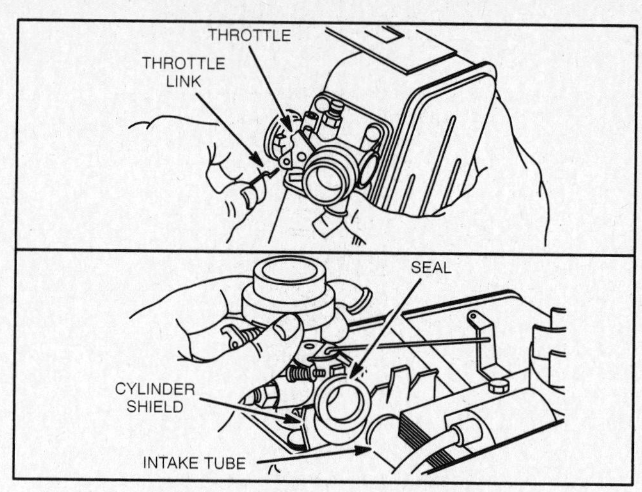

Fig. 87 – Removing Carburetor
Model Series 100900, 113900 Type #2999, 130900, 131900, 132900, Vertical Crankshafts

DISASSEMBLE CARBURETOR

Disassemble Choke-A-Matic® Linkage, Slide Choke, (Except Model Series 100900, 130900 131900, 132900)

1. To remove choke link, remove speed adjustment lever and stop switch insulator plate.

2. Remove speed adjustment lever from choke link.

3. Then pull out choke link through hole in choke slide, Fig. 88.

NOTE: On Model Series 100900, 130900, 131900, and 132900, the Choke-A-Matic® valve lever is operated by the carburetor control plate. Removing the plate is all that is required.

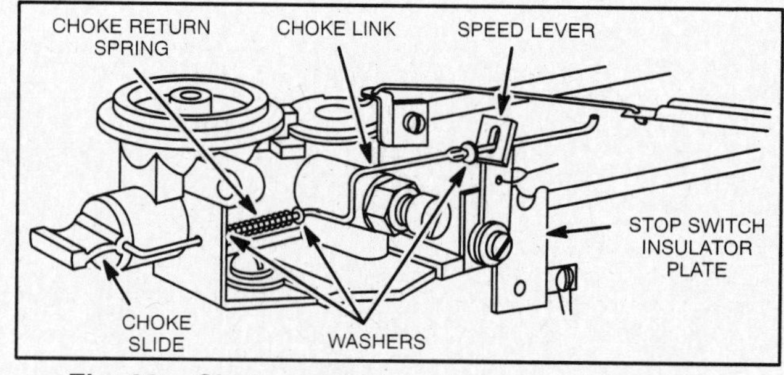

Fig. 88 – Choke-A-Matic® Linkage, Slide Choke

Disassemble Choke-A-Matic® Linkage, Rotary Choke, Horizontal Crankshaft

1. To remove choke link, remove speed adjustment lever and stop switch insulator plate.

NOTE: METRIC EQUIVALENTS ARE LISTED ON PAGE 68 OF THIS SECTION.

2. Work link out through hole in choke shaft, Fig. 89.

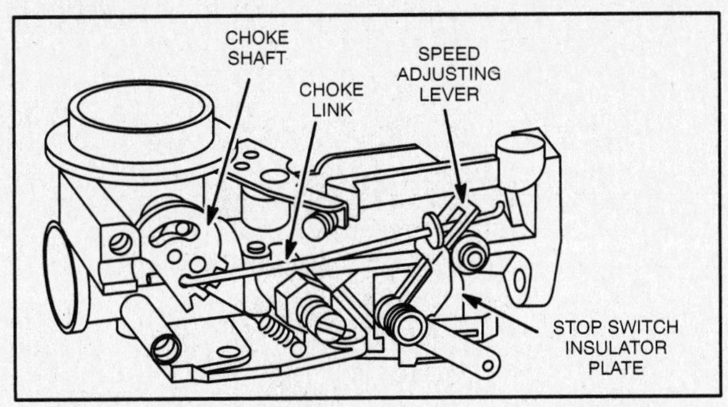

Fig. 89 – Choke-A-Matic® Linkage, Rotary Choke

Remove Spiral

NOTE: Some carburetor models have a spiral in carburetor bore.

1. To remove, clamp carburetor in a vise with smooth jaws about half an inch below top of jaws.
2. Grasp spiral firmly with a pair of pliers, as shown, Fig. 90.
3. Place a screwdriver under ledge of pliers.
4. Using edge of vise, push down on screwdriver handle to pry out spiral, Fig. 90.
5. Inspect gasket surface of carburetor. Repair if mounting surface is damaged.

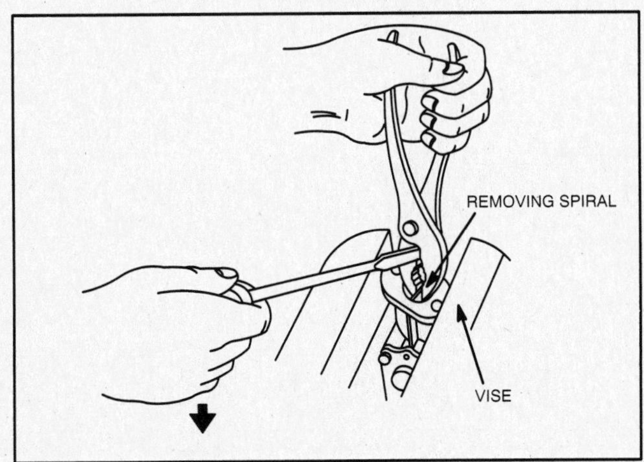

Fig. 90 – Removing Spiral

Remove Throttle, All

1. Throttle, Fig. 91, is removed by using a Phillips or standard screwdriver to remove throttle valve screw.
2. After removal of valve, throttle shaft and dust seal may be lifted out, Fig. 92.

NOTE: Some Pulsa-Jet carburetors have a throttle shaft seal in addition to the dust seal. Remove and discard.

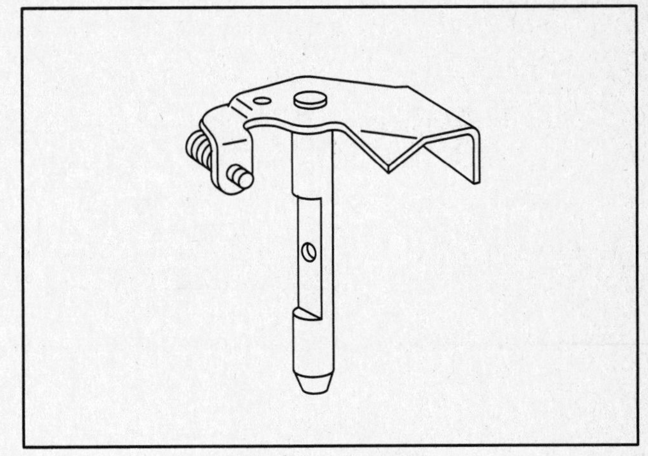

Fig. 91 – Throttle

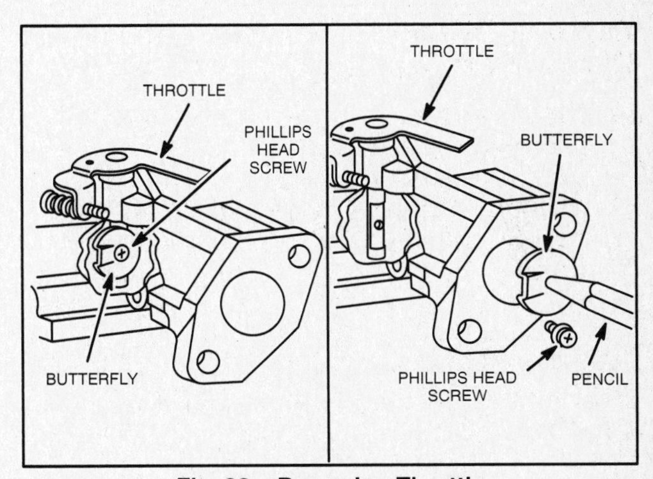

Fig. 92 – Removing Throttle

Remove Nylon Choke and Shaft, Model Series 92000, 100900, 130900, Vertical Crankshaft

1. To remove choke parts, first disconnect choke return spring, Fig. 93.
2. Then pull nylon choke shaft sideways to separate choke shaft from choke valve.

NOTE: If choke valve is heat-sealed to choke shaft, loosen by sliding sharp pointed tool along edge of choke shaft.

NOTE: METRIC EQUIVALENTS ARE LISTED ON PAGE 68 OF THIS SECTION.

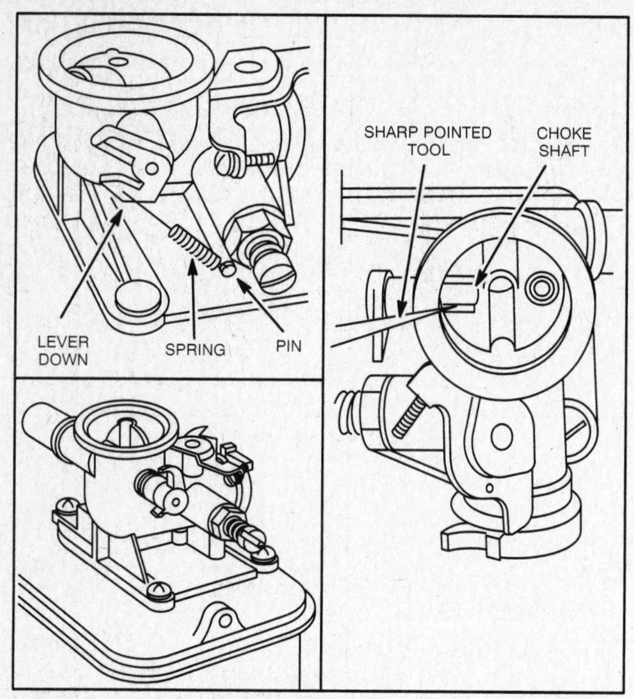

Fig. 93 – Choke Shaft and Valve – Choke-A-Matic®

Remove Nylon Choke and Shaft, Rotary Choke-A-Matic®, Manual, and Remote, Model Series 80000, 110000, 130000, Horizontal Crankshaft

1. Pull nylon choke shaft sideways to separate choke shaft from choke valve.
2. Remove spring (Choke-A-Matic® only), felt washer, and metal washer from choke shaft, Fig. 94.

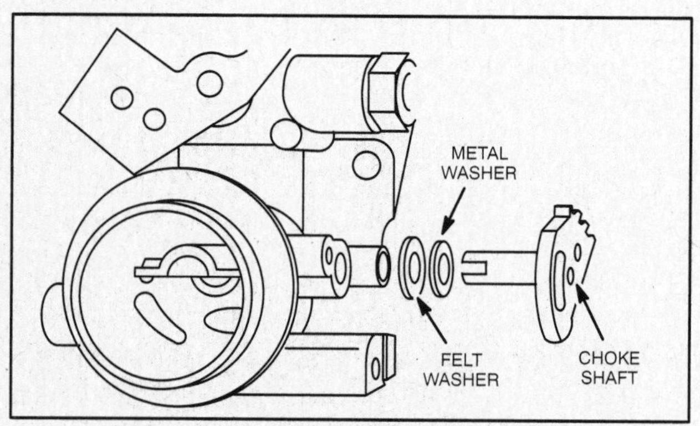

Fig. 94 – Removing Choke Shaft and Valve, Rotary Choke

Remove Fuel Pipe (Vacu-Jet)

The fuel pipe contains a check ball and a fine mesh screen. To function properly, screen must be clean and check ball free, Fig. 95. Replace pipe if screen and ball cannot be satisfactorily cleaned in carburetor cleaner. DO NOT LEAVE CARBURETOR IN CLEANER MORE THAN 1/2 HOUR WITHOUT REMOVING NYLON PARTS.

- Nylon fuel pipes, Fig. 95, are removed and replaced with a 6 point 3/8" or 9/16" socket, Fig. 96.

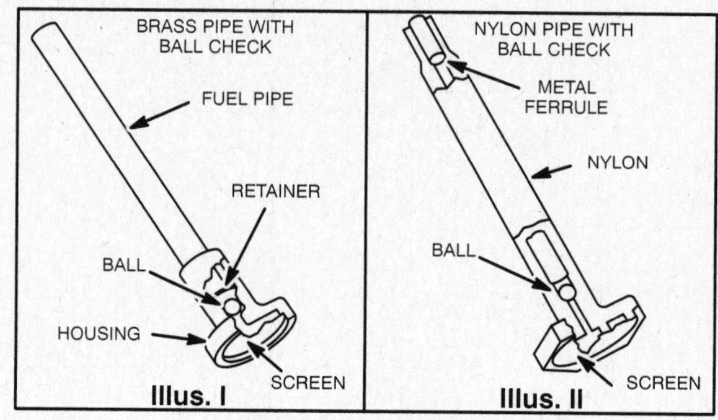

Fig. 95 – Fuel Pipes

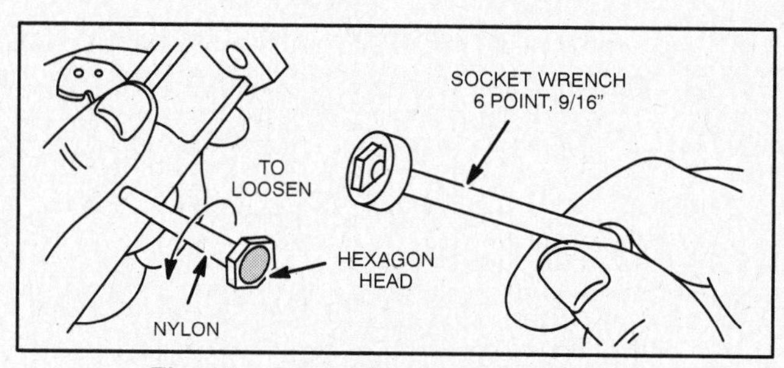

Fig. 96 – Replacing Nylon Fuel Pipe

Remove Fuel Pipe (Pulsa-Jet)

Check balls are not used in these fuel pipes. Screen housing or pipe must be replaced if screen can not be satisfactorily cleaned. Long pipe supplies fuel from tank to fuel pump and tank cup. Short pipe supplies fuel from tank cup to carburetor venturi, Fig. 98. Fuel pipes are nylon or brass. Short nylon pipes are removed and replaced by using a six point socket, or open end wrench, Fig. 97. WHERE BRASS PIPES ARE USED, NYLON OR BRASS SCREEN HOUSING ONLY IS REPLACED, Fig. 99.

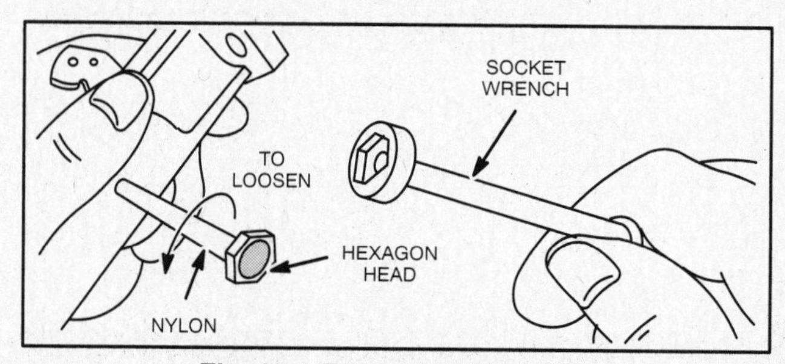

Fig. 97 – Removing Fuel Pipe

NOTE: METRIC EQUIVALENTS ARE LISTED ON PAGE 68 OF THIS SECTION.

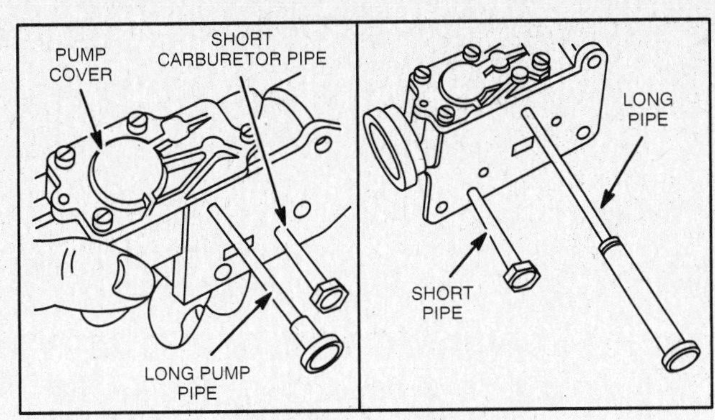

Fig. 98 – Fuel Pipes

1. Clamp fuel pipe in a vise (do not overtighten).
2. Drive off brass filter housing with a screwdriver or flat punch, Fig. 99.
3. New filter housing is installed by tapping it on pipe with a soft hammer.
4. Slide new retainer clip onto brass pipe.
5. Heat small end of new nylon tube in hot water and push onto brass tube until nylon tube covers groove on brass tube.
6. Slide retaining clip down onto nylon tube over groove on brass pipe, Fig. 98.

NOTE: DO NOT remove brass pipe.

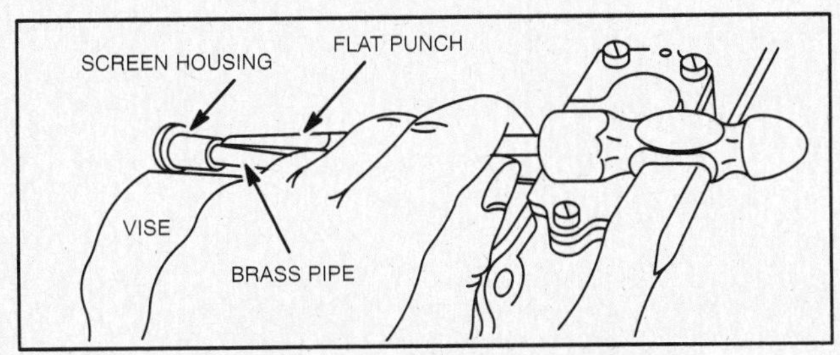

Fig. 99 – Removing Fuel Pipe

Remove Needle Valve and Seat

1. Remove needle valve to inspect.
2. Replace needle valve if needle is bent, grooved, or broken.
3. Replace seat if screwdriver slot is damaged.
4. If carburetor is gummy or dirty, remove seat to allow better cleaning of metering holes, Fig. 100.
5. Use only compressed air to clean metering holes.

NOTE: Do not change metering hole sizes, Fig. 100.

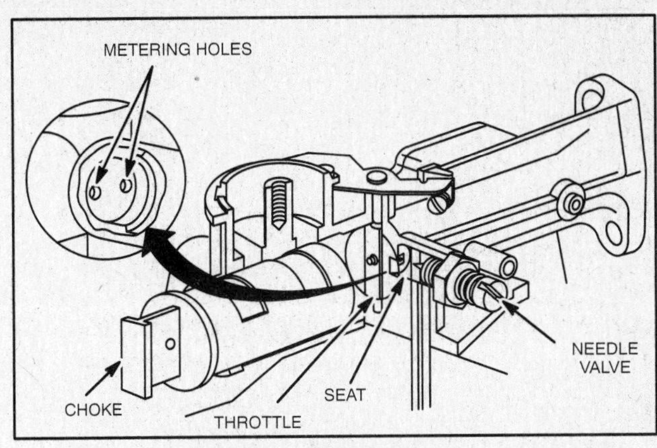

Fig. 100 – Metering Holes

Disassemble Fuel Pump, Pulsa-Jet Model Series 80000, 100000, 110000, 130000, Horizontal and Vertical Crankshafts

1. Remove fuel pump cover, diaphragm, spring and cup, Fig. 101.
2. Inspect diaphragm for punctures, cracks and fatigue.
3. Replace if damaged.
4. Smooth side of cup must rest against diaphragm. This prevents spring from cutting diaphragm.

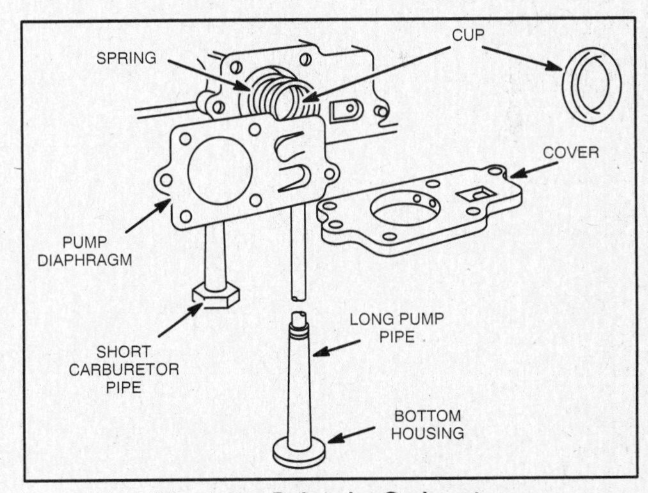

Fig. 101 – Pulsa-Jet Carburetor

Breather and Intake Manifold

1. Intake manifold is bolted to cylinder on vertical crankshaft Model Series 90000, 100000, 110000, and 130000, Fig. 102.
2. Check for good fit or damaged gaskets to prevent air leaks or entry of dirt.

NOTE: METRIC EQUIVALENTS ARE LISTED ON PAGE 68 OF THIS SECTION.

NOTE: When installing reinforced plastic or metal intake manifold and new gasket, torques screws to 40 in. lbs.

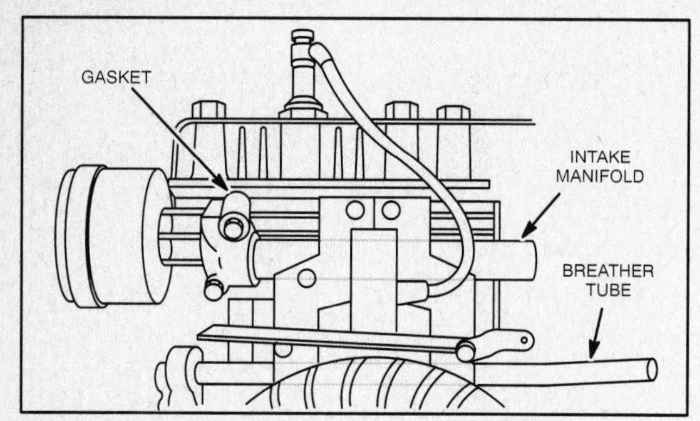

Fig. 102 – Breather and Intake Manifold

3. Place "O" ring in groove in throttle bore, Fig. 103.

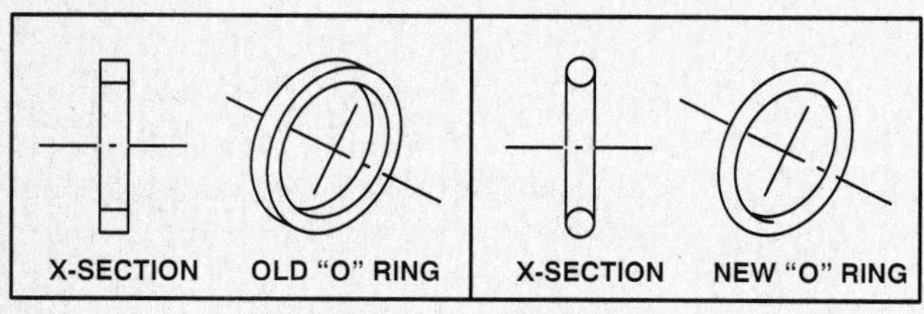

Fig. 103 – "O" Ring

INSPECTION AND REPAIR

Check all parts for wear and replace as needed. Examine fuel pipe screens for gum deposits and dirt. Replace if dirty. Replace diaphragm if worn, torn, punctured or stiff. Inspect mixture adjustment needle, Fig. 104, and replace if damaged.

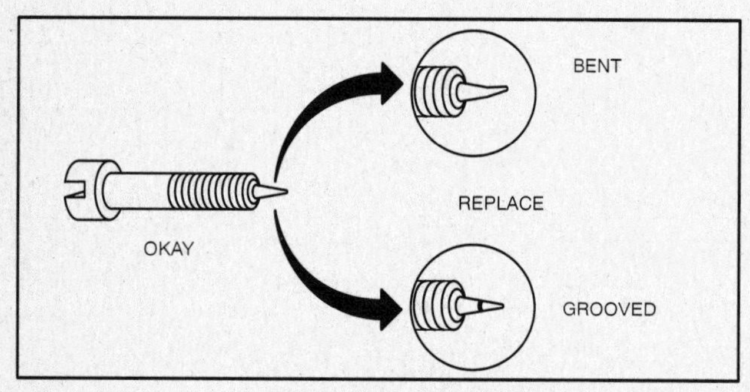

Fig. 104 – Mixture Needle

NOTE: On Vacu-Jet carburetors there is a check ball in fuel pickup tube. To function properly, screen must be clean and check ball free. Replace pipe if screen is clogged or check ball is not free to move.

Clean Fuel System

Gummy or dirty fuel tanks, lines and carburetors should be cleaned in a carburetor cleaner, such as Bendix. Do not soak diaphragms or nylon parts in cleaner.

After removal of carburetor from fuel tank, inspect tank for deposits of dirt and/or varnish.

ASSEMBLE CARBURETOR

Assemble Fuel Pump – Pulsa-Jet

1. Smooth side of cup must rest against diaphragm. This prevents spring from cutting diaphragm.

2. When installing pump cover, tighten screws evenly in staggered sequence to ensure a good seal.

3. Inspect all sealing surfaces for nicks or damages and repair or replace as required, Fig. 105.

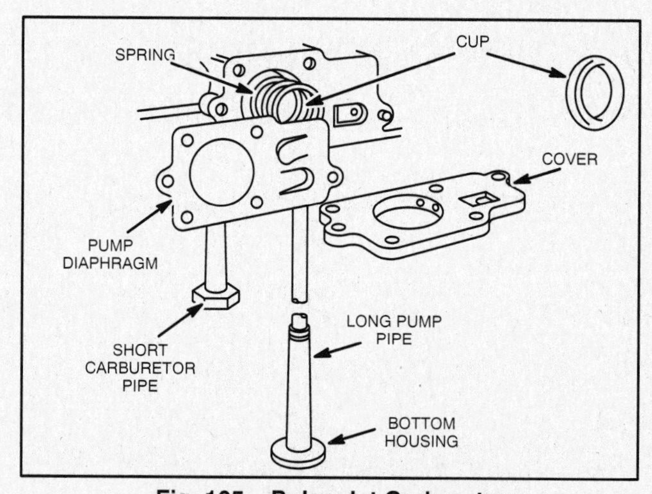

Fig. 105 – Pulsa-Jet Carburetor

Assemble Rotary Choke Valve and Shaft

1. Place choke valve in carburetor throat with short shaft on choke valve towards breather opening and insert short shaft in shaft hole, Fig. 110.

2. Insert choke shaft with metal washer and felt seal into choke shaft hole.

NOTE: On manual choke carburetors, bottom tooth of choke shaft engages top tooth on manual choke lever including Model Series 113900 Type #2999, Fig. 106.

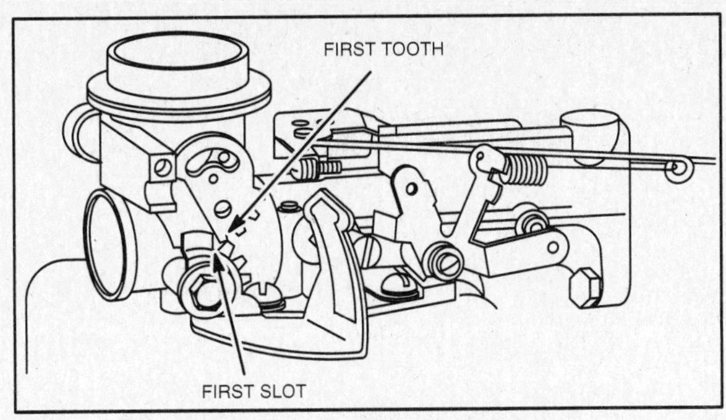

Fig. 106 – Choke Shaft Engagement

NOTE: On horizontal crankshaft model Choke-A-Matic® carburetors, hook small end of spring on spring post and long hook in bottom hole of choke shaft, Fig. 107.

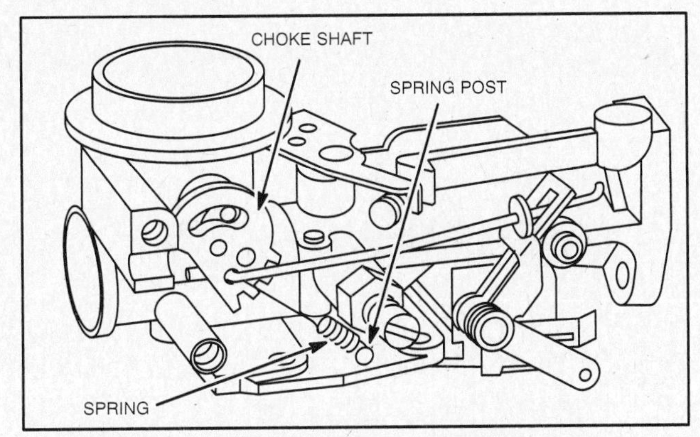

Fig. 107 – Assemble Choke-A-Matic® Spring

NOTE: On vertical crankshaft Model Series 100900, 130900, 131900, 132900 hook small loop on post on carburetor body and square hook in notch on choke shaft, Fig. 108.

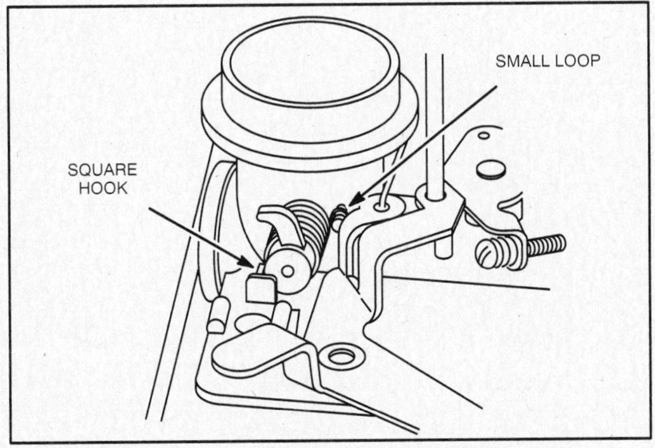

Fig. 108 – Assemble Choke-A-Matic® Spring

Assemble Carburetor Choke Shaft, Choke-A-Matic® Model Series 92000

1. When assembling carburetor, use new "O" rings, gaskets and/or diaphragms.
2. Install choke plate and choke shaft.
3. Choke shaft lever should be as shown in Fig. 109, Illus. I, II.

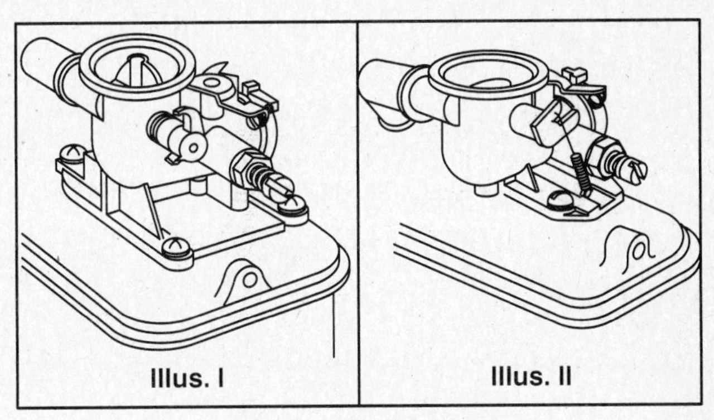

Fig. 109 – Choke Lever

Assemble Choke Valve (With Poppet Valve)

- Do not reseal parts on assembly. When replacing choke valve and shaft, install choke valve so poppet valve spring is visible when valve is in full choke position on carburetors using poppet valve, Fig. 110.

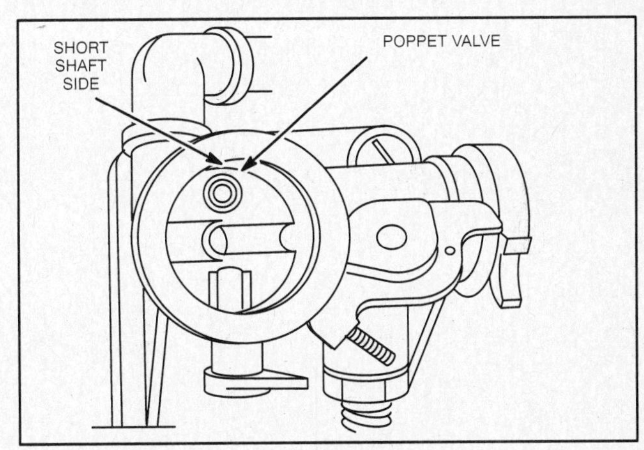

Fig. 110 – Poppet Valve

Assemble Choke-A-Matic® Linkage, Slide Choke

1. To assemble, slip washers and spring over choke link, Fig. 111.
2. Hook choke link through hole in choke slide. Place other end of choke link through hole in speed adjustment lever.
3. Mount lever and stop switch insulator plate to carburetor.

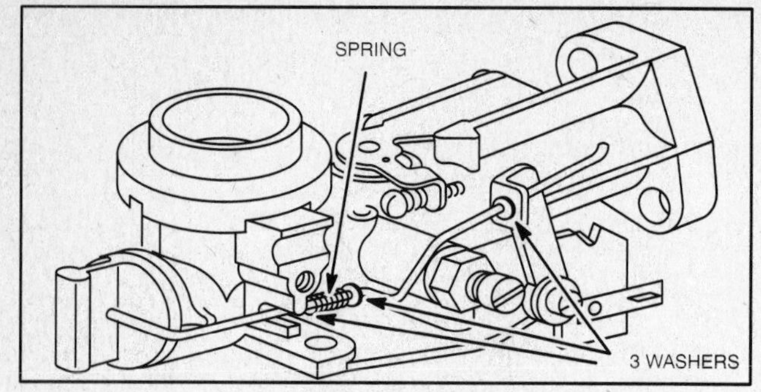

Fig. 111 – Assembling Choke-A-Matic® Linkage

Assemble Choke-A-Matic® Linkage, Rotary Choke

1. Insert "Z" bend of Choke-A-Matic® linkage into same hole as return spring.
2. Slide washer on the end of linkage and then slide Choke-A-Matic® lever onto shaft.
3. Install lever assembly and stop switch on carburetor, Fig. 112.

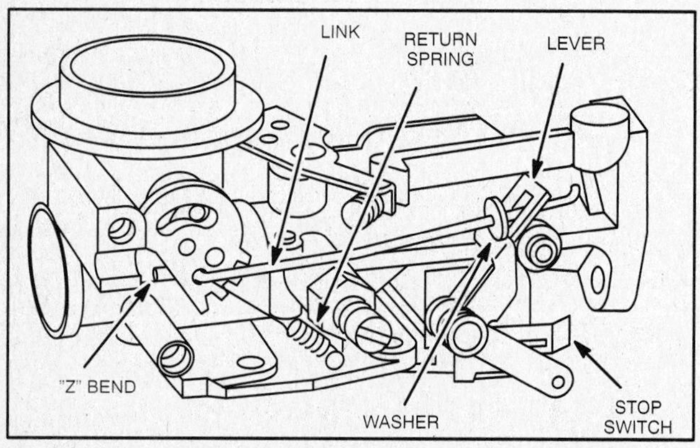

Fig. 112 – Assembling Choke-A-Matic® Linkage

Install Throttle

1. If Pulsa-Jet carburetor body had a throttle shaft seal, install new seal with sealing lip up.
2. Place new dust seal on throttle shaft and install in carburetor body, Fig. 113.
3. Install throttle valve in carburetor body and install Phillips or slotted screws, Fig. 113.

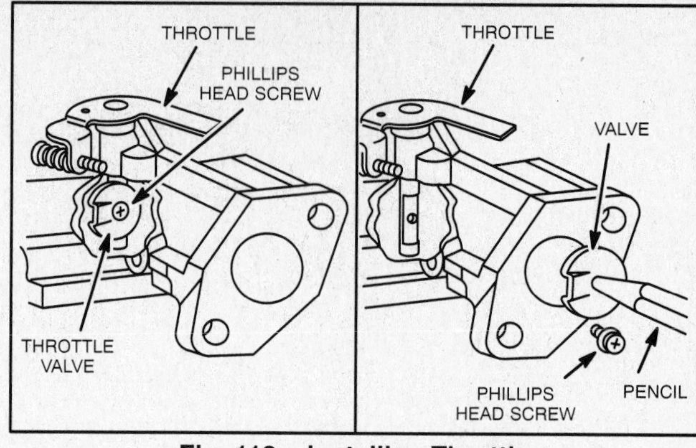

Fig. 113 – Installing Throttle

Install Spiral

- When inserting spiral, top must be flush to 1/32" below carburetor flange, and spiral parallel with fuel tank mounting surface, Fig. 114.

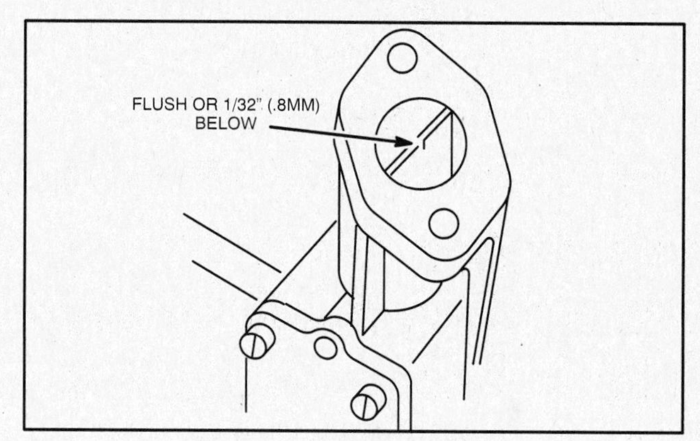

Fig. 114 – Installing Spiral

Install Carburetor and Tank Assembly Choke-A-Matic®, Model Series 92000, Pulsa-Jet, Vacu-Jet, Vertical Crankshaft

1. Put a light film of oil on "O" ring in throttle bore.
2. With governor link hooked to governor blade, connect link to throttle and slip carburetor into place.
3. Align carburetor with intake tube and breather tube grommet.
4. Hold choke lever as shown in Fig. 115, so it does not catch on control plate.
5. Be sure "O" ring in carburetor does not distort when fitting carburetor to intake tube.
6. Install mounting bolts. Fig. 116 shows routings of stop switch wires.

NOTE: METRIC EQUIVALENTS ARE LISTED ON PAGE 68 OF THIS SECTION.

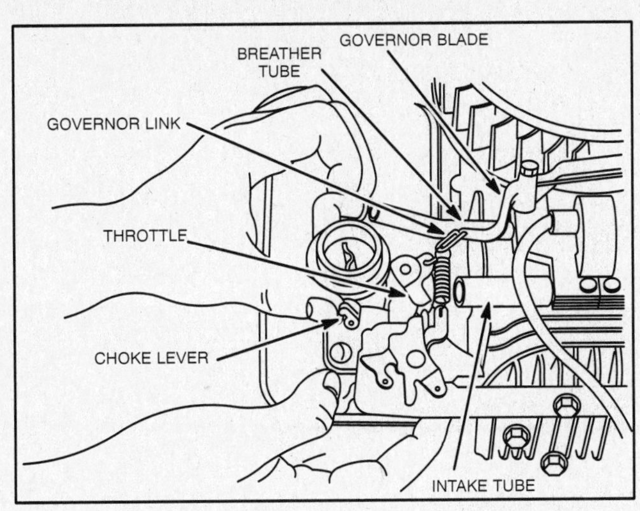

Fig. 115 - Install Carburetor and Tank Assembly

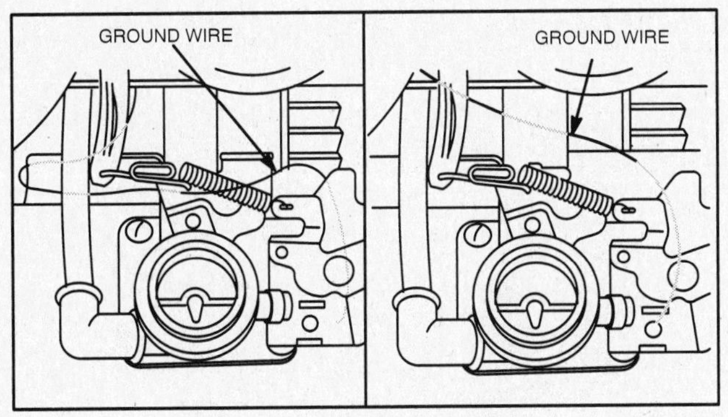

Fig. 116 - Stop Switch Wires

Install Carburetor, Horizontal Crankshaft Model Series 80000, 110000, 130000

1. Install carburetor and tank as one assembly on engine.

2. Hook throttle link into carburetor throttle and governor blade (For various illustrations, see Section 4).

3. Raise carburetor into place, insert a new gasket and fasten with mounting screws.

4. Install governor spring, Fig. 117.

5. Install stop switch wire and remote control where used.

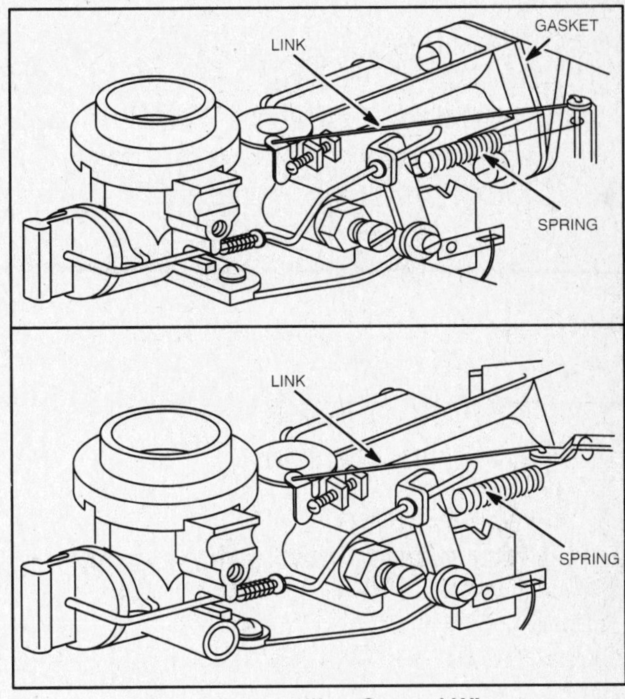

Fig. 117 - Installing Ground Wire

Install Carburetor and Tank, Model Series 100900, 113900 Type #2999, 130900, 131900, and 132900, Vertical Crankshaft

1. Assemble carburetor and new gasket to tank.

2. Hook throttle link to throttle lever, Fig. 118.

3. Slip carburetor over notch in cylinder shield and around intake tube, Fig. 118.

4. Oil seal in carburetor body to prevent damage, when installing.

5. Mount carburetor and tank assembly to cylinder.

6. Torque two head bolts to 140 in. lbs. Install rear tank mounting screw.

NOTE: Model 113900 type #2999 has a stud and a tank mounting screw. Torque stud to 140 in. lbs.

7. Hook up stop switch wire and governor spring.

NOTE: METRIC EQUIVALENTS ARE LISTED ON PAGE 68 OF THIS SECTION.

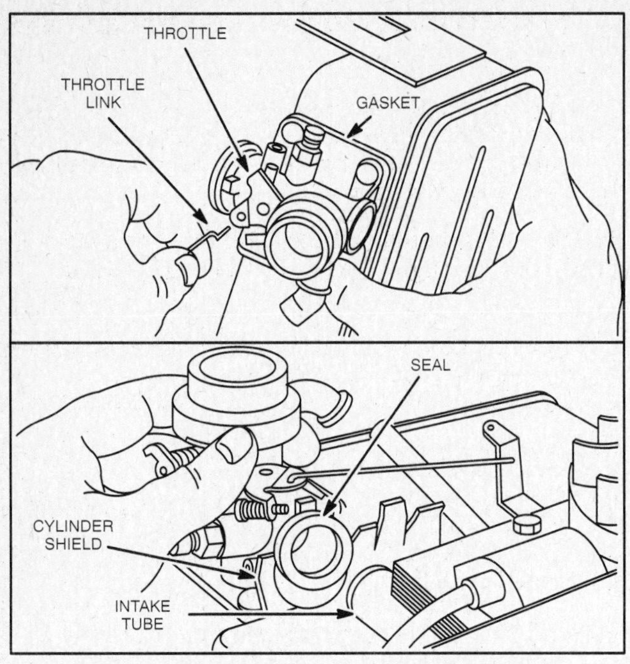

Fig. 118 – Installing Carburetor Model Series 100900, 130900, 131900, 132900

Install Carburetor and Tank Assembly, Model Series 60000, 80000, 110000, 130000, Horizontal Crankshaft

1. Install carburetor and fuel tank as an assembly.
2. Hook throttle link into carburetor throttle and governor lever. (For various hook-ups, see Remote Control, Section 4.)
3. Raise carburetor into place, insert a new gasket and fasten with mounting screws.
4. Install governor spring. Install stop wire and remote control where used, Fig. 119.

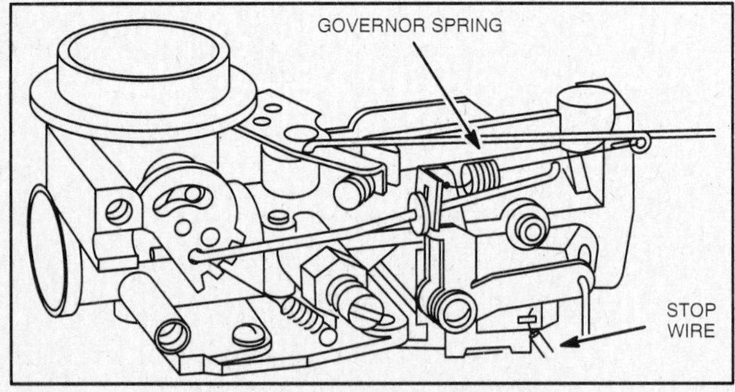

Fig. 119 – Install Carburetor

Adjust Choke-A-Matic® Model Series 92000, Vertical Crankshaft

The Choke-A-Matic® feature was standard on Model Series 92500 (type nos. lower than 0600) 92900 (type nos. lower than 0500) engines. Remote control must be of type in which control wire moves out of casing, when control lever is moved from "STOP" position to "CHOKE" or "START" position. A minimum travel of 1-3/8" is required when remote control is mounted, Fig. 120.

1. Remove air cleaner and move control lever to a position about midway between idle and fast.
2. Then mount remote control with casing clamp as shown in Fig. 121.

To adjust remote control assembly proceed as follows:

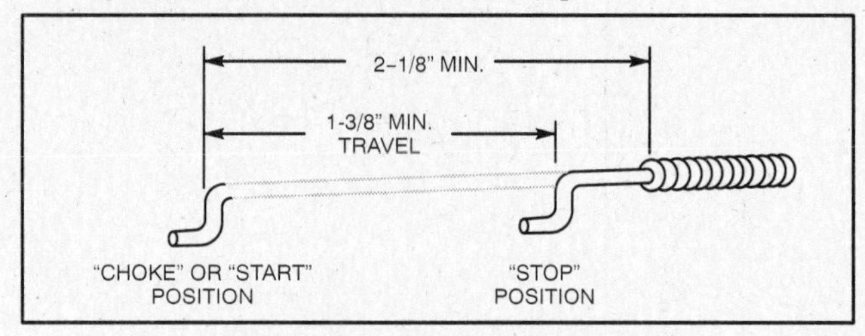

Fig. 120 – Remote Control

3. Place control lever on equipment in "FAST" (high speed) position.

NOTE: CONTROL MUST BE MOUNTED ON EQUIPMENT TO MAKE AN ACCURATE ADJUSTMENT.

4. Lever "A" on carburetor should be just touching choke shaft at "B."
5. Move casing "D" forward or backwards until correct position is obtained.
6. Tighten screw "C." Recheck operation of controls after adjustment, Fig. 121.

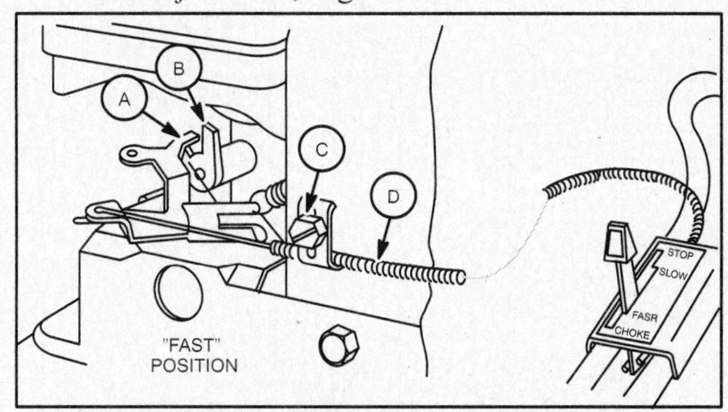

Fig. 121 – Choke-A-Matic® Control (Typical)

Adjust Choke-A-Matic® Linkage Model 100900, 130900, 131900, and 132900, Vertical Crankshaft

Manual or remote control for choke and stop is done by a lever on control plate mounted to carburetor by two screws "A," Fig. 122. Lever for remote control has a loose fit; for manual control, a friction fit.

1. To check lever action, move lever to left until it snaps into "RUN" detent.
2. Lever "B" should just touch choke lever at "C."
3. If it does not, loosen screws "A" slightly and move control plate to right or left until lever just touches choke lever at "C."
4. Tighten screws.

NOTE: METRIC EQUIVALENTS ARE LISTED ON PAGE 68 OF THIS SECTION.

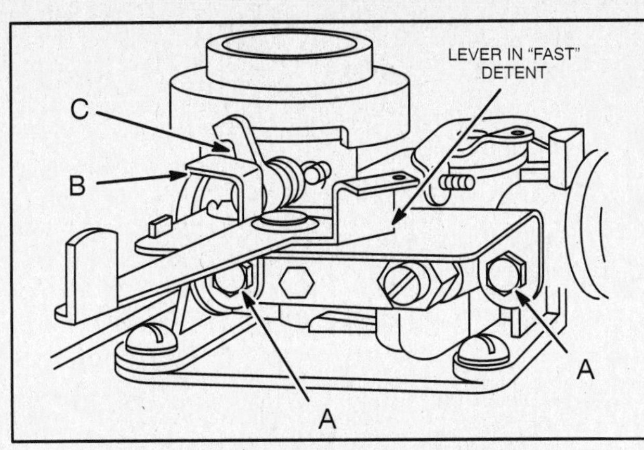

Fig. 122 – Choke-A-Matic® Linkage – Model 100900, 130900, 131900, 132900

CHOKE-A-MATIC® LINKAGE

Adjust Choke-A-Matic® Linkage, Slide Choke

The following covers Choke-A-Matic® parts installed as a part of carburetor assembly. See Section 4 for Choke-A-Matic® remote controls.

1. To check operation of Choke-A-Matic® linkage, move speed adjustment lever to "CHOKE" position.
2. If choke slide does not fully close, replace link or use flat nose pliers to bend choke link, Fig. 123 (do not over bend).
3. Speed adjustment lever must make good contact against stop switch when moved to stop position.

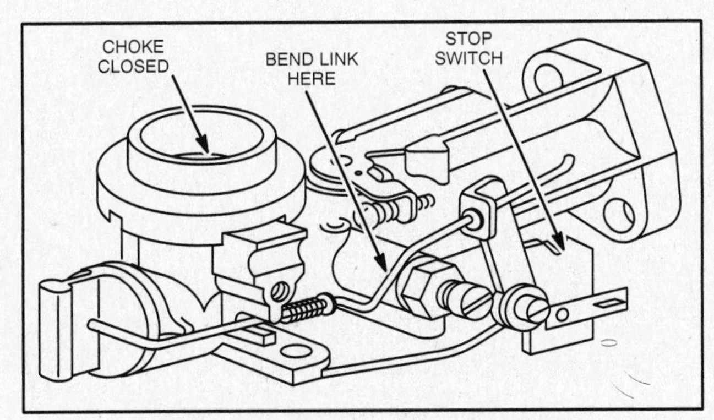

Fig. 123 – Adjust Choke Link

CARBURETOR ADJUSTMENT

Initial Adjustment

1. Turn needle valve clockwise until it just closes. DO NOT FORCE.

   NOTE: Valve may be damaged by turning it in too far.

2. The initial setting of needle valve, Fig. 124, is made by turning needle valve all the way in, then turning out 1-1/2 turn. Final adjustment is made with engine running.

NOTE: All carburetor adjustments must be made with air cleaner on engine and with fuel tank 1/2 full.

NOTE: When starting a Pulsa-Jet engine for first time, fill fuel tank completely full. This eliminates priming the fuel pump, thus ensuring a quick start.

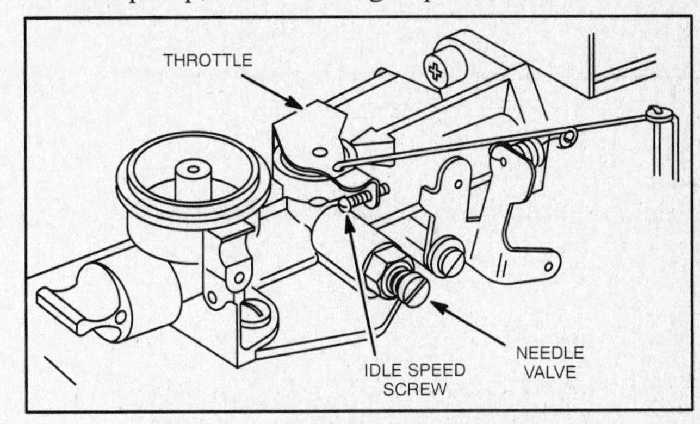

Fig. 124 – Carburetor Adjustment

Final Adjustment

1. Start and run engine at half throttle for five minutes to bring engine up to operating temperature.
2. Place governor speed control lever in "FAST" position.
3. Turn needle valve in until engine misses (clockwise – lean mixture) then turn it out past smooth operation point until engine runs unevenly (counterclockwise – rich mixture).
4. Now turn needle valve to midpoint between rich and lean so engine runs smoothly.
5. Next, adjust idle RPM. Rotate throttle counterclockwise and hold against stop.
6. Adjust idle speed adjusting screw to obtain 1750 RPM.
7. Release throttle – engine should accelerate without hesitation or sputtering.
8. If engine does not accelerate properly, carburetor should be re-adjusted, usually to a slightly richer mixture.

CHOKE-A-MATIC® REMOTE CONTROLS

See Section 4 for illustrations by engine model.

BRIGGS & STRATTON/WALBRO SMALL ONE-PIECE FLO-JET CARBURETORS

Model Series 83400 Horizontal Crankshaft, 90700, 91700, 100700, 110700, 111700, 112700, 114700, 121700, 122700, 124700, 130700, 131700, Vertical Crankshafts

These carburetors are made in three basic types, FIXED HIGH SPEED MAIN jet ADJUSTABLE HIGH SPEED MAIN jet, and FIXED HIGH SPEED jet with primer system and no choke valve, Fig's. 125, 126, 127, 128, and 129.

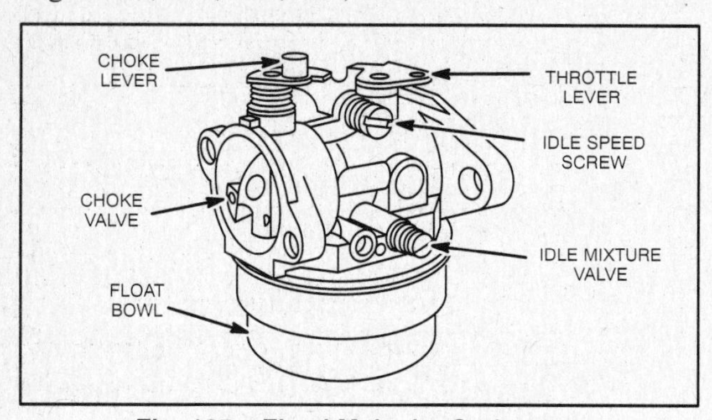

Fig. 125 - Fixed Main Jet Carburetor

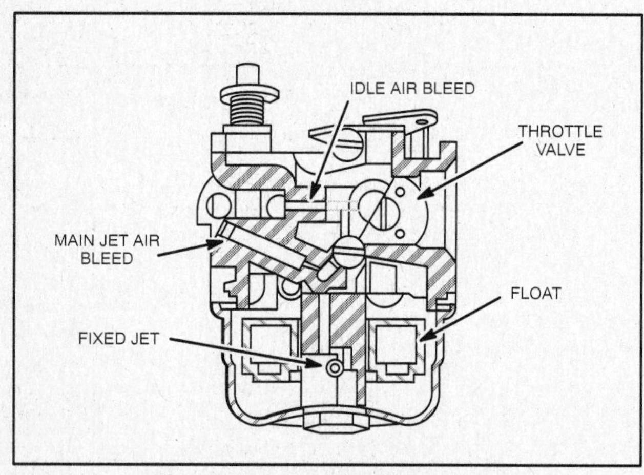

Fig. 126 - Fixed Jet Carburetor

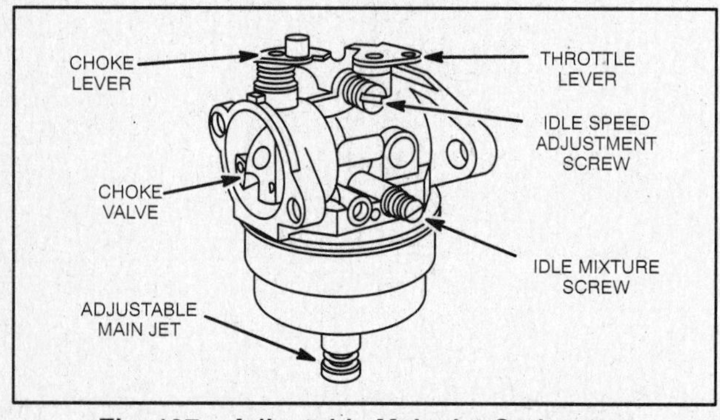

Fig. 127 - Adjustable Main Jet Carburetor

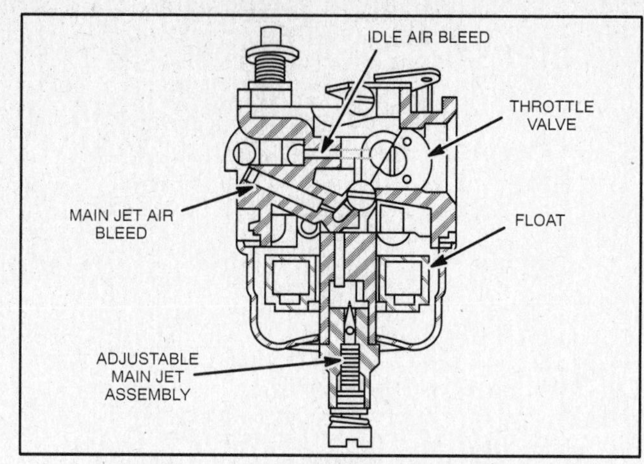

Fig. 128 - Adjustable Main Jet Carburetor

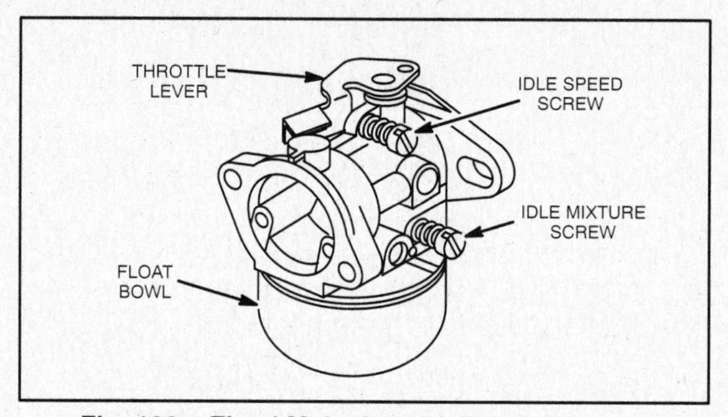

Fig. 129 - Fixed Main Jet with Primer System

Disassemble Carburetor Fixed and Adjustable High Speed

NOTE; Low emission carburetors do not have an idle mixture needle and spring.

1. Remove bowl nut/high speed needle nut and fiber washer.
2. Remove float bowl and bowl gasket from carburetor.
3. Remove float hinge pin, float and inlet valve.

   NOTE: On Model Series 120000 engines bowl nut may be a removable fixed main jet.

4. Remove idle mixture screw with spring and idle speed screw with spring.
5. Rotate throttle shaft to closed position and remove throttle valve screw.
6. Remove throttle valve and throttle shaft with foam seal.
7. Grasp choke valve and remove from choke shaft.
8. Remove choke shaft and felt or foam washer.

NOTE: METRIC EQUIVALENTS ARE LISTED ON PAGE 68 OF THIS SECTION.

9. With a modified 5/32 inch pin punch, remove welch plug(s) from carburetor body, Fig. 130.

10. Remove inlet valve seat from carburetor.

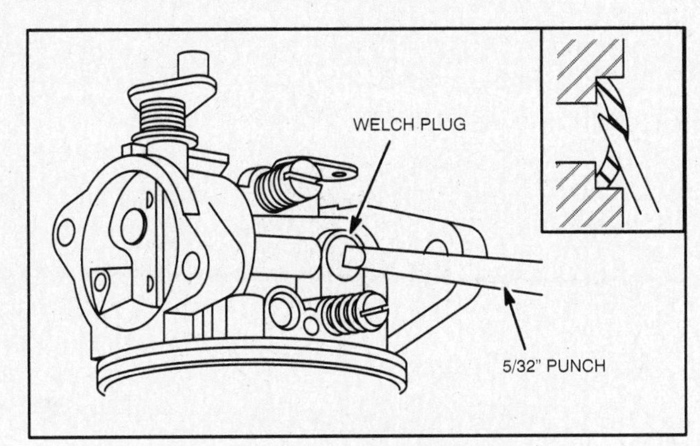

Fig. 130 – Removing Welch Plug

High Altitude Compensation – LMS 1 through LMS-15, LMS-21, 22, 24, 28, 29, 29, 36

NOTE: When carburetor is used at high altitudes, and performance is poor, refer to Table No. 3 by basic Model Number and carburetor I.D. number.and remove main jet air bleed. If carburetor I.D. number is not in Table No. 3, go to Table No. 4.

Table No. 3

Model Series	Carburetor Identification #	
83400	LMS-30	
90700	LMS-3 LMS-10	LMS-13 LMS-14
91700	LMS-14	
100700	LMS-5 LMS-15	
110700	LMS-1 LMS-3 LMS-4	LMS-10 LMS-11
111700	LMS-2 LMS-7	LMS-12
112700	LMS-1 LMS-3	LMS-11 LMS-14
114700	LMS-7 LMS-12	

Table No. 3, cont'd

Model Series	Carburetor Identification #
12A700	LMS-5
12A800	LMS-24
121700	LMS-5 LMS-24
121800	LMS-24
122700	LMS-5 LMS-24
122800	LMS-24
123700	LMS-5 LMS-24
123800	LMS-24
124700	LMS-5 LMS-24
124800	LMS-24
125700	LMS-5
126700	LMS-5
127700	LMS-24
127800	LMS-24
128700	LMS-24
128800	LMS-24
129800	LMS-24
130700	LMS-9 LMS-19
131700	LMS-9 LMS-19

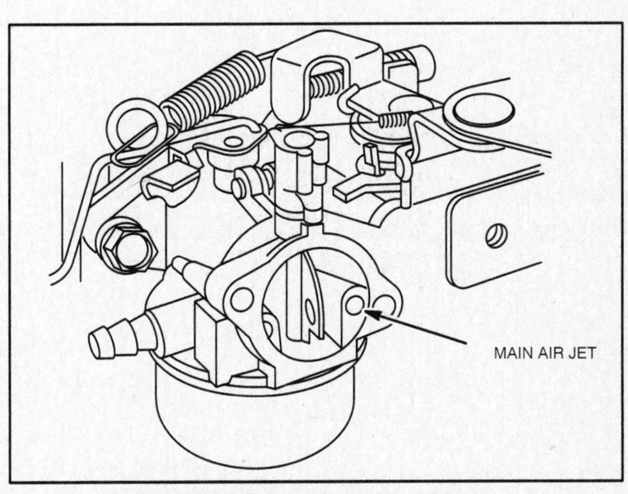

Fig. 131 – Removing Main Air Jet

NOTE: METRIC EQUIVALENTS ARE LISTED ON PAGE 68 OF THIS SECTION.

High Altitude Compensation – LMS 25, 26, 27, 31, 32, 34, 35, 37 and up

NOTE: When carburetor is used at high altitudes, and performance is poor, remove fixed main jet, Fig. 132. Refer to Table No. 4 to identify standard and high altitude jets by number or letter.

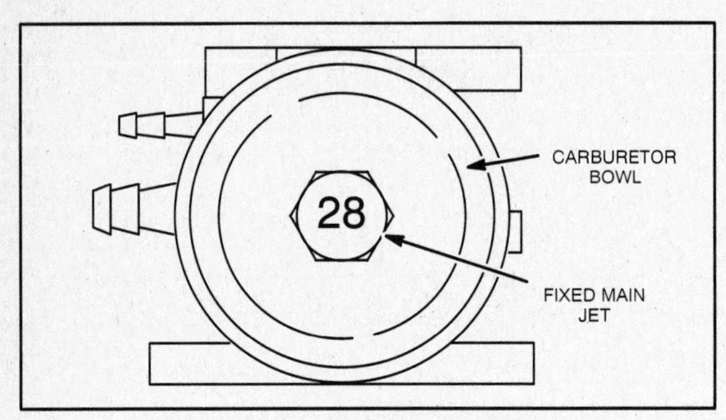

Fig. 132 – Removing Fixed Main Jet

Table No. 4

Model Series	Carburetor Identification #	Standard Jet # or Letter	High Altitude Jet # or Letter
121700	LMS-26, LMS-25, LMS-31, LMS-35	27 or E 27 or E 28 or F 28 or F	26 or D 26 or D 26 or D 26 or D
121800	LMS-25, LMS-31, LMS-35	27 or E 28 or F 28 or F	26 or D 26 or D 26 or D
122700	LMS-25, LMS-26, LMS-31, LMS-35	27 or E 28 or F 28 or F 28 or F	26 or D 26 or D 26 or D 26 or D
122800	LMS-25 LMS-31 LMS-35	27 or E 30 or G 28 or F	26 or D 28 or F 26 or D
123700	LMS-25 LMS-32 LMS-35	27 or E 28 or F 28 or F	26 or D 26 or D 26 or D
123800	LMS-25 LMS-32 LMS-35	27 or E 31 or H 28 or F	26 or D 30 or G 26 or D
124700	LMS-25 LMS-27 LMS-32 LMS-35	28 or F 31 or H 31 or H 28 or F	26 or D 30 or G 30 or G 26 or D

Table No. 4 (Cont'd.)

Model Series	Carburetor Identification #	Standard Jet # or Letter	High Altitude Jet # or Letter
124700	LMS-25 LMS-32 LMS-35	28 or F 31 or H 28 or F	26 or D 30 or G 26 or D
124800	LMS-27 LMS-32	31 or H 31 or H	30 or G 30 or G
125700	LMS-27 LMS-32	31 or H 31 or H	30 or G 30 or G
126700	LMS-25 LMS-27 LMS-32 LMS-35	28 or F 31 or H 31 or H 28 or F	26 or D 30 or G 30 or G 26 or D
126800	LMS-25 LMS-32 LMS-35	28 or F 31 or H 28 or F	26 or D 30 or G 26 or D
127700	LMS-25 LMS-32 LMS-35	28 or F 31 or H 28 or F	26 or D 30 or G 26 or D
127800	LMS-25 LMS-35	28 or F 28 or F	26 or D 26 or D
128700	LMS-41	28 or F	27 or E
128800	LMS-32 LMS-41	28 or F 28 or F	27 or E 27 or E
129700	LMS-32 LMS-41	28 or F 28 or F	27 or E 27 or E
129800	LMS-32 LMS-41	28 or F 28 or F	27 or E 27 or E
12A800	LMS-25 LMS-35	28 or F 28 or F	26 or D 26 or D
12D800	LMS-25 LMS-32	28 or F 28 or F	26 or D 26 or D
133400	LMS-34	33 or K	1 or I
133700	LMS-36	31 or H	30 or G
135700	LMS-36	31 or H	30 or G

Clean and Inspect Carburetor

Carburetor can be cleaned in any commercially available carburetor cleaner. After cleaning, inspect for wear, damage, cracks, or plugged openings. Replace body if any of the above conditions exist. Use only compressed air to clear plugged openings.

Inspect idle mixture needle for bent needle point or a groove in tip of needle. Replace if bent or grooved.

NOTE: METRIC EQUIVALENTS ARE LISTED ON PAGE 68 OF THIS SECTION.

Assemble Carburetor

Install Welch Plug

1. Install welch plug(s) with pin punch slightly smaller than outside diameter of plug.

2. Press in until plug is flat. DO NOT cave in plug.

3. After plug is installed, seal outside edge of plug with fingernail polish or non-hardening sealant, Fig. 133.

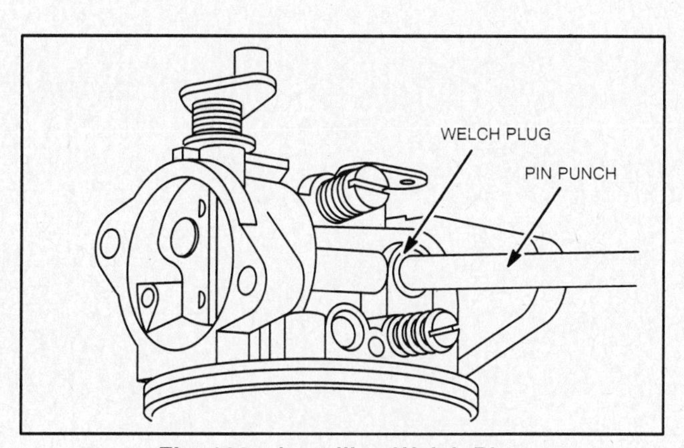

Fig. 133 – Installing Welch Plug

Install Choke Shaft (Return Spring on Lever)

1. Install choke shaft and felt washer.

2. Rotate choke shaft until lever is as shown in Fig. 134.

3. Insert choke valve in slot of choke shaft until valve is centered on choke shaft.

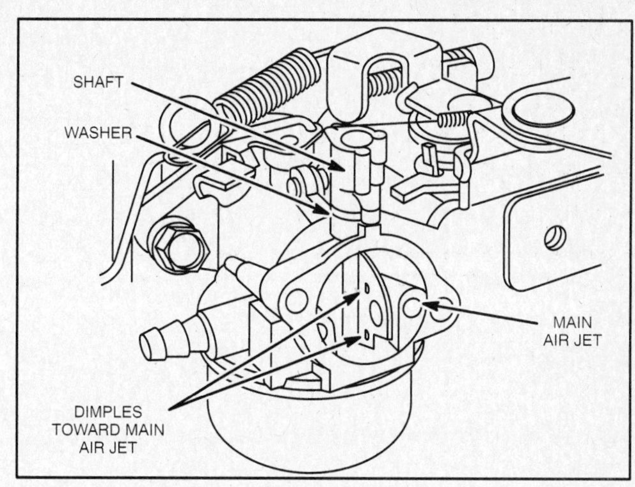

Fig. 134 – Installing Choke Shaft

Install Choke Shaft (Return Spring on Shaft)

1. Install choke shaft, return spring, and felt washer.

2. Rotate choke shaft counterclockwise until arm on shaft is approximately 90° to carburetor bore.

3. Insert choke valve so numbers will be visible when choke is closed, Fig. 135.

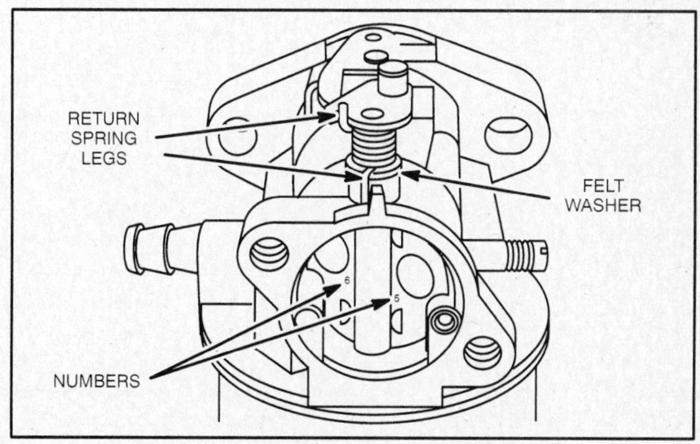

Fig. 135 – Installing Choke Shaft

Install Choke Shaft (Manual Choke, except low emission carburetors)

Install foam seal and choke shaft in carburetor body with detent against detent spring, Fig. 136.

NOTE: METRIC EQUIVALENTS ARE LISTED ON PAGE 68 OF THIS SECTION.

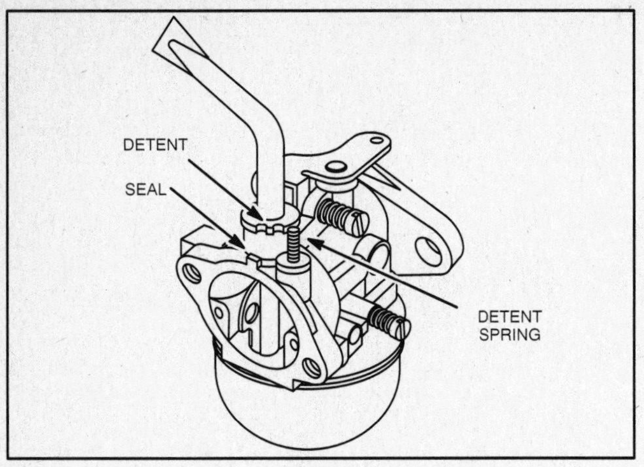

Fig. 136 – Installing Choke Shaft

Install Choke Shaft (Manual Choke, low emission carburetors)

Install foam seal and choke shaft in carburetor body with choke valve detent against detent spring, Fig. 136.

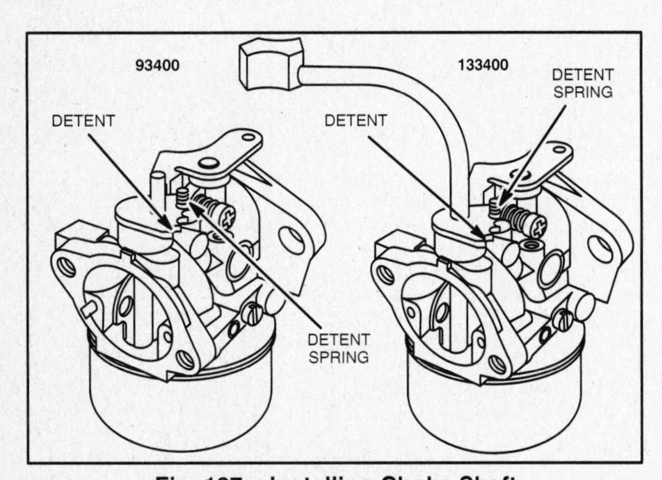

Fig. 137 – Installing Choke Shaft

Install Throttle Shaft

1. Install throttle shaft and foam washer.
2. Turn shaft until flat is facing out.
3. Lay throttle valve on shaft with numbers facing out and install screw, Fig. 138.

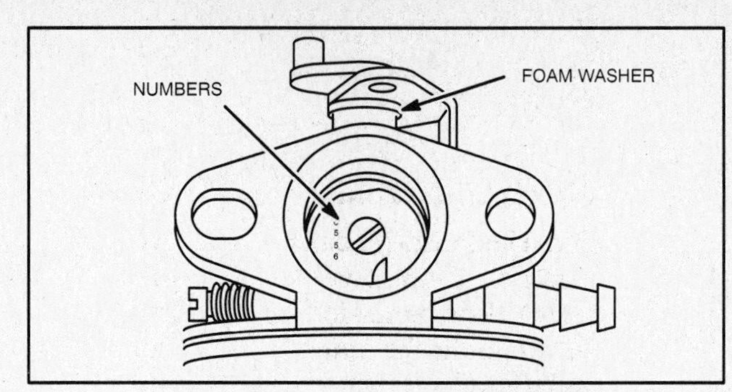

Fig. 138 – Installing Throttle Shaft

Install Inlet Needle Seat

Install inlet needle seat with GROOVE DOWN using Tool #19057, Bushing Driver, until seated, Fig. 139.

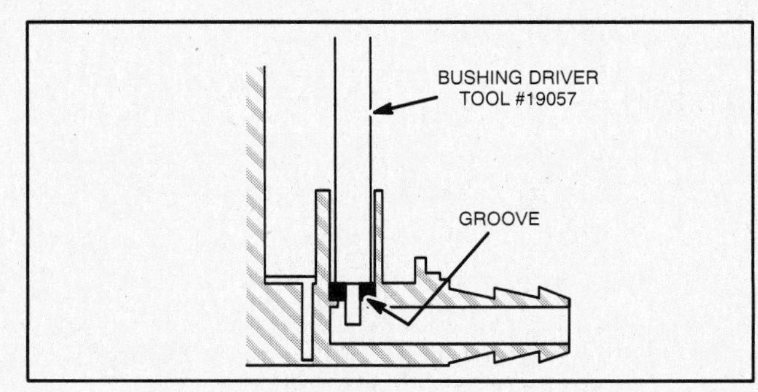

Fig. 139 – Installing Inlet Needle Seat

Install Inlet Needle and Float

1. Install inlet needle on float and install assembly on carburetor body.
2. Insert float hinge pin and center pin. Float height is non-adjustable.
3. Install rubber gasket on carburetor and lay float bowl on body.
4. Place fiber washer over bowl nut hole and install bowl nut/high speed needle nut.
5. Tighten nut to 50 in. lbs. torque.

Install Carburetor

Place fuel intake pipe seal in chamfer of carburetor and install carburetor with two mounting screws torquing screws to 75 in. lbs., Fig. 140.

NOTE: METRIC EQUIVALENTS ARE LISTED ON PAGE 68 OF THIS SECTION.

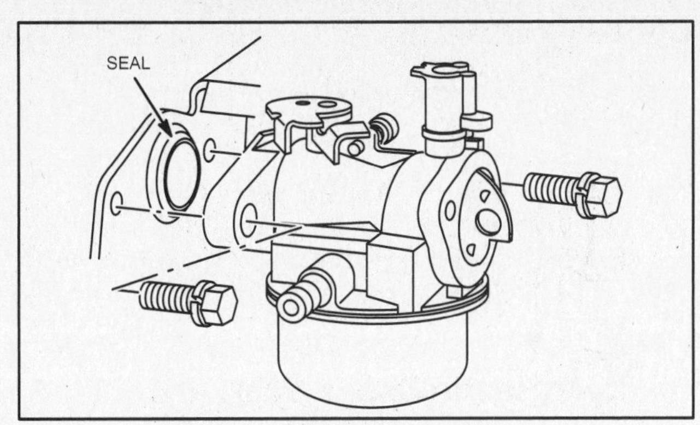

Fig. 140 – Installing Carburetor

Install Air Cleaner

1. Install carburetor back plate with two (2) sealant coated screws into carburetor. Do not tighten at this time.
2. Then install third screw but do not tighten.
3. Torque two (2) screws into carburetor to 40 in. lbs.
4. Then torque remaining screw to 40 in. lbs., Fig. 141.

NOTE: On Choke-A-Matic® carburetors install spring on choke shaft as shown in Fig. 140.

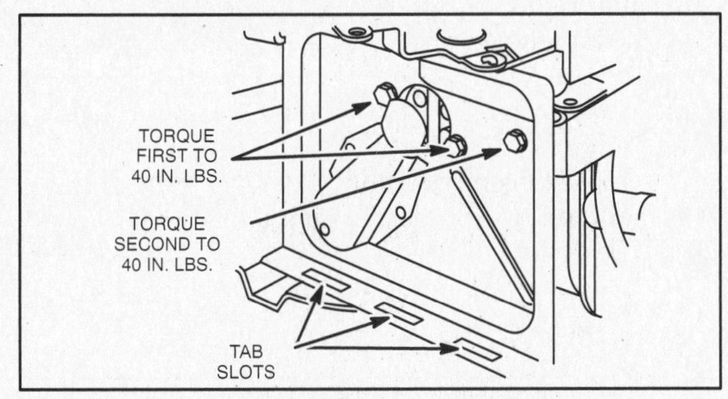

Fig. 141 – Installing Air Cleaner Back Plate

5. Install air cleaner cartridge, Pre-Cleaner (optional) and cover making sure that three (3) tabs engage three (3) slots in back plate, Fig. 141.

Initial Adjustment

1. Install idle speed screw and spring.
2. Install idle mixture screw and spring.
3. Turn screw in until it just bottoms.
4. Then back out screw 1-1/4 turn. This will permit engine to start.

NOTE: On carburetors with adjustable high speed needle, turn high speed adjustment needle clockwise until it just touches needle seat. Then back off 1-1/4 turn.

Final Adjustment

1. Install complete air cleaner before starting engine.
2. Start and run engine for five minutes at 1/2 throttle to bring engine up to operating temperature.
3. Move equipment speed control to idle position.
4. Turn idle speed screw to obtain 1750 RPM minimum.
5. Then turn idle mixture screw clockwise slowly until engine just begins to slow.
6. Then turn screw opposite direction until engine just begins to slow.
7. Turn screw back to midpoint.

   NOTE: On carburetors with adjustable high speed needle, move speed control to fast position. Adjust high speed mixture needle same as idle mixture screw.

8. Move equipment speed control from idle to high speed position.
9. Engine should accelerate smoothly.
10. If it doesn't, open idle mixture needle screw 1/8 turn open.

BRIGGS & STRATTON/WALBRO LARGE ONE-PIECE FLO-JET CARBURETORS

Model Series 176400, 194700, 195700, 196400, 196700, 226400, 254700, 256400, 257700, 258700, 259700, 282700, 283700, 284700, 285700, 286700, 288700, 289700, 28A700, 28B700, 28C700, 28D700, 28M700

These carburetors have a FIXED HIGH SPEED MAIN jet with ADJUSTABLE IDLE, Fig's. 142 and 143. The different carburetors are identified as LMT 1 and up. The letters LMT are cast into the body of the carburetor while the numbers are stamped into carburetor mounting flange next to idle mixture screw.

NOTE: METRIC EQUIVALENTS ARE LISTED ON PAGE 68 OF THIS SECTION.

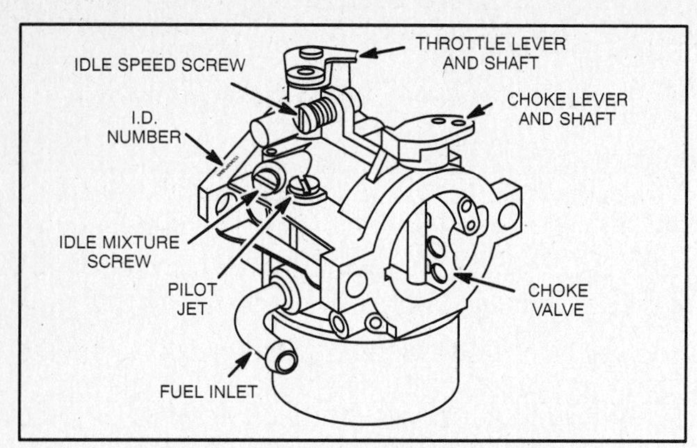

Fig. 142 - Outside View, Carburetor

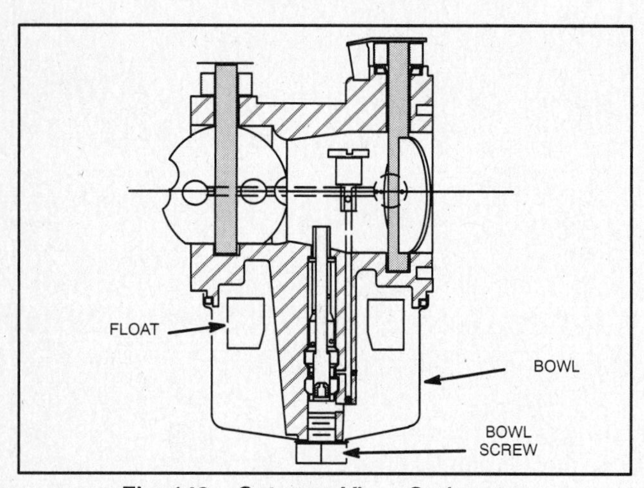

Fig. 143 - Cutaway View, Carburetor

Disassemble Carburetor

1. Remove bowl screw and fuel bowl washer.
2. Remove float bowl and float bowl gasket from carburetor.
3. Remove float hinge pin, float and inlet valve.
4. With a small hook or crochet hook remove inlet valve seat.
5. Remove idle mixture needle limiter cap, if so equipped.
6. Remove idle mixture screw with spring and idle speed screw with spring.
7. Rotate throttle shaft and lever to closed position and remove two (2) throttle screws.
8. Remove throttle valve and throttle shaft and lever with foam seal.
9. Remove throttle shaft seal from carburetor body.

Choke Shafts

These carburetors are equipped with two styles of choke shafts:

A. Plastic shaft with snap in choke valve or;

B. Metal shaft with screw mounted choke valve.

Remove Plastic Choke Shaft and Valve

1. Pull choke valve out of choke shaft and lever.
2. Remove choke shaft and lever, return spring, and foam washer.

Remove Metal Choke Shaft and Valve

1. Rotate choke shaft and lever to closed position.

   NOTE: Service replacement carburetors may have a spring detent that will hold choke in closed position.

2. Hold choke closed and remove two (2) screws holding choke valve.
3. Remove valve.
4. Release tension on choke shaft and remove choke shaft and lever, return spring and seal assembly.
5. Remove brass pilot jet from carburetor body, Fig. 144.

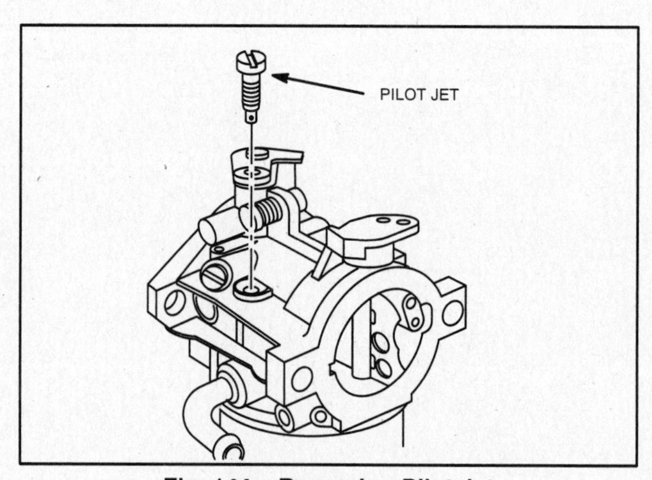

Fig. 144 - Removing Pilot Jet

6. Using Tool #19280, Carburetor Nozzle Screwdriver, remove main carburetor jet nozzle, Fig. 145.

NOTE: METRIC EQUIVALENTS ARE LISTED ON PAGE 68 OF THIS SECTION.

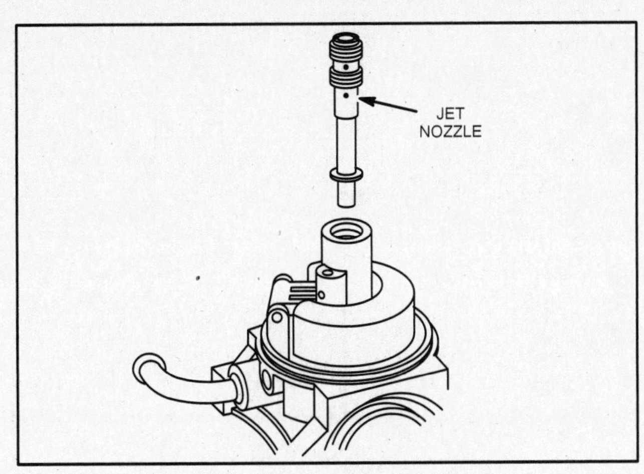

Fig. 145 - Removing Jet Nozzle

7. With a modified 5/32 inch pin punch, remove welch plug from carburetor body, Fig. 146.

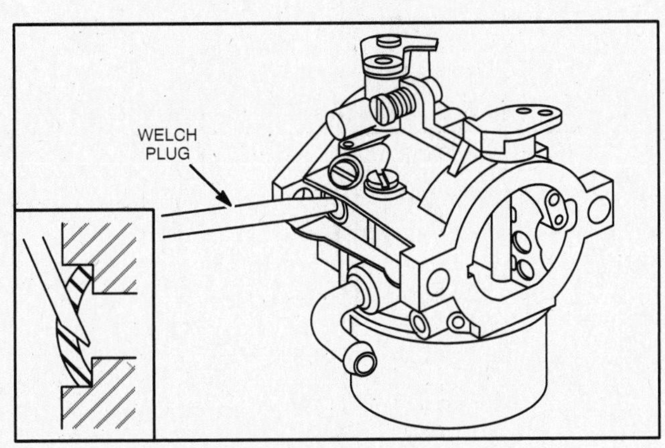

Fig. 146 - Removing Welch Plug

8. Remove inlet seat, Fig. 147.

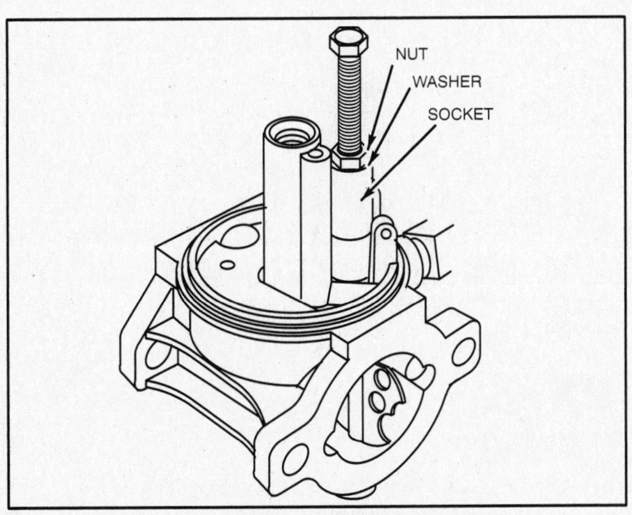

Fig. 147 - Removing Fuel Inlet Seat

High Altitude Compensation

If poor performance is experienced at higher altitudes, high altitude kits are available. These kits consist of a new pilot jet and new nozzle with main jet. Table No. 5 below shows how to identify standard and high altitude nozzles by engine model series and color.

Table No. 5

Model Series	LMT #	Standard Nozzle Color	High Altitude Nozzle Color
176400	LMT-69	Blue	Yellow
194700	LMT-20, LMT-21, LMT-22, LMT-23, LMT-25, LMT-50, LMT-51, LMT-53	Green	Brown
195700	LMT-20, LMT-21, LMT-22, LMT-23, LMT-25, LMT-46, LMT-49, LMT-50, LMT-51, LMT-53	Green	Brown
196400	LMT-69	Blue	Yellow
196700	LMT-14, LMT-15, LMT-16, LMT-19, LMT-20, LMT-25, LMT-46, LMT-47, LMT-49, LMT-50, LMT-53	Green	Brown
226400	LMT-71	Green	Brown

NOTE: METRIC EQUIVALENTS ARE LISTED ON PAGE 68 OF THIS SECTION.

Table No. 5, (Cont'd.)			
Model Series	LMT #	Standard Nozzle Color	High Altitude Nozzle Color
254700	LMT-8, LMT-13	White	Black
	LMT-26, LMT-27, LMT-28, LMT-31, LMT-54, LMT-55, LMT-57	Blue	Yellow
257700	LMT-8, LMT-9, LMT-10, LMT-12, LMT-13	White	Black
	LMT-27, LMT-31	Blue	Yellow
	LMT-42, LMT-43, LMT-44, LMT-45	White	Black
256400	LMT-71	Green	Brown
257700	LMT-54, LMT-57	Blue	Yellow
258700	LMT-27, LMT-28, LMT-31, LMT-54, LMT-55, LMT-57	Blue	Yellow Blue
259700	LMT-8, LMT-9, LMT-10, LMT-13, LMT-42, LMT-43, LMT-45	White	Black
270700	LMT-63	Brass	Red
271700	LMT-63	Brass	Red
272700	LMT-63	Brass	Red
273700	LMT-63	Brass	Red

Table No. 5, (Cont'd.)			
Model Series	LMT #	Standard Nozzle Color	High Altitude Nozzle Color
28A700	LMT-63, LMT-66	Brass	Red
28B700	LMT-63, LMT-65, LMT-66	Brass	Red
28C700	LMT-63, LMT-66	Brass	Red
28D700	LMT-63, LMT-64, LMT-66	Brass	Red
282700	LMT-1, LMT-5, LMT-37, LMT-41	Brass	Red
28M700	LMT-37, LMT-39, LMT-41	Brass	Red
283700	LMT-1, LMT-2, LMT-4, LMT-5, LMT-6, LMT-7, LMT-32, LMT-37, LMT-38, LMT-39, LMT-40, LMT-41	Brass	Red
284700	LMT-1, LMT-5, LMT-37, LMT-41	Brass	Red
285700	LMT-1, LMT-5, LMT-6, LMT-37, LMT-41	Brass	Red

NOTE: METRIC EQUIVALENTS ARE LISTED ON PAGE 68 OF THIS SECTION.

Table No. 5, (Cont'd.)			
Model Series	LMT #	Standard Nozzle Color	High Altitude Nozzle Color
286700	LMT-1, LMT-2, LMT-3, LMT-4, LMT-5, LMT-6, LMT-7, LMT-37, LMT-38, LMT-39, LMT-40, LMT-41	Brass	Red
288700	LMT-1, LMT-5, LMT-37, LMT-41	Brass	Red
289700	LMT-1, LMT-5, LMT-6, LMT-37, LMT-41	Brass	Red

Clean and Inspect Carburetor

Carburetor can be cleaned in any commercially available carburetor cleaner. After cleaning, inspect for wear, damage, cracks, or plugged openings. Replace body if any of the above conditions exist. Use only compressed air to clear plugged openings.

Inspect idle mixture needle for bent needle point or a groove in tip of needle. Replace if bent or grooved.

ASSEMBLE CARBURETOR

Install Welch Plug

1. Install welch plug with pin punch slightly smaller than outside diameter of plug.
2. Press in until plug is flat. DO NOT cave in plug.
3. After plug is installed, seal outside edge of plug with fingernail polish or non-hardening sealant, Fig. 148.

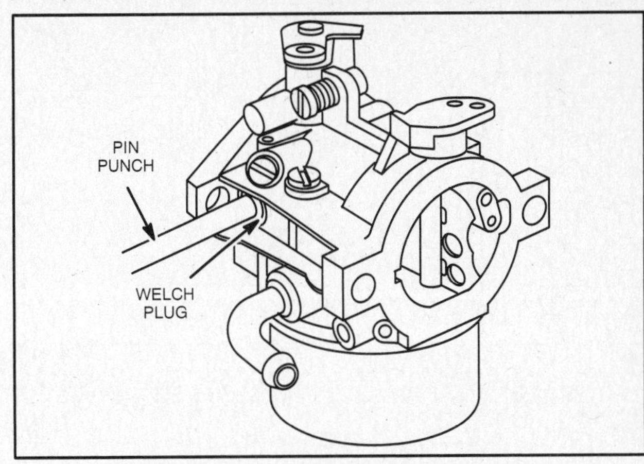

Fig. 148 – Installing Welch Plug

4. Press fuel inlet seat in until flush, Fig. 149.

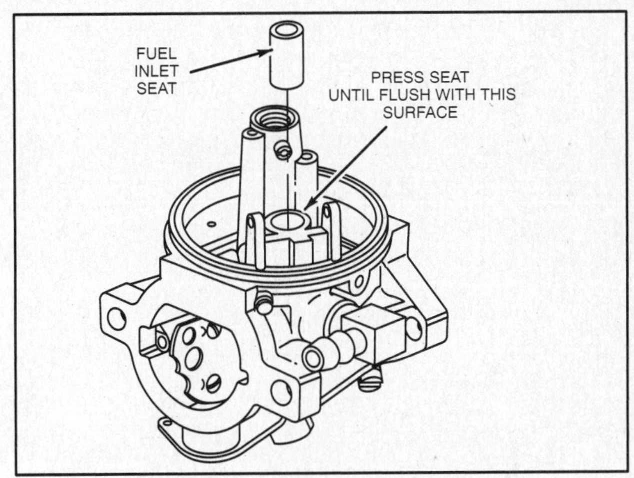

Fig. 149 – Installing Fuel Inlet Seat

Install Plastic Choke Shaft

1. Insert spring inside large foam seal and slide seal and spring onto choke shaft with straight end of spring up toward choke shaft lever.
2. Insert choke shaft into carburetor body until hook of spring hooks on spring anchor.
3. Lift choke shaft and lever up slightly and turn counterclockwise until stop on lever clears spring anchor and push shaft down, Fig. 150.
4. Insert choke valve into choke shaft and lever with dimples toward fuel inlet side of carburetor. Dimples help to hold and align choke valve on shaft.

NOTE: METRIC EQUIVALENTS ARE LISTED ON PAGE 68 OF THIS SECTION.

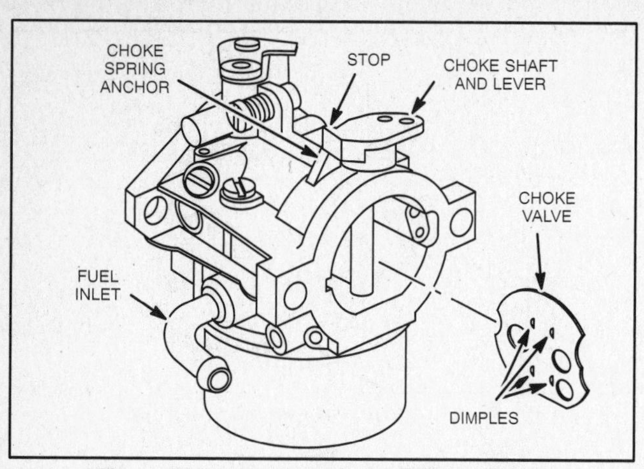

Fig. 150 – Installing Plastic Choke Shaft

Install Metal Choke Shaft

1. Install foam seal and return spring on choke shaft hooking small hook in notch on choke lever, Fig. 151, inset.
2. Insert choke shaft assembly into carburetor body and engage large end of return spring on boss.
3. If carburetor has spring detent, guide detent spring into slot on choke shaft lever, Fig. 151.
4. Place choke valve on shaft with single notch on edge towards fuel inlet. Two (2) half moon dimples will help to position valve on shaft.

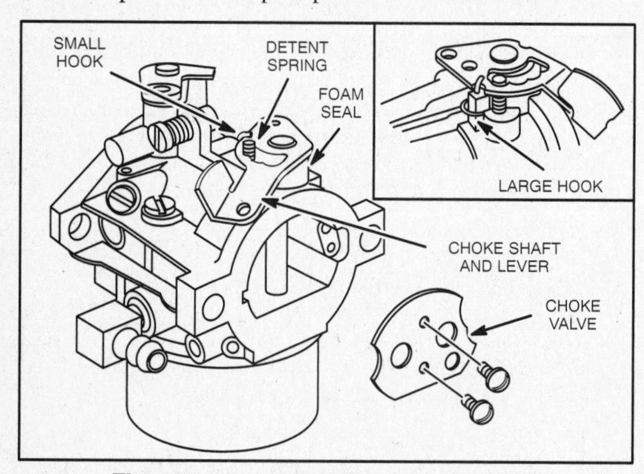

Fig. 151 – Installing Metal Choke Shaft

Install Throttle Shaft

1. Install throttle shaft seal with sealing lip down in carburetor body until top of seal is flush with top of carburetor.
2. Install throttle shaft and small foam washer.
3. Turn shaft until flat is facing out.
4. Lay throttle valve on shaft with numbers toward idle mixture screw and dimples facing in, resting on edge of shaft. Install two (2) screws, Fig. 152.

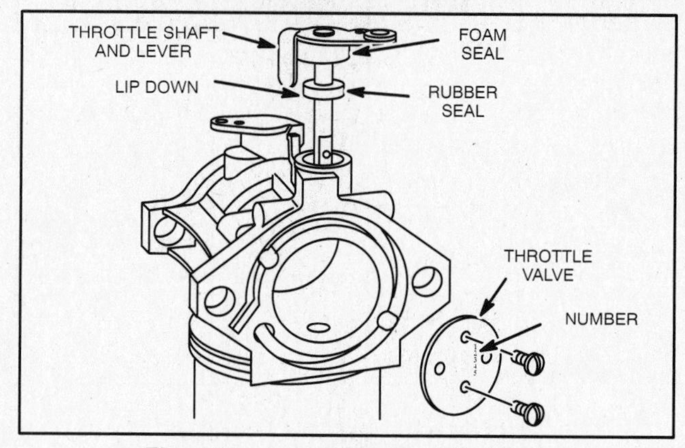

Fig. 152 – Installing Throttle Shaft

Install Inlet Valve Seat

These carburetors are equipped with a tan or black inlet valve seat for gravity feed fuel systems and a brown inlet valve seat for fuel pump feed fuel systems. Both seats are installed the same way.

1. Be sure inlet valve seat area is clean.
2. Install inlet needle seat with GROOVE DOWN using Tool #19057, Bushing Driver, until seated, Fig. 153.
3. After installing seat use compressed air to remove any debris that may be in carburetor.
4. Blow from seat out to fuel inlet.
5. Check to be sure that inlet seat is fully seated.

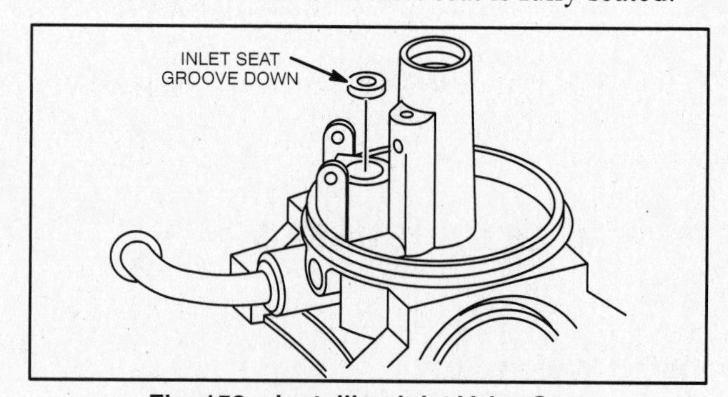

Fig. 153 – Installing Inlet Valve Seat

Install Jet Nozzle

1. Install jet nozzle using Tool #19280, Carburetor Nozzle Screwdriver, until nozzle seats, Fig. 154.
2. After installing jet nozzle, use compressed air to blow out any chips or debris that may have been loosened while installing jet nozzle.

NOTE: METRIC EQUIVALENTS ARE LISTED ON PAGE 68 OF THIS SECTION.

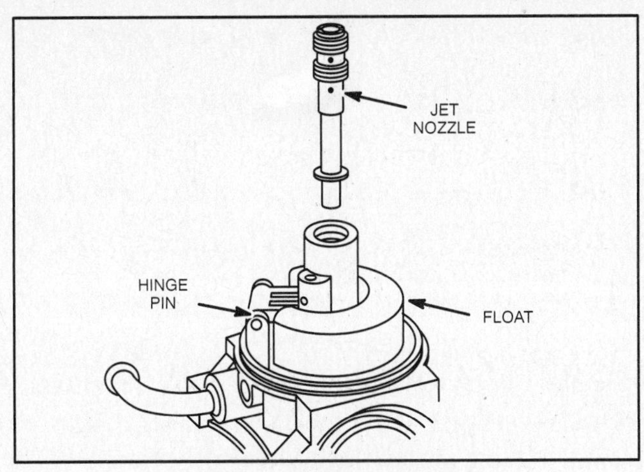

Fig. 154 – Installing Jet Nozzle

Install Inlet Needle Valve and Float

1. Insert inlet needle valve in slot on float.
2. Place float and needle on carburetor and install float hinge pin centering hinge pin.
3. Place bowl gasket on carburetor body.
4. Place bowl on carburetor and install bowl screw and float bowl washer torquing bowl screw to 40 in. lbs.

Install Idle Screw and Pilot Jet

1. Install pilot jet until it seats securely.
2. Install idle mixture screw with spring and turn until head of screw touches spring.

Install Carburetor Elbow

- If carburetor elbow was removed, place new gasket and elbow on intake port and torque screws to 100 in. lbs.

Install Carburetor to Elbow

1. Place two (2) studs on carburetor and new gasket on studs with long edge on side of gasket opposite fuel inlet.
2. Hook governor link spring in throttle lever hole without grommet.
3. Hook governor link in throttle lever hole with grommet, with link on top of lever.

Install Choke-A-Matic® Link, Horizontal Control Plate

1. Insert "Z" bend of Choke-A-Matic® link in outer hole of choke lever from bottom of lever.
2. Slide "U" bend of link into slot on governor control bracket and place carburetor on intake elbow.
3. Torque studs to 65 in. lbs., Fig. 155.

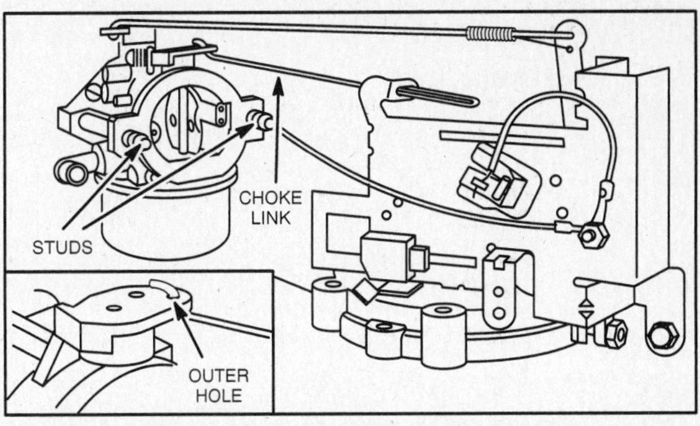

Fig. 155 – Installing Carburetor

Install Choke-A-Matic® Link, Vertical Control Plate

1. Insert "Z" bend of Choke-A-Matic® link in inner hole of choke lever from bottom of lever.
2. Slide "U" bend of link into slot on governor control bracket and place carburetor on intake elbow.
3. Torque studs to 65 in. lbs., Fig. 156.

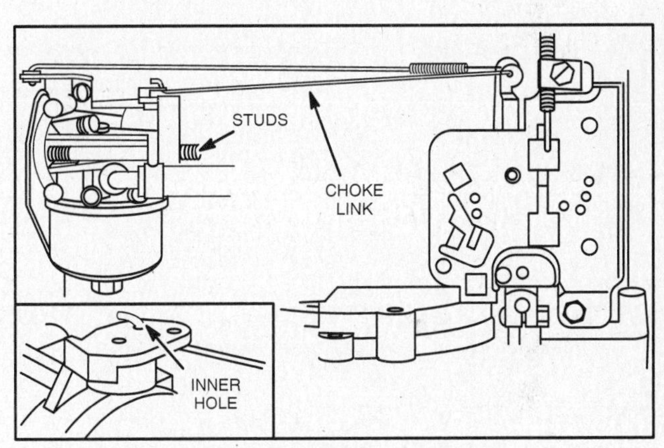

Fig. 156 – Installing Carburetor

4. Install air cleaner body and torque nuts to 55 in. lbs.
5. Be sure breather tube is on air cleaner body opening.
6. Install air cleaner brace.

Install Dual Element Air Cleaner

1. Install air cleaner cartridge and pre-cleaner with small air cleaner knob.
2. Install air cleaner cover and large nut.

Install Oil Foam® Air Cleaner Element

1. Place foam element into air cleaner body, making sure lip of foam extends over edges of body to form protective seal.
2. Inserts slots of cover into tabs on body and press down on cover until latch snaps into place.

NOTE: METRIC EQUIVALENTS ARE LISTED ON PAGE 68 OF THIS SECTION.

3

ADJUST CARBURETOR

Initial Adjustment

1. Turn idle mixture screw in until it bottoms lightly.
2. Then back out screw 1-1/2 turns. This will permit engine to start.

Final Adjustment

1. Start and run engine for 5 minutes at 1/2 throttle to bring engine up to operating temperature.
2. Move equipment control to idle position.
3. Turn idle speed screw to obtain 1750 RPM Minimum.
4. Then turn idle mixture screw slowly clockwise until engine just begins to slow.
5. Then turn screw opposite direction until engine just begins to slow.
6. Turn screw back to midpoint.
7. Install limiter cap at midpoint position, Fig. 157, when used.

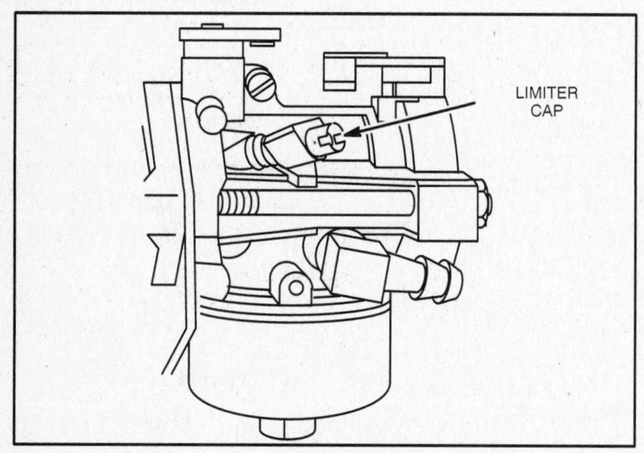

Fig. 157 – Installing Limiter Cap

8. Move equipment speed control from idle to high speed position.
9. Engine should accelerate smoothly.
10. If it does not, open idle mixture needle screw 1/8 turn open.

NOTE: If engine is adjusted for governed idle, reset idle speed screw to 1200 RPM.

ONE-PIECE FLO-JET CARBURETORS SMALL AND LARGE VERTICAL CRANKSHAFT ENGINES

The small One-Piece Flo-Jet carburetor is illustrated in Fig's. 158 and 159 and was used on early Model Series 170700. These are float feed carburetors with high speed and idle needle valve adjustments.

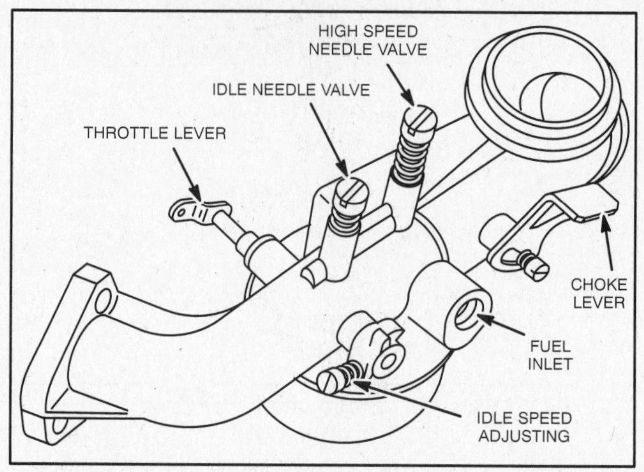

Fig. 158 – Small One-Piece Flo-Jet Carburetor

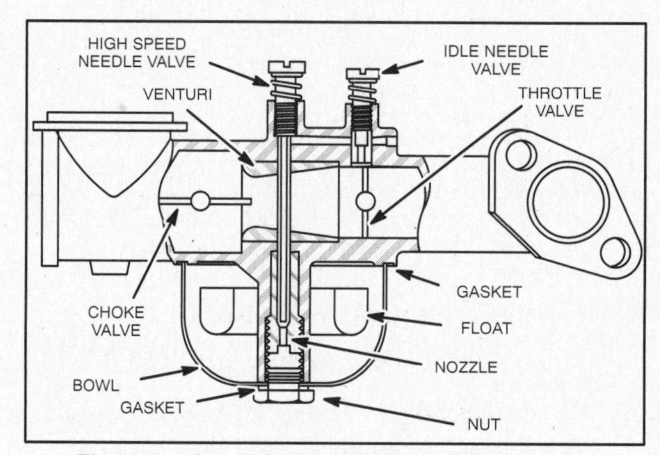

Fig. 159 – Small One-Piece Flo-Jet Carburetor

The large One-Piece Flo-Jet carburetor is similar to the small One-Piece Flo-Jet. The main difference is that high speed needle is below float bowl, Fig's. 160 and 161.

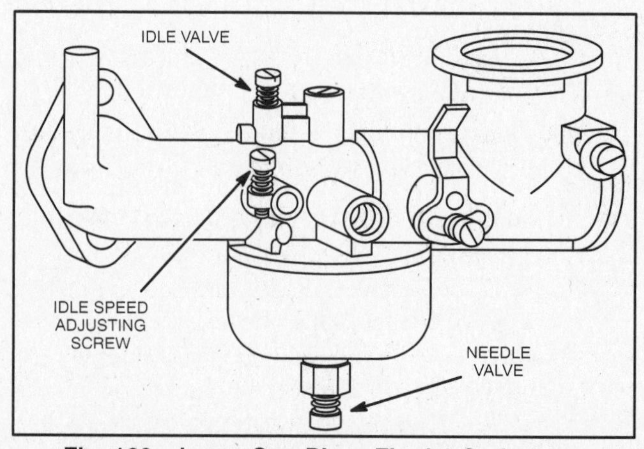

Fig. 160 – Large One-Piece Flo-Jet Carburetor

NOTE: METRIC EQUIVALENTS ARE LISTED ON PAGE 68 OF THIS SECTION.

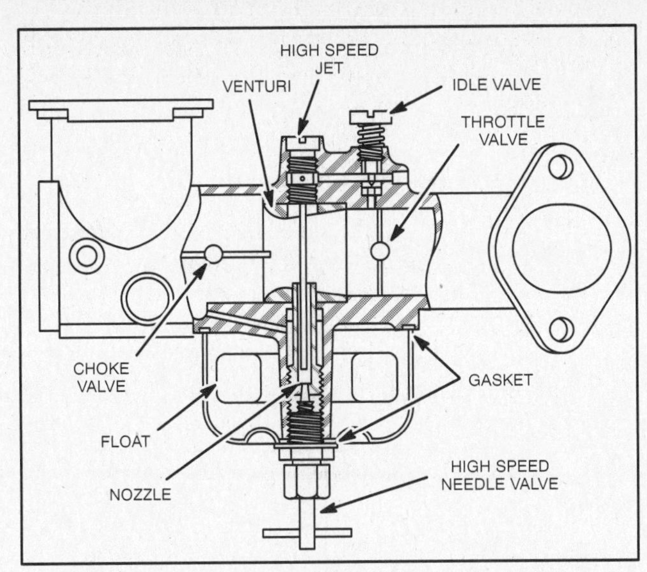

Fig. 161 – Large One-Piece Flo-Jet Carburetor

Repair procedures for small and large One-Piece Flo-Jet carburetors are similar except for location of adjusting needles.

Disassemble Carburetor, Small One-Piece Flo-Jet

1. Remove idle and high speed adjusting needles, Fig. 159.
2. Remove bowl nut and float bowl.
3. Use Tool #19280, Carburetor Nozzle Screwdriver, to remove nozzle, Fig. 162.
4. Remove float pin to remove float and float needle.
5. Use a large wide screwdriver to remove float valve seat.

Disassemble Carburetor, Large One-Piece Flo-Jet

1. Remove idle needle valve, Fig. 161.
2. Remove high speed needle valve assembly from float bowl and remove float bowl.
3. Use Tool #19280, Carburetor Nozzle Screwdriver, to remove nozzle, then remove jet from top of carburetor.
4. Remove float pin to remove float and float needle.

Disassembly Continued, Small and Large One-Piece Flo-Jet

1. If necessary to remove choke shaft, venturi, or throttle shaft, proceed in following sequence.
2. Pry out welch plug.
3. Remove choke valve. On carburetors with nylon choke shaft, remove choke valve as shown in Fig. 163.
4. Venturi can now be removed, Fig. 162. (Large One-Piece Choke-A-Matic® carburetors have a choke valve stop pin which must be pulled out to remove venturi.)
5. To check for throttle shaft wear, refer to two piece Flo-Jet for checking procedure, Section 3, page 56.
6. Remove throttle shaft seals, when so equipped.

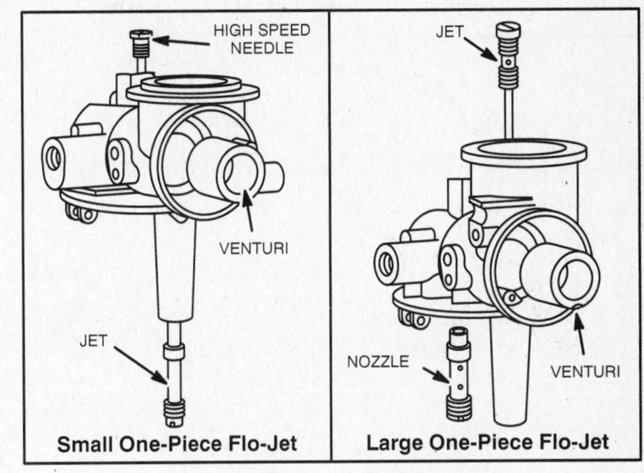

Fig. 162 – Repair Carburetors

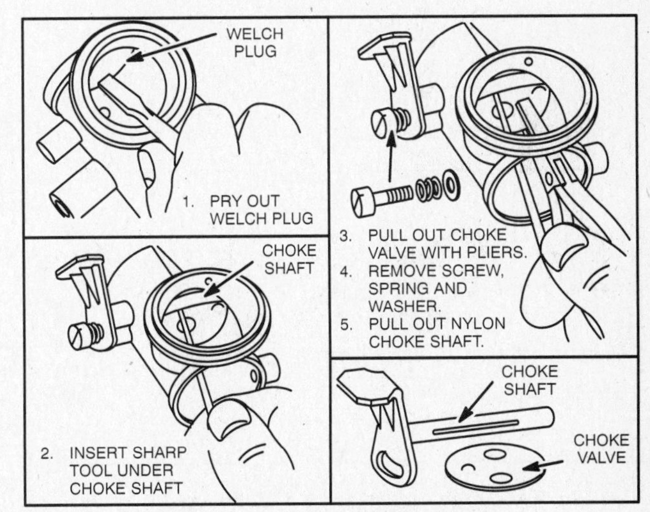

Fig. 163 – Nylon Choke Shaft

Inspection

Reject idle and high speed mixture needles if damaged, Fig. 164.

Check float for leakage. If it contains fuel or is crushed, it must be replaced. Replace float needle, if worn. If carburetor leaks with new float needle on carburetors with pressed in float needle seat, refer to next paragraph.

NOTE: METRIC EQUIVALENTS ARE LISTED ON PAGE 68 OF THIS SECTION.

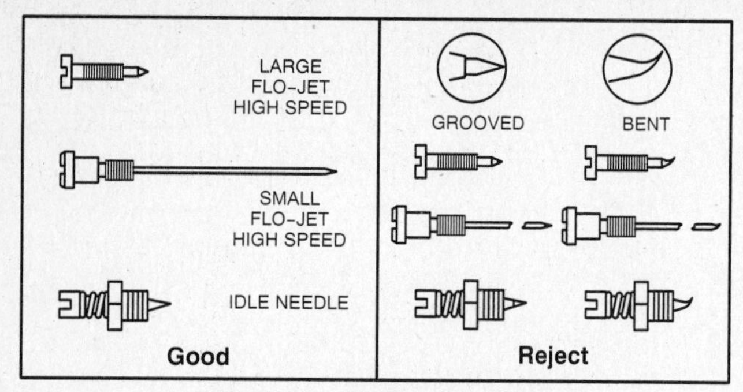

Fig. 164 - Mixture Needles

Replace Pressed in Float Valve Seat

1. Use a Part #93029 self-threading screw or remove one self-threading screw from Tool #19069, Flywheel Puller, and clamp head of screw in a vise.

   NOTE: On carburetors with removable viton inlet seat, use a 1/4-20 tap and screw Part #93029 or a screw extractor to remove pressed in seat.

2. Turn carburetor body to thread screw or screw extractor into seat, Fig. 165.
3. Continue turning carburetor body drawing seat out.
4. Leave screw or screw extractor fastened to seat. Insert new seat from repair kit Part #394682 into carburetor body (seat has chamfer).

   NOTE: If engine is equipped with a fuel pump, install repair kit Part #394683.

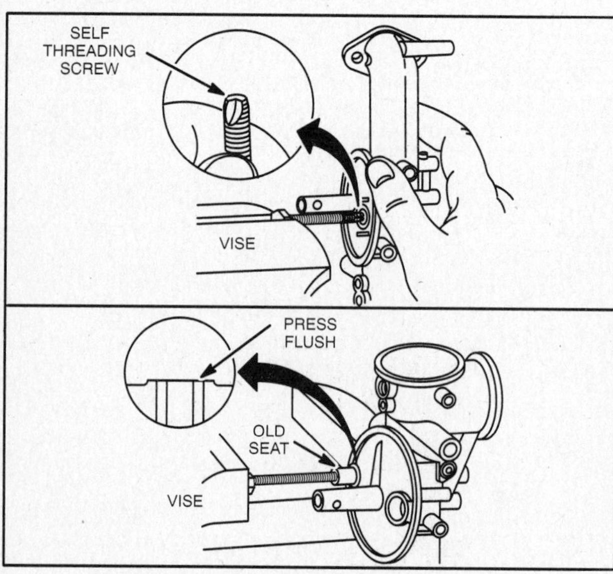

Fig. 165 - Replacing Float Valve Seat

5. Press new seat flush with body using screw/screw extractor and old seat as driver, Fig. 165.
6. Use care to ensure seat is not pressed below body surface or improper float to float valve contact will occur.

Assemble Carburetor

1. On carburetors equipped with throttle shaft seals, rubber lipped seals are installed with lip out on both sides. Foam seals can be installed either way.
2. Install float needle to float as shown, Fig. 166.
3. Open end of hook on spring must face away from venturi.

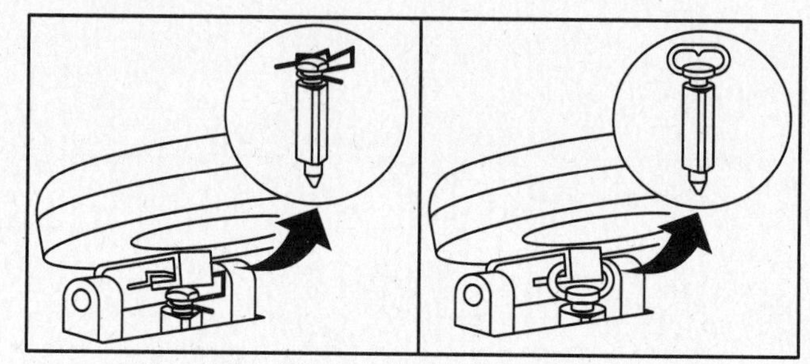

Fig. 166 - Float Needle Valve Variations

Check Float Level

1. With body gasket in place on upper body and float valve and float installed, float should be parallel to body mounting surface. Fig. 167.
2. If not, bend tang on float until they are parallel. DO NOT PRESS ON FLOAT, Fig. 167.

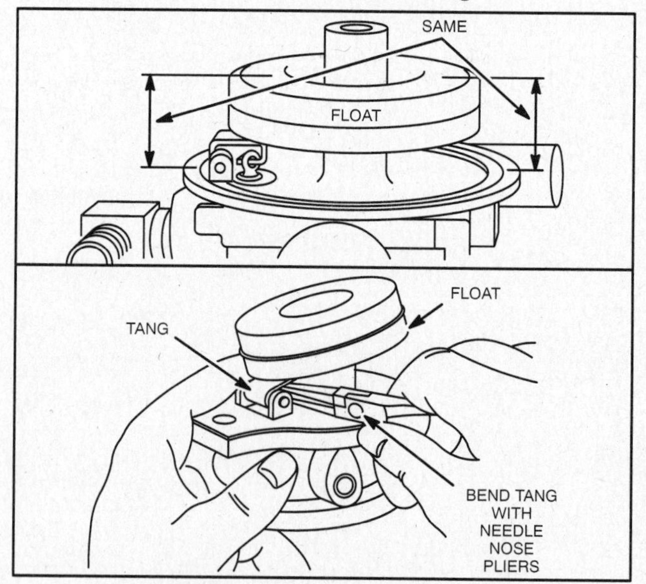

Fig. 167 - Checking Float Level

Repair Carburetor

Use new parts where necessary. Always use new gaskets. Carburetor repair kits are available. See Illustrated Parts List for particular model.

NOTE: METRIC EQUIVALENTS ARE LISTED ON PAGE 68 OF THIS SECTION.

1. If throttle shaft and/or venturi have been removed, install throttle and throttle shaft first.
2. Then install venturi.
3. Now install jet on small One-Piece or nozzle on large One-Piece Flo-Jet. The nozzle or jet holds venturi in place, Fig. 162.
4. Replace choke shaft and valve.
5. Install new welch plug using sealer around edge of plug.
6. Stake plug in eight places. Sealer is to prevent entry of dirt into engine.
7. Install float bowl, idle and high speed adjustment needles.

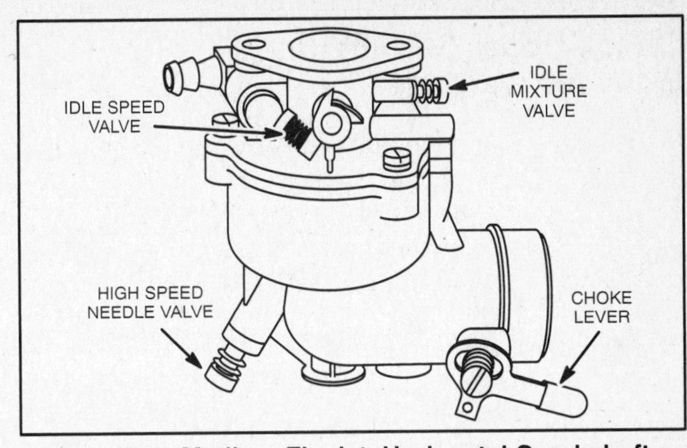

Fig. 169 – Medium Flo-Jet, Horizontal Crankshaft

ADJUST CARBURETOR
Initial Adjustment

1. Turn both idle and high speed needles in until they just bottom.
2. Then turn both valves 1-1/2 turns open.

These settings will allow engine to start. Final adjustment should be made when engine is running and has warmed up. See carburetor adjustment (two piece Flo-Jet carburetor), page 59.

Choke-A-Matic® Remote Control Adjustment

On Choke-A-Matic® carburetors, remote control must be correctly adjusted in order to obtain proper operation of choke and stop switch. See Section 4 for illustration by engine model.

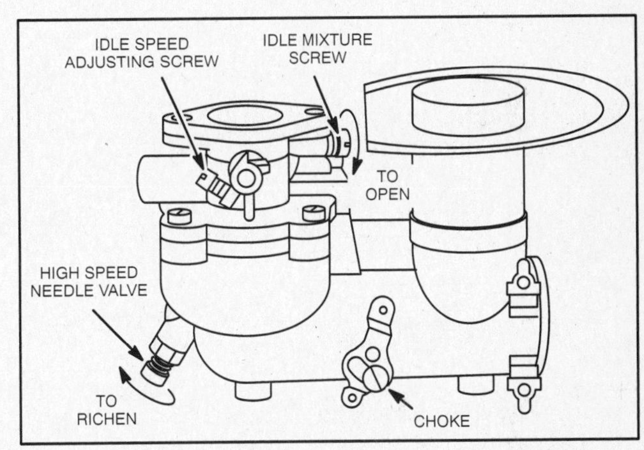

Fig. 170 – Large Flo-Jet, Horizontal Crankshaft

TWO-PIECE FLO-JET CARBURETORS, SMALL, MEDIUM AND LARGE FLO-JET

Fig. 168 – Small Flo-Jet, Horizontal and Vertical Crankshaft

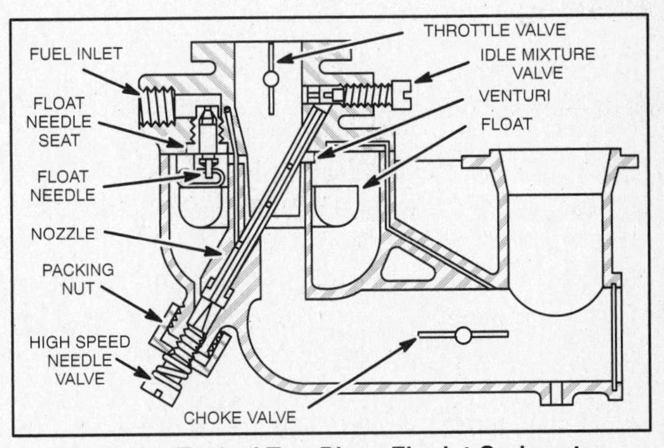

Fig. 171 – Typical Two Piece Flo-Jet Carburetor

NOTE: METRIC EQUIVALENTS ARE LISTED ON PAGE 68 OF THIS SECTION.

Check Upper Carburetor Body for Warpage

With carburetor assembled and body gasket in place, if a .002" feeler gauge can be inserted between upper and lower bodies at air vent boss, just below idle valve, upper body is warped or gasket surfaces are damaged and should be replaced, Fig. 172.

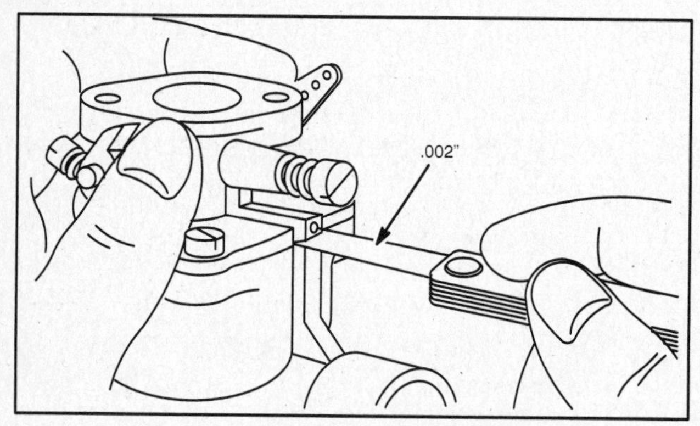

Fig. 172 – Checking Carburetor Body

Check Throttle Shaft and Bushings for Wear

1. Wear between throttle shaft and bushings should not exceed .010".
2. Check wear by placing a short iron bar on upper carburetor body as shown in Fig. 173.
3. Measure distance between bar and shaft with feeler gauge while holding shaft down and then holding shaft up.
4. If difference is over .010", either upper body should be rebushed, throttle shaft replaced, or both.
5. Wear on throttle shaft can be checked by comparing worn and unworn portions of shaft.
6. To replace bushings, see "Remove Throttle Shaft and Bushings," page 57.

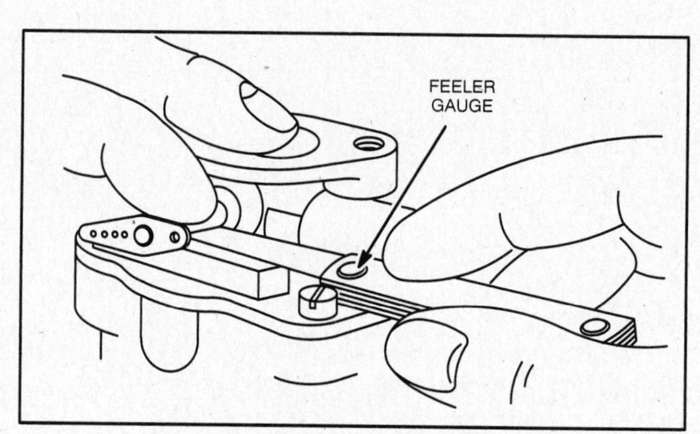

Fig. 173 – Checking Throttle Wear

Disassemble Carburetor

1. Remove idle needle valve.
2. On early small Flo-Jet loosen high speed packing nut. Remove packing nut and high speed needle valve together. On current small, medium and large Flo-Jets remove high speed needle valve assembly.
3. Remove nozzle with Tool #19280, Carburetor Nozzle Screwdriver. Use of Tool #19280 will help to prevent damage to threads in lower carburetor body.

   NOTE: If threads have been damaged in lower carburetor body Tool #19245, Tap Set, can be used to clean damaged threads.

4. Because nozzle projects diagonally into a recess in upper body, it must be removed before separating upper and lower bodies, Fig. 171.
5. Remove screws holding upper and lower bodies together and separate the two bodies.

NOTE: METRIC EQUIVALENTS ARE LISTED ON PAGE 68 OF THIS SECTION.

6. Remove float pin and remove float and float needle as an assembly.
7. With a wide blade screwdriver that completely fills slot, remove float inlet seat.
8. On carburetors with pressed in seats, see "Replacing Pressed in Float Seats," page 58, this section.

On small Flo-Jet carburetors, venturi is a separate part and can be slipped out of lower body.

Some two piece Flo-Jet carburetors have a welch plug and it should be removed only if choke shaft or choke valve is going to be removed. Some carburetors have a nylon choke shaft. Remove as shown, Fig. 174.

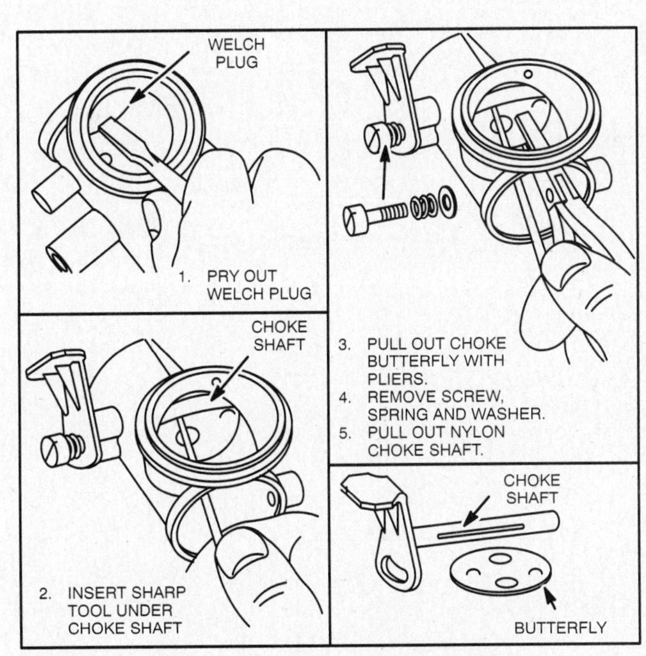

Fig. 174 - Nylon Choke Shaft

Remove Throttle Shaft and Bushing

Throttle shaft should be removed only when necessary to replace throttle shaft and/or bushings.

1. To remove throttle shaft, use a thin punch to drive out pin holding throttle stop to shaft, remove throttle valve, then pull out shaft, Fig. 175.

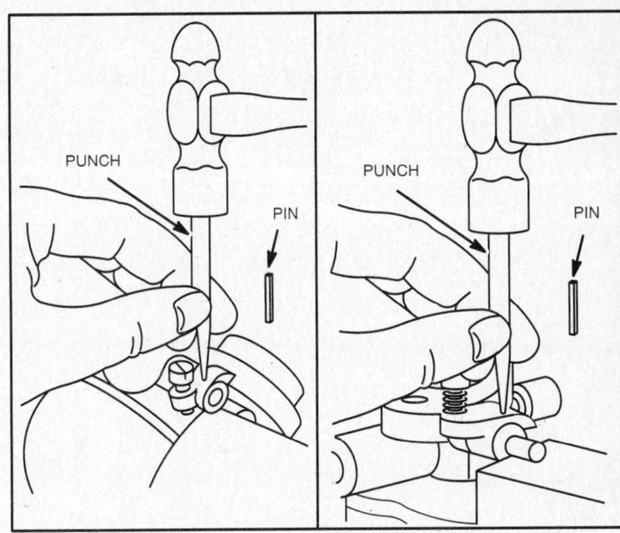

Fig. 175 - Remove Throttle Shaft and Bushings

Replace Throttle Shaft Bushings

1. Place a 1/4" x 20 tap or an E-Z out in a vise.
2. Turn carburetor body so as to thread tap or E-Z out into bushings enough to pull bushings out of body, Fig. 176.
3. Press new bushings into carburetor body with a vise.
4. Insert throttle shaft to be sure it is free in bushings.
5. If not, run a size 7/32" drill through both bushings to act as a line reamer.
6. Install throttle shaft, valve and stop.

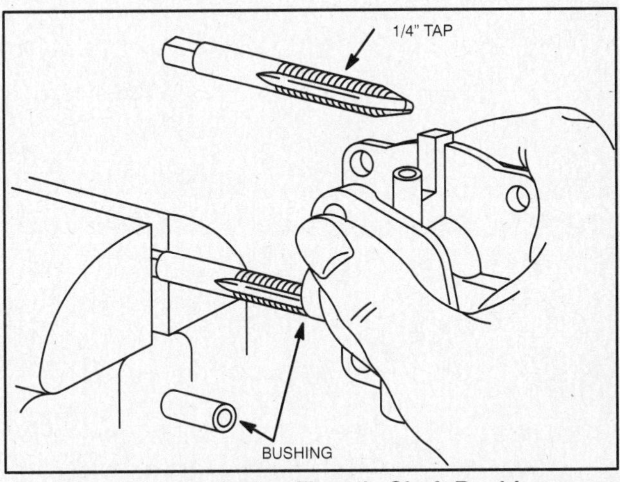

Fig. 176 - Replacing Throttle Shaft Bushings

NOTE: METRIC EQUIVALENTS ARE LISTED ON PAGE 68 OF THIS SECTION.

REPAIR CARBURETOR

Replace Float Needle Bushing or Seat

Use new parts when necessary. Always use new gaskets. Old gaskets take a set or harden and may leak. Carburetor repair kits are available. See Illustrated Parts List for part number for specific model.

1. Tighten inlet seat with gasket securely in place, if used. Some float valves have a spring clip to connect float valve to float tang. Others are nylon with a stirrup which fits over float tang. Older type float valves and earlier engines with fuel pumps have neither spring or stirrup.
2. A viton tip float valve is used on later models of Flo-Jet carburetors. These needles are used with inlet needle seat pressed into upper carburetor body and does not need replacement unless damaged.
3. Use a Part #93029 self-threading screw or remove one self-threading screw from Tool #19069, Flywheel Puller, and clamp head of screw in a vise.

   NOTE: On carburetors with removable viton inlet seat, use a 1/4-20 tap and screw Part #93029 or a screw extractor to remove pressed in seat.
4. Turn carburetor body to thread screw or screw extractor into seat, Fig. 165.
5. Continue turning carburetor body drawing seat out.
6. Leave screw or screw extractor fastened to seat. Insert new seat from repair kit Part #394682 into carburetor body (seat has chamfer).

NOTE: If engine is equipped with a fuel pump, install repair kit Part #394683, Fig. 177.

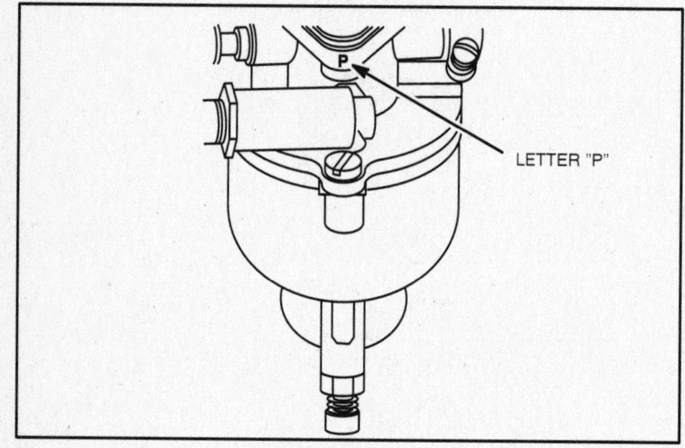

Fig. 177 - Flange Marking, Fuel Pump

7. Press new seat flush with body using screw and old seat as a driver, Fig. 176.
8. Use care to ensure seat is not pressed below body surface or improper float to float valve contact will occur.

Check Float Level

1. With body gasket in place on upper body and float valve and float installed, float should be parallel to body mounting surface.
2. If not, bend tang on float until they are parallel. DO NOT PRESS ON FLOAT TO ADJUST, Fig. 178 A/B.

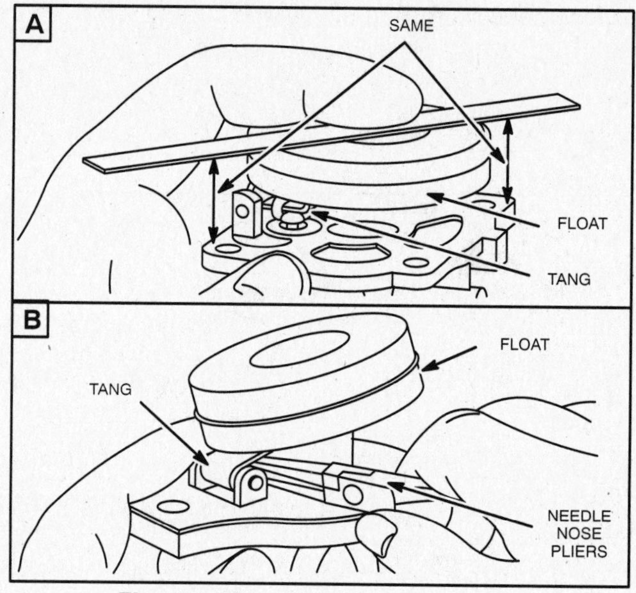

Fig. 178 A/B - Checking Float Level

Assemble Carburetor

1. Assemble venturi and venturi gasket, when used, to lower body. Be sure holes in venturi and venturi gasket are aligned. Most models do not have a removable venturi.
2. Install choke parts and welch plug if previously removed.
3. Use a sealer around welch plug to prevent entry of dirt.
4. Stake welch plug at least twice on small two-piece Flo-Jets and eight places on large two-piece Flo-Jets.
5. Fasten upper and lower bodies together with mounting screws.
6. Screw in nozzle with Tool #19280, Carburetor Nozzle Screwdriver, being careful that nozzle tip enters recess in upper body, Fig. 179.

7. Tighten nozzle securely. Screw in needle valve and idle valve until they just seat.

8. Back off high speed needle valve 1-1/2 turns. Do not tighten packing nut.

9. Back off idle needle valve 1-1/4 turn. These settings are approximately correct. Final adjustment will be made when engine is running.

NOTE: All carburetor adjustments must be made with air cleaner installed.

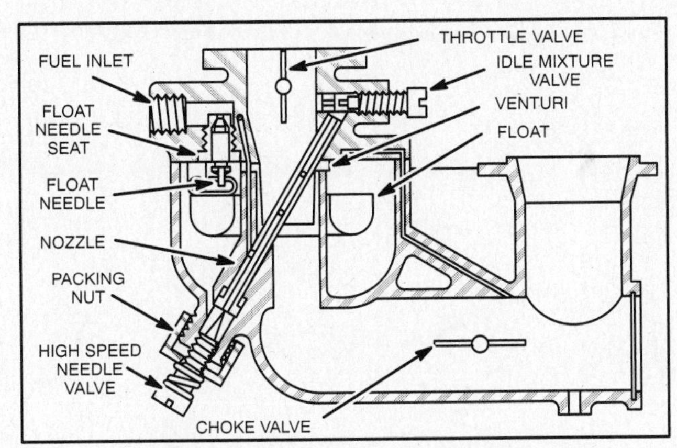

Fig. 179 – Assemble Carburetor

Carburetor Adjustment (All 2 Piece Flo-Jet Carburetors)

1. Start engine and run to warm up.

2. Then place governor speed control lever in "FAST" position.

3. Turn high speed needle valve in until engine slows (clockwise – lean mixture).

4. Then turn it out past smooth operating point (rich mixture).

5. Now turn high speed needle valve to midpoint between rich and lean.

6. Next, adjust idle RPM. Rotate throttle counterclockwise and hold against stop.

7. Adjust idle speed adjusting screw to obtain 1750 RPM, aluminum engines; 1200 RPM, cast iron engines, Fig. 180.

8. Holding throttle against idle stop, turn idle valve in (lean) and out (rich).

9. Set at midpoint between rich and lean.

10. Recheck idle RPM. Release throttle.

11. If engine will not accelerate properly, carburetor should be readjusted, usually to a slightly richer mixture.

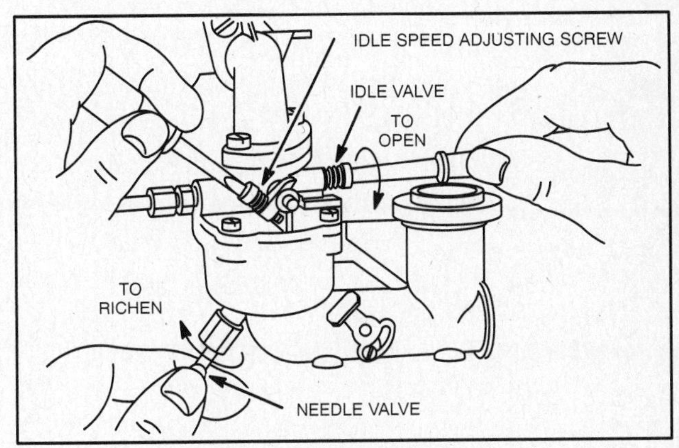

Fig. 180 – Adjusting Carburetor

Governed Idle

To adjust for governed idle, refer to Section 4 for specific model of engine.

Choke-A-Matic® Remote Control Adjustment

On Choke-A-Matic® carburetors, remote control must be correctly adjusted in order to obtain proper operation of choke and stop switch. For adjustment, see Section 4.

Idling Device and Throttle Control (Two-Piece Flo-Jet)

A manual friction control may be used to limit throttle movement, to any pre-set position. It is commonly used for two purposes:

1. To return throttle to a "no-load" position on a pump, generator, etc;

2. For cold weather starting on governed idle engines. Throttle can easily be kept in a "near closed" position, while starting, which is most favorable for cold weather starts, Fig. 181.

NOTE: METRIC EQUIVALENTS ARE LISTED ON PAGE 68 OF THIS SECTION.

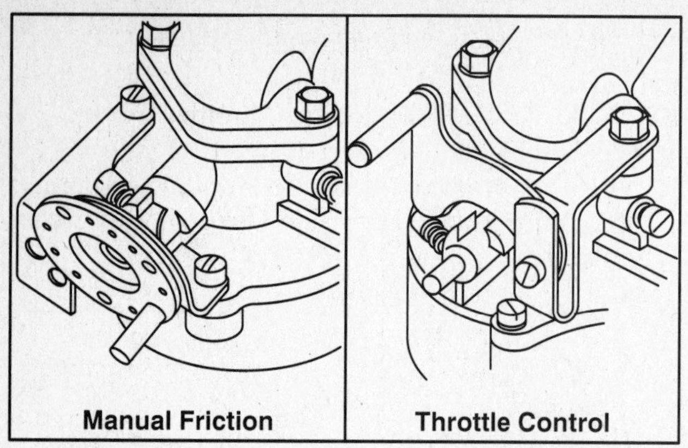

Fig. 181 – Idling Device and Throttle Control

Remote Throttle Control (Two Piece Flo-Jet)

The remote throttle control opens carburetor throttle until full governed speed is obtained, at which point governor takes over control of throttle. At any point below governed speed, throttle is held in fixed position and engine speed will vary with load, Fig. 182.

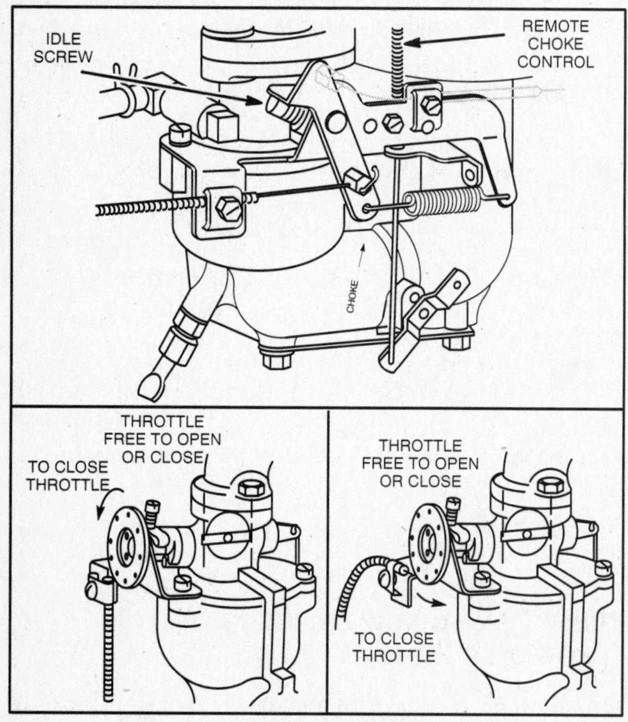

Fig. 182 – Remote Throttle Control

CROSS-OVER FLO-JET CARBURETORS, HORIZONTAL CRANKSHAFT ENGINES

The cross-over Flo-Jet carburetor is used on Model Series 253400, 255400 engines and is a float type carburetor with idle and high speed adjustment needles. This carburetor also has an integral fuel pump. All adjustments can be made from top of carburetor, Fig's. 183 and 184.

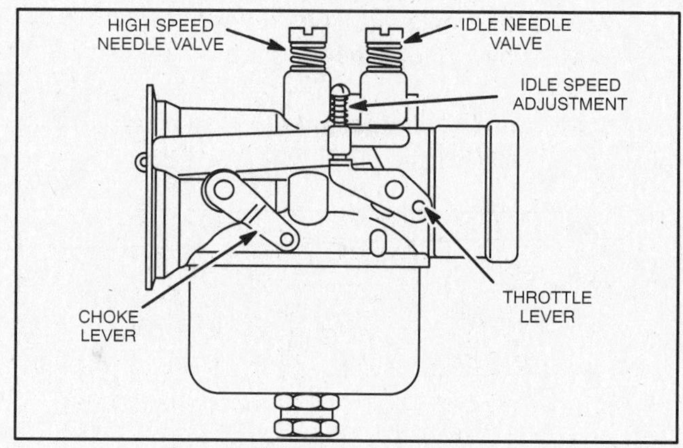

Fig. 183 – Cross-Over Flo-Jet

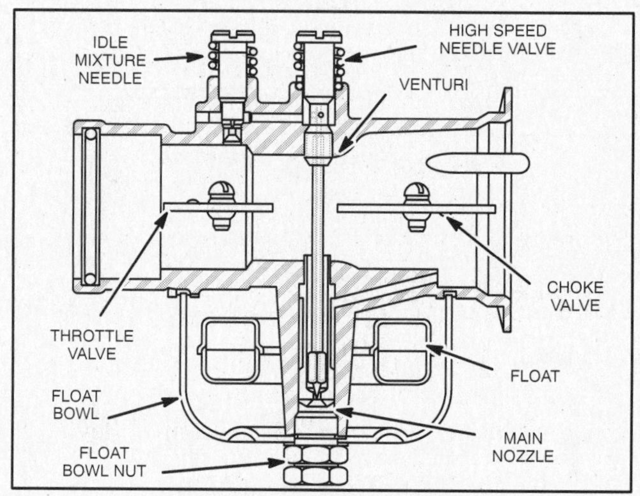

Fig. 184 – Sectional View

Disassemble Cross-Over Flo-Jet

1. Remove idle and high speed needle adjustment valves.
2. Remove float bowl mounting screw, washer and float bowl.
3. Using a large blunt screwdriver, remove nozzle screw.
4. Remove float hinge pin, float and float inlet needle.
5. Use screwdriver to remove two screws from choke shaft.

NOTE: METRIC EQUIVALENTS ARE LISTED ON PAGE 68 OF THIS SECTION.

6. Then remove choke plate and choke shaft.
7. Use screwdriver to remove screw from throttle shaft.
8. Then remove throttle plate and throttle shaft.
9. Use screwdriver to remove three screws from fuel pump body.
10. Remove fuel pump from carburetor taking care not to lose pump valve springs.

Inspection

Check idle and high speed needle valves for burrs, grooves or bent needle tips. Replace if damaged, Fig. 185. Check float for fuel in float, damage or leaks. If it contains fuel or is crushed, it must be replaced. If carburetor leaks with new inlet needle valve, replace inlet needle seat. See next paragraph.

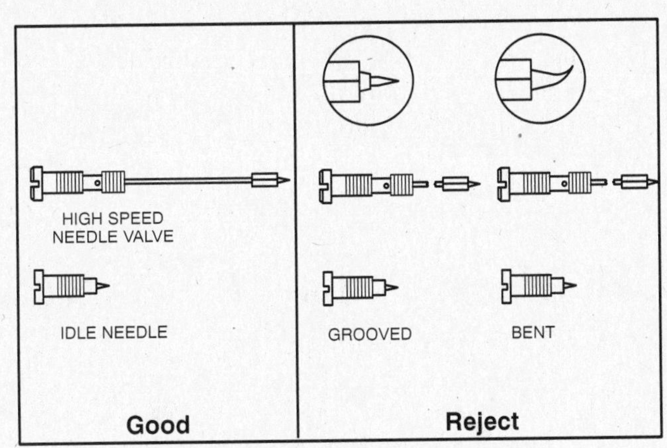

Fig. 185 - Checking Needle Valves

Replace Pressed-In Float Valve Seat

1. Use a #93029 self-threading screw or remove one self-threading screw from Tool #19069, Flywheel Puller, and clamp head of screw in a vise.
2. Turn carburetor body to thread screw into seat, Fig. 186.
3. Continue turning carburetor body drawing seat out. Leave seat fastened to screw.
4. Insert new seat from repair kit Part #394683 into carburetor body (seat has starting chamfer).

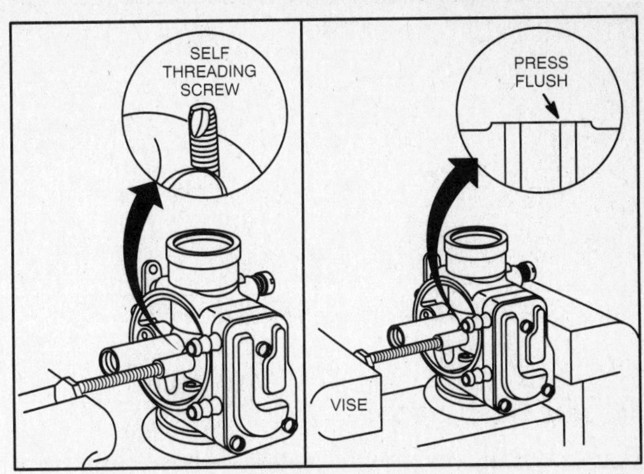

Fig. 186 - Replacing Float Valve Seat

5. Press new seat flush with body using screw and old seat as a driver, Fig. 186. Use care to ensure seat is not pressed below body surface or improper float to float needle valve contact will occur.
6. Install float valve as shown in Fig. 187. Hook on spring must face away from venturi.

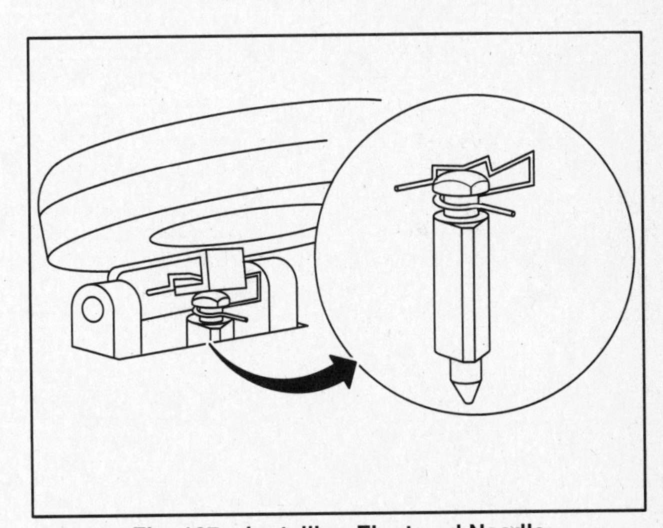
Fig. 187 - Installing Float and Needle

Check Float Level

1. With float needle valve, float and float hinge pin installed, hold carburetor upside down.
2. Float should be parallel to bowl mounting surface.
3. If not, bend tang on float until they are parallel. DO NOT PRESS ON FLOAT TO ADJUST, Fig. 188.

NOTE: METRIC EQUIVALENTS ARE LISTED ON PAGE 68 OF THIS SECTION.

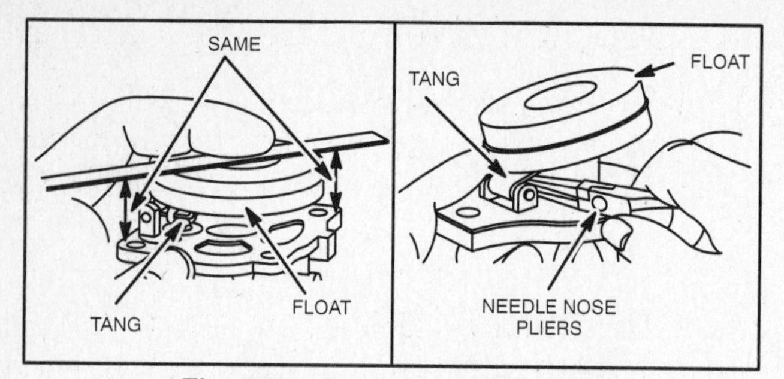

Fig. 188 - Checking Float Level

Repair Carburetor

Use new parts where necessary. Always use new gaskets. Old gaskets take a set or harden and may leak. Carburetor repair kits are available. See Illustrated Parts List for part numbers. These carburetors use a viton tip float needle and a pressed-in needle seat. Seat does not need replacement unless seat is damaged or leaks with a new float needle.

Assemble Carburetor

1. Install main nozzle using blunt screwdriver to prevent damage to slot and metering hole.
2. Place bowl on carburetor and install bowl nut and washer.
3. Install one (1) pump valve spring on spring boss, Fig. 189, and then place diaphragm on carburetor.

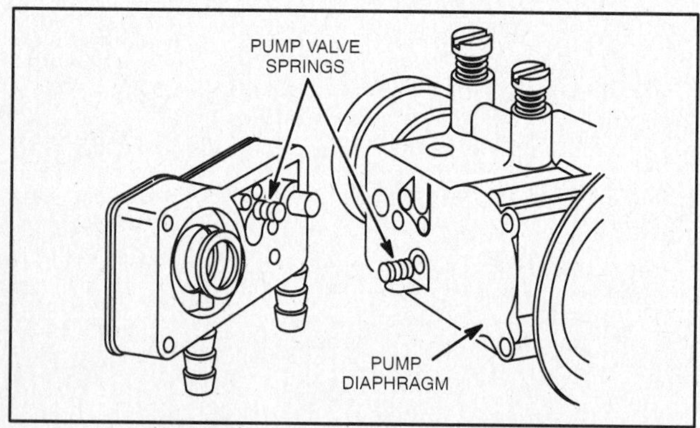

Fig. 189 - Pump Spring Location (Valve Flap Bent Down for Clarity)

4. Place a pump valve spring on spring boss in pump body, Fig. 189, and place pump body on carburetor.
5. Place damping diaphragm, pump gasket and pump cover on pump body and install three screws, Fig. 190. A fuel pump repair kit is available. See Illustrated Parts List for part number.

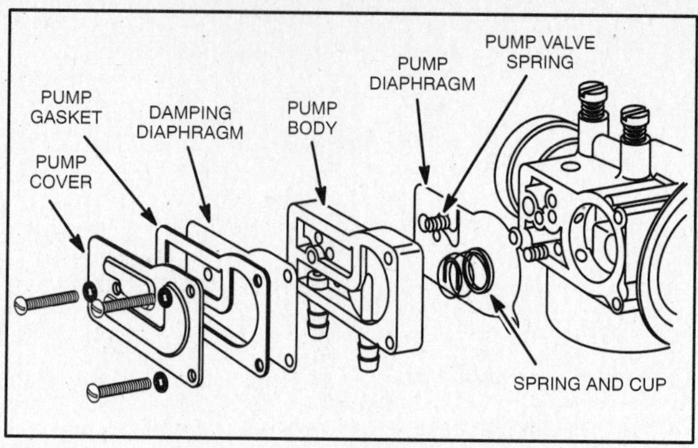

Fig. 190 - Assemble Fuel Pump

6. Place choke shaft in carburetor body and slide in choke valve with notch out and dimple down toward float bowl, Fig. 191A.
7. Install two (2) screws using a screwdriver.
8. Slide in throttle shaft and then slide in throttle plate with two (2) dimples facing toward idle valve.
9. When valve is installed correctly, dimples will be down and number on plate is visible with throttle in closed or idle position, Fig. 191B.
10. Install idle and high speed needle valves.

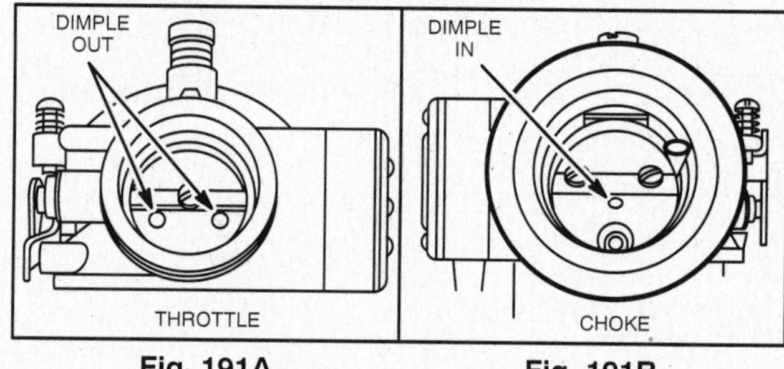

Fig. 191A **Fig. 191B**

CARBURETOR ADJUSTMENTS

INITIAL ADJUSTMENT

1. Turn idle and high speed needle valves clockwise until they just close, Fig. 192.

   NOTE: Valves may be damaged by turning them too far.

2. Now open high speed needle valve 1-1/2 turns counterclockwise and idle needle valve one turn. This initial adjustment will permit engine to be started and warmed up prior to final adjustment.

NOTE: METRIC EQUIVALENTS ARE LISTED ON PAGE 68 OF THIS SECTION.

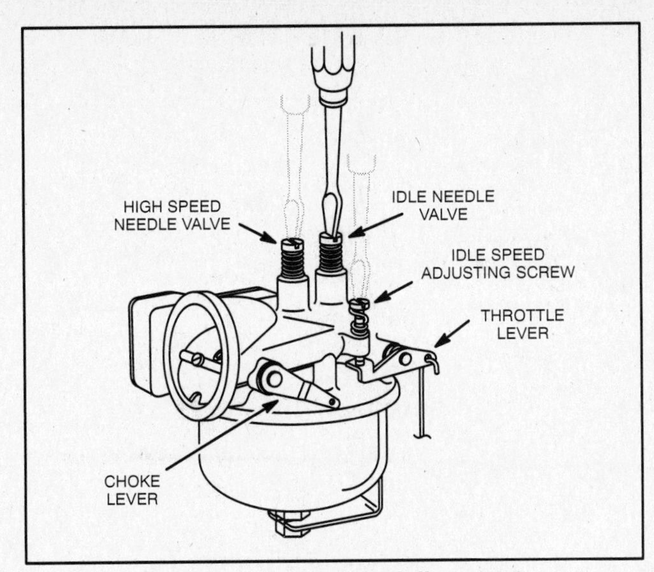

Fig. 192 - Carburetor Adjustment

NOTE: Carburetor adjustments should be made with air cleaner installed on engine.

FINAL ADJUSTMENT PROCEDURE

Idle Needle Valve Mixture

1. Place governor speed control lever in "IDLE" position.
2. Set idle speed adjusting screw to obtain 1750 RPM minimum while holding throttle lever against screw.
3. Turn idle needle valve in until RPM slows or misses (clockwise – lean mixture), then turn it out past smooth idling point until engine runs unevenly (rich mixture).
4. Now turn idle needle valve to midpoint between rich and lean so engine runs smoothly.
5. Release throttle lever.
6. Readjust idle speed to 1750 RPM, if required.

High Speed Needle Valve Mixture

1. Move governor speed control lever to "FAST" position.
2. Turn high speed needle valve in until engine slows or misses (lean mixture), then turn it out past smooth operating point until engine runs unevenly (rich mixture).
3. Now turn high speed needle valve to midpoint between rich and lean so engine runs smoothly, Fig. 192.
4. Engine should accelerate smoothly.
5. If engine does not accelerate properly, carburetor should be readjusted usually to a slightly richer mixture.

LP GAS FUEL SYSTEM

NOTE: Engines converted for use with LPG fuel for use in the state of California after January 1, 1995 must be certified by the company doing the conversion to assure that the engine meets or exceeds CARB certification requirements.

The following information is provided to assist you in servicing LP gas fuel systems. This information applies only to Garretson Equipment Company systems installed by Briggs & Stratton. For parts information refer to MS-3915. Parts for Garretson system must be obtained from a Garretson parts distributor.

For additional information about LP conversion kits, contact:

Garretson Equipment Co, Inc.
Box 111
Mount Pleasant, Iowa 52641

or

Beam Products Manufacturing Co.
P.O. Box 2082
Artesia, California 90702-2082

For LP fuel systems not covered in this section contact manufacturer of fuel system.

WARNING: LP gas fuel system should only be worked on in a very well ventilated area. Many state, county and city governments require that service be performed only outdoors. Before loosening any fuel line connections, have a fan blowing directly across engine.

Check and Adjust Fuel System

1. Loosen fuel line at primary regulator.
2. Open valve on cylinder for an instant, to be sure there is pressure in fuel cylinder.
3. Escaping gas can be heard.
4. Shut off valve at cylinder, Fig. 193.
5. Remove fuel line between primary and secondary regulator (fuel controller).

NOTE: METRIC EQUIVALENTS ARE LISTED ON PAGE 68 OF THIS SECTION.

6. Attach pressure gauge to outlet of primary regulator, leaving gauge connection loose enough to permit a slight leakage of gas. (This will permit adjustment of regulator under conditions of actual gas flow.)
7. Remove cap or top of primary regulator, Fig. 193.
8. Open fuel cylinder valve.
9. Turn pressure regulating screw in p.s.i. primary regulator, until a pressure of 1-1/2 p.s.i. is obtained at pressure gauge.
10. Shut off fuel cylinder valve.
11. Reassemble cap.
12. Remove pressure gauge.
13. Loosen secondary regulator bracket from carburetor.
14. Pull secondary regulator away from carburetor so that short rubber fuel line is disconnected.
15. Assemble fuel line between primary regulator and secondary regulator (fuel controller).
16. Secondary regulator must remain mounted so diaphragm is in a vertical plane, Fig. 193.
17. Open fuel cylinder valve.
18. Apply soap suds to outlet at center of secondary regulator to which rubber fuel line has been attached.
19. If a bubble forms, it indicates that valve is leaking or not locking off.
20. If no bubble appears, press primer button.
21. A bubble should appear, indicating fuel is flowing into regulator.
22. Put soap suds on outlet again, then slowly turn adjusting screw at bottom of secondary regulator counterclockwise until a bubble forms at outlet.
23. Turn adjusting screw in (clockwise) slowly until soap bubbles on outlet no longer form.
24. Hold adjusting screw at this point and tighten locknut.
25. Press primer button to allow fuel to flow.
26. Release and again put soap suds on outlet to make certain fuel shuts off.
27. Repeat several times.
28. If bubble should form after primer button is released, adjusting screw should be turned in until flow stops and soap bubble does not break or enlarge.
29. Loosen fuel line between regulators.
30. Re-assemble secondary regulator to carburetor with short rubber fuel line in place.
31. Retighten fuel line connections, Fig. 193.

Adjust Carburetor, LP Fuel System

1. Loosen locknut on load needle screw and turn needle screw in until it seats.
2. Do not force; open 2-1/2 turns.
3. Turn idle needle in until it seats, then open one turn.
4. If engine will not be required to idle, leave idle needle closed.
5. Depress primer button momentarily, then start engine, run engine to allow it to warm up before final adjustment.
6. With engine running at normal operating speed, turn load needle screw in slowly (clockwise) until engine starts to miss (lean mixture).
7. Then turn load screw out slowly past point of best operation until engine begins to run unevenly (rich mixture).
8. Then turn load screw in just enough so engine will run smoothly.
9. Hold load screw and tighten locknut.
10. Hold throttle at idle position, then release throttle.
11. Engine should accelerate quickly and smoothly.
12. If engine will be required to run at idle, turn idle speed adjusting screw on throttle until engine runs at proper idle speed for engine model. See Repair Check Chart.
13. Hold throttle at this point and turn idle needle slowly in or out until engine runs at maximum idle speed.
14. Then readjust idle speed screw until proper idle speed is obtained.
15. Allow throttle to open. Engine should accelerate quickly and smoothly.
16. If not, readjust load screw, usually to a richer mixture.

NOTE: METRIC EQUIVALENTS ARE LISTED ON PAGE 68 OF THIS SECTION.

17. To stop engine, turn off fuel supply valve at fuel cylinder.

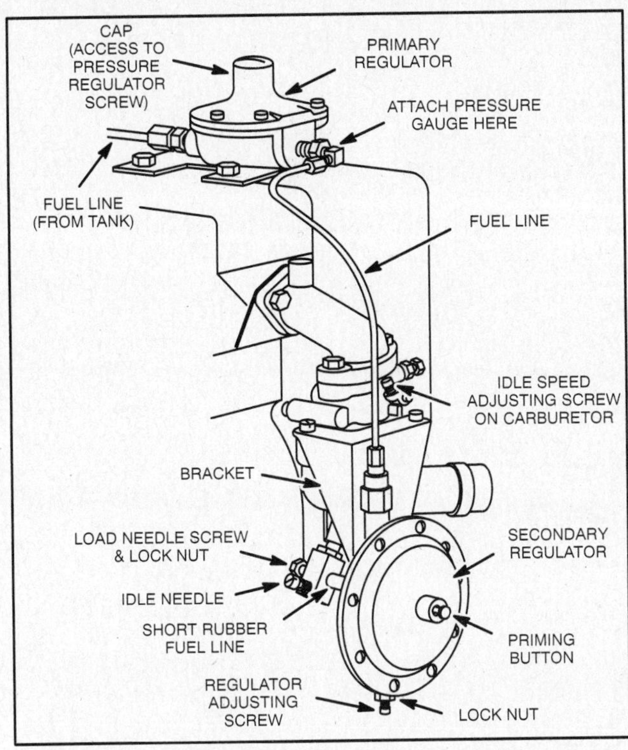

Fig. 193 - Adjusting Carburetor, LP Fuel System

Start Engine

1. To start engine, do not use choke, but depress primer button momentarily, then start engine immediately.
2. In cold weather, it may be necessary to partially close carburetor choke valve to permit engine to run smoothly until engine warms up.

Clean LP Gas Filter (Optional)

1. Unscrew filter head from filter body. Remove element assembly from head, Fig. 194.
2. Wash element in commercial solvent cleaner or gasoline.
3. If accumulated dirt is gummy, we suggest a short soaking period in solvent cleaner.
4. Element should then be rinsed in clean gasoline and blown with compressed air.

   ALWAYS USE REVERSE FLOW FROM INSIDE OUT. NEVER USE COMPRESSED AIR ON OUTSIDE SURFACE OF ELEMENT. NEVER DIP ELEMENT IN "BRIGHT DIP" OR OTHER ACID SOLUTION.

5. To re-assemble filter, insert element into filter head with round washer entering first.
6. Gasket is put on filter body. Spring is located in filter body so that when filter body and head are put together, spring will hold element against head.
7. Tighten body and head with 75 ft. lbs. torque.
8. After filter has been re-assembled to engine, point at gasket and other line connections should be checked with soap suds, with fuel turned on, to be sure there are no leaks.

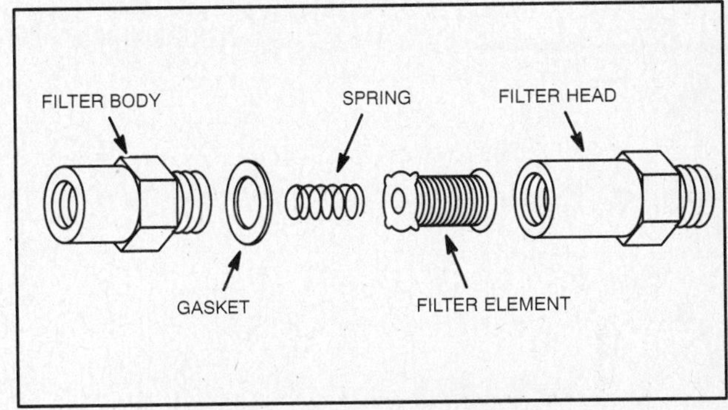

Fig. 194 - Element Assembly

KEROSENE SYSTEM OPERATION

Efficient engine performance will be obtained only when following changes are accomplished:

1. A low compression cylinder head is required for models 131400, 132400, 233000, and 243000. Other models may use two cylinder head gaskets.
2. A special spark plug - #291835 - must be used on models 233000, and 243000. Spark plug gap .030" all models.
3. A reduced breaker gap, .015", is used on models 233000 and 243000. Engine must be retimed using reduced breaker gap. Follow timing procedure in Section 2, Ignition.

Power loss will vary between 15% to 25% and fuel consumption will be approximately 15% less while running on kerosene.

Fig's. 195 through 197 illustrate various types of Briggs & Stratton combination fuel systems used.

Due to the low volatility of kerosene, engines operated on kerosene-gasoline fuel systems can be started on kerosene, only when engine is at operating temperature. Cold engines must be started on gasoline and switched over to kerosene operation only after warmed up.

NOTE: METRIC EQUIVALENTS ARE LISTED ON PAGE 68 OF THIS SECTION.

1. After warm-up and while operating on kerosene, adjust carburetor needle valves to a point where engine runs smoothest, and accelerates without hesitation when throttle is quickly opened.
2. When shutting down engine, carburetor must be emptied of kerosene so engine can be started on gasoline when cold.
3. Refer to Flo-Jet carburetor for adjustment of carburetor and adjust carburetor while running on kerosene.

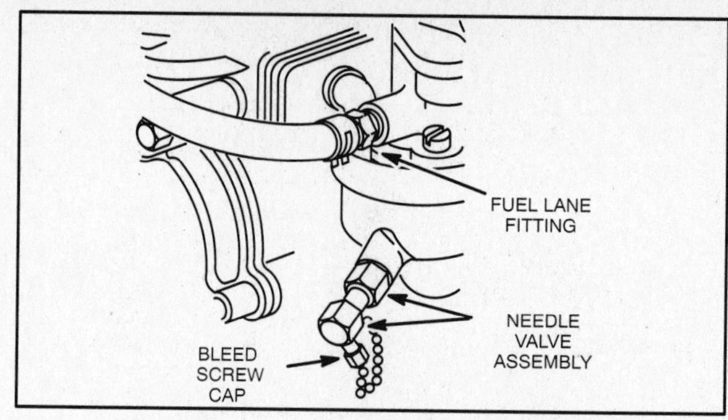

Fig. 197 – Combination Fuel Carburetor

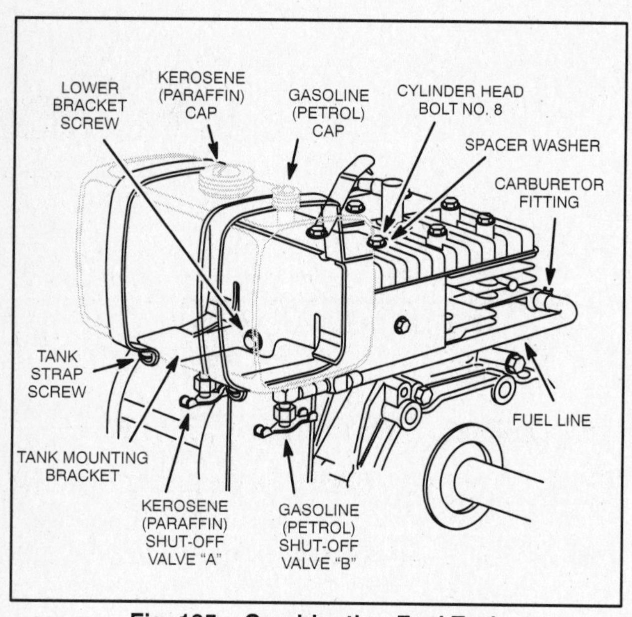

Fig. 195 – Combination Fuel Tank

Fuel Pumps (Crankcase Vacuum Operated)

Some models are factory or field equipped with fuel pumps operated by crankcase vacuum. Fuel pumps may be mounted directly to carburetor or on a mounting bracket, Fig's. 198 or 199. Crankcase vacuum is obtained by a fitting on dipstick tube, Fig. 199, a hollow bolt and fitting, Fig. 200, or from crankcase breather valve, Fig. 198.

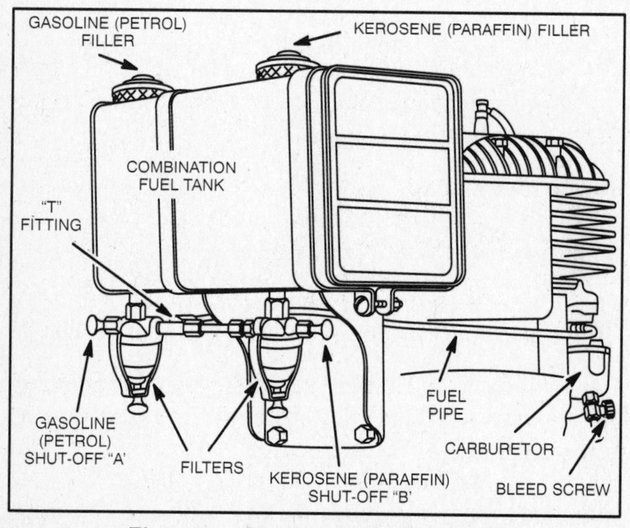

Fig. 196 – Combination Fuel Tank

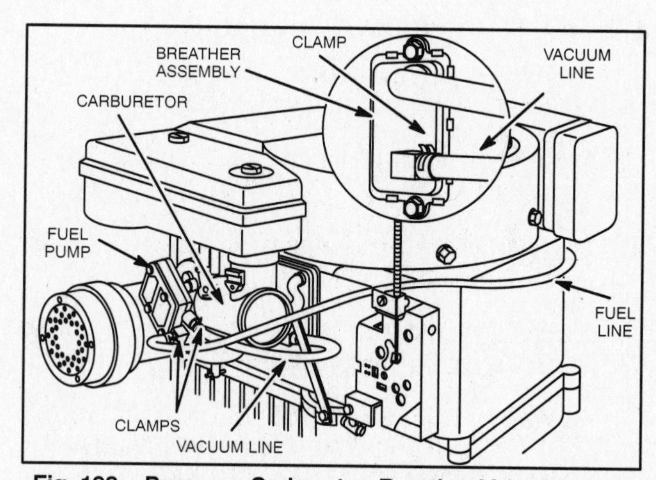

Fig. 198 – Pump on Carburetor, Breather Valve Vacuum

NOTE: METRIC EQUIVALENTS ARE LISTED ON PAGE 68 OF THIS SECTION.

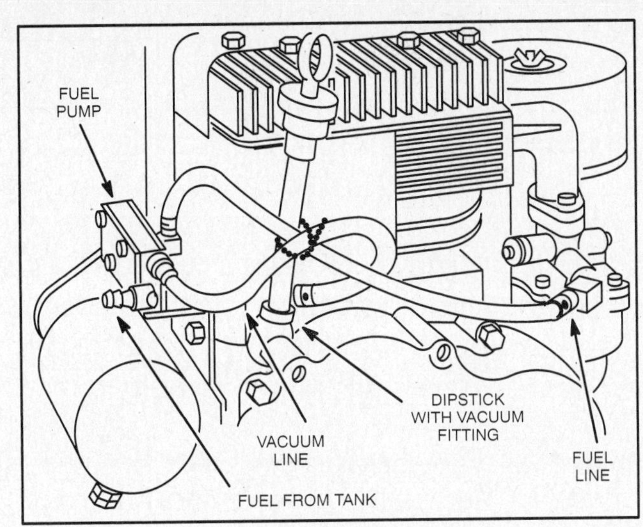

Fig. 199 - Pump on Bracket, Dipstick Tube Vacuum

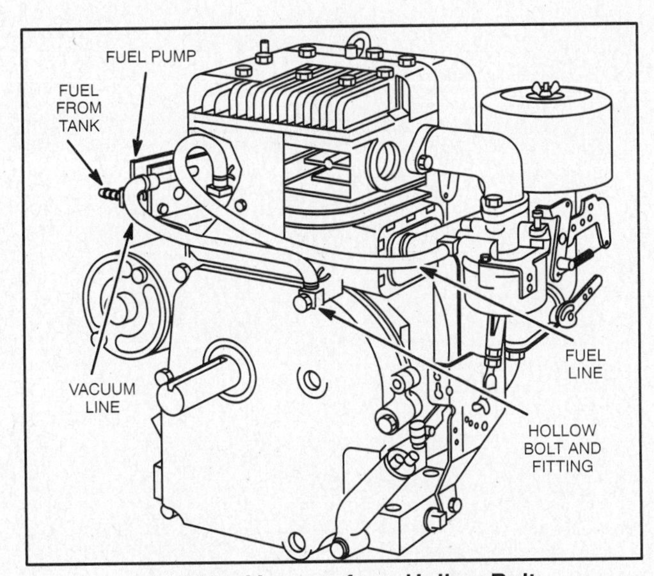

Fig. 200 - Vacuum from Hollow Bolt

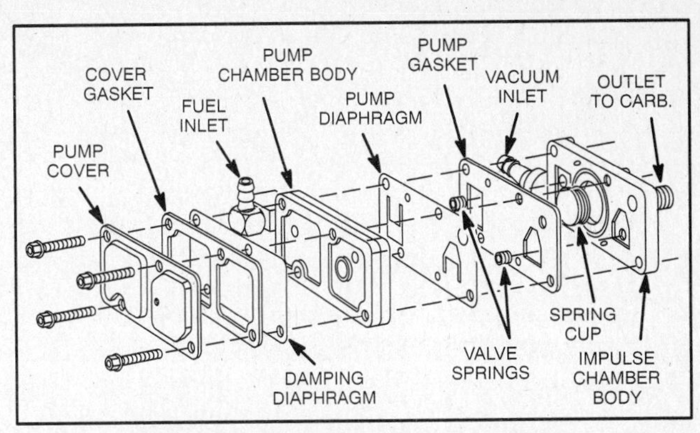

Fig. 201 - Exploded View, Fuel Pump

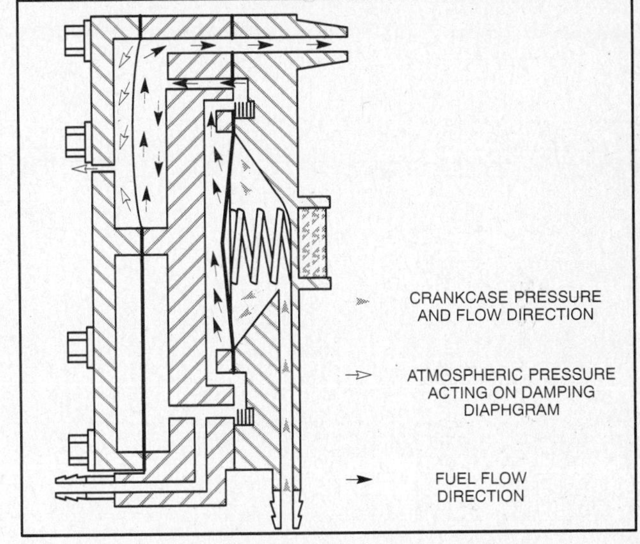

Fig. 202 - Fuel Flow with Crankcase Pressure

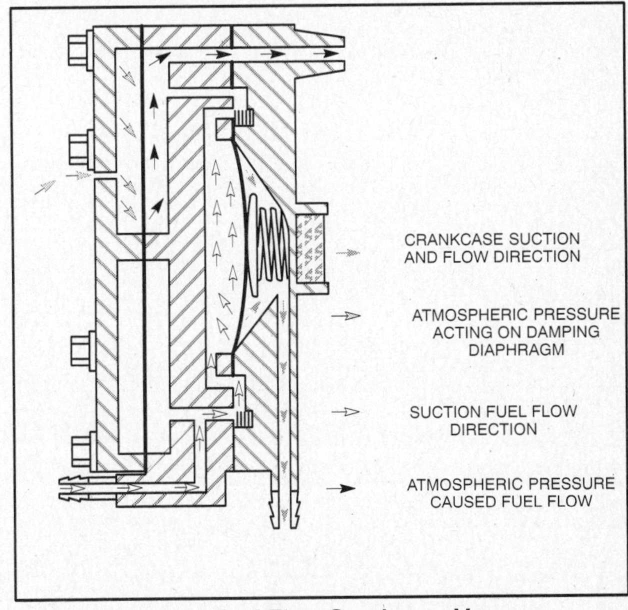

Fig. 203 - Fuel Flow Crankcase Vacuum

Operation

Operation of fuel pump is illustrated in Fig's. 201, 202, and 203. Any restriction in fuel or vacuum lines will affect operation. Also any leaks that cause air to get into fuel line or reduce vacuum in vacuum line will reduce performance.

1. To service fuel pump, remove pump from carburetor or mounting bracket.

NOTE: METRIC EQUIVALENTS ARE LISTED ON PAGE 68 OF THIS SECTION.

2. When removing fuel supply line from tank to pump, be sure to plug fuel line or turn off fuel valve, if so equipped.
3. Disassemble fuel pump by removing four 1/4" head cap screws from pump cover.
4. Separate pump cover, pumping chamber and impulse chamber.
5. Discard old gaskets, diaphragms and springs. Clean pump parts in carburetor solvent or lacquer thinner.

A repair kit is available. See Illustrated Parts List. Kit includes all parts needed.

6. Install chamber gasket using locator pins.
7. Place springs in spring recesses and install pump diaphragm on locator pins.
8. Place pump chamber body on impulse body using locator pins.
9. Place damping diaphragm and cover gasket on pump body.
10. Install cover and four screws.
11. Torque screws to 10 to 15 in. lbs., See Fig. 201 for exploded view.

METRIC EQUIVALENTS

DIMENSION DECIMAL	
Inches	**Millimeters**
.002	.05
.010	.25
.015	.38
.030	.76
DIMENSION FRACTIONAL	
Inches	**Millimeters**
1/32	.8
5/32	3.9
7/32	5.5
1/4	6.4
15/16	23.8
1	25.4
1-7/64	28.2
1-1/8	28.6
1-7/32	30.9
1-5/16	33.3
1-3/8	35
2–1/8	54

TORQUE		
In. Lbs.	**Kgcm Kpcm**	**Nm**
10	12	1.1
15	17	1.7
30	35	3.4
40	46	4.5
50	58	5.6
55	63	6.2
65	75	7.3
75	86	8.5
100	115	11.3
140	162	15.8
Ft. Lbs.	**Kgm**	**Nm**
75	.7	101.7
PRESSURE		
P.S.I.	**Kgcm²**	**Bar**
1-1/2	.1	

NOTE: METRIC EQUIVALENTS ARE LISTED ON PAGE 68 OF THIS SECTION.

Section 4
GOV. CONTROLS, CARB. LINKAGE & FLYWHEEL BRAKES

SECTION INDEX

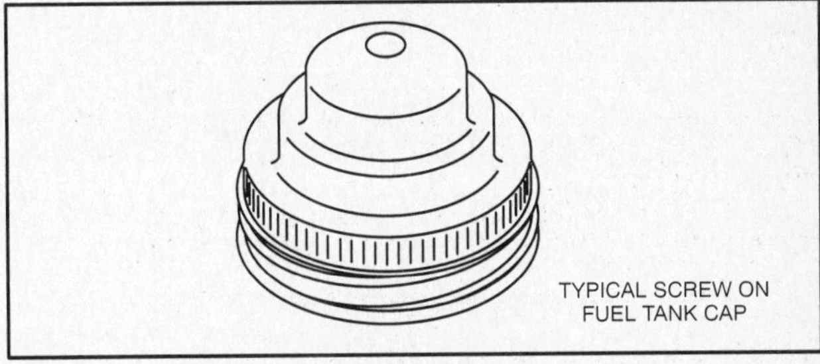

TYPICAL SCREW ON FUEL TANK CAP

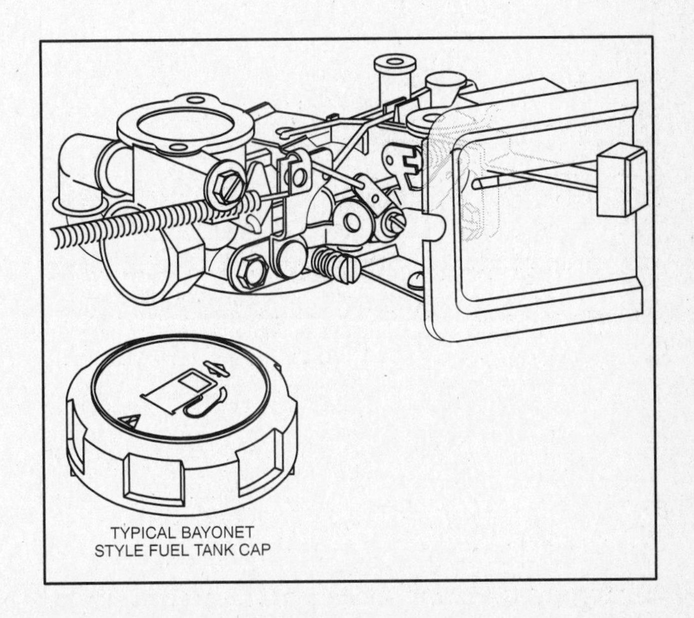

TYPICAL BAYONET STYLE FUEL TANK CAP

NOTE: METRIC EQUIVALENTS ARE LISTED ON PAGE 26 OF THIS SECTION.

SECTION INDEX, CONT'D

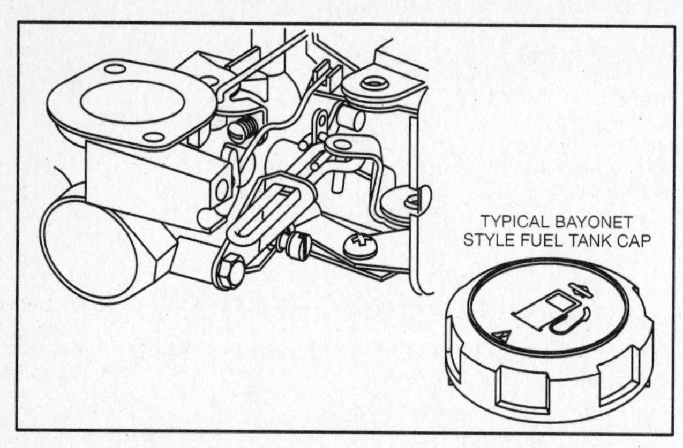

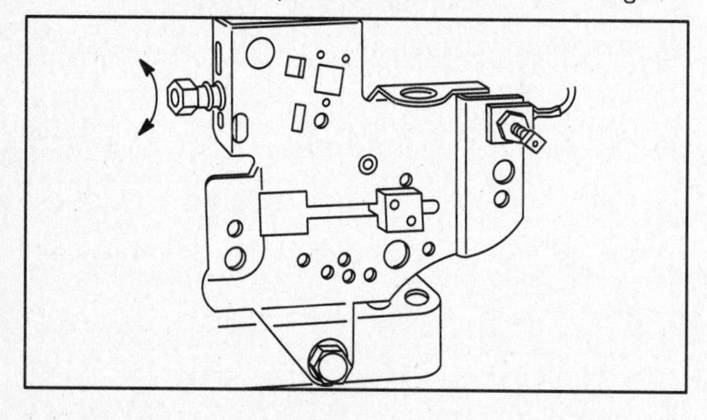

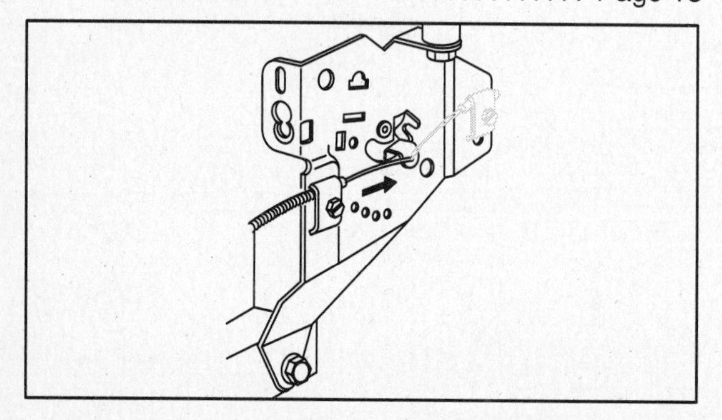

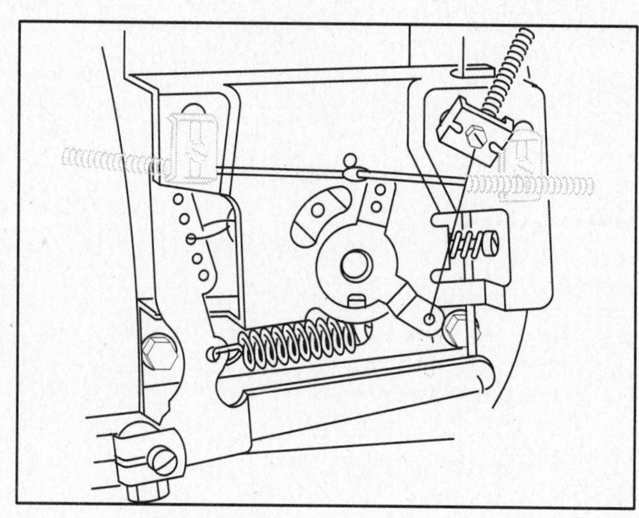

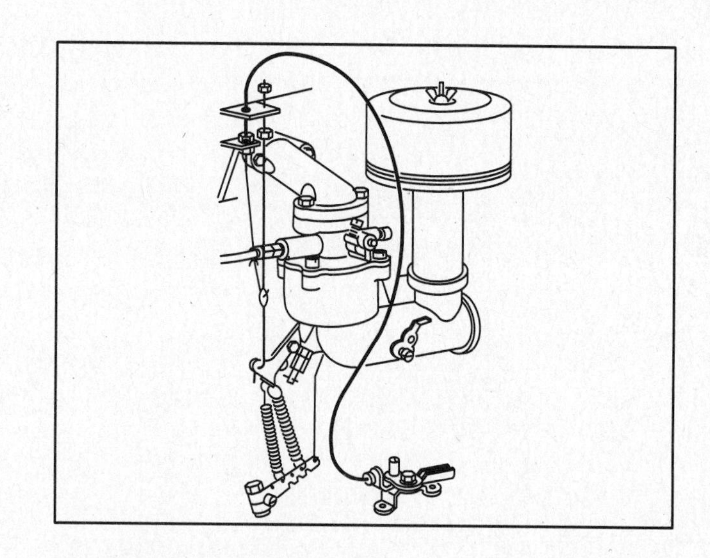

Vertical Crankshaft

NOTE: METRIC EQUIVALENTS ARE LISTED ON PAGE 26 OF THIS SECTION.

SECTION INDEX, (Cont'd.)

REMOTE CONTROLS

In general, there are three types of remote controls: remote governor control, remote throttle control, and Choke-A-Matic® control. Fig's. 1 to 6, show the operation of these control systems. See following pages for specific control assemblies and installation hook-up by engine model.

NOTE: METRIC EQUIVALENTS ARE LISTED ON PAGE 26 OF THIS SECTION.

GOVERNOR CONTROLS, CARBURETOR LINKAGE & FLYWHEEL BRAKES

REMOTE GOVERNOR CONTROL

The remote governor control regulates the engine speed by changing the governor spring tension, thus allowing the governor to control the carburetor throttle at all times and maintain any desired speed, Fig. 1.

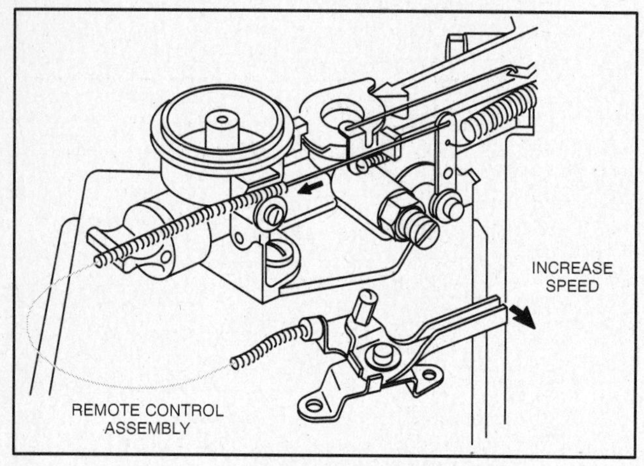

Fig. 1 - Remote Governor Control

REMOTE THROTTLE CONTROL

The remote throttle control is used on an engine having a fixed no load governed speed setting such as 3600 or 4000 RPM.

This control enables an operator to control the speed of an engine, similar to an accelerator used on an automobile. However, when full governed speed is obtained, the governor prevents overspeeding and possible damage to the engine. At any point below the governed speed, the throttle is held in a fixed position and the engine speed will vary with the load. See Fig. 2

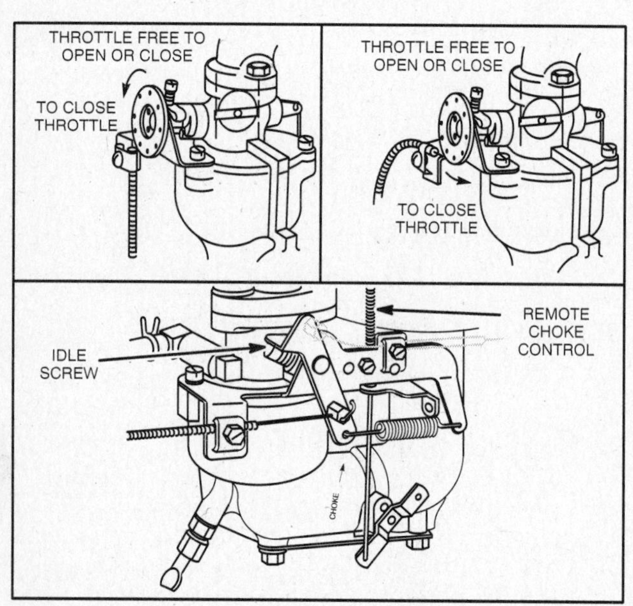

Fig. 2 - Remote Throttle Control

CHOKE-A-MATIC® REMOTE CONTROL

On Choke-A-Matic® carburetors, the remote control must be correctly adjusted in order to obtain proper operation of the choke and stop switch.

NOTE: REMOTE CONTROL SYSTEM MUST BE MOUNTED ON POWERED EQUIPMENT IN NORMAL OPERATING POSITION BEFORE ADJUSTMENTS ARE MADE.

CHOKE-A-MATIC® ADJUSTMENT (EXCEPT MODEL SERIES 120000)

Fig. 3 illustrates typical remote control installations used with Choke-A-Matic® carburetors.

1. To adjust, move remote control lever to "FAST" position. Choke actuating lever "A" should just contact choke shaft "B" or link "B" as shown in Fig. 3.

2. If not, loosen screw "C" slightly and move casing and wire "D" in or out to obtain this condition.

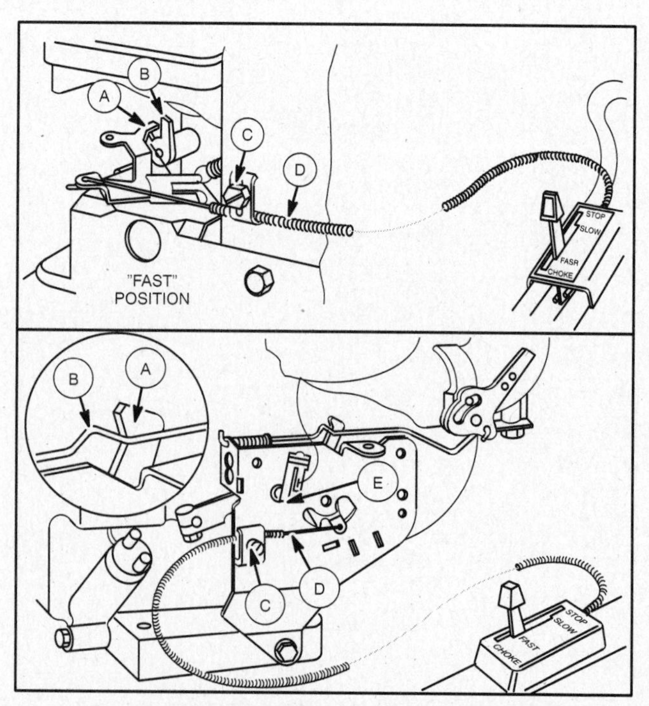

Fig. 3 - Choke-A-Matic® Control (Typical)

NOTE: METRIC EQUIVALENTS ARE LISTED ON PAGE 26 OF THIS SECTION.

3. Check operation by moving remote control lever to "START" or "CHOKE" position.
4. Choke valve should be completely closed, Fig. 4, Illus. 1.
5. Then move remote control lever to "STOP" position. Control must contact stop switch blade, Fig. 4, Illus. 2 or "E," Fig. 3.

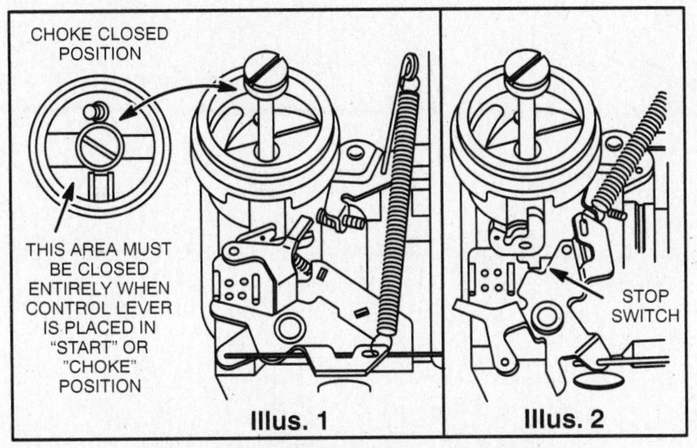

Fig. 4 - Choke and Stop Position

Choke-A-Matic®, Model Series 120000

1. Move control lever until a 1/8" dia. rod can be inserted through control plate and control lever, Fig. 5.
2. Place equipment control in "RUN" position and install casing and wire on control lever and control bracket, Fig. 5.

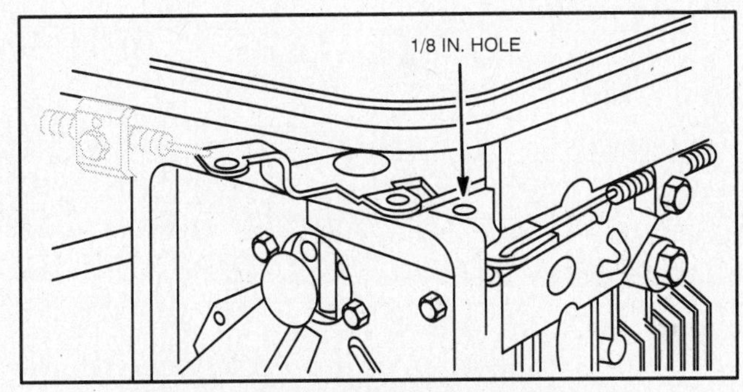

Fig. 5 - Choke-A-Matic® Adjustment, Model Series 120000

Travel of remote control wire must be a minimum of 1-3/8" in order to achieve full "CHOKE" and "STOP" position, Fig. 6.

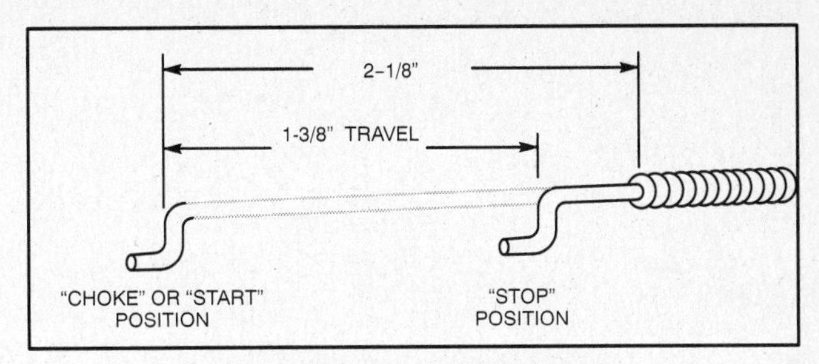

Fig. 6 - Control Wire Travel

4

CHOKE-A-MATIC® DIAL CONTROL ADJUSTMENTS

Dial controls seldom require adjustment unless blower housing has been removed.

1. To Adjust: Place dial control knob in "START" position.
2. Loosen control wire screw "A" - move lever "C" to full choke position. Allow a 1/8" gap between lever and bracket as shown, Fig. 7.
3. While holding lever, tighten screw "A."

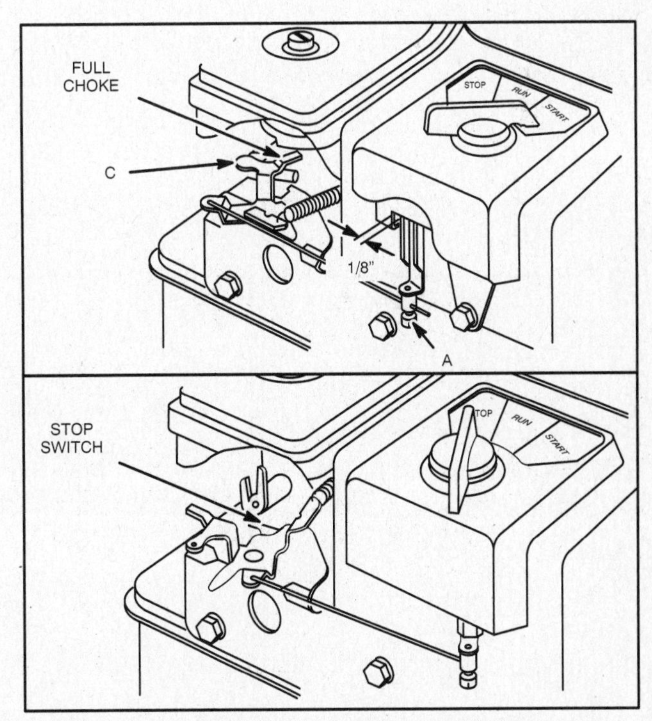

Fig. 7 - Choke-A-Matic® Dial Control Adjustments

NOTE: METRIC EQUIVALENTS ARE LISTED ON PAGE 26 OF THIS SECTION.

GOVERNOR CONTROLS, CARBURETOR LINKAGE & FLYWHEEL BRAKES

The following drawings of governor controls (Figs. 9 through 49 and 61 through 136) are to show how governor links and springs are to be installed on carburetors. For governor control adjustments, see Section 5, GOVERNORS.

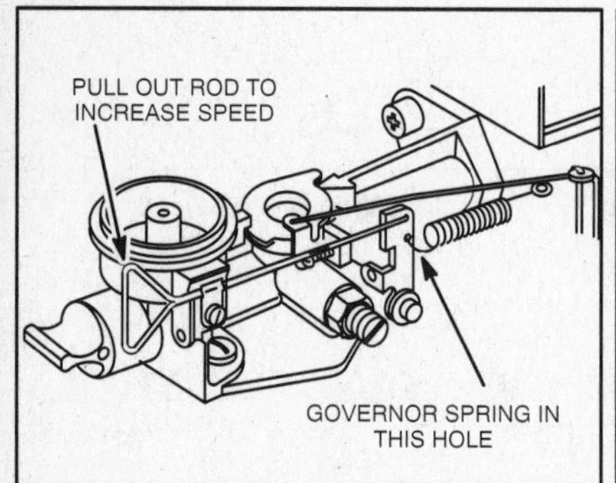

Fig. 8

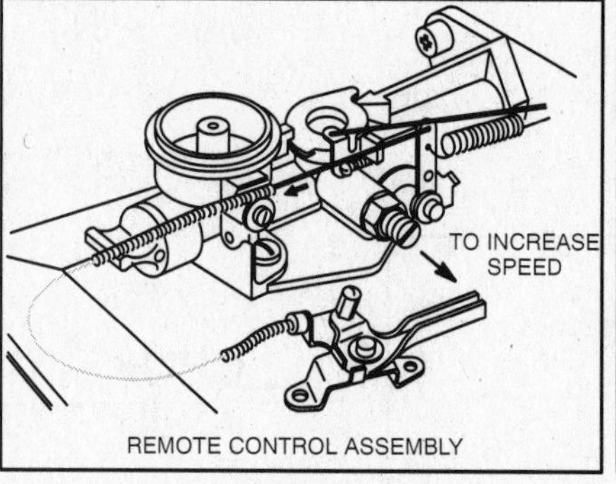

Fig. 9

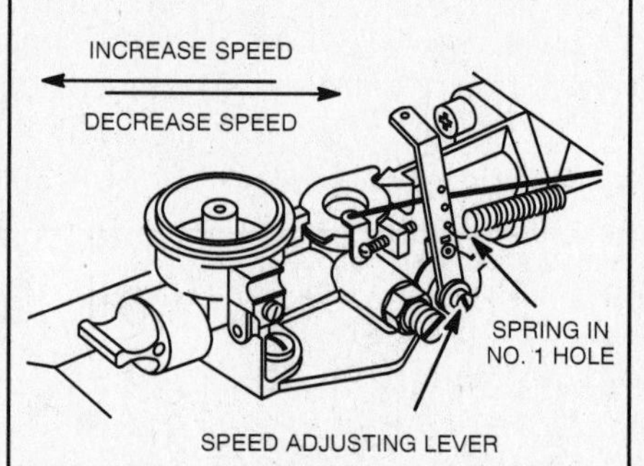

Fig. 10

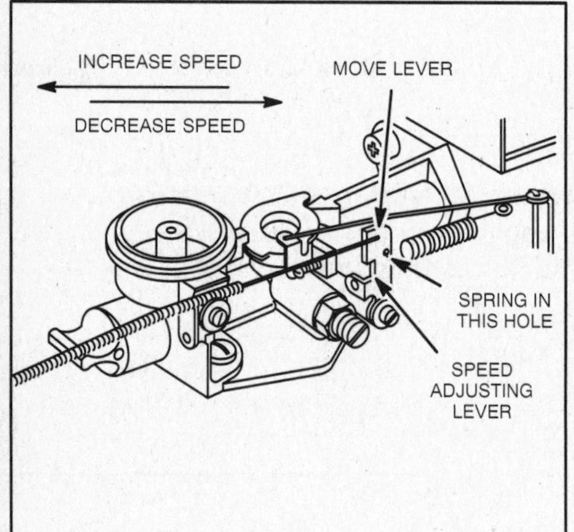

Fig. 11

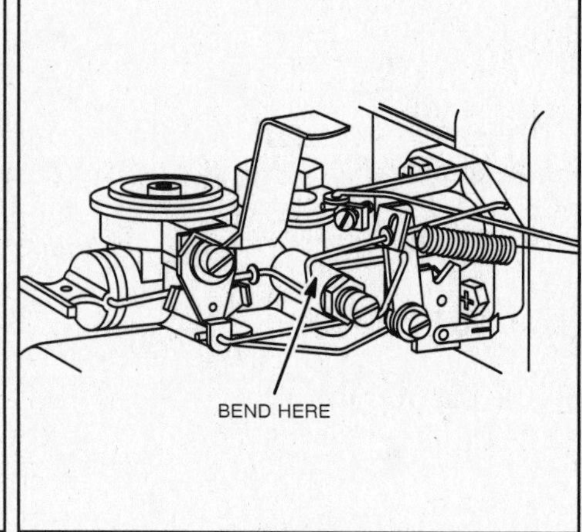

Fig. 12

Place lever in choke detent. If choke is not fully closed, bend link where show to attain full choke.

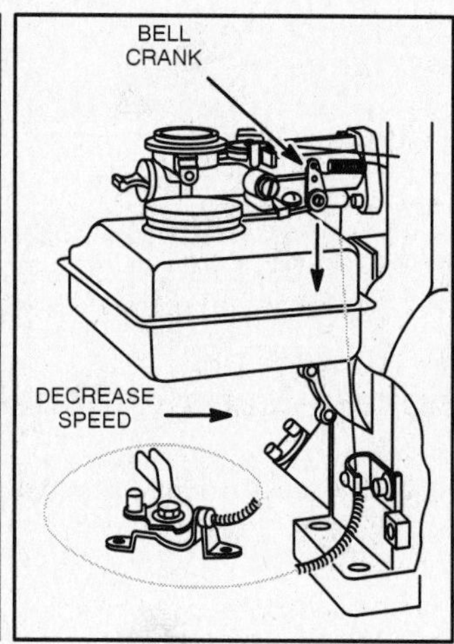

Fig. 13

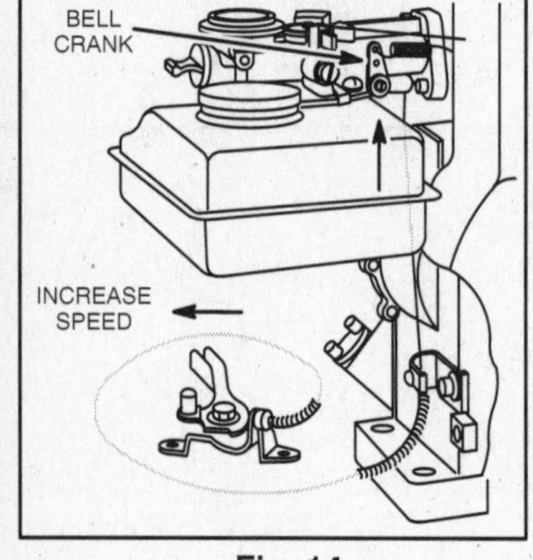

Fig. 14

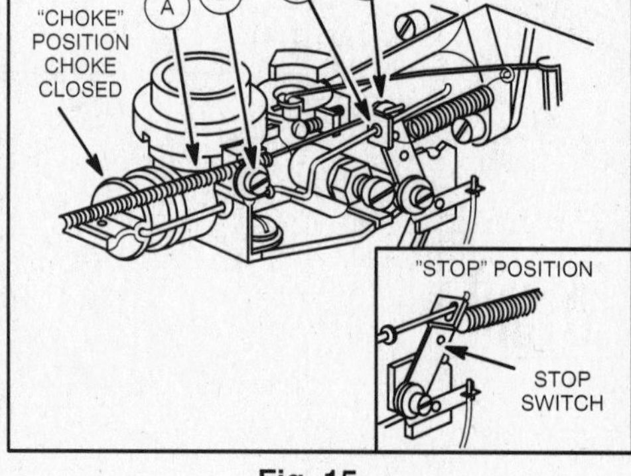

Fig. 15

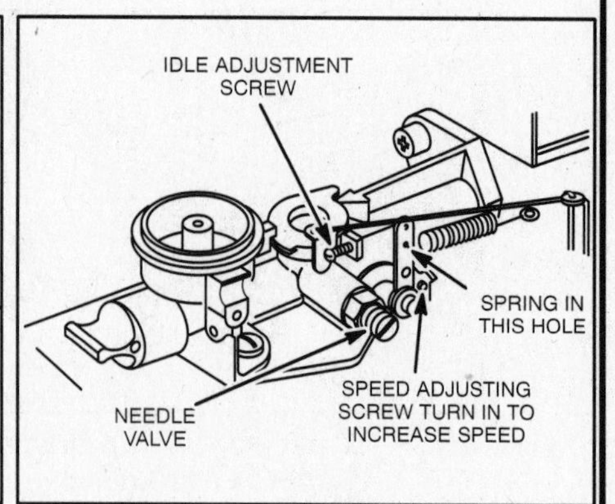

Fig. 16

Model 60100, 61100, 80100, 81100 Horizontal Crankshaft

NOTE: METRIC EQUIVALENTS ARE LISTED ON PAGE 26 OF THIS SECTION.

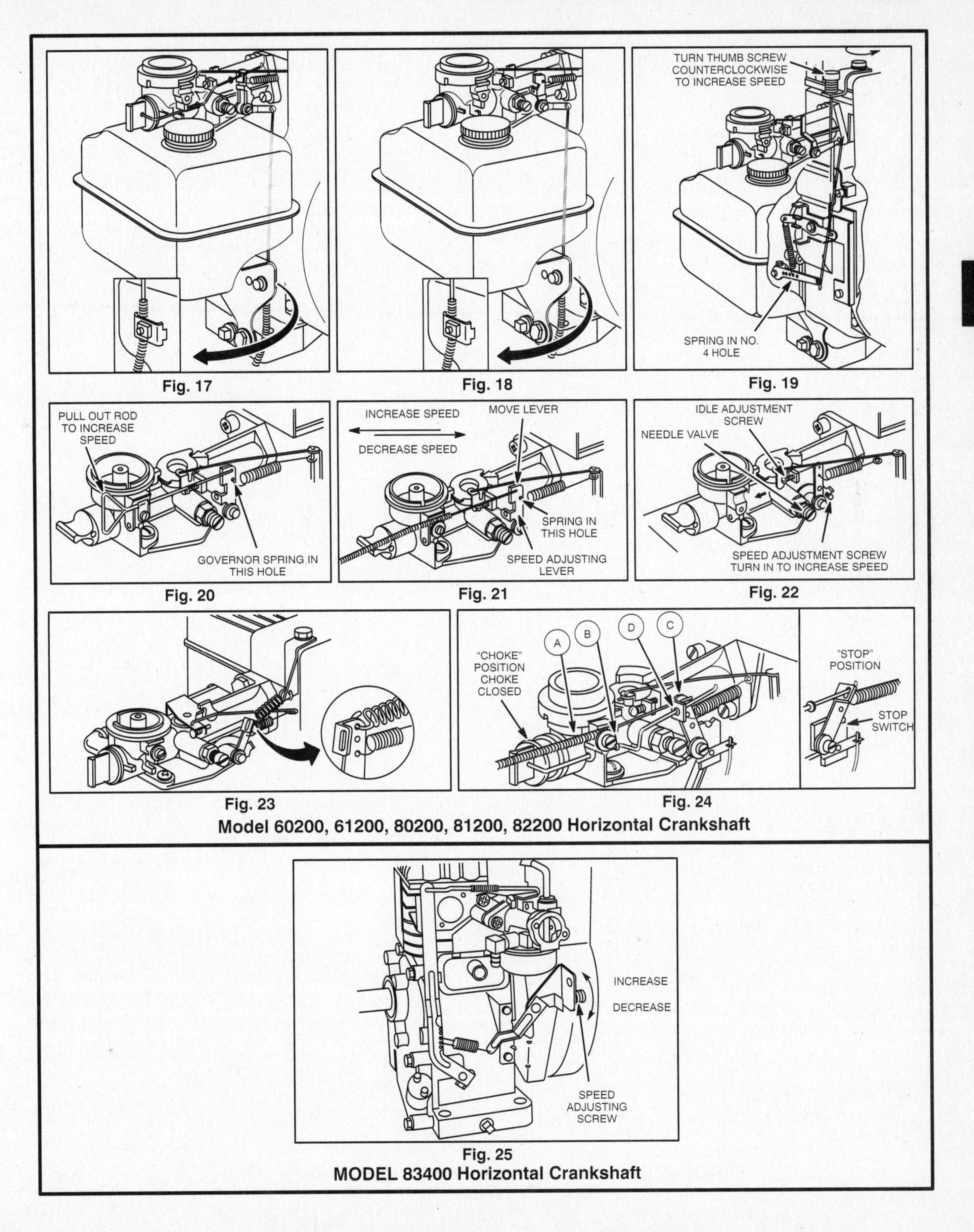

Fig. 17

Fig. 18

Fig. 19

Fig. 20

Fig. 21

Fig. 22

Fig. 23

Fig. 24

Model 60200, 61200, 80200, 81200, 82200 Horizontal Crankshaft

Fig. 25

MODEL 83400 Horizontal Crankshaft

NOTE: METRIC EQUIVALENTS ARE LISTED ON PAGE 26 OF THIS SECTION.

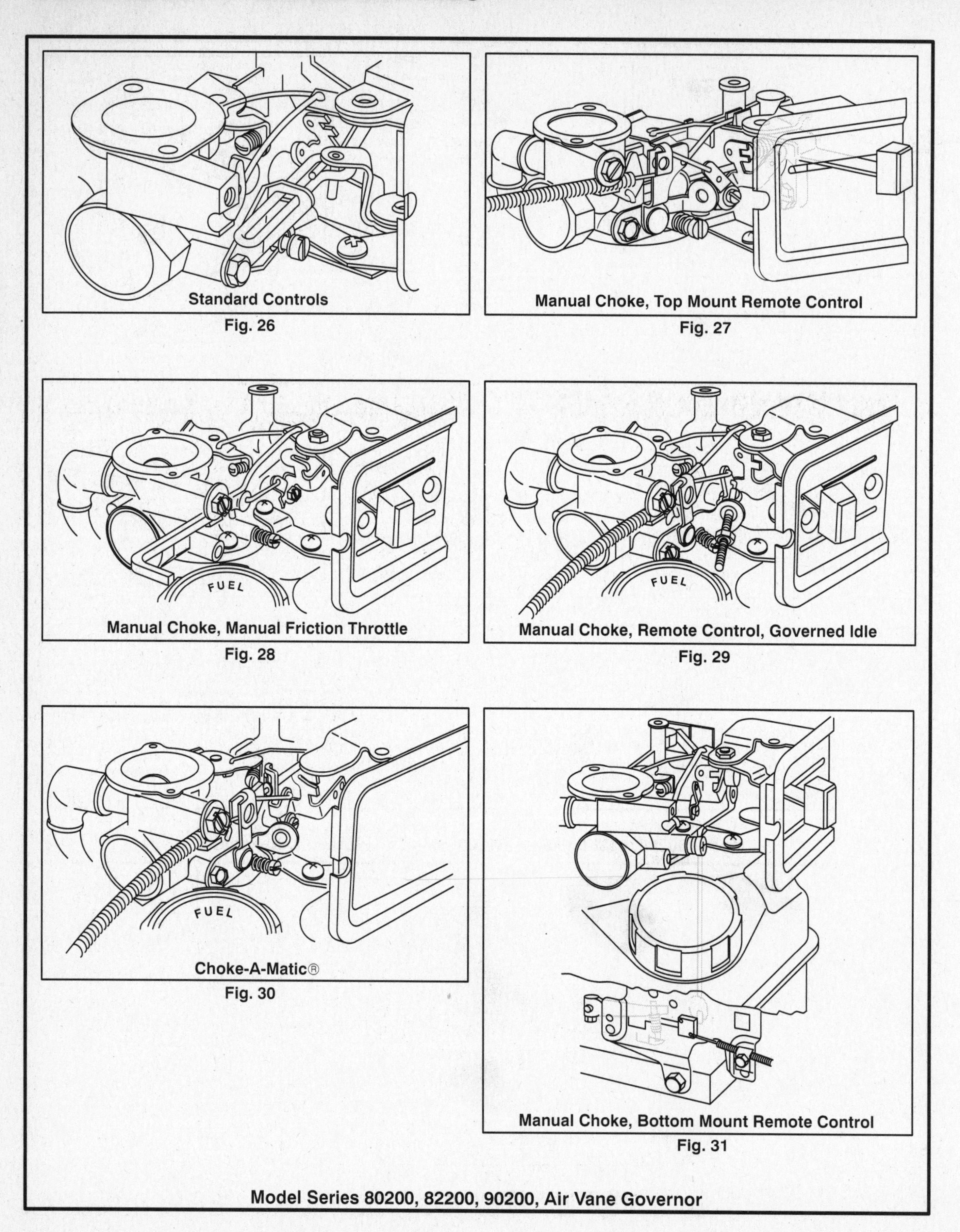

Standard Controls
Fig. 26

Manual Choke, Top Mount Remote Control
Fig. 27

Manual Choke, Manual Friction Throttle
Fig. 28

Manual Choke, Remote Control, Governed Idle
Fig. 29

Choke-A-Matic®
Fig. 30

Manual Choke, Bottom Mount Remote Control
Fig. 31

Model Series 80200, 82200, 90200, Air Vane Governor

NOTE: METRIC EQUIVALENTS ARE LISTED ON PAGE 26 OF THIS SECTION.

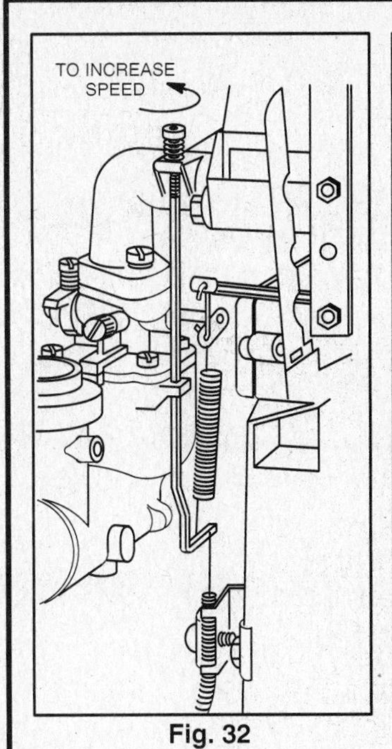

Fig. 32

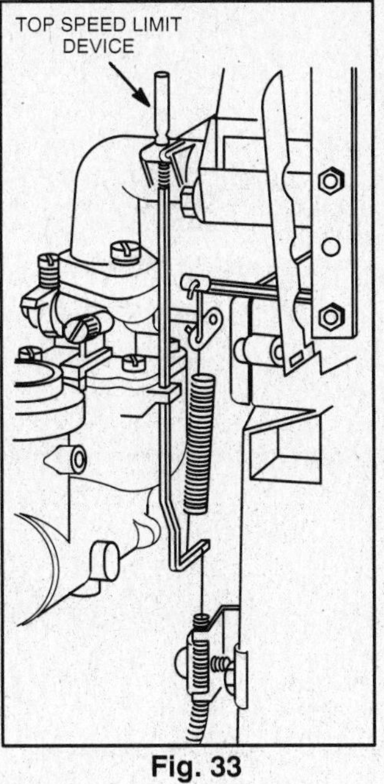

Fig. 33

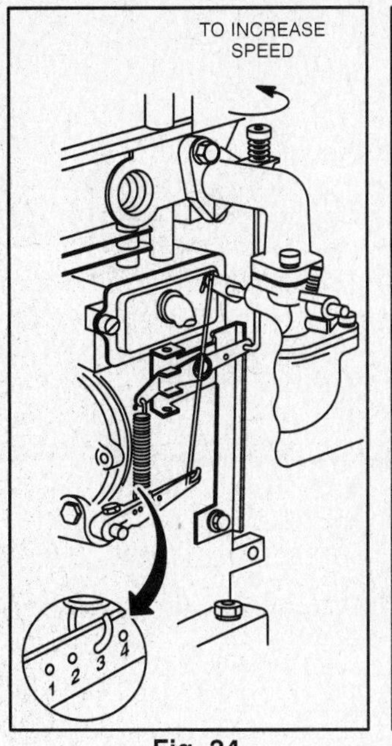

Fig. 34

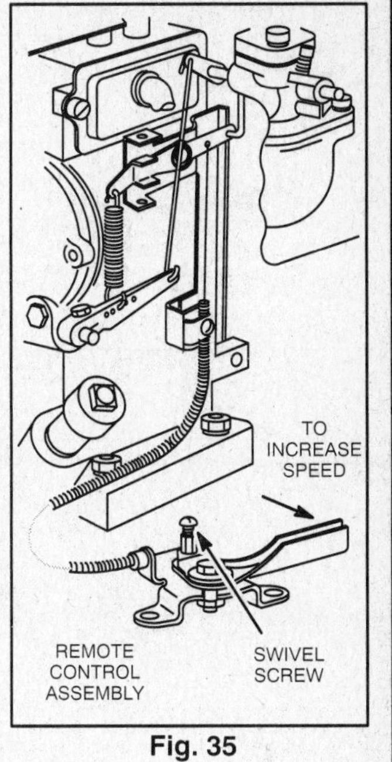

Fig. 35

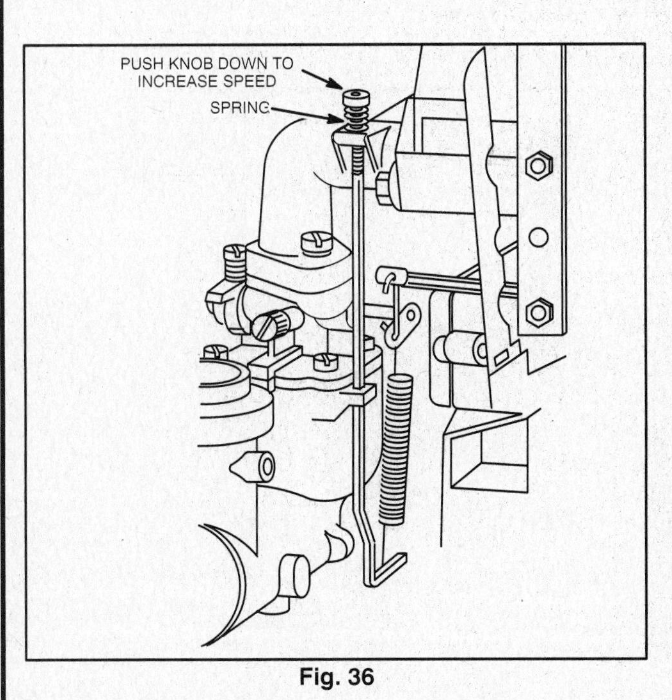

Fig. 36

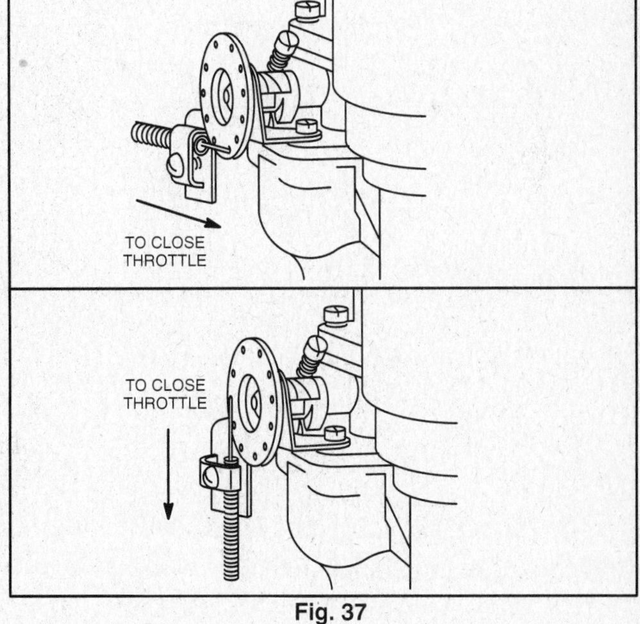

Fig. 37

Models 60300, 60400, 61300, 80300, 80400, 81400 Horizontal Crankshaft

NOTE: METRIC EQUIVALENTS ARE LISTED ON PAGE 26 OF THIS SECTION.

GOVERNOR CONTROLS, CARBURETOR LINKAGE & FLYWHEEL BRAKES

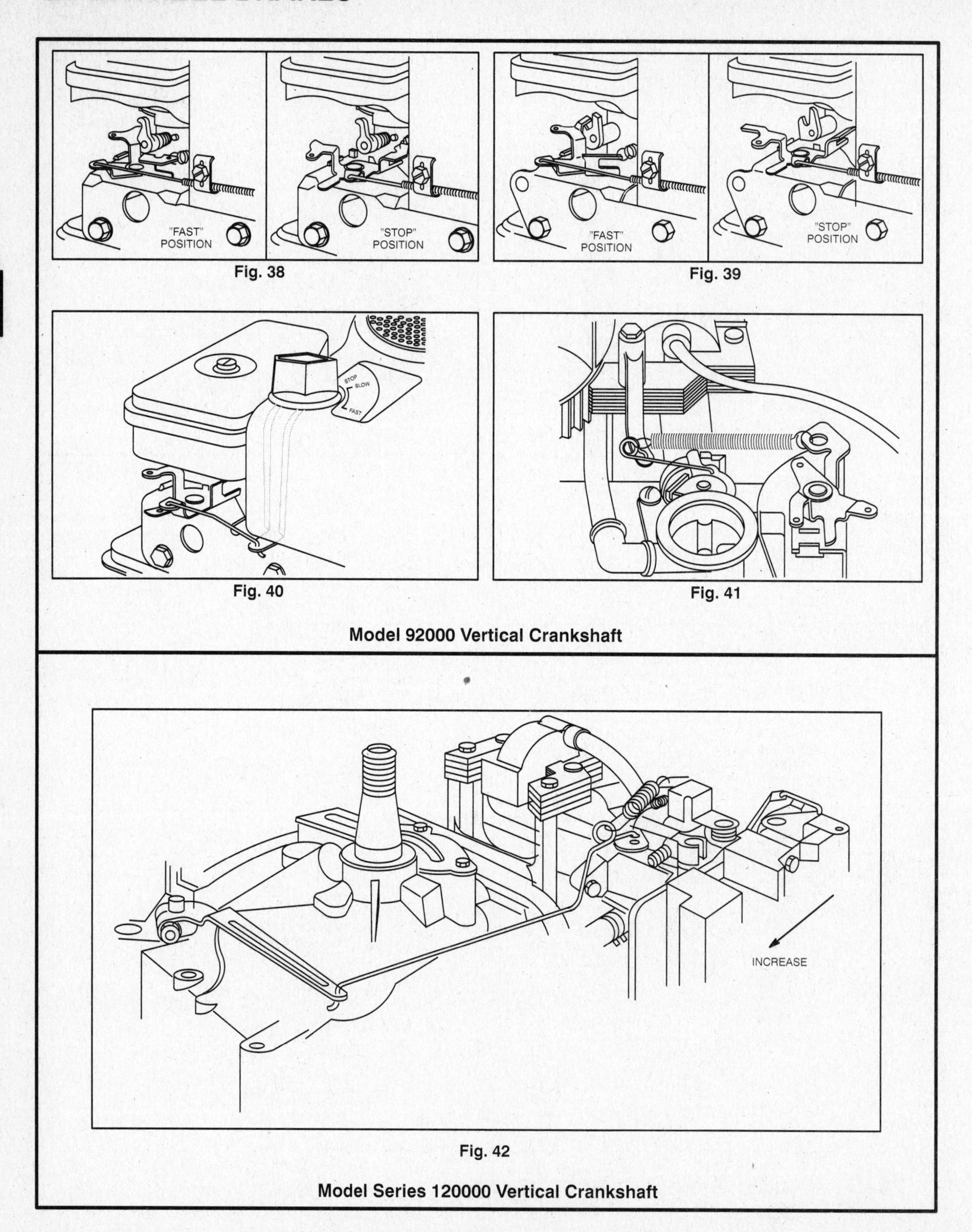

Fig. 38

Fig. 39

Fig. 40

Fig. 41

Model 92000 Vertical Crankshaft

Fig. 42

Model Series 120000 Vertical Crankshaft

NOTE: METRIC EQUIVALENTS ARE LISTED ON PAGE 26 OF THIS SECTION.

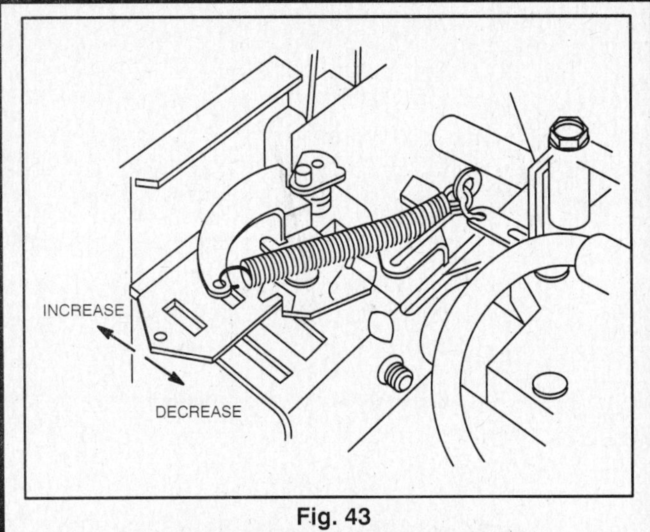

Fig. 43
**Models 90700, 110700, 112700
Vertical Crankshaft**

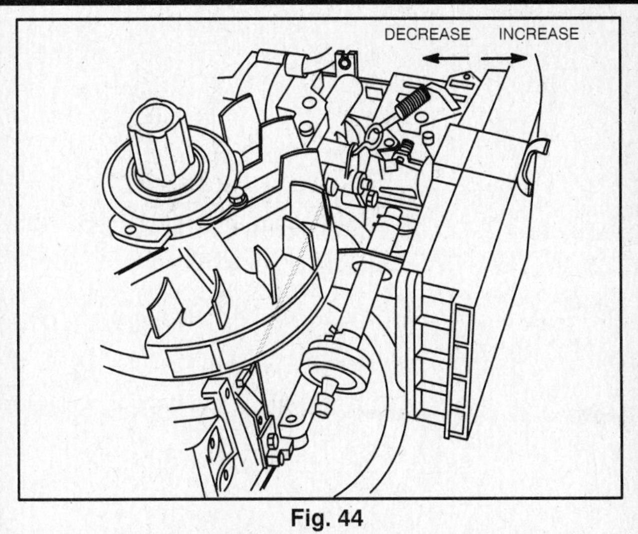

Fig. 44
**Models 91700, 111700, 114700
Vertical Crankshaft**

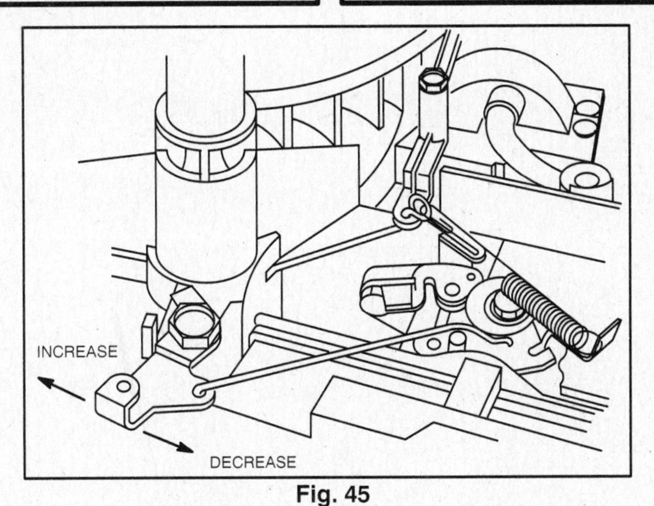

Fig. 45
Model 100700 Vertical Crankshaft

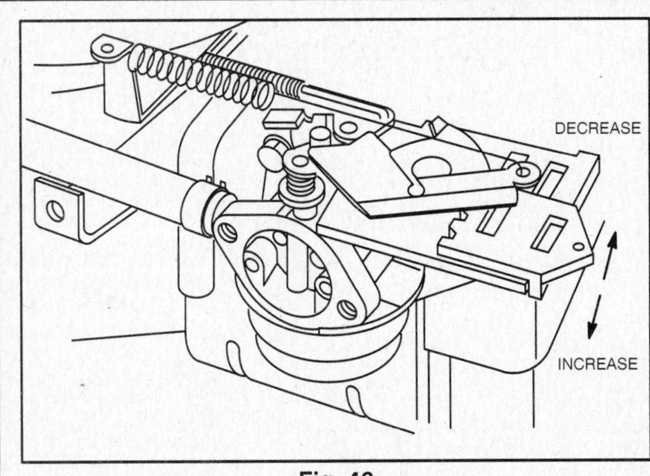

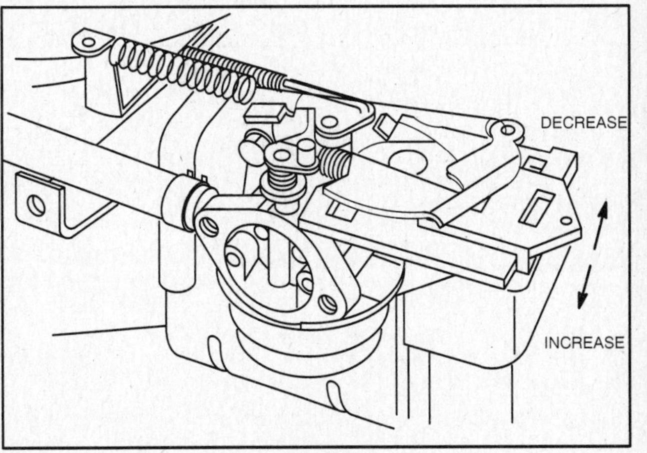

Fig. 46

Fig. 47

Model 130700, 131700, 132700 Vertical Crankshaft

NOTE: METRIC EQUIVALENTS ARE LISTED ON PAGE 26 OF THIS SECTION.

GOVERNOR CONTROLS, CARBURETOR LINKAGE & FLYWHEEL BRAKES

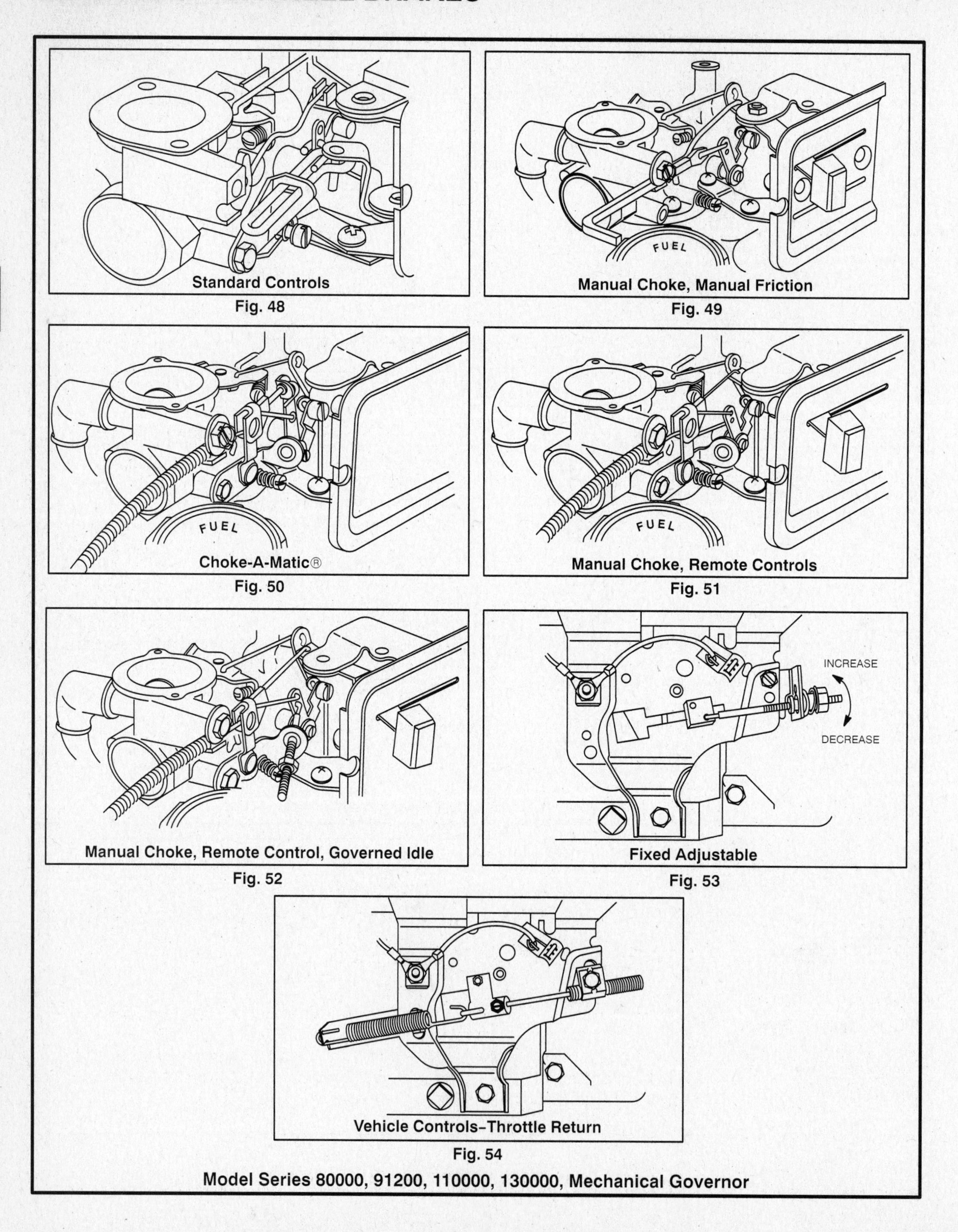

Standard Controls
Fig. 48

Manual Choke, Manual Friction
Fig. 49

Choke-A-Matic®
Fig. 50

Manual Choke, Remote Controls
Fig. 51

Manual Choke, Remote Control, Governed Idle
Fig. 52

Fixed Adjustable
Fig. 53

Vehicle Controls–Throttle Return
Fig. 54

Model Series 80000, 91200, 110000, 130000, Mechanical Governor

NOTE: METRIC EQUIVALENTS ARE LISTED ON PAGE 26 OF THIS SECTION.

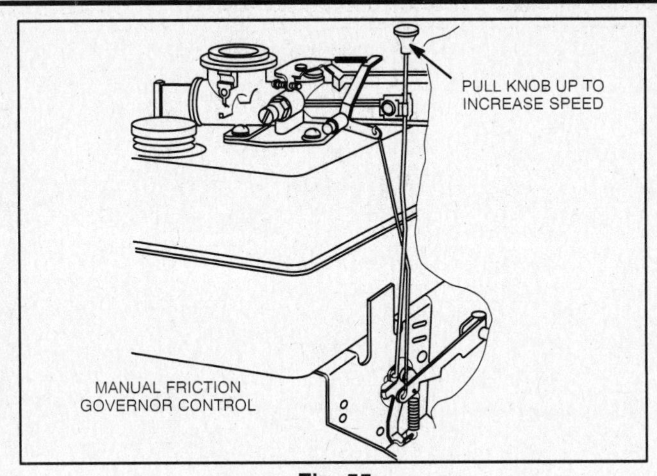

Fig. 55

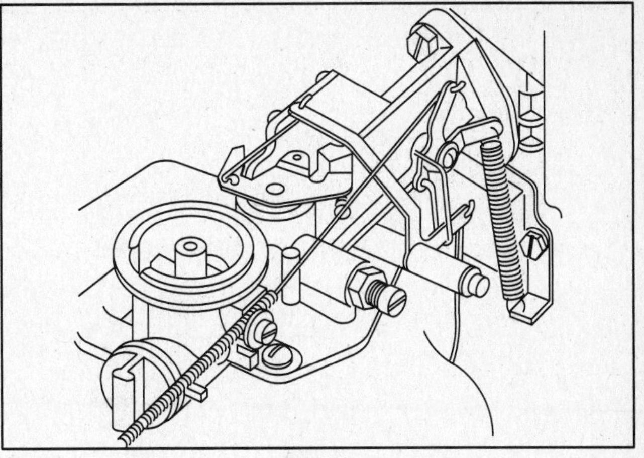

Fig. 56

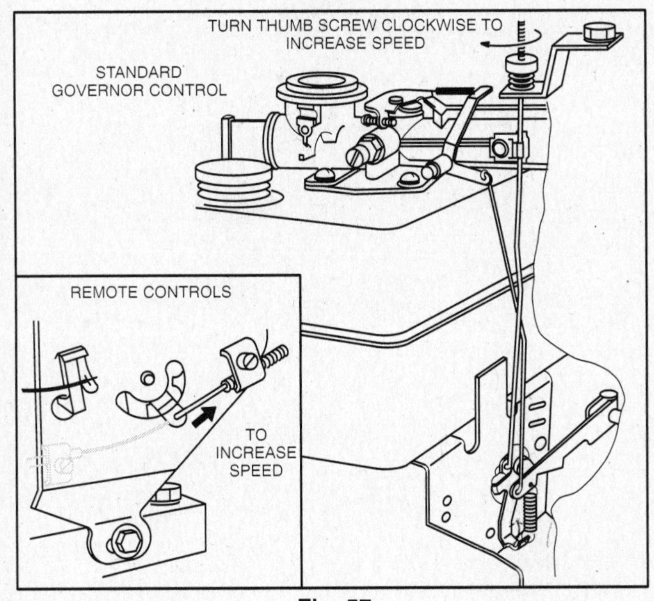

Fig. 57

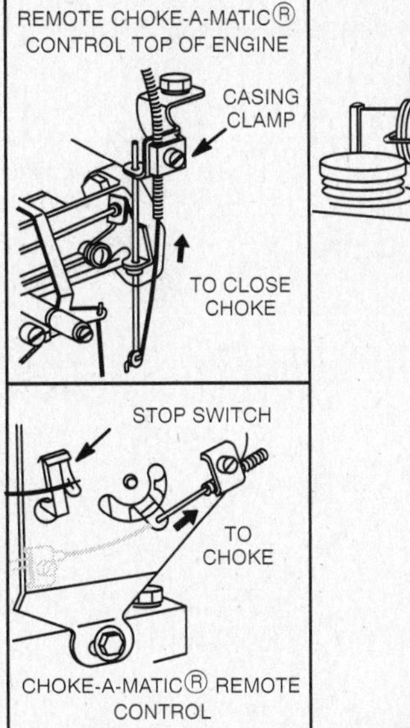

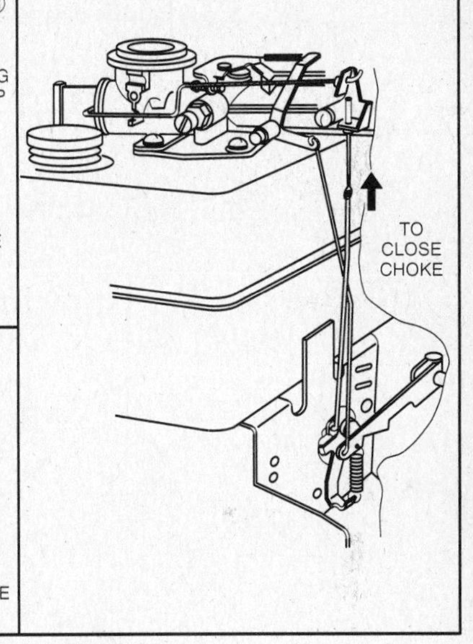

Fig. 58

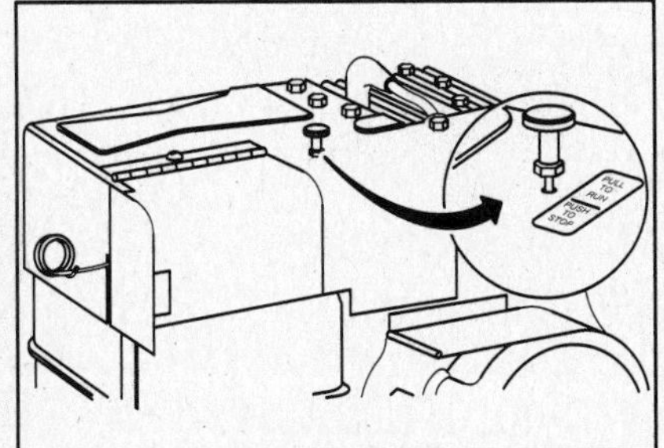

Fig. 59

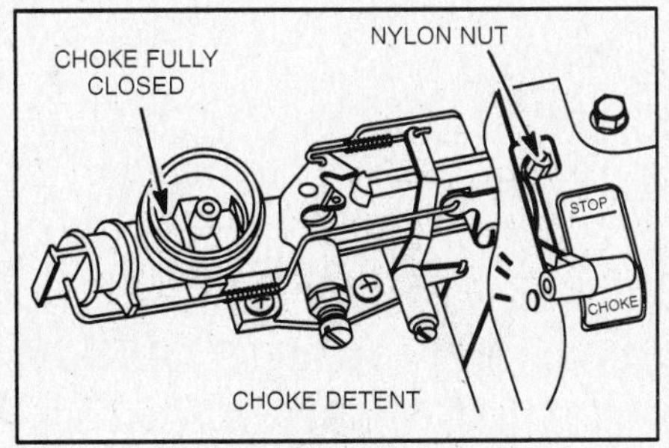

Fig. 60

Place lever in choke detent. If choke is not fully closed, adjust nylon nut (with socket wrench) until choke just closes.

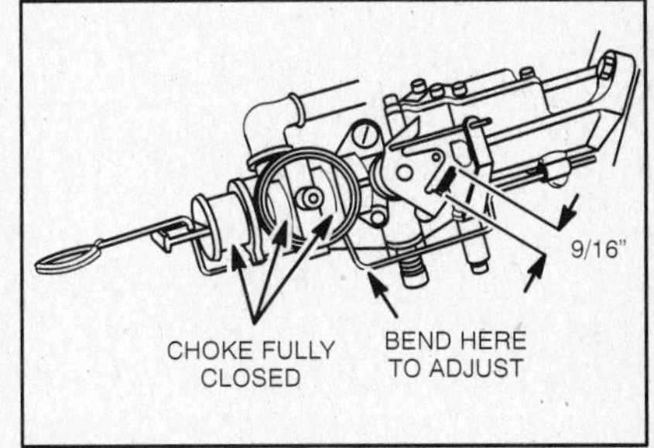

Fig. 61

Pull lever to choke position. The distance between throttle stamping and throttle screw stop must be 9/16". To adjust, bend lever where shown.

Models 100200, 130200 Horizontal Crankshaft

NOTE: METRIC EQUIVALENTS ARE LISTED ON PAGE 26 OF THIS SECTION.

GOVERNOR CONTROLS, CARBURETOR LINKAGE & FLYWHEEL BRAKES

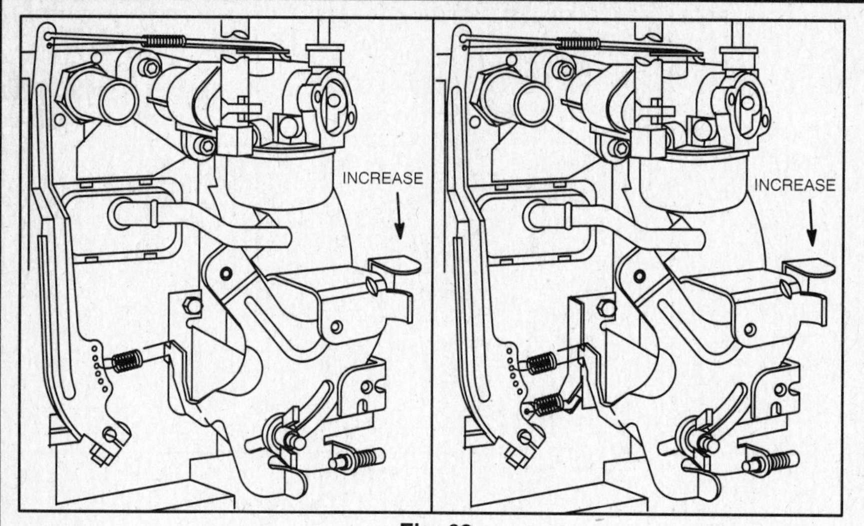

Fig. 62

Model 93400 Horizontal Crankshaft

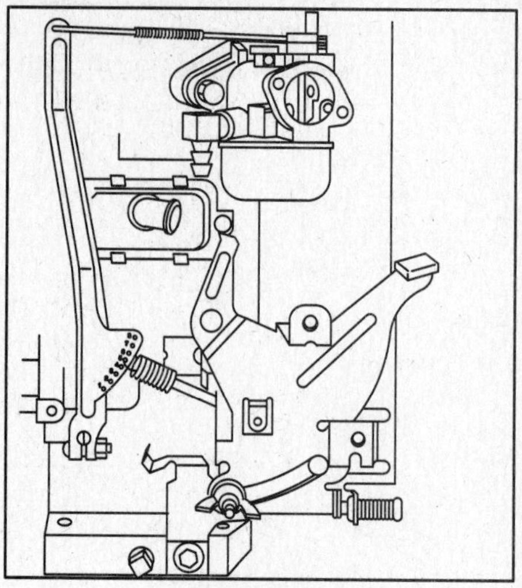

Fig. 63

Model 133400 Horizontal Crankshaft

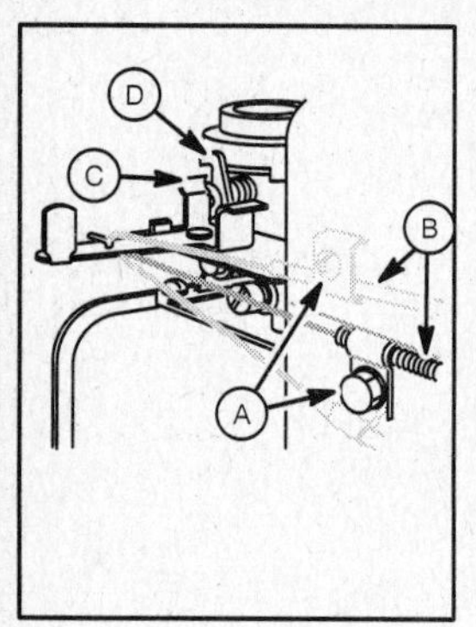

Fig. 64

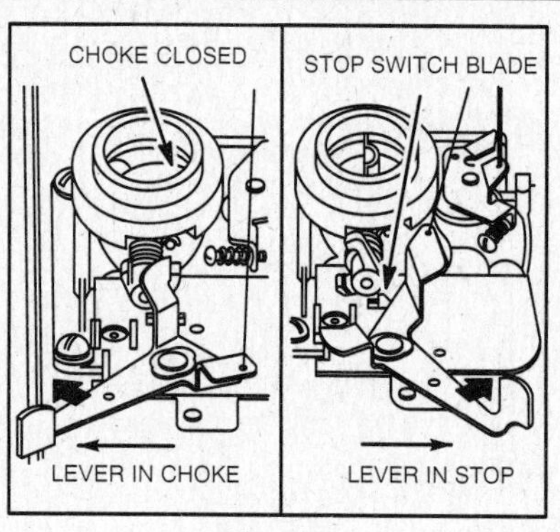

Fig. 65

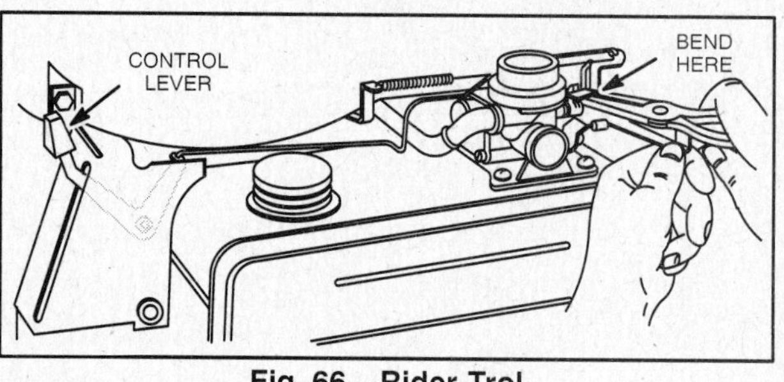

Fig. 66 – Rider-Trol

Place control in choke detent; if choke does not fully close, bend as shown until choke is closed.

Models 100900, 130900 Vertical Crankshaft

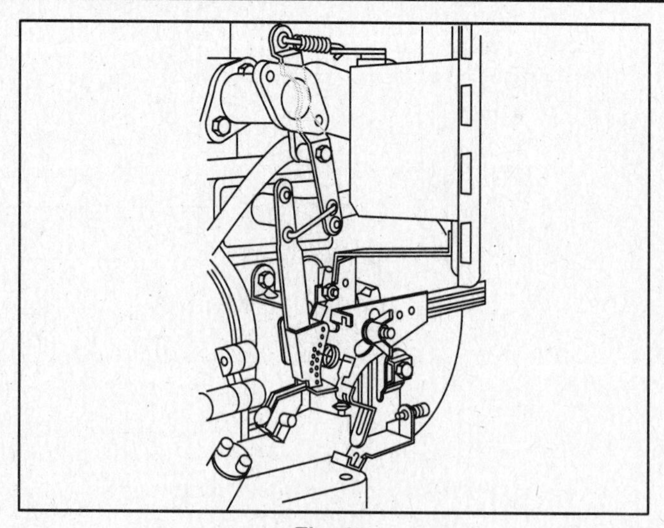

Fig. 67

Models 176400, 19B400, 19E400, 19F400, 19G400, 192400, 196400, 197400 Horizontal Crankshaft

NOTE: METRIC EQUIVALENTS ARE LISTED ON PAGE 26 OF THIS SECTION.

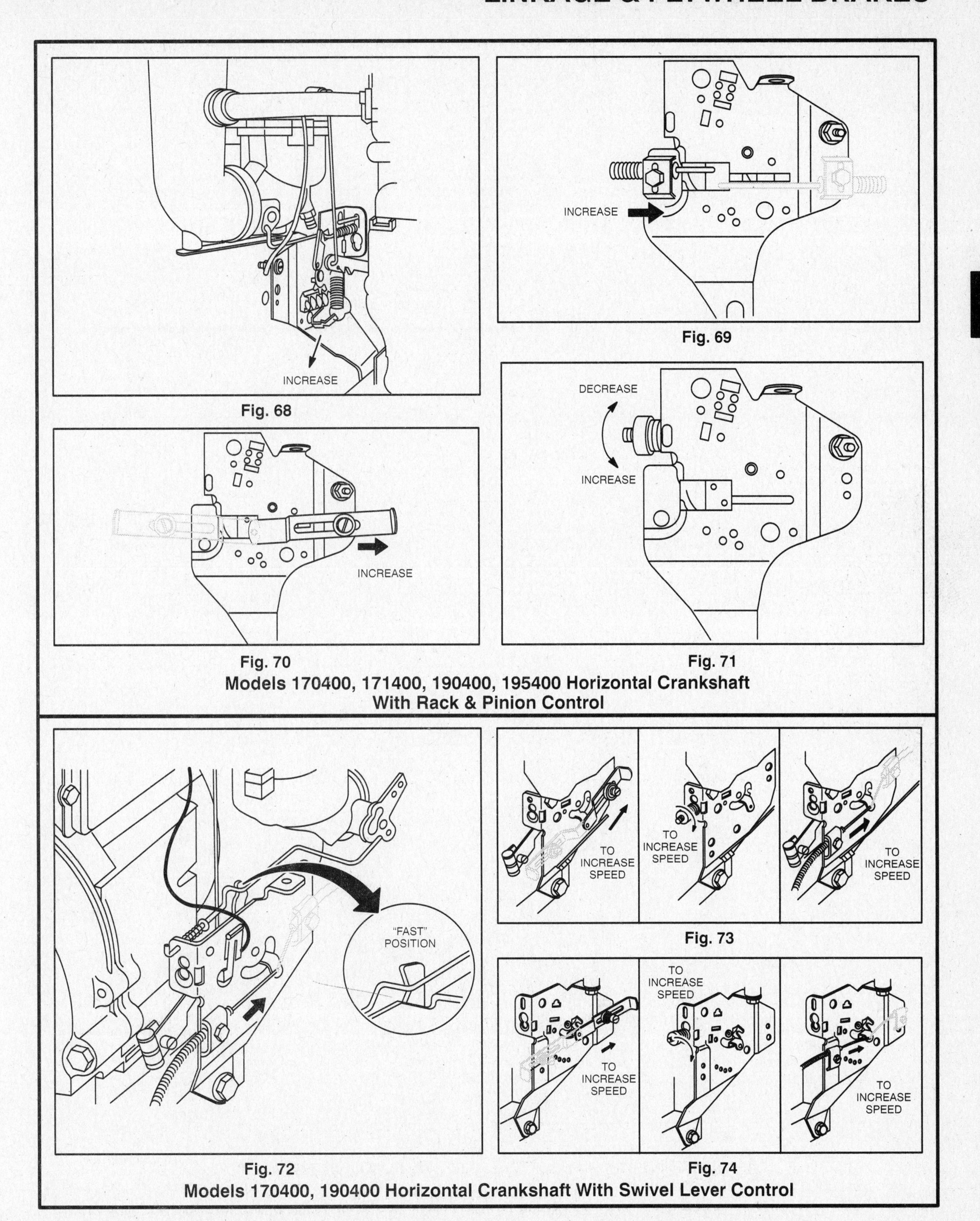

Fig. 68

Fig. 69

Fig. 70

Fig. 71

Models 170400, 171400, 190400, 195400 Horizontal Crankshaft With Rack & Pinion Control

Fig. 72

Fig. 73

Fig. 74

Models 170400, 190400 Horizontal Crankshaft With Swivel Lever Control

NOTE: METRIC EQUIVALENTS ARE LISTED ON PAGE 26 OF THIS SECTION.

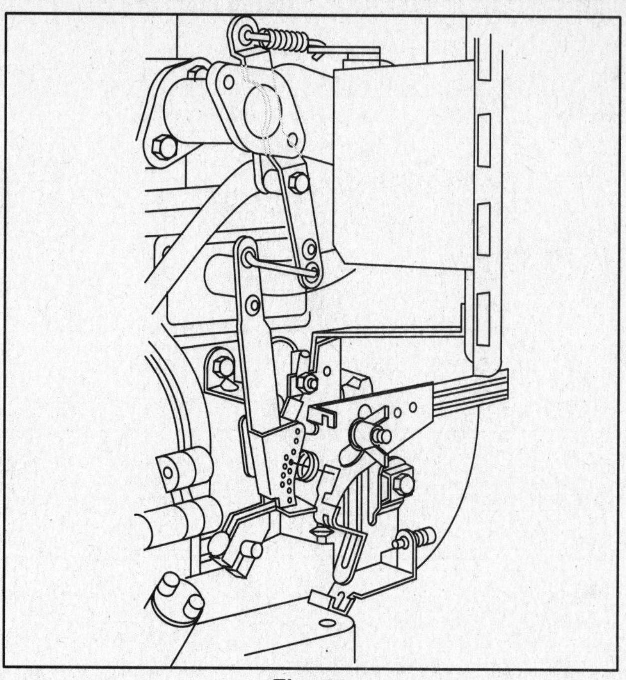

Fig. 75

Models 226400, 250400, 256400 Horizontal Crankshaft Control

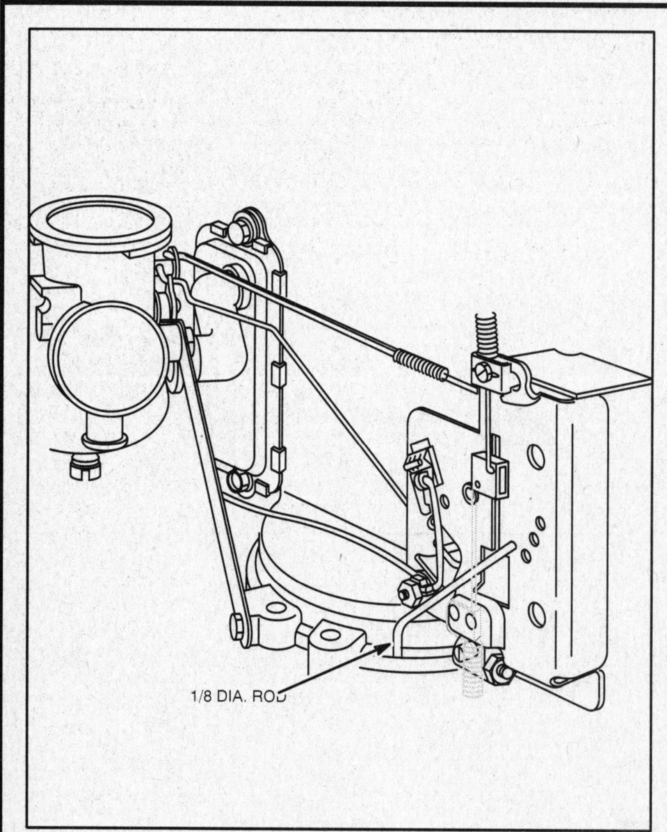

Fig. 76

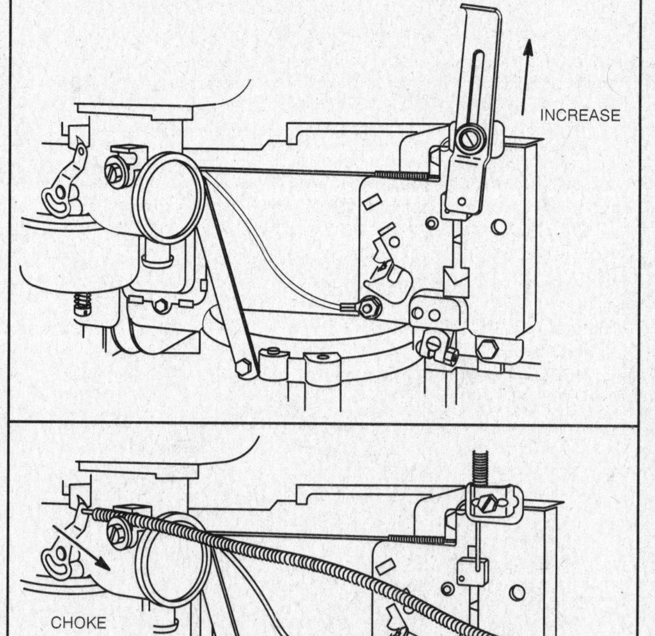

Fig. 77

Models 170700, 190700, 191700, 192700, 193700, 220700, 252700, 253700, 280000 Vertical Crankshaft with Rack & Pinion Control Except Model 286700

NOTE: METRIC EQUIVALENTS ARE LISTED ON PAGE 26 OF THIS SECTION.

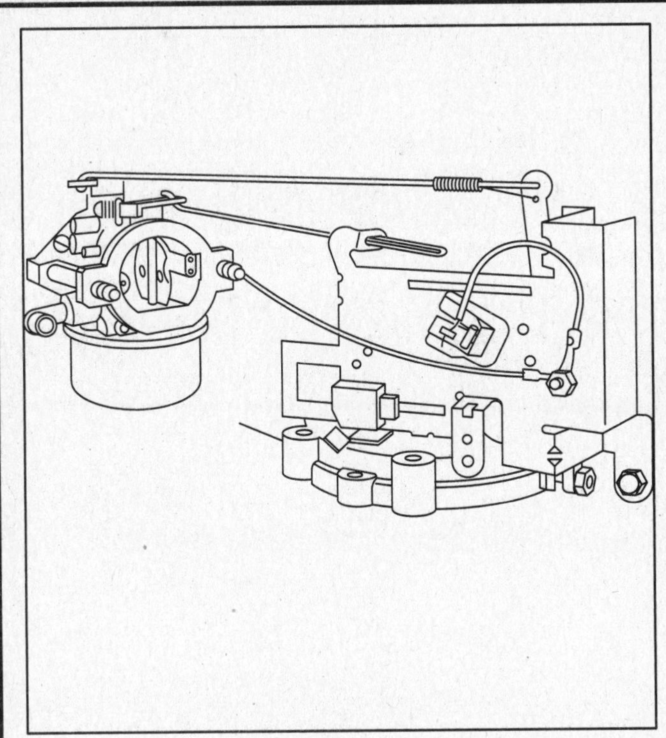

Fig. 78

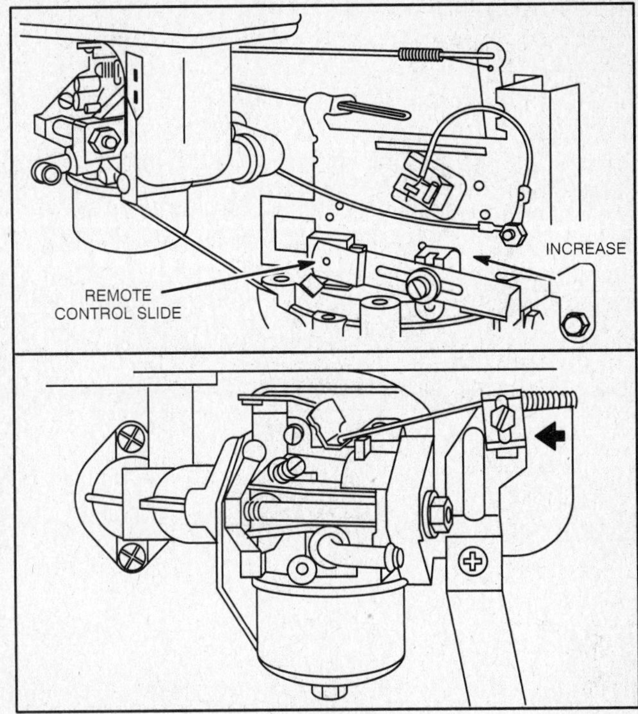

Fig. 79

Models 194700, 195700, 254700, 257700, 283700, 286700
Vertical Crankshaft With Horizontal Control Rack & Pinion Control

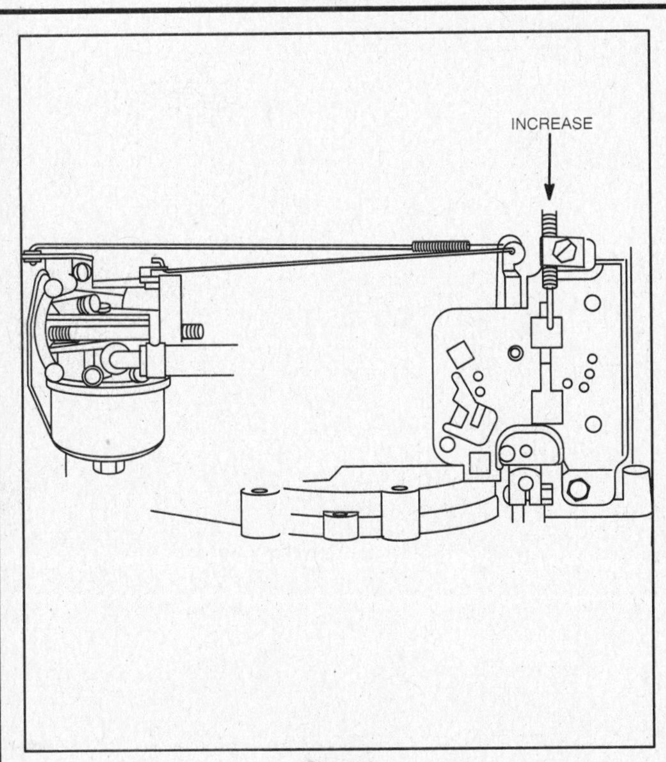

Fig. 80

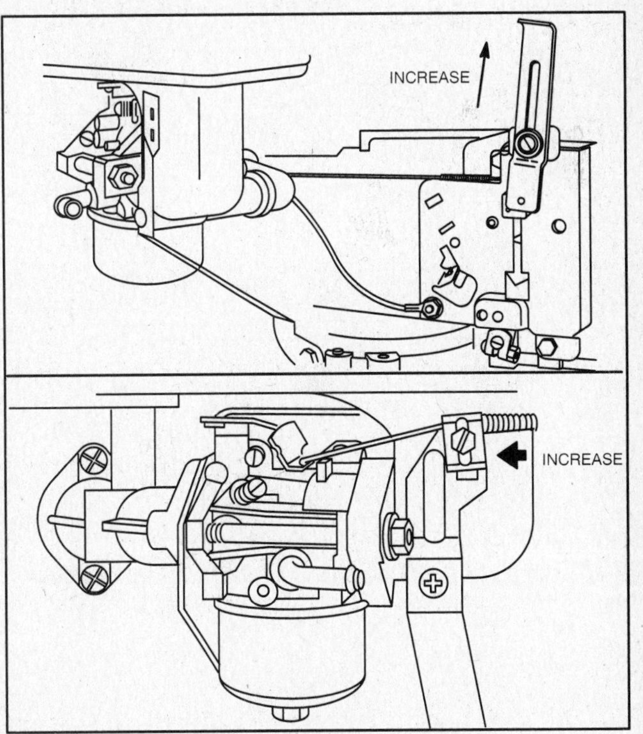

Fig. 81

Models 194700, 195700, 196700, 254700, 257700, 283700, 286700
Vertical Crankshaft With Vertical Rack & Pinion Control

NOTE: METRIC EQUIVALENTS ARE LISTED ON PAGE 26 OF THIS SECTION.

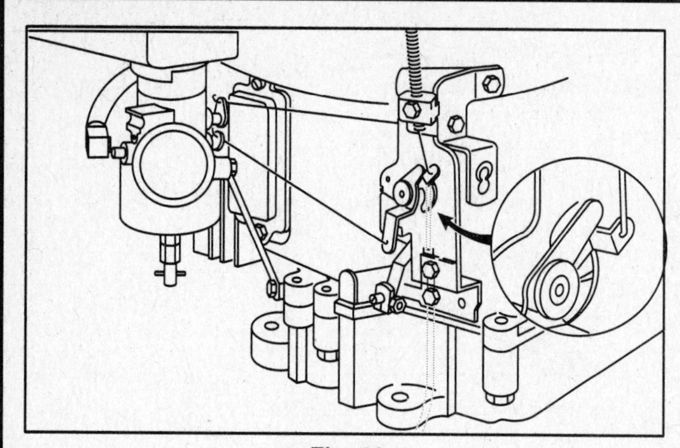

Fig. 82

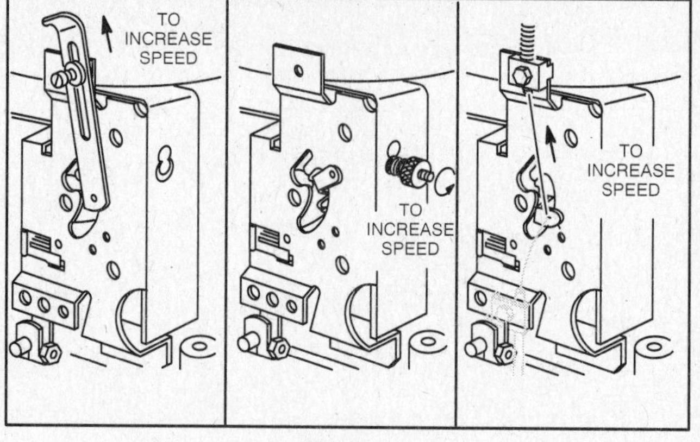

Fig. 83

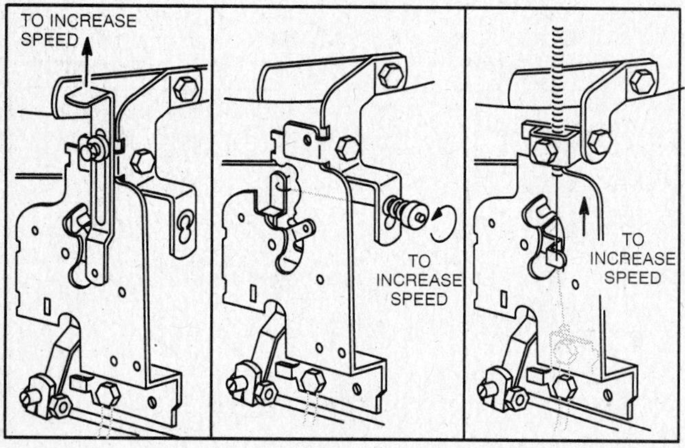

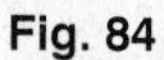

Fig. 84

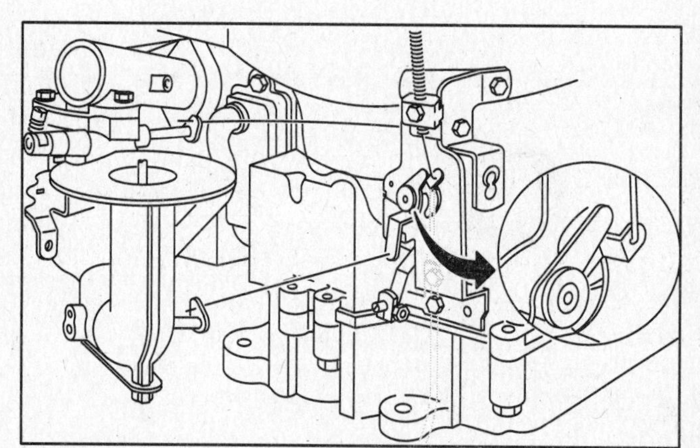

Fig. 85

Models 170700, 171700, 190700, 191700 Vertical Crankshaft with Swivel Lever Control

NOTE: METRIC EQUIVALENTS ARE LISTED ON PAGE 26 OF THIS SECTION.

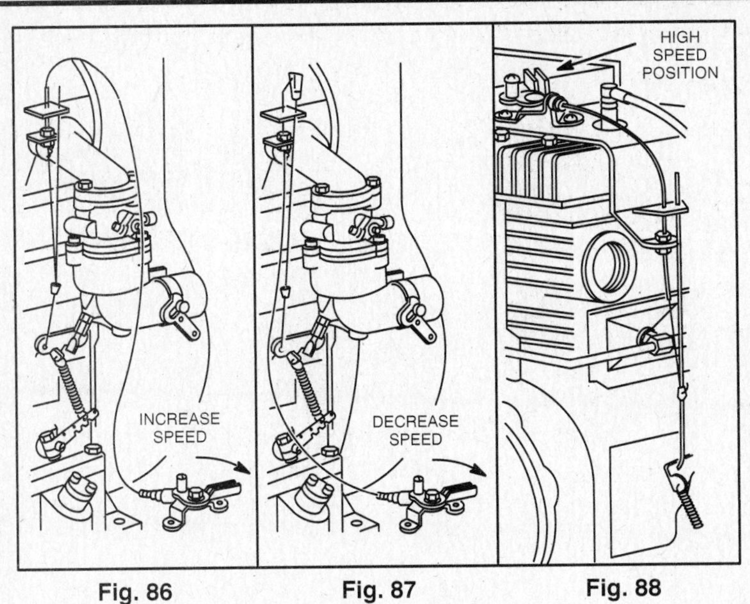

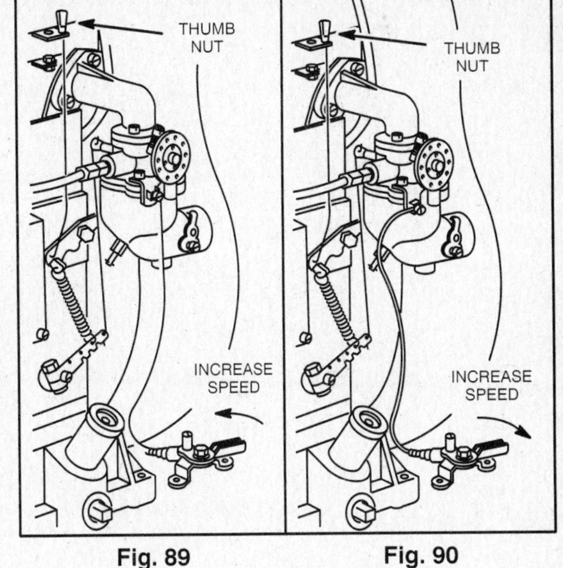

Fig. 86 Fig. 87 Fig. 88 Fig. 89 Fig. 90

REMOTE GOVERNOR CONTROL

Attach remote control casing and wire as shown in Figs. 86 or 87. Do not change the position of the small elastic stop nuts. They provide for a governed idle speed and protection against overspeeding.

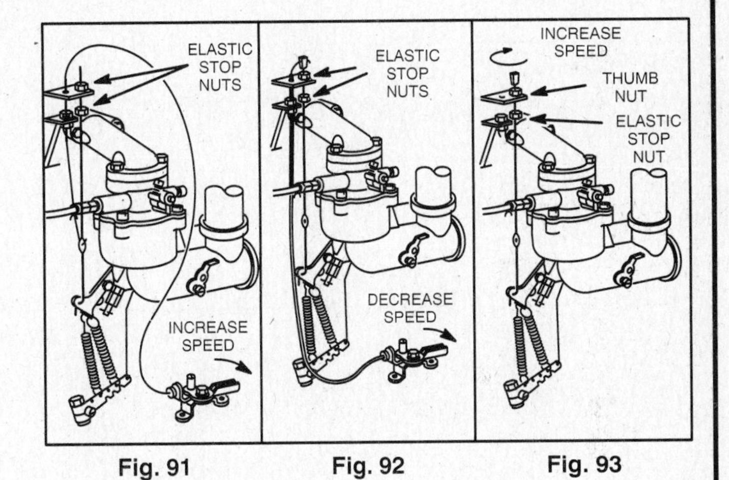

Fig. 91 Fig. 92 Fig. 93

THUMB NUT ADJUSTMENT

Remove thumb nut and upper elastic stop nut. Replace thumb nut and adjust to desired operating speed. See Fig. 88. Do not change the position of the lower elastic stop nut. It provides protection against overspeeding.

GOVERNED IDLE

All engines in Model Series 243400, 300400, 320400 and some Model Series 23D and 233400 engines use two governor springs as shown in Figs. 89 and 90. The shorter spring keeps the engine on governor, even at idle speed. If moderate loads are applied at idle, the engine will not stall.

TO INCREASE SPEED

TO INCREASE SPEED

Fig. 94

MODELS 230000 , 240000, 300000, 320000 Horizontal CRANKSHAFT

NOTE: METRIC EQUIVALENTS ARE LISTED ON PAGE 26 OF THIS SECTION.

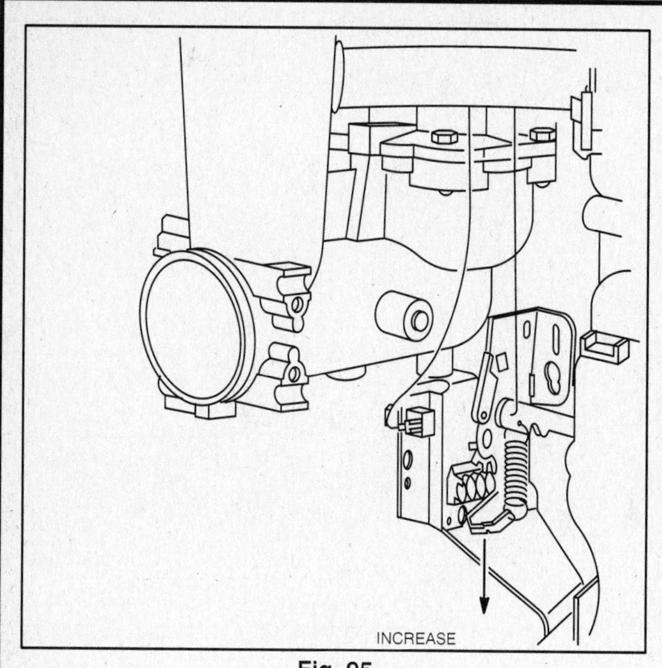

Fig. 95

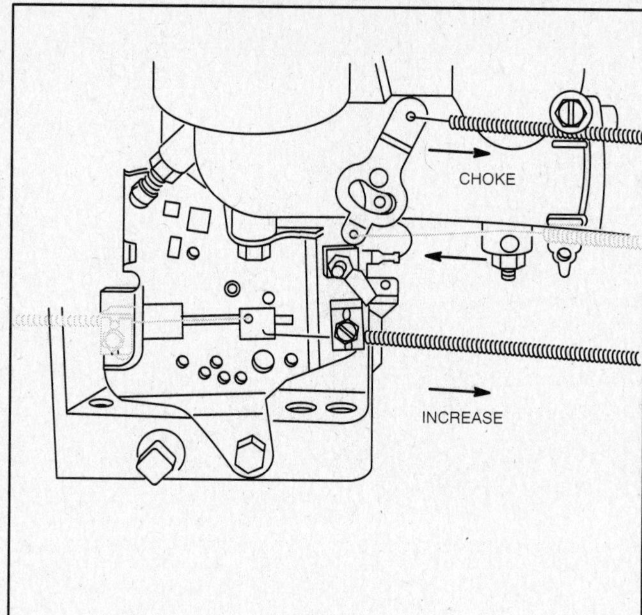

Fig. 96

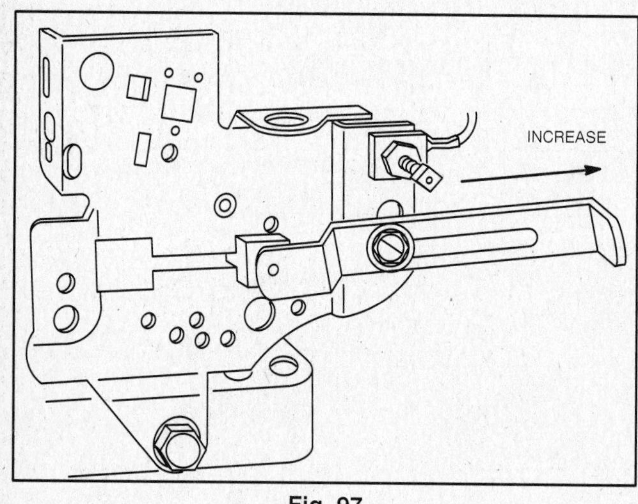

Fig. 97

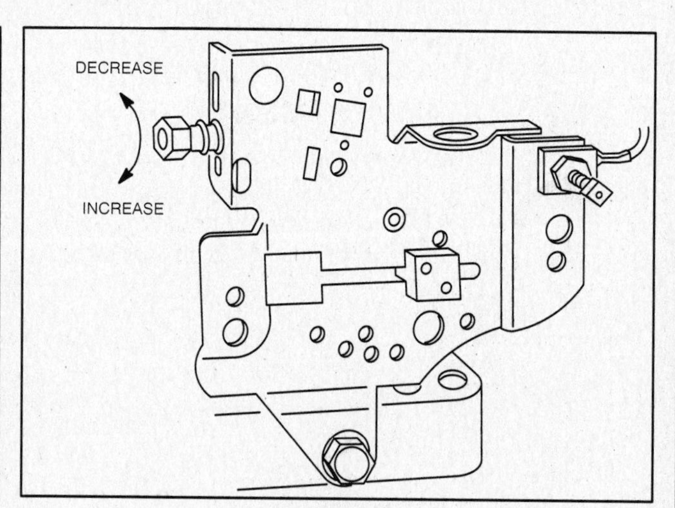

Fig. 98

MODELS 220000, 250000 Horizontal Crankshaft with Rack & Pinion Control, Except 253400, 255400

NOTE: METRIC EQUIVALENTS ARE LISTED ON PAGE 26 OF THIS SECTION.

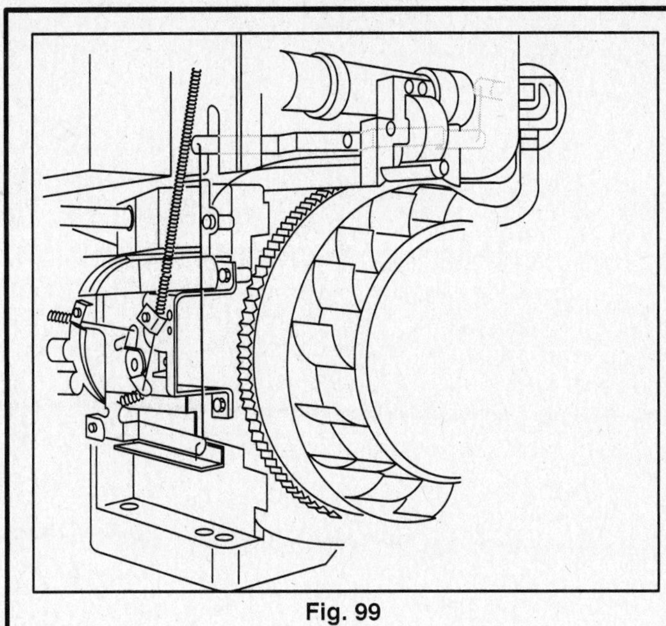

Fig. 99

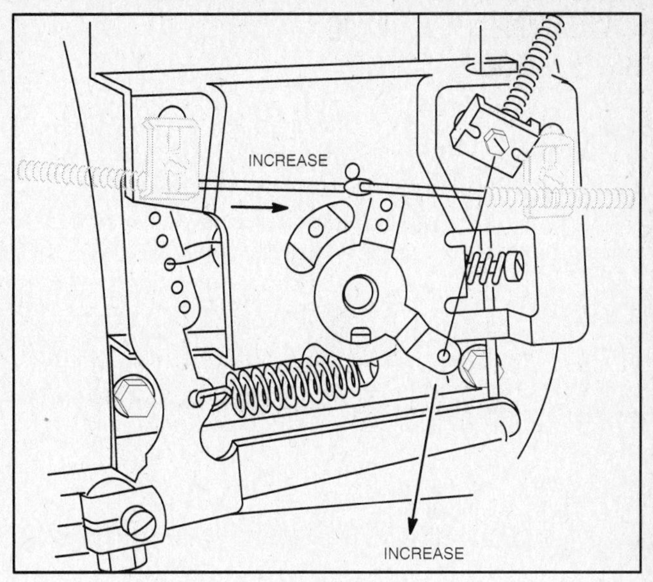

Fig. 100

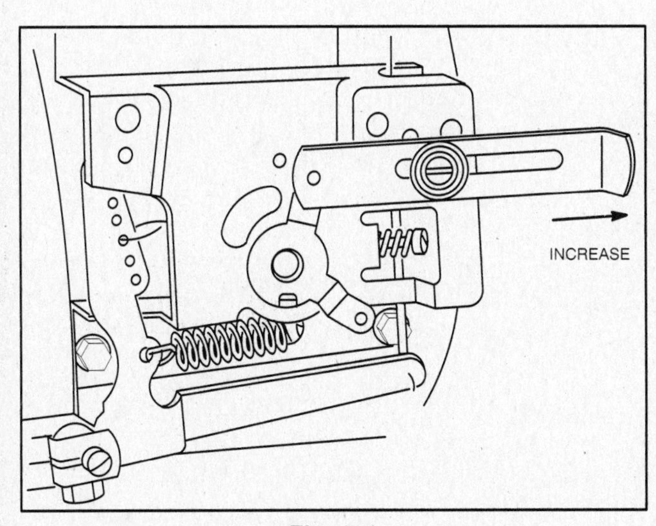

Fig. 101

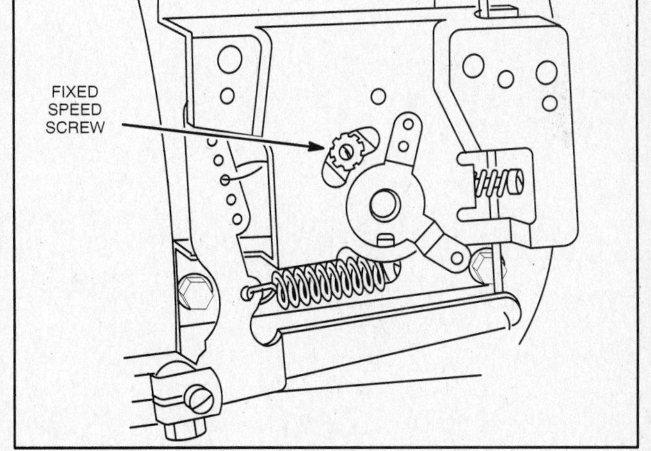

Fig. 102

MODEL 253400, 255400 Horizontal Crankshaft

NOTE: METRIC EQUIVALENTS ARE LISTED ON PAGE 26 OF THIS SECTION.

BAND BRAKE CONTROLS – MODEL SERIES 92000, 93000, 94000, 95000, 110000

System 2® and 4® engines are equipped with the band brake feature, Fig. 103. The band brake **MUST STOP** the engine (cutter blade) within three seconds after operator releases equipment safety control, Fig. 104. Cutter blade stopping time can be checked using **BLADE MONITOR®**, Tool #19255.

If engine (cutter blade) stopping time exceeds three seconds with equipment speed control set in "FAST" position, examine following for adjustment, alignment, or damage:

A. Brake band, worn or damaged.

B. Anchor post, misaligned or bent.

C. Brake spring, not securely anchored or loose.

D. Control bracket lever, rivet worn or loose. (Check ignition system as noted in Section 2.)

E. Control bracket, misadjusted.

F. Equipment controls, damaged.

To examine, adjust, or replace band brake, place spark plug wire in holding tab and disconnect battery wires at connector, System 4® only. Loosen battery holder screws and remove battery, System 4® only.

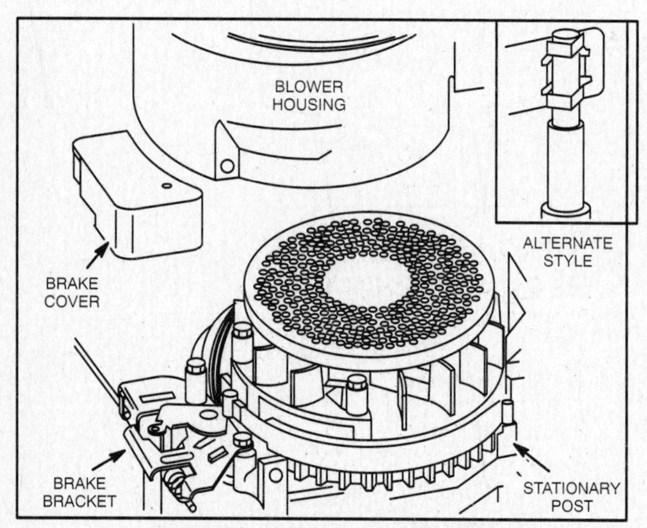

Fig. 103 – Band Brake System

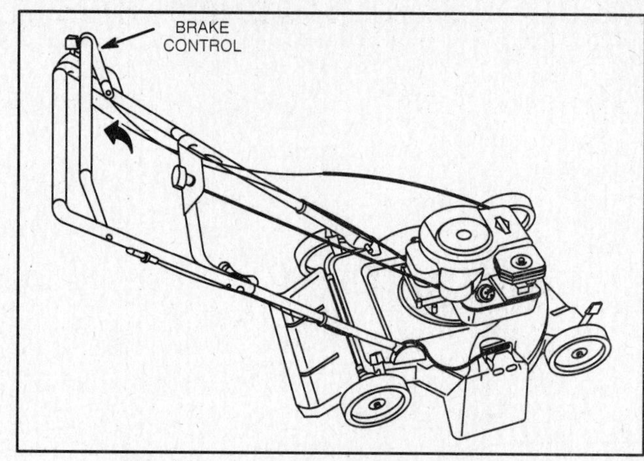

Fig. 104 – Typical Equipment Control

DISASSEMBLY OF BAND BRAKE

1. Remove brake control bracket cover.

2. Loosen cable clamp screw and remove cable from control lever, Fig. 103.

   NOTE: Contact equipment manufacturer for control cable specifications or replacement.

3. Remove two switch cover screws. On System 4® engines, move cover as shown in Fig. 105. Handle with care to prevent damage to lever caused by link when moving switch cover.

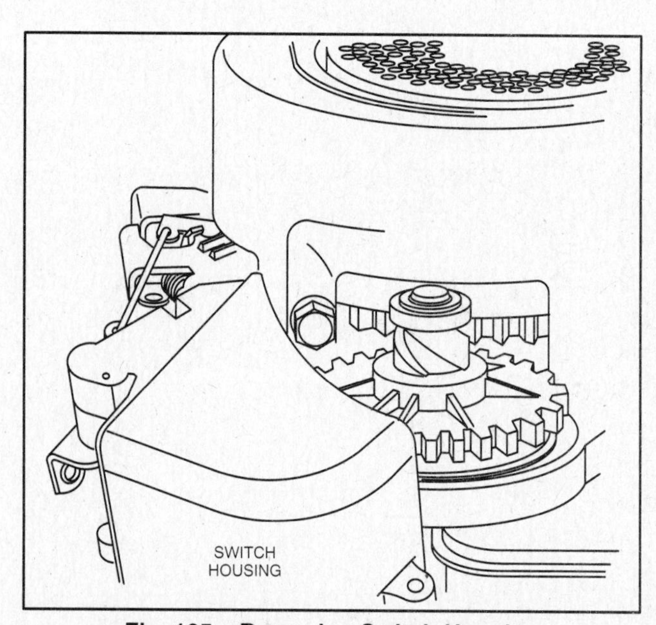

Fig. 105 – Removing Switch Housing

NOTE: METRIC EQUIVALENTS ARE LISTED ON PAGE 26 OF THIS SECTION.

REMOVE BRAKE BAND, NEW STYLE BAND BRAKE BRACKET

1. Remove blower housing and rotating screen, Fig. 103.

2. On new style band brake brackets, release brake spring and lift brake band up off both stationary and moving posts, Fig. 106.

3. Replace brake band if brake material is damaged or worn to less than .030" thick.

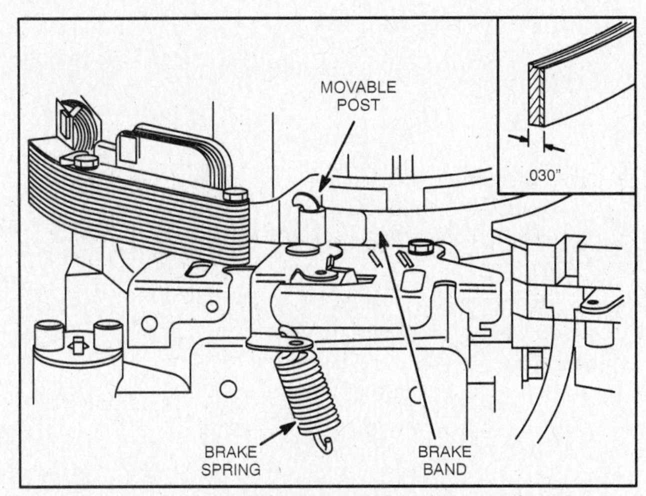

Fig. 106 - Removing Brake Band, New Style Band Brake Bracket

REMOVE BRAKE BAND, OLD STYLE BAND BRAKE BRACKET

1. Remove blower housing and rotating screen, Fig. 103.

2. Bend control lever tang to clear band brake loop, Fig. 107.

3. Release brake spring tension and remove brake band.

4. Replace brake band if brake material is damaged or worn to less than .030" thick.

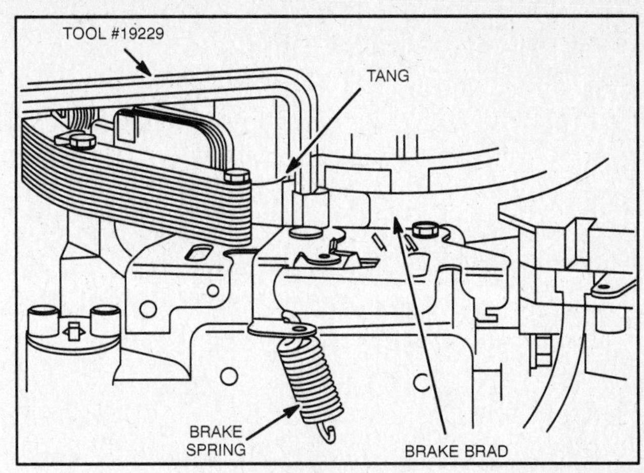

Fig. 107 - Removing Brake Band, Old Style Band Brake Bracket

5. Loosen screw "A" (System 4® engines only).
6. Remove two screws "B," Fig. 107. Remove control bracket from cylinder.

   NOTE: Disconnect control lever from starter link (System 4® engines only) using care to prevent switch cover lever damage.

7. Remove stop switch wire from stop switch terminal.

ASSEMBLE CONTROL BRACKET AND BRAKE BAND, NEW STYLE BRACKET

1. Reinstall stop switch wire on control bracket.
2. Assemble control bracket to cylinder with screws finger tight.
3. Place brake band on stationary post and hook over end of movable post until band bottoms, Fig. 106.

   NOTE: Brake material on steel band **MUST** be on flywheel side after assembly.

ASSEMBLE CONTROL BRACKET AND BRAKE BAND, OLD STYLE BRACKET

1. Reinstall stop switch wire on control bracket stop switch terminal.
2. Assemble control bracket to cylinder with screws finger tight.
3. Install brake band on stationary and movable posts, Fig. 107.

NOTE: METRIC EQUIVALENTS ARE LISTED ON PAGE 26 OF THIS SECTION.

4. Bend lever retainer tang over brake band loop.

NOTE: Brake material on steel band **MUST** be on flywheel side after assembly.

NOTE: Some manufacturers install a cable clamp bracket using a pop rivet in the control bracket cable clamp screw hole. Place bayonet end of gauge in control lever as shown in Fig. 108. Rotate control lever sufficiently to install other end of gauge into pop rivet hole. Check as noted above for tension at bayonet end of gauge.

Adjusting Band Brake

1. Place bayonet end of Band Brake Adjusting Gauge, Tool #19256, in control lever, Fig. 108.

2. Rotate control lever far enough to install other end of gauge in cable clamp screw hole.

3. Install brake spring.

   NOTE: For ease of assembly, brake spring must be temporarily removed from control bracket spring anchor.

4. Re-attach brake spring to control bracket spring anchor **IMMEDIATELY** after installing control bracket screws finger tight and gauge.

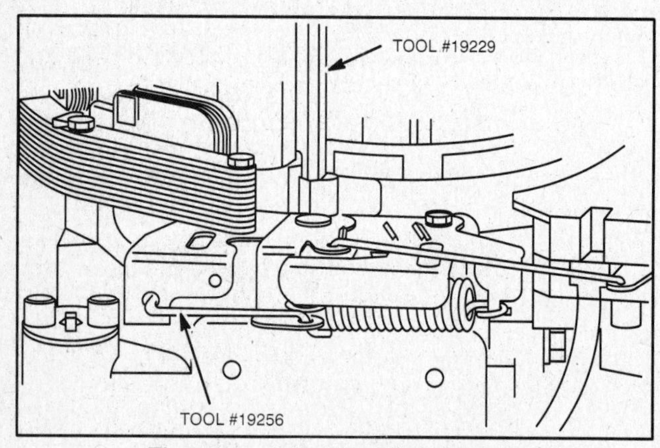

Fig. 108 - Adjusting Band Brake

5. With brake spring installed, apply pressure to the control bracket **ONLY**. Move it in direction indicated by arrow, Fig. 108, until gauge link tension is **JUST** eliminated.

6. Hold control bracket in this position while torquing screws to 25 to 30 in. lbs.

7. Remove gauge.

TEST BAND BRAKE

1. To test band brake adjustment, use Torque Wrench, Tool #19197, Starter Clutch Wrench, Tool #19244, and/or a 7/8" socket.

2. With band brake engaged, rotate flywheel clockwise, Fig. 109, and note torque wrench reading.

3. If less than 45 in. lbs. of torque is required to rotate flywheel, check the following for damage, misalignment, or misadjustment:

   A. Brake Band Lining;

   B. Contour or Wear;

   C. Brake Band Anchors;

   D. Control Bracket;

   E. Brake Spring;

   F. Brake Spring Anchor. Correct, readjust, and repeat band brake test.

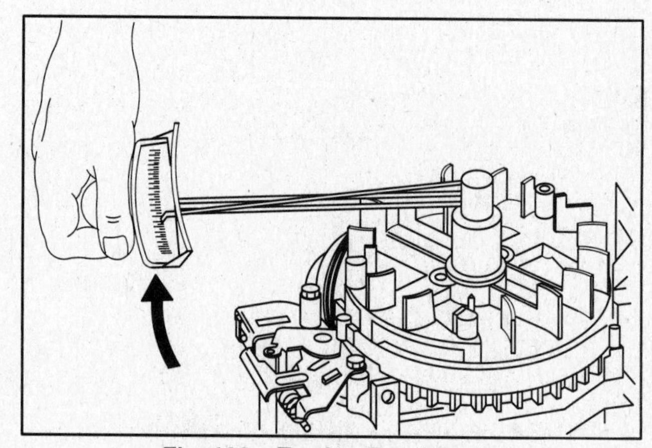

Fig. 109 - Testing Band Brake

When band brake is released, engine must turn freely. If brake band drags against flywheel restricting movement, check for damaged brake band or anchors.

NOTE: METRIC EQUIVALENTS ARE LISTED ON PAGE 26 OF THIS SECTION.

FINAL ASSEMBLY

Install rotating screen and blower housing on engine. Tighten screws. Note location of blower housing guard, Fig. 110.

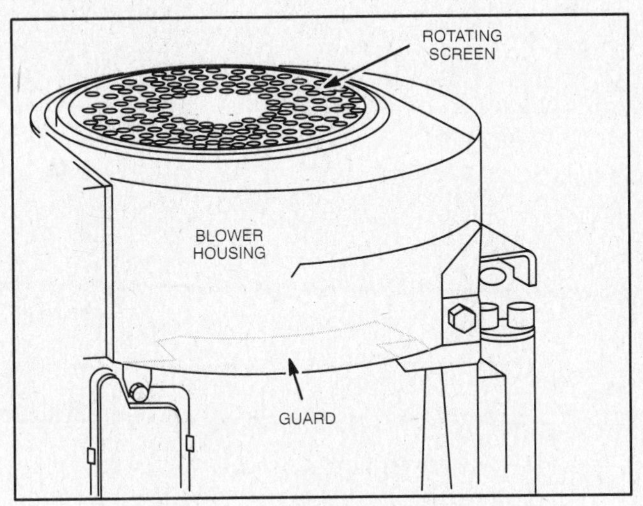

Fig. 110 – Installing Blower Housing

INSTALL ELECTRIC STARTER CONTROLS, SYSTEM 4®

1. Install starter link into control lever.
2. Carefully insert other end of link in switch cover lever.
3. Rotate switch cover into position on starter motor.
4. Fasten screws securely, Fig. 105.

   NOTE: If equipped with key switch, ignition link may be omitted.

5. Install equipment safety control cable to control lever.
6. Tighten cable clamp screw securely.
7. Conduct Stop Switch and Stop Switch Wire Tests described in Section 2, Ignition.
8. Install brake control bracket cover and tighten screws.
9. Place battery in holder and tighten screws (System 4® engines only).
10. After engine is installed on equipment, connect battery wires to connector and place wire on spark plug.
11. Service engine. Test blade stopping time, using **BLADE MONITOR®**, Tool #19255.

FLYWHEEL BRAKE, MODEL SERIES 120000

DESCRIPTION

The flywheel brake is part of the safety control required for some applications of this engine model. The flywheel brake **MUST** stop the engine within three seconds, while running at **FAST** speed position, when the operator releases the equipment safety control.

REMOVE FLYWHEEL BRAKE

1. Remove finger guard and fuel tank, Fig. 111.

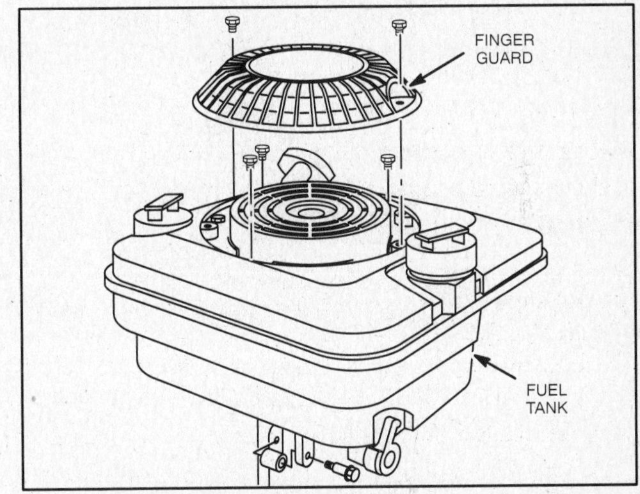

Fig. 111 – Removing Static Guard and Fuel Tank

2. Remove dipstick and oil fill tube.
3. Remove blower housing and rewind starter, Fig. 112.

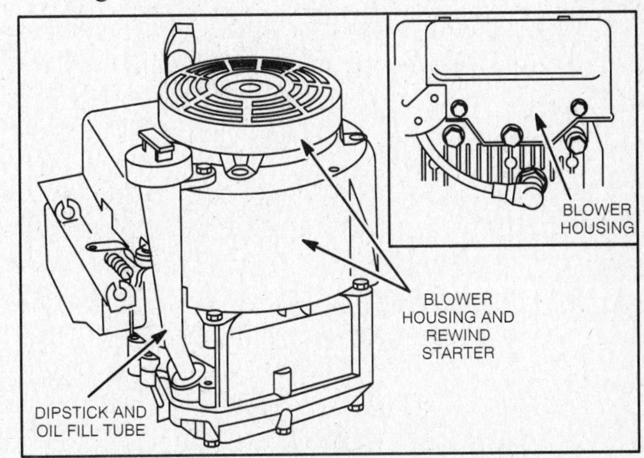

Fig. 112 – Removing Dipstick and Oil Fill Tube, Blower Housing and Rewind Starter

4. Disconnect spring from brake anchor, Fig. 113.
5. Disconnect stop switch wire from stop switch.

NOTE: METRIC EQUIVALENTS ARE LISTED ON PAGE 26 OF THIS SECTION.

GOVERNOR CONTROLS, CARBURETOR LINKAGE & FLYWHEEL BRAKES

NOTE: If engine is equipped with electric starter, disconnect both wires from starter interlock switch. Remove two screws from brake bracket and remove bracket, Fig. 113.

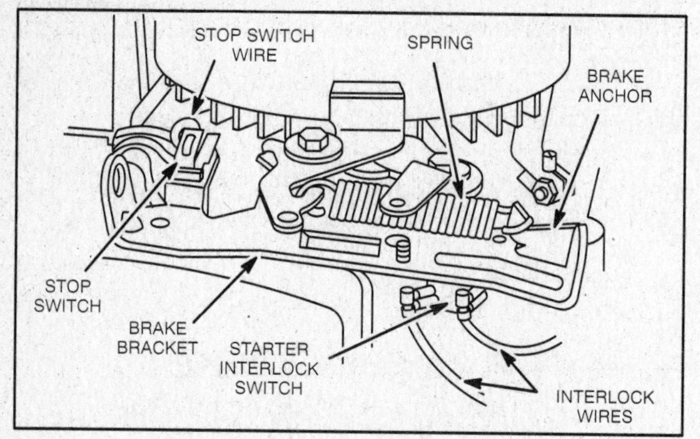

Fig. 113 - Removing Brake Bracket

INSPECT FLYWHEEL BRAKE AND SWITCHES

1. Inspect brake lining on brake lever. Replace brake assemble if lining is less than .090"
2. Test stop switch as described in Section 2, STOP SWITCH - REMOTE CONTROL.
3. Test electric starter interlock switch as described in Section 7B, INTERLOCK SWITCH - ELECTRIC STARTER.

ASSEMBLE FLYWHEEL BRAKE

1. Install brake assembly on crankcase and torque mounting screws to 40 in. lbs.
2. Install stop switch wire and bend end of wire 90°. Install interlock switch wires on interlock switch, if used.
3. Install blower housing as described in Section 7A, SERVICE STARTER.
4. Install dipstick tube and dipstick.
5. Install fuel tank and finger guard.

METRIC EQUIVALENTS

DIMENSIONS, FRACTIONAL	
Inches	**Millimeters**
1/8	3.18
9/16	14.27
1-3/8	35
2-1/8	54
DIMENSIONS, DECIMAL	
.030	.76
.090	2.46

TORQUE		
Inch Lbs.	**Kgcm**	**Nm**
25	29	2.8
30	35	3.4
40	46	4.5
45	52	5.1

NOTE: METRIC EQUIVALENTS ARE LISTED ON PAGE 26 OF THIS SECTION.

Section 5
GOVERNORS

SECTION INDEX

5

NOTE: METRIC EQUIVALENTS ARE LISTED ON PAGE 28 OF THIS SECTION.

SECTION INDEX (Cont'd.)

NOTE: METRIC EQUIVALENTS ARE LISTED ON PAGE 28 OF THIS SECTION.

GOVERNED SPEED LIMITS ALL MODEL SERIES

THE PURPOSE OF THE GOVERNOR IS TO MAINTAIN WITHIN CERTAIN LIMITS, A DESIRED ENGINE SPEED, EVEN THOUGH THE LOAD MAY VARY.

To comply with specified top governed speed limits, Briggs & Stratton supplies manufacturers with engines using either calibrated governor springs or an adjustable top speed limit. Calibrated springs or an adjustable top speed limit will allow no more than a desired top governed speed when the engine is operated on a rigid test stand at our own Factory. However, the design of the cutter blade, deck, etc., can affect engine speeds. Therefore, the top governed speed should be checked with a tachometer when the engine is operated on a completely assembled machine. If on a lawn mower, it should be operated on a hard surface to eliminate cutting load on the blade.

If a governor spring must be replaced, consult the appropriate Illustrated Parts List. Choose the proper governor spring by engine type number. AFTER A NEW GOVERNOR SPRING IS INSTALLED, CHECK ENGINE TOP GOVERNED SPEED WITH AN ACCURATE TACHOMETER.

Run engine at half throttle to allow the engine to reach normal operating temperature before measuring speed with a tachometer. To account for tolerances, which may be required by tachometer manufacturers, we suggest that the top governed speed of the engine be adjusted at least 200 RPM lower than the maximum speeds shown.

Since blade tip speed is a function of engine RPM, lower tip speeds require lower engine speeds.

Table No. 1 lists various lengths of rotary lawn mower cutter blades, and the maximum blade rotational speeds, which will produce blade tip speeds of 19,000 feet per minute.

TABLE NO. 1

Blade Length	Maximum Rotational RPM
18"	3800
19"	3600
20"	3400
21"	3250
22"	3100
23"	2950
24"	2800
25"	2700

NOTE: For correct no load RPM by model and type, see Engine Sales Manual, MS-4052 or MS-6225, Service Engine Sales Manual microfiche under note column, or MAXIMUM RPM TABLE at end of each manual for the model engine.

AIR VANE GOVERNOR OPERATION ALL MODEL SERIES

The governor spring tends to open the throttle. Air pressure against the air vane tends to close the throttle. The engine speed at which these two forces balance is called the governed speed. The governed speed can be varied by changing governor spring tension, Fig. 1 or changing governor spring, Fig. 2.

CHECK GOVERNOR

Worn linkage or damaged governor springs should be replaced to ensure proper governor operation. If spring or linkage is changed, check and adjust TOP NO LOAD RPM, Fig. 1 or check TOP NO LOAD RPM, Fig. 2 with engine assembled.

NOTE: METRIC EQUIVALENTS ARE LISTED ON PAGE 28 OF THIS SECTION.

ADJUST TOP NO LOAD RPM, MODEL SERIES 80000, HORIZONTAL CRANKSHAFT, AIR VANE WITH CONTROL PANEL

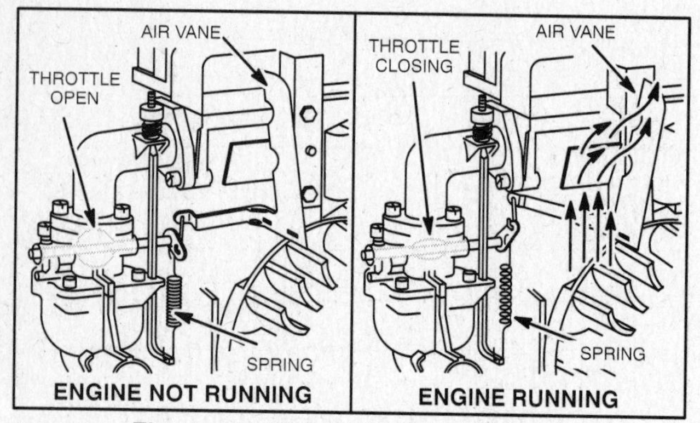

Fig. 1 - Air Vane Governor (Typical)

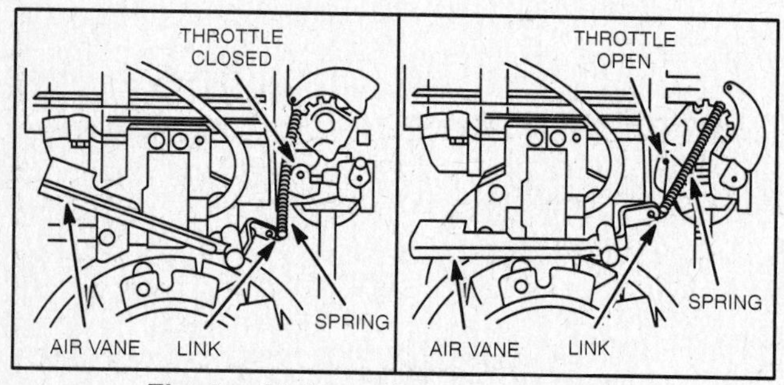

Fig. 2 - Air Vane Governor (Typical)

1. Set control lever to maximum speed position, with engine running.

   NOTE: See Section 3 for proper idle speed adjusting procedure for small Briggs & Stratton/Walbro carburetors.

2. Use Tool #19229, Tang Bending Tool, to bend spring anchor tang to obtain the proper top no load RPM, Fig. 3.

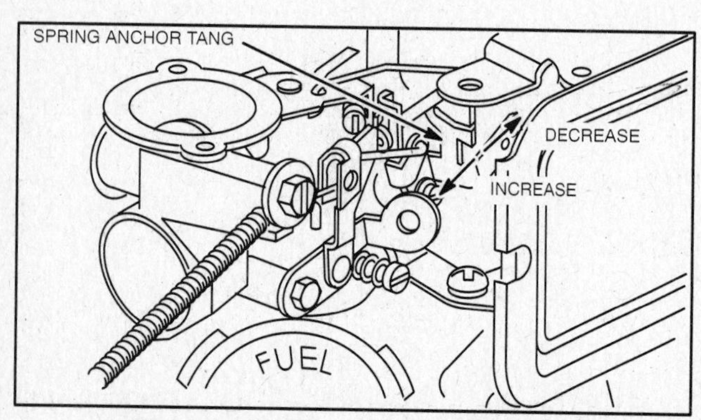

Fig. 3 - Adjusting Top No Load RPM

If a service replacement engine is used, check the top governed speed using a tachometer, with the engine operating on a completely assembled mower, to be sure the blade tip speed will not exceed 19,000 feet per minute. If necessary, change the governor spring or adjust the top speed limit device, so the engine will not exceed the recommended speed, based on blade length as shown. See page 6 for adjustment procedure for mechanical governor.

Some engines are equipped with governed idle. Governed idel permits the governor to operate at idle speeds while the engine is operating under light loads.

ADJUST GOVERNED IDLE, MODEL SERIES 80000, HORIZONTAL CRANKSHAFT, AIR VANE WITH CONTROL PANEL

1. Place control lever in minimum speed position with engine running.

2. Adjust Idle speed screw to obtain 1600 RPM.

3. Turn governed idle stop nut to obtain 1750 RPM, Fig. 4.

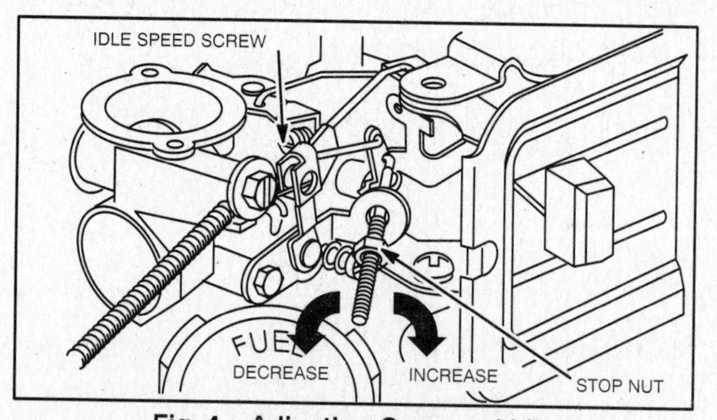

Fig. 4 - Adjusting Governed Idle

REMOVAL AND INSTALLATION OF GOVERNOR SPRING ON MODEL SERIES 90000, 110000, VERTICAL CRANKSHAFT

The governor springs used on engine Model Series 90000, 110000 are made with double end loops for a secure attachment and proper governor regulation. Springs with double end loops are easily removed and installed by following the procedure shown below. DO NOT use a needle-nosed pliers, or the end loops of the governor spring will be deformed. When the governor spring is correctly installed, the spring must be positioned as shown in Fig. 5.

NOTE: METRIC EQUIVALENTS ARE LISTED ON PAGE 28 OF THIS SECTION.

LOOP HORIZONTAL
NOTE END OF LOOP TOWARD ENGINE
LOOP VERTICAL
NOTE END OF LOOP DOWN

Fig. 5 - Correct Position of Spring

INSTALLING SPRING

①

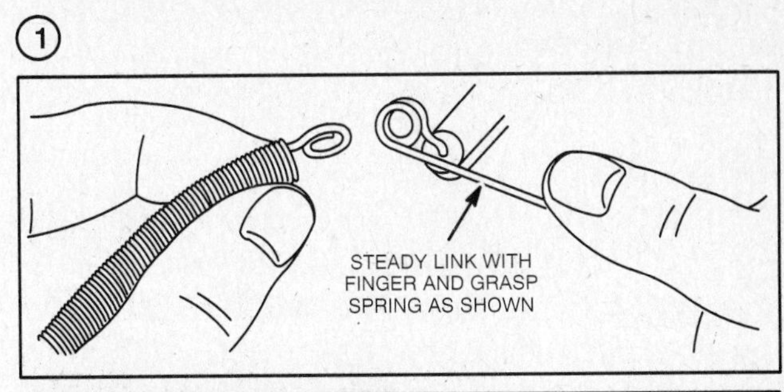

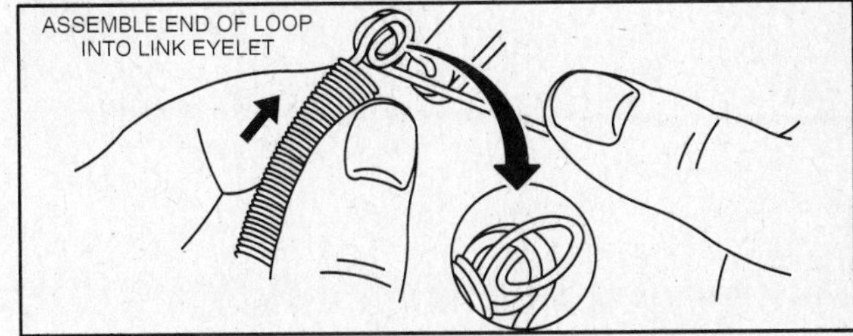

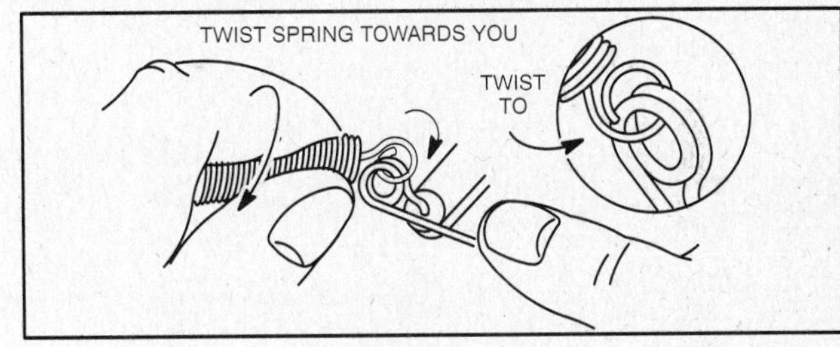

Fig. 8 - Assemble Spring to Link Eyelet

REMOVING SPRING

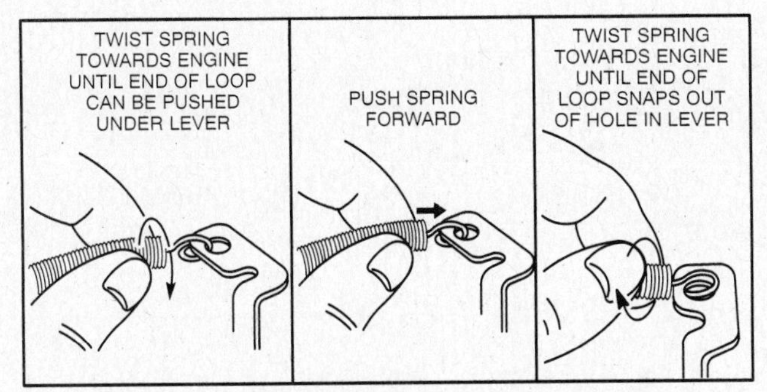

Fig. 6 - Remove Spring from Control Lever

REMOVING SPRING

②

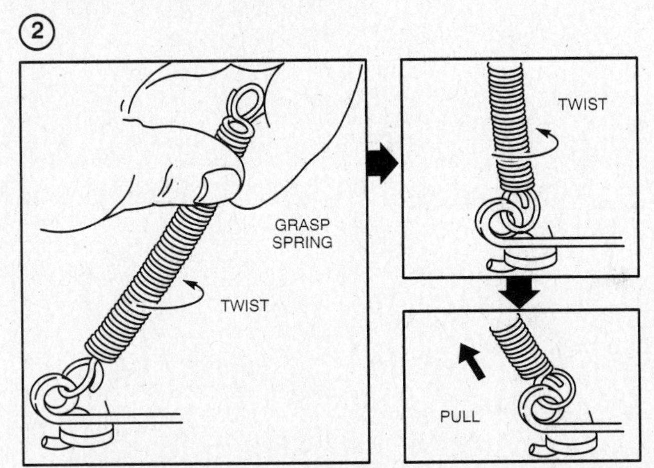

Fig. 7 - Remove Spring from Eyelet in Link

②

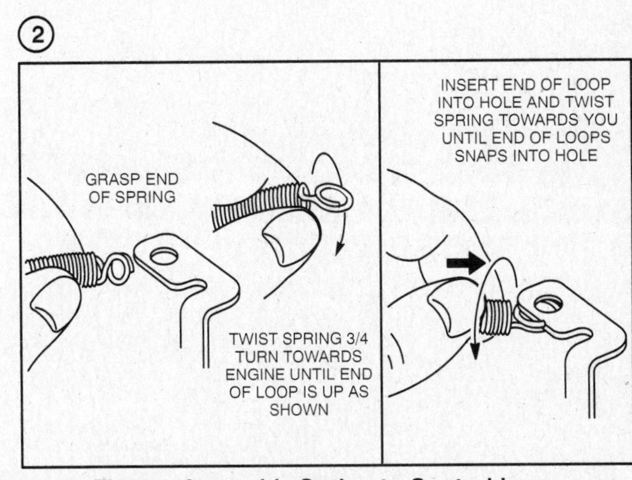

Fig. 9 - Assemble Spring to Control Lever

NOTE: METRIC EQUIVALENTS ARE LISTED ON PAGE 28 OF THIS SECTION.

MECHANICAL GOVERNOR OPERATION – ALL MODEL SERIES

The governor spring tends to pull the throttle open. The force of the counterweights, which are operated by centrifugal force, tends to close the throttle. The engine speed at which these two forces balance is called the governed speed. The governed speed can be varied by changing governor spring tension or governor spring, Fig. 10.

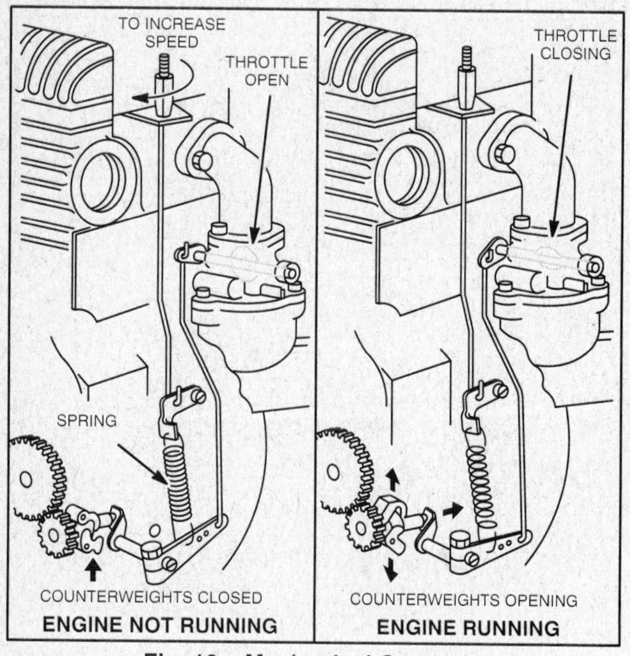

Fig. 10 – Mechanical Governor

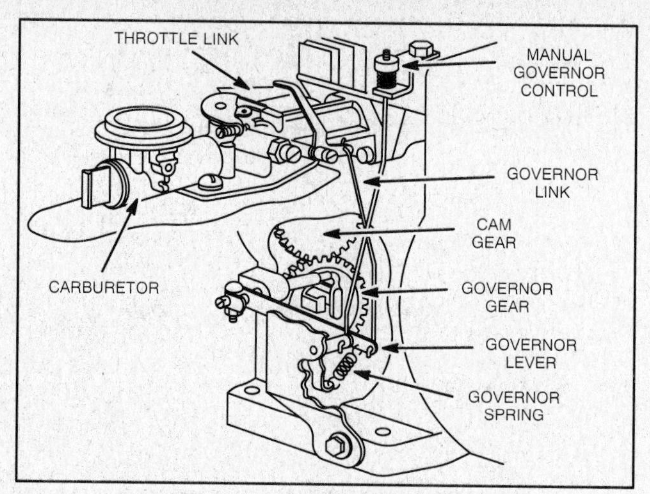

Fig. 11 – Horizontal Shaft

MECHANICAL GOVERNORS HORIZONTAL CRANKSHAFT MODEL SERIES

Aluminum Cylinders Model Series 80000, 83400, 100200, 130000, 170000, 190000, 220000, 251400, 252400, 254400 With Governor Crank in Cylinder

Typical governors used on the horizontal shaft models is illustrated in Fig's. 11 and 12.

The only disassembly necessary is removing the governor assembly as one unit from the shaft on the crankcase cover on horizontal models, Fig. 13.

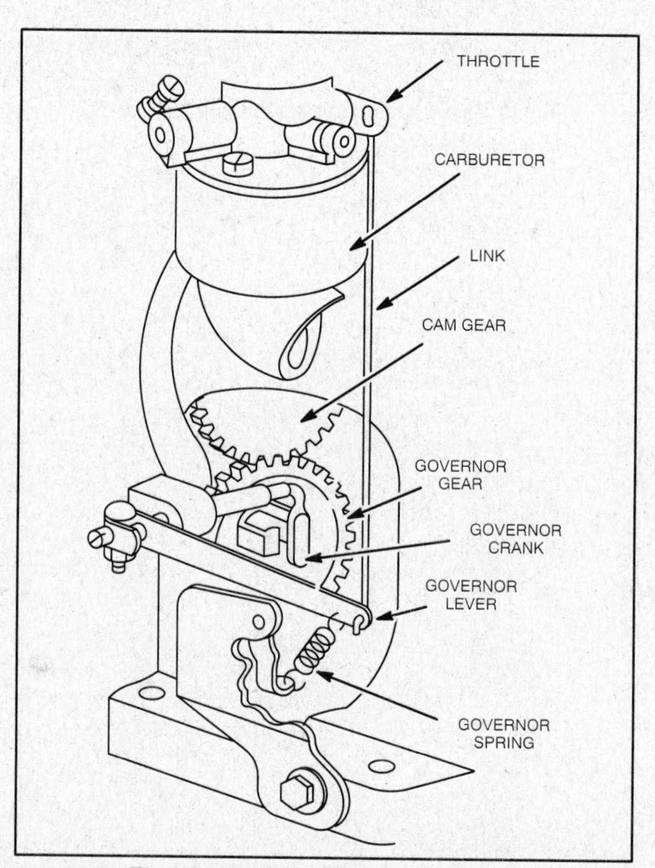

Fig. 12 – Large Aluminum Engines

NOTE: METRIC EQUIVALENTS ARE LISTED ON PAGE 28 OF THIS SECTION.

ASSEMBLE, HORIZONTAL CRANKSHAFT

1. On horizontal crankshaft models, the governor rides on a short stationary shaft and is retained by the governor shaft, with which it comes in contact after the crankcase cover is secured in place.

2. Press governor cup against crankcase cover to seat retaining ring on shaft, prior to installing crankcase cover.

   NOTE: It is suggested that the assembly of the crankcase cover be made with the crankshaft in a horizontal position.

3. The governor crank should hang straight down parallel to the cylinder axis, Fig. 13.

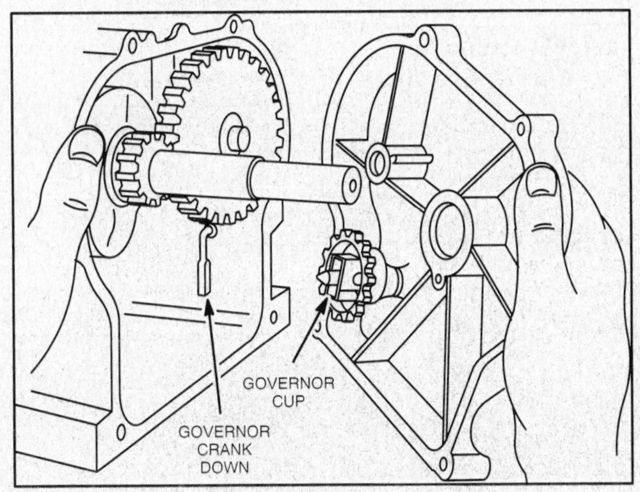

Fig. 13 - Showing Governor Crank Proper Position

NOTE: If the governor crank is clamped in an angular position, pointing toward the crankcase cover, it is possible for the end of the shaft to be jammed into the inside of the governor assembly, resulting in broken parts when the engine is started.

4. After the crankcase cover and gasket are in place, install cover screws. Be sure that screw "A," Fig. 63, has nonhardening sealant, such as Permatex® II on threads of screw.

5. Complete installation of remaining governor linkages and carburetor and then adjust governor shaft and lever. See "Adjust Governor, Static."

   NOTE: See page 21, 3/16" inside diameter, or page 16, 1/4" inside diameter, for procedure to replace governor crank bushing.

ADJUST GOVERNOR, STATIC

1. Loosen screw holding governor lever to governor crank.

2. Place throttle in high speed position.

3. While holding throttle in this position with a screwdriver, turn governor crank clockwise as far as it will go.

4. Tighten screw holding governor lever to governor crank. Torque to 35-45 in. lbs., Fig. 14.

5. Before starting engine, manually move governor linkage to check for any binding.

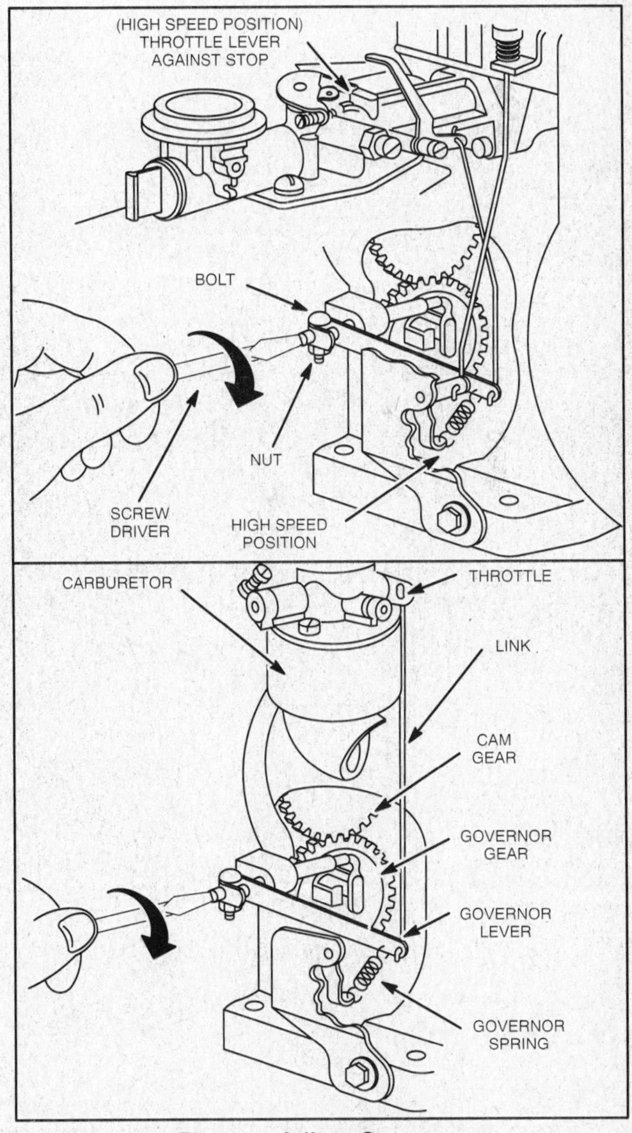

Fig. 14 - Adjust Governor

NOTE: METRIC EQUIVALENTS ARE LISTED ON PAGE 28 OF THIS SECTION.

ADJUST GOVERNOR, ENGINE RUNNING ALUMINUM MODEL SERIES 100200, 130000, 170000, 190000, 220000, 250000 (EXCEPT 253400, 255400)

1. Set control lever to maximum speed position, with engine running.
2. Insert a 1/8" rod through hole in control plate and governor tang, Fig. 15, on rack and pinion control plates. See note below for engines using Top Speed Limit Screws.

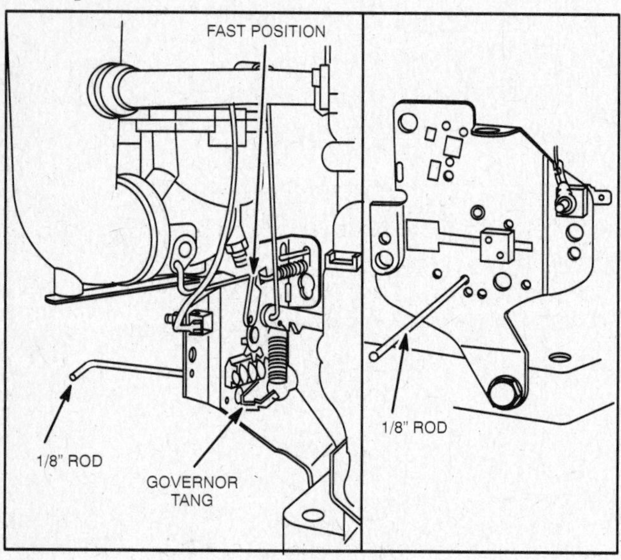

Fig. 15

3. Use Tool #19229, Tang Bending Tool, to bend spring anchor tang to obtain the proper TOP NO LOAD RPM, Fig. 16. For engines using Top Speed Limit Screws, adjust tang to 4000 RPM. Top Speed Limit screw must be removed while adjusting tang.

NOTE: If Tool #19229 is not available, make tool, Fig. 19.

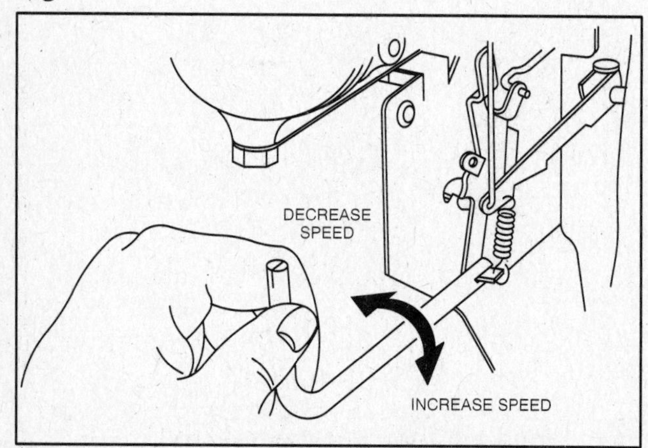

Fig. 16 – Adjusting TOP NO LOAD RPM

Choke-A-Matic® top speed range is 3700 to 4000 RPM with standard spring. (Top speed limit screw cannot be used.)

NOTE: Refer to Fig.'s 17 and 18 to identify the type of control and refer to table above that figure for correct hole ot use after adjusting governor tang, Step 3, and installing Top Speed Limit Screw.

SETTING TOP SPEED

Top Speed Limit Screw Position	No Load Top Speed Range
None	3800 to 4000 RPM
No. 1 Position	3400 to 3700 RPM
No. 2 Position	3000 to 3300 RPM
No. 3 Position	2500 to 2900 RPM
No. 4 Position	1800 to 2400 RPM

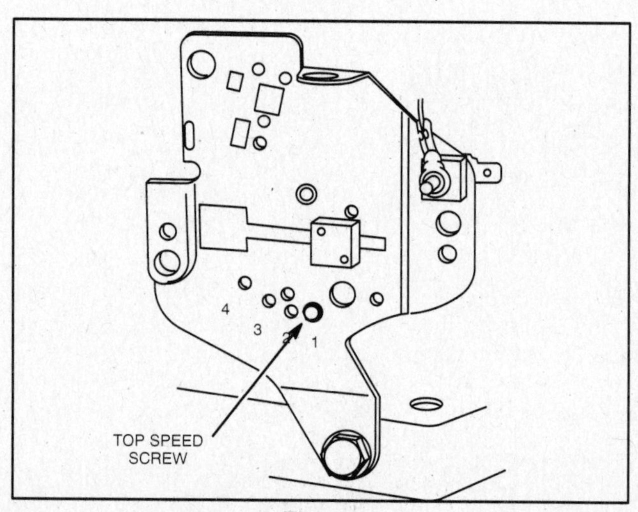

Fig. 17

NOTE: METRIC EQUIVALENTS ARE LISTED ON PAGE 28 OF THIS SECTION.

Top Speed Limit Screw Position	No Load Top Speed Range
None	4000 to 3800 RPM
No. 1 Position	3700 to 3400 RPM
No. 2 Position	3300 to 3000 RPM
No. 3 Position	2900 to 2500 RPM
No. 4 Position	2400 to 1800 RPM

Fig. 18

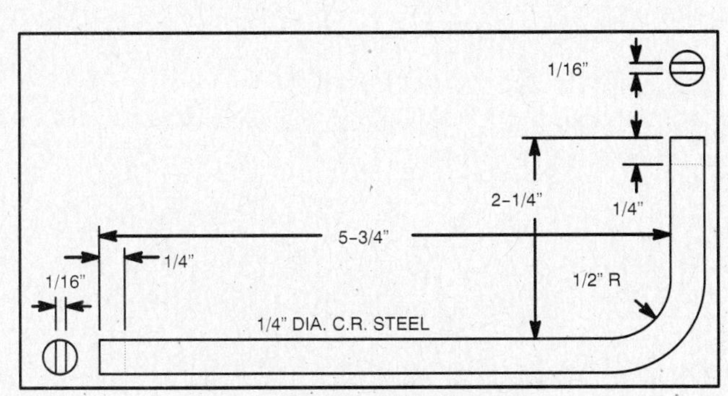

Fig. 19 – Tang Bending Tool

ADJUST GOVERNED IDLE RACK AND PINION CONTROL HORIZONTAL CRANKSHAFT MODELS

1. To adjust, first make final carburetor mixture adjustment.
2. Then place remote control in idle position.
3. Hold throttle in closed position with finger, adjust idle speed screw to 1550 RPM.
4. Release throttle.
5. Set remote control to 1750 RPM. Turn screw in until it contacts remote control lever, Fig. 20.

Always set desired TOP NO LOAD speed by bending end of control lever at the spring anchor, Fig. 16, this Section.

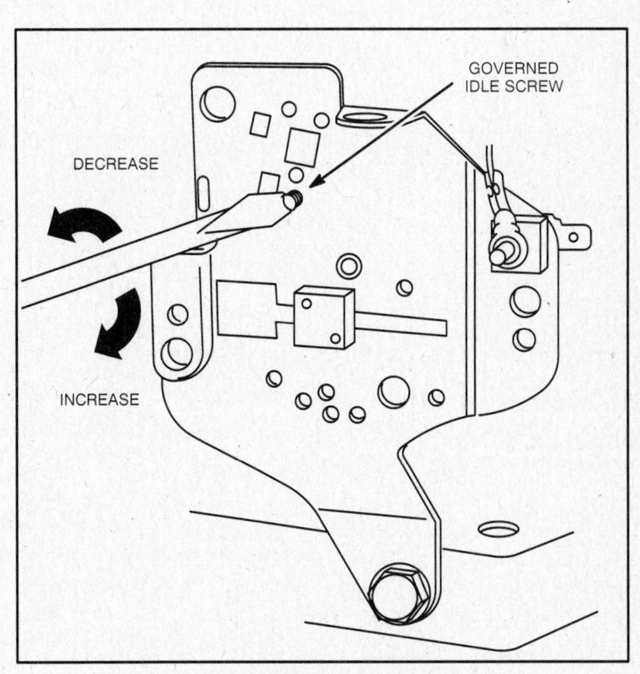

Fig. 20 – Adjusting Governed Idle

NOTE: METRIC EQUIVALENTS ARE LISTED ON PAGE 28 OF THIS SECTION.

ALUMINUM MODEL SERIES 83400 ADJUSTING TOP NO LOAD SPEED

Turn screw to 3750 RPM, Fig. 21, unless a load bank is available to load engine to full generator rated output. Then load generator to full rated output with load bank and turn screw to obtain 3600 RPM, Fig. 21.

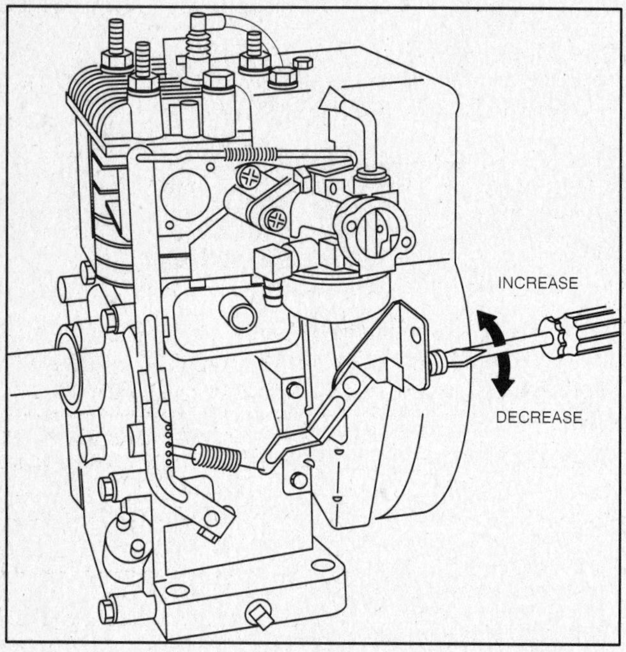

Fig. 21 – Adjusting Top RPM, Model Series 83400

TABLE NO. 2, Model Series 93400 before Date Code 941114

RPM Range	Hole No.
2800 – 3000	2
3100 – 3500	3
3600 – 3900	4
4000 – 4200	6

TABLE NO. 3, Model Series 93400 after Date Code 941113

RPM Range	Hole No.
2800 – 3000	2
3100 – 3500	3
3600 – 3900	4
4000 – 4200	5

ALUMINUM MODEL SERIES 93400, 133400, 176400, 196400, 226400, 256400

MODEL SERIES 93400 GOVERNOR SPRING LOCATION

Place governor spring in holes 1 through 6, Fig. 22, for the RPM specified in Engine Sales Manual, MS-4052 or Service Engine Sales Manual microfiche, MS-6225 under note column or MAXIMUM RPM TABLE at end of each manual, Table No. 2 or Table No. 3, depending on date code, EXCEPT FOR GENERATOR ENGINES. See ALUMINUM MODEL SERIES 93400, GENERATOR ENGINES, page 12, this section. To adjust Top No Load RPM for engine other than on generators, see page 12. To adjust governed idle, see page 13.

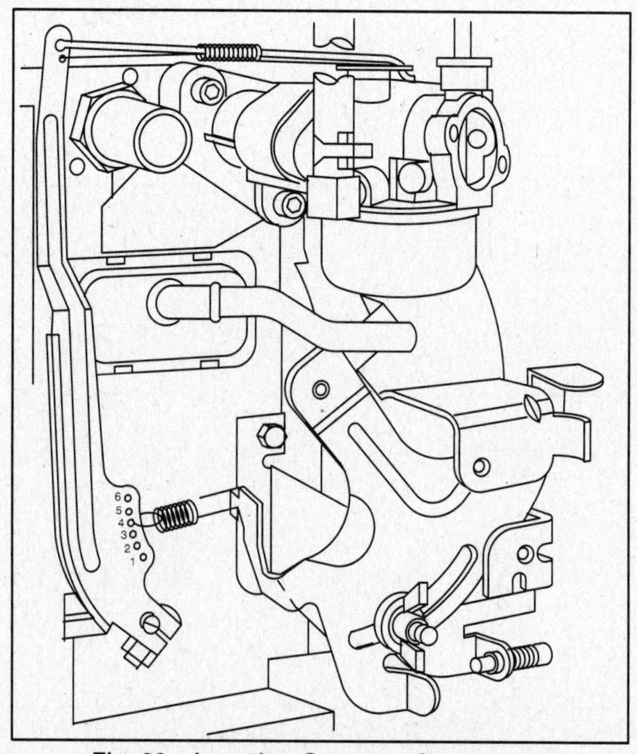

Fig. 22 – Locating Governor Spring Hole

NOTE: METRIC EQUIVALENTS ARE LISTED ON PAGE 28 OF THIS SECTION.

MODEL SERIES 133400 GOVERNOR SPRING LOCATION

Place governor spring in holes 1 through 8, Fig. 23, for the RPM specified in Engine Sales Manual, MS-4052 or Service Engine Sales Manual microfiche, MS-6225 under note column or MAXIMUM RPM TABLE at end of each manual, Table No. 4, EXCEPT FOR GENERATOR ENGINES. See ALUMINUM MODEL SERIES 133400, GENERATOR ENGINES, page 12, this section. To adjust Top No Load RPM for engine, other than on generators, see page 12. To adjust governor idle, see Sec. 3, page 17.

TABLE NO. 4
Model Series 133400

RPM Range	Hole No.
2800 – 3100	3
3200 – 3400	4
3500 – 3700	5
3800 – 4000	6
4100 – 4200	7

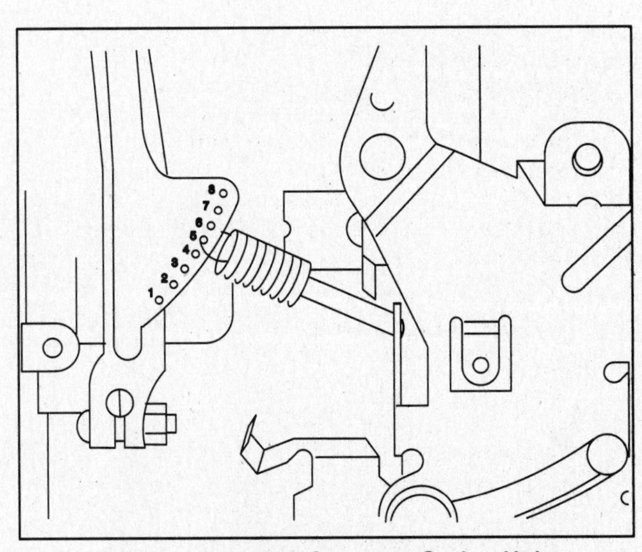

Fig. 23 – Locating Governor Spring Hole Model Series 133400

GOVERNOR SPRING LOCATION MODEL SERIES 176400, 196400, 226400, 250400, 256400

Place governor spring in holes 1 through 12, Fig. 24, for the RPM specified in Engine Sales Manual, MS-4052 or Service Engine Sales Manual microfiche, MS-6225 under note column or MAXIMUM RPM TABLE at end of each manual, Table No. 5, EXCEPT FOR GENERATOR ENGINES. See ALUMINUM MODEL SERIES 176400, 196400, 226400, 250400, 256400 GENERATOR ENGINES, page 12. To adjust TOP NO LOAD RPM for engines, other than on generators, see page 12. To adjust governed idle RPM, see page 13.

TABLE NO. 5
Model Series 176400, 196400, 226400, 250400, 256400

RPM Range	Hole No.
2600 – 2800	2
2900 – 3100	4
3200 – 3400	6
3500 – 3700	8
3800 – 4000	11

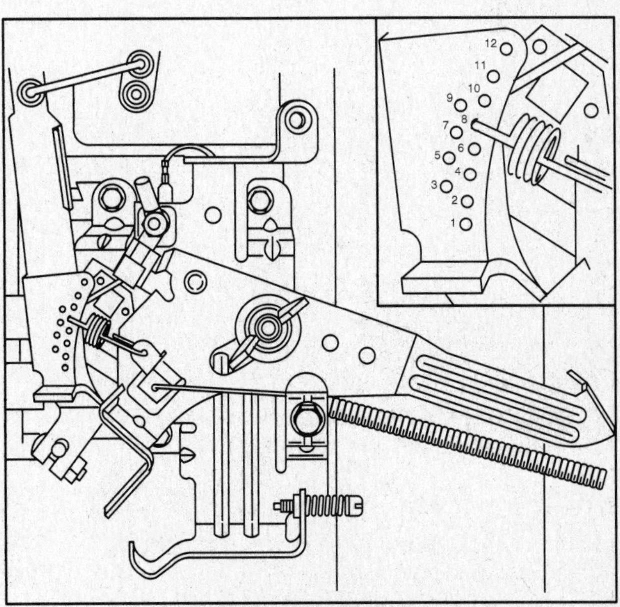

Fig. 24 – Locating Governor Spring Hole Model Series, 176400, 196400, 226400, 250400, 256400

NOTE: METRIC EQUIVALENTS ARE LISTED ON PAGE 28 OF THIS SECTION.

ADJUSTING TOP NO LOAD SPEED

1. Start and run engine at half throttle for five minutes to bring engine to operating temperature.
2. Move speed control lever to maximum RPM position.

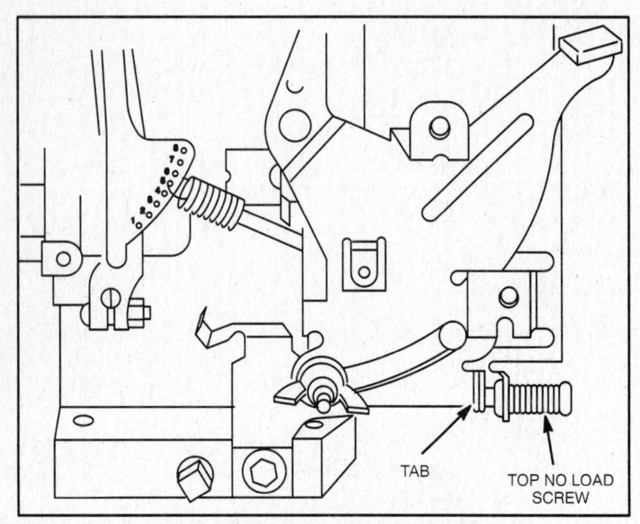

Fig. 25 – Maximum RPM Position, Model Series 93400, 133400

3. If tab on lever is touching head of TOP NO LOAD RPM adjusting screw, back out screw until tab no longer touches screw when control lever is in maximum RPM position, Fig. 25.
4. Bend spring anchor tang, using Tool #19229, Tang Bender, to 100 to 200 RPM above specified speed, Fig. 26, Table No. 2 or Table No. 3, (Model Series 93400, fig. 23, Table No. 4 (133400) or Table No. 5 (Model Series 176400, 196400, 226400, 250400, 256400) Fig. 26.
5. Turn TOP NO LOAD RPM screw clockwise until specified speed is obtained, Fig. 26.

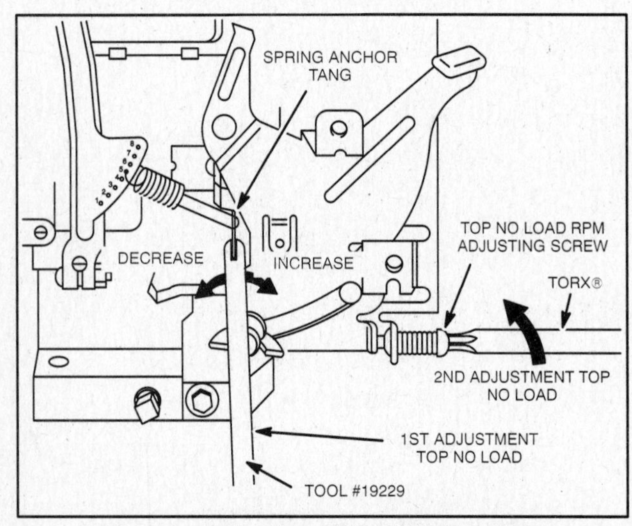

Fig. 26 – Adjusting TOP NO LOAD RPM

NOTE: If specified TOP NO LOAD RPM cannot be obtained, recheck spring anchor hole location for that speed. If location is correct, repeat procedure beginning at Step 2.

GOVERNOR SPRING LOCATION – GENERATOR ENGINES, MODEL SERIES 93400

Place governor spring in governor lever hole number 2 for 50 Cycle (3000 RPM) or hole number 3 for 60 Cycle (3600 RPM) generators. DO NOT USE HOLE LOCATIONS SHOWN IN TABLES.

GOVERNOR SPRING LOCATION – GENERATOR ENGINES, MODEL SERIES 133400

Place governor spring in governor lever hole number 2 for 50 Cycle (3000 RPM) or hole number 4 for 60 Cycle (3600 RPM) generators. DO NOT USE HOLE LOCATIONS SHOWN IN TABLES.

GENERATOR ENGINES, MODEL SERIES 176400, 196400, 226400, 250400, 256400

Place governor spring in governor lever hole number 4 for 50 Cycle (3000 RPM) or hole number 8 for 60 Cycle (3600 RPM) generators. DO NOT USE HOLE LOCATIONS SHOWN IN TABLES.

ADJUSTING TOP NO LOAD SPEED, GENERATOR ENGINES

1. Start and run engine at half throttle for five minutes to bring engine to operating temperature.
2. Then move speed control lever to maximum RPM position.
3. If tab on lever is touching head of TOP NO LOAD RPM adjusting screw, back out screw until tab no longer touches screw when control lever is in maximum RPM position, Fig. 26.
4. Bend spring anchor tang, using Tool #19229, Tang Bender, to 3300 for 50 cycle or 3800 for 60 cycle, Fig. 26.
5. Turn TOP NO LOAD RPM screw clockwise until 3150 RPM, 50 Cycle or 3750 RPM, 60 Cycles is obtained, Fig. 26, No load.

NOTE: METRIC EQUIVALENTS ARE LISTED ON PAGE 28 OF THIS SECTION.

NOTE: If available, use a load bank to load engine to full generator rated output. With generator at full rate output, turn screw to obtain 3000 RPM, 50 Cycle or 3600 RPM, 60 Cycle, Fig. 26.

ADJUST GOVERNED IDLE, MODEL SERIES 93400

1. If governed idle is specified, move speed control down until engine is at minimum RPM and adjust carburetor idle speed screw to 1600 RPM.

   NOTE: See Section 3 for proper idle speed adjusting procedure for small Briggs & Stratton/Walbro carburetors.

2. While holding speed control lever at minimum RPM, bend governed idle tang to obtain 1800 RPM, Fig. 27.

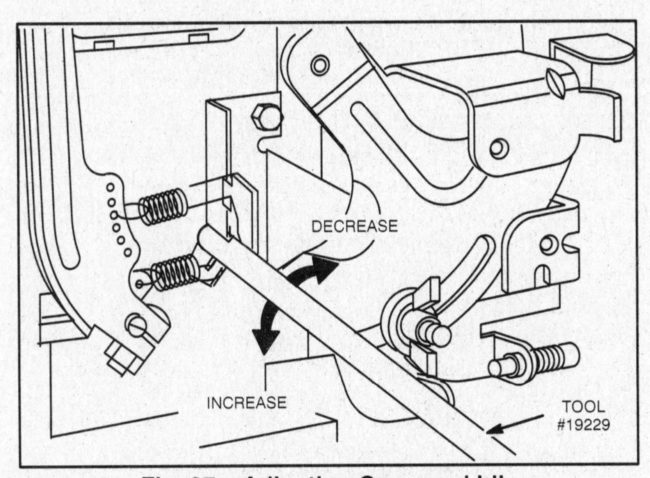

Fig. 27 - Adjusting Governed Idle

ADJUST GOVERNED IDLE, MODEL SERIES 133400, 176400, 196400, 226400, 256400

1. If governed idle is specified, move speed control down until engine is at minimum RPM and adjust carburetor idle speed screw to 1600 RPM.

   NOTE: See Section 3 for proper idle speed adjusting procedure for small or large Briggs & Stratton/ Walbro carburetors.

2. Then move speed control lever to obtain 1800 RPM. Bend governed idle speed tang up against speed control lever, Fig. 28.

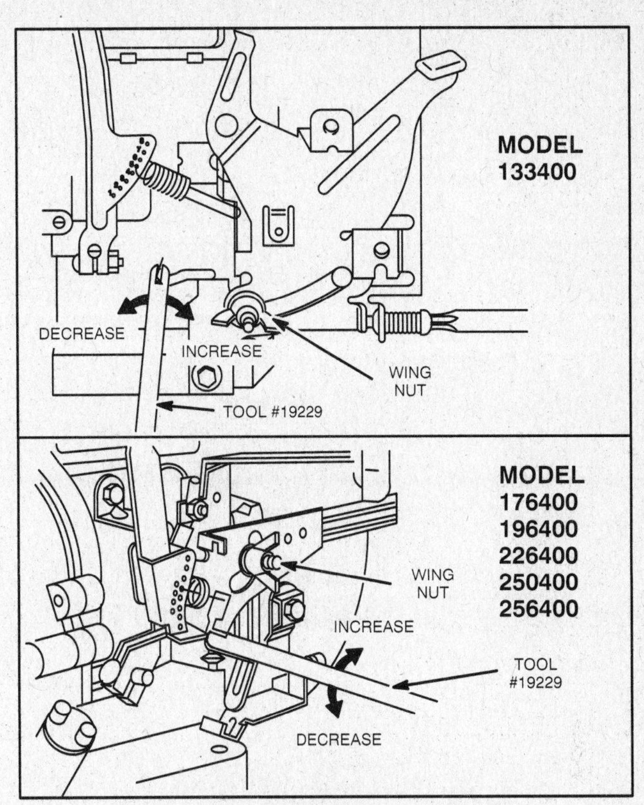

Fig. 28 - Adjusting Governed Idle

ADJUST FOR MANUAL FRICTION CONTROL

For fixed speed place speed control lever in maximum RPM position and tighten wing nut down until lever cannot be moved, Fig. 28.

For manual friction, tighten wing nut until lever will stay in any position without moving while engine is running, Fig. 28.

ADJUST FOR REMOTE CONTROL ADJUST

For remote control, loosen wing nut until speed control lever drops of its own weight down to idle, Fig. 28.

MODEL SERIES 253400, 255400 Adjusting Top No Load Speed

1. On Model Series 253400, 255400 with speed control at fast position, turn screw "A" to set top no load RPM, Fig. 29.

2. Turn clockwise to increase or counterclockwise to decrease speed.

NOTE: METRIC EQUIVALENTS ARE LISTED ON PAGE 28 OF THIS SECTION.

NOTE: For correct top no load RPM by model and type, see Engine Sales Manual, MS-4052 or MS-6225, Service Engine Sales Manual microfiche under NOTE column, or MAXIMUM RPM TABLE at end of each manual for the engine model.

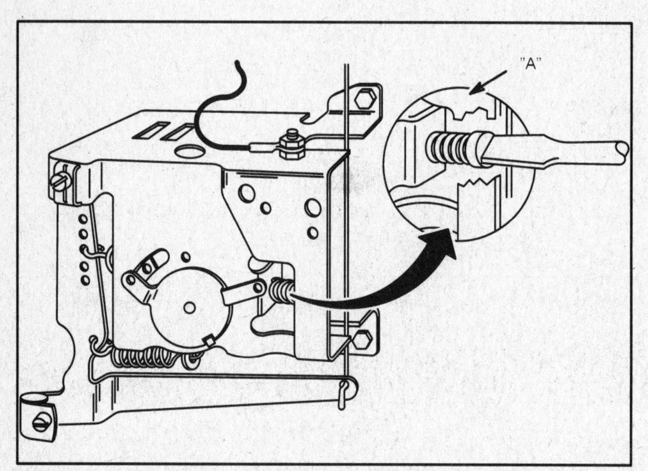

Fig. 29 - Setting Top No Load RPM

Set Speed control to desired RPM and tighten fixed speed screw, Fig. 30.

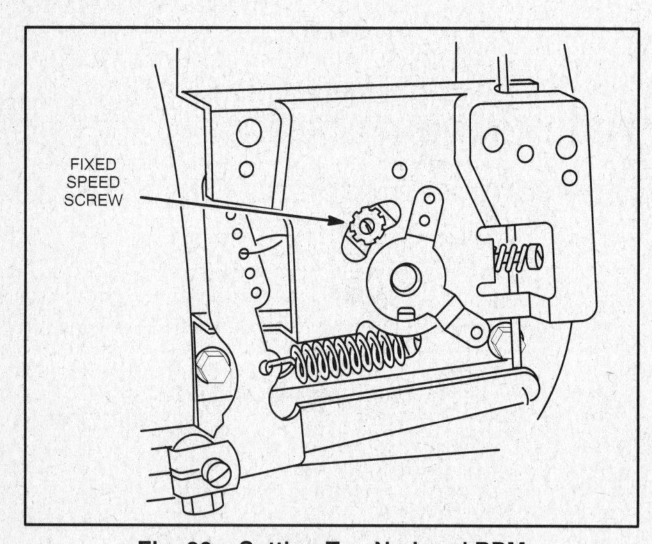

Fig. 30 - Setting Top No Load RPM

GOVERNED IDLE

1. Turn carburetor idle speed adjusting screw to obtain 1600 RPM while holding throttle lever against screw.
2. Release throttle lever.
3. Align holes in control bracket and inside lever with 1/8" diameter rod. Governor speed control lever of equipment should be in "IDLE" position. Fig. 31.
4. Adjust if necessary. Bend spring tang to obtain 1750 RPM.
5. Remove 1/8" diameter rod, Fig. 31.

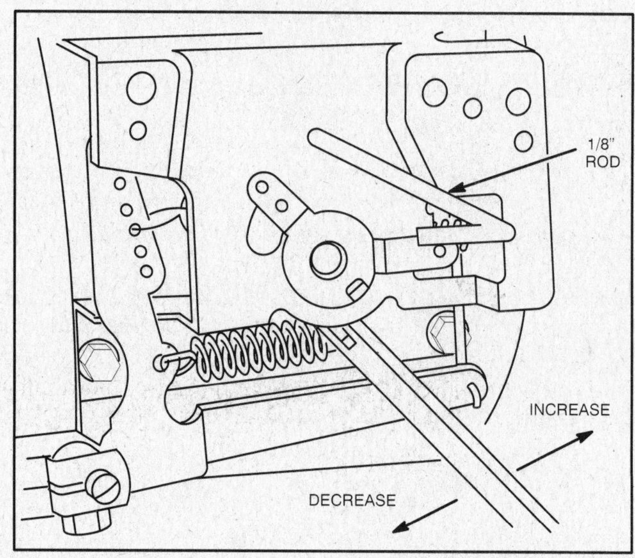

Fig. 31 - Governed Idle Adjustment

GENERATOR APPLICATIONS ONLY

Governor regulation to within two cycles of either 60 or 50 cycles can be obtained if the procedures indicated below are followed:

1. Push speed adjusting nut in and up to release spring tension on nut.
2. Start engine and pull out on speed adjusting nut to maximum length of travel, Fig. 32.

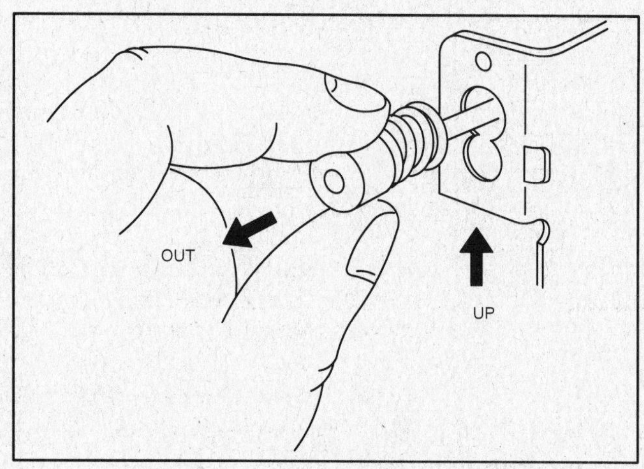

Fig. 32 - Speed Adjusting Nut

3. Set engine speed per Table No. 6 by bending governor tang, Fig. 33.

NOTE: METRIC EQUIVALENTS ARE LISTED ON PAGE 28 OF THIS SECTION.

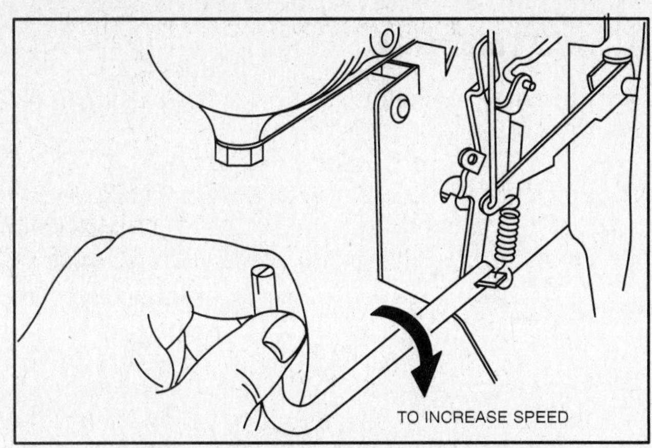

Fig. 33 – Adjusting TOP NO LOAD RPM

4. With engine still running, return speed adjusting nut to slot, push in to compress spring and push nut down into slot.

5. Then turn speed adjusting nut to obtain:

1600 RPM Top No Load for 1500 RPM 50 cycle generator

1875 RPM Top No Load for 1800 RPM 60 cycle generator

3100 RPM Top No Load for 3000 RPM 50 cycle generator

3700 RPM Top No Load for 3600 RPM 60 cycle generator

ALUMINUM MODEL SERIES 80000, 112200, 130000 (EXCEPT 133400), 170000, 190000, 220000, 250000

TABLE NO. 6

Model Series	Governor Type	Governor Pre-Set RPM	Notes
80000	Mechanical	4600	Without Flat Cartridge Air Cleaner
80000	Mechanical	4400	With Flat Cartridge Air Cleaner
112200	Mechanical	4300	Type Numbers below 0799
112200	Mechanical	4400	Type Numbers above 0800
130200, 131200, 132200	Mechanical	4600	Without Flat Cartridge Air Cleaner
130200 & 132200	Mechanical	4000	60 Cycle, 3600 RPM with Flat Cartridge Air Cleaner
130200 & 132200	Mechanical	3600	50 Cycle, 3000 RPM With Flat Cartridge Air Cleaner
131400	Mechanical	4200	60 Cycle, 3600 RPM
132400	Mechanical	4600	50 & 60 Cycle, 3000 & 3600 RPM
170000 & 190000	Mechanical	4250	50 & 60 Cycle, 3000 & 3600 RPM, with Standard Air Cleaner
170000 & 190000	Mechanical	4150	50 & 60 Cycle, 3000 & 3600 RPM, with Front Mount Air Cleaner
170000 & 190000	Mechanical	2400	60 Cycle, 1800 RPM
220000 & 250000	Mechanical	4200	50 & 60 Cycle, 3000 & 3600 RPM
220000 & 250000	Mechanical	2400	60 Cycle, 1800 RPM

CAST IRON MODEL SERIES 230000, 240000, 300000, 320000

DISASSEMBLE

1. Remove engine base.
2. Loosen governor lever bolt and nut.
3. Remove governor lever from governor crank assembly.
4. Remove hair pin and washer from governor crank.

NOTE: METRIC EQUIVALENTS ARE LISTED ON PAGE 28 OF THIS SECTION.

5. Remove any paint or burrs from governor crank.

6. Remove governor crank.

   NOTE: Current production engines have a spacer on the governor crank. Earlier production engines have a long bushing without spacer.

7. Slide governor gear assembly off governor shaft.

REPLACE GOVERNOR SHAFT BUSHING

1. Press old bushing out of cylinder.

2. Press new bushing into cylinder until bushing is flush with outside surface of cylinder.

3. Ream new bushing with Tool #19333, Finish Reamer, using Stanisol or kerosene as lubricant.

ASSEMBLE GOVERNOR

1. Assemble governor gear and cup assembly on governor shaft in cylinder.

2. Slide governor crank (and spacer, when used) through bushing from inside cylinder, Fig. 34.

3. Install lever, governor spring, and links.

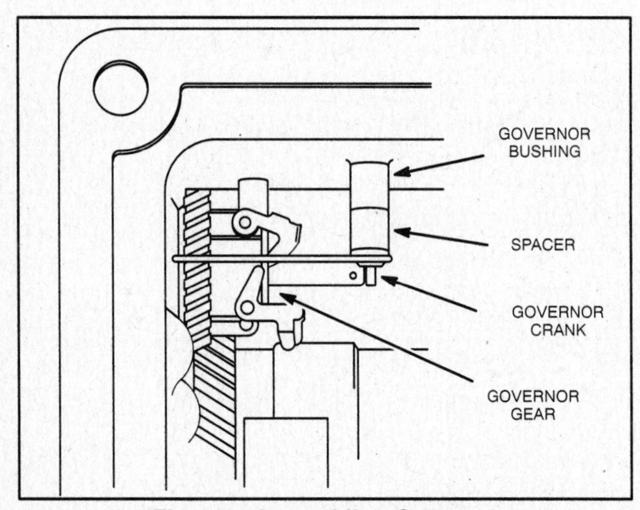

Fig. 34 - Assembling Governor

ADJUSTMENT, STATIC

1. Loosen screw holding governor lever to governor shaft.

2. Place throttle in high speed position.

3. Hold throttle in this position and with a screwdriver turn governor shaft COUNTERCLOCKWISE as far as it will go.

4. Tighten screw holding governor lever to governor shaft to 35-45 in. lbs. torque, Fig. 35.

5. Before starting engine, manually move governor linkage to check for any binding.

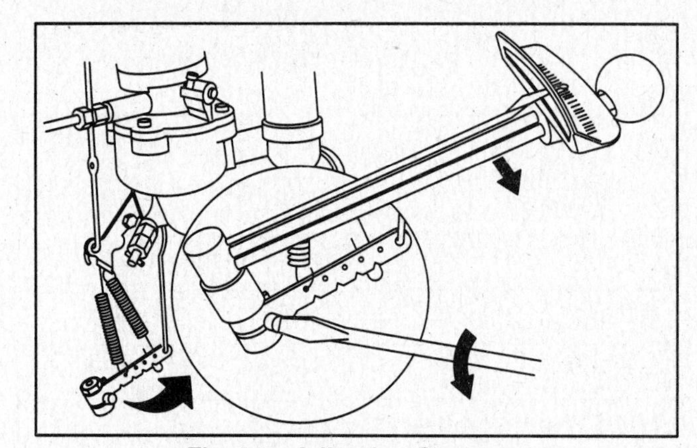

Fig. 35 - Adjusting Governor

Adjust Top No Load Speed

FIXED SPEED OPERATION

1. Loosen lower stop nut.

2. Adjust top stop nut to obtain top no load RPM as listed in Engine Sales Manual, MS-4052 or MS-6225, Service Engine Sales Manual microfiche under note column, or MAXIMUM RPM TABLE at end of each manual for the engine model.

3. After speed is set, tighten lower stop nut, Fig. 36.

REMOTE CONTROL OPERATION

Adjust lower stop nut to obtain top no load RPM as listed in Service Engine Sales Manual, MS-4052 or MS-6225, Service Engine Sales Manual microfiche under NOTE column, or MAXIMUM RPM TABLE at end of each manual for the engine model, Fig. 36.

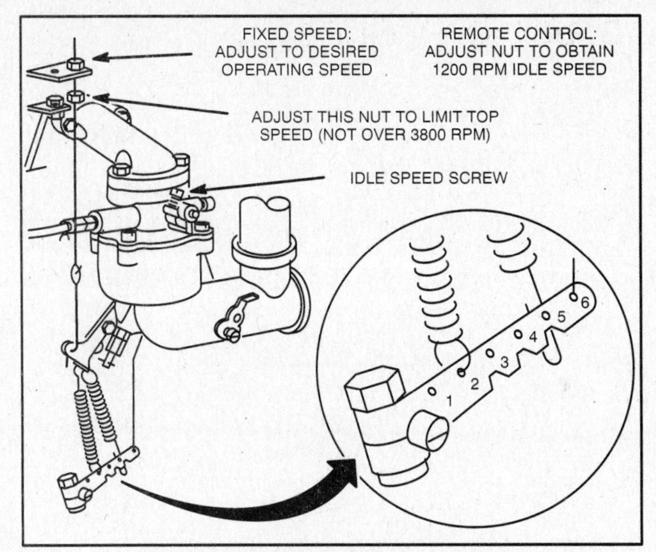

Fig. 36 - Adjusting Top Load RPM

ADJUST GOVERNED IDLE

First make final carburetor mixture adjustments. Then place remote control in idle position. Hold throttle shaft in closed position and adjust idle screw to 1000 RPM. Release the throttle. With remote control in idle position, adjust upper elastic stop nut to 1200 RPM. See Fig. 37.

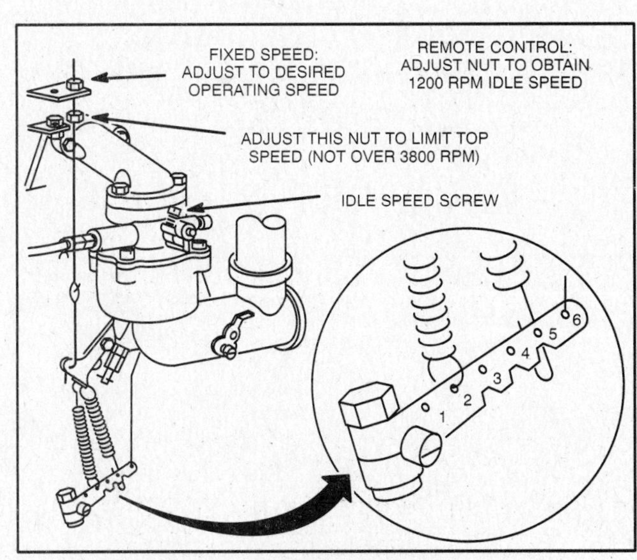

Fig. 37 - Adjusting Governed Idle

ALUMINUM CYLINDERS MODEL SERIES 60000, 80000 With Governor Lever and Shaft Mounted on Crankcase Cover

DISASSEMBLE

1. To service governor, remove crankcase cover.
2. Loosen the screw on the governor lever and pull lever from governor shaft.
3. Loosen the two mounting screws to remove gear housing, Fig. 38. As the housing is removed, the governor gear will slip off the shaft. There is a steel thrust washer on the shaft between the gear and the governor housing.

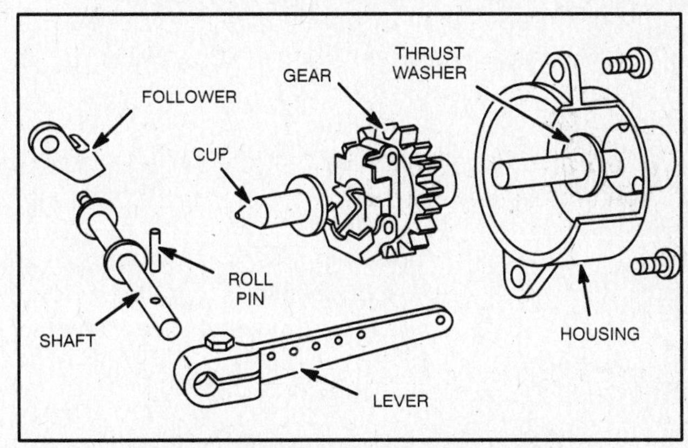

Fig. 38 - Mechanical Governor Parts

4. To remove governor shaft, remove roll pin and washer.
5. Unscrew governor shaft by turning clockwise.
6. Remove governor lever shaft, Fig. 38.

ASSEMBLE

1. Push governor shaft into crankcase cover, with threaded end in.
2. Assemble small washer on the inner end of the shaft, then screw shaft into governor follower by turning shaft counterclockwise.
3. Tighten securely. Turn shaft until follower points down as illustrated, Fig. 39.
4. Place washer on outside end of shaft.
5. Install roll pin. The leading end of the pin should just go through the shaft so pin protrudes from only one side of shaft.

NOTE: METRIC EQUIVALENTS ARE LISTED ON PAGE 28 OF THIS SECTION.

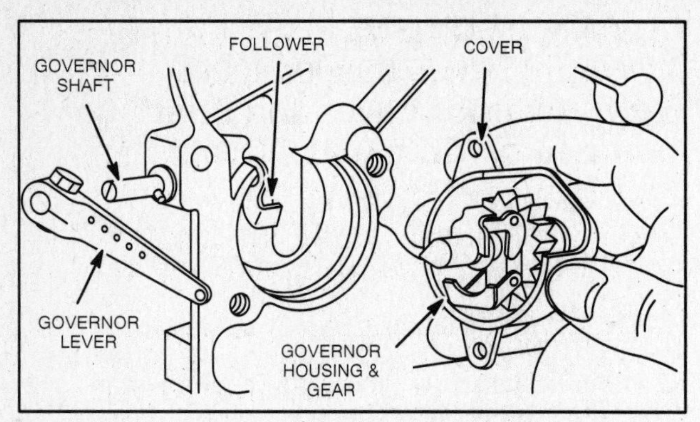

Fig. 39 – Assembling Mechanical Governor

6. Place thrust washer and then governor gear on shaft in gear housing.
7. Hold crankcase cover in a vertical (normal) position and then assemble housing with gear in position so that point of steel cup on gear rests against crank follower.
8. Tighten housing in place with two mounting screws, Fig. 39.
9. Assemble governor lever to lever shaft with lever pointing downward at about a 30° angle. Adjustment will be made later when carburetor linkage is assembled.

ADJUSTMENT – STATIC

1. With crankcase cover, carburetor and all linkage installed, loosen screw holding govérnor lever to governor shaft.
2. Place throttle in high speed position.
3. Hold throttle in this position and with a screwdriver turn governor shaft COUNTERCLOCKWISE as far as it will go.
4. Tighten screw holding governor lever to governor shaft to 35-45 in. lbs. torque, Fig. 40.
5. Before starting engine, manually move governor linkage to check for any binding.
6. Correct any binding in linkage or carburetor.

Adjust Top No Load Speed

1. Start and run engine at half throttle for five minutes to bring engine to operating temperature.
2. Move speed control lever to maximum rpm position.
3. Turn knurled knob to increase or decrease RPM to desired speed, Fig. 40.

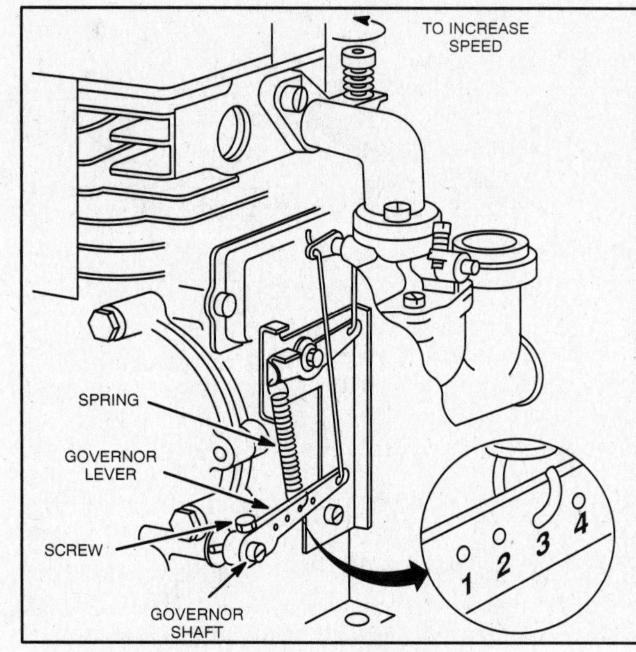

Fig. 40 – Governor Adjustment

MECHANICAL GOVERNORS – VERTICAL CRANKSHAFT MODEL SERIES 100900, 130000, 170000, 190000, 220000, 250000, 280000

The governor used on the vertical shaft models is incorporated with the oil slinger, Fig's. 42 and 43. It is removed as part of the oil slinger, Fig. 41. Further disassembly is unnecessary.

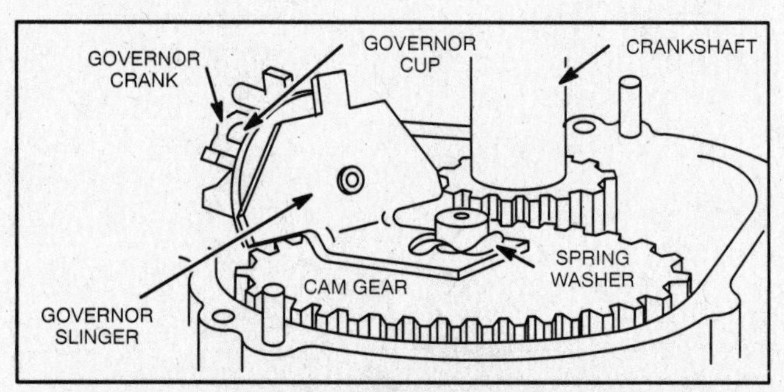

Fig. 41 – Vertical Shaft Governor and Oil Slinger Assembly, Typical

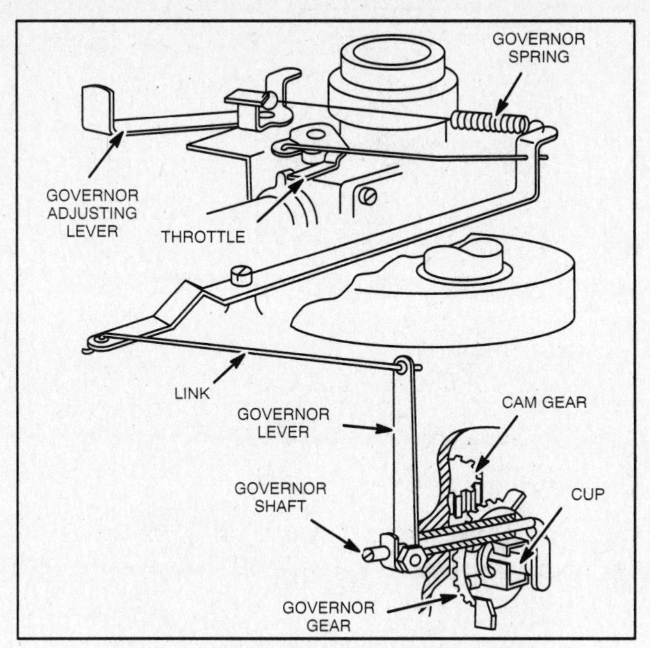

Fig. 42 - Model Series 100900, 130000

Fig. 43 - Model Series 170000, 190000, 220000, 250000, 280000, Typical

MODEL SERIES 91700, 94500, 94900, 111700, 113900, 114700, 114900, (NEW STYLE)

The mechanical governor for Model Series listed above is illustrated in Fig. 44. The governor gear is part of the oil slinger assembly.

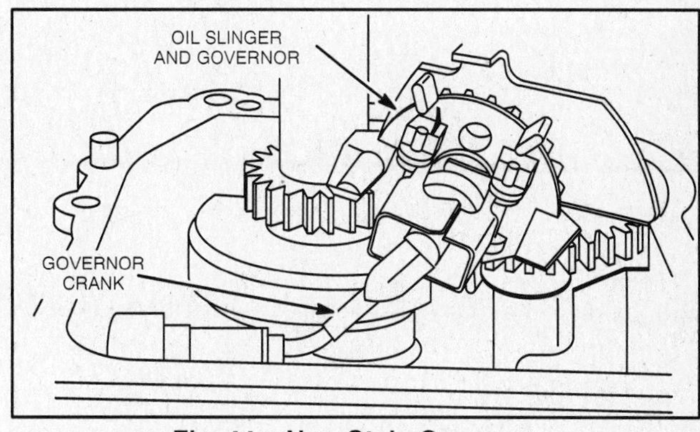

Fig. 44 - New Style Governor

DISASSEMBLE

1. Before governor can be serviced, the engine sump must be removed.
2. Loosen governor lever bolt and nut.
3. Slide lever off governor crank and snap out governor link.
4. Remove hair pin and washer from governor crank.
5. Remove any paint and burrs from governor crank.
6. Remove governor crank, Fig. 45.

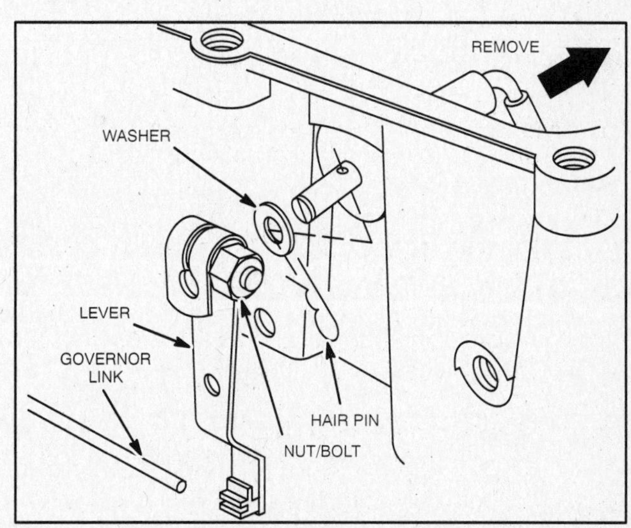

Fig. 45 - Removing Governor Crank

NOTE: METRIC EQUIVALENTS ARE LISTED ON PAGE 28 OF THIS SECTION.

REPLACE GOVERNOR SHAFT BUSHING

1. Press old governor shaft bushing out of cylinder.
2. Press new bushing into cylinder until bushing is 1/16 inch above outside surface of cylinder.
3. Ream bushing using Tool #19058, Finish Reamer, using Stanisol or kerosene for lubricant.

ASSEMBLE GOVERNOR

1. Install governor crank from inside cylinder.
2. Slide washer onto governor crank and install hair pin.
3. Slide governor lever onto governor crank and tighten bolt and nut on lever until governor crank turns with resistance.
4. Turn crank counterclockwise until paddle contacts governor cup on oil slinger, Fig. 46.

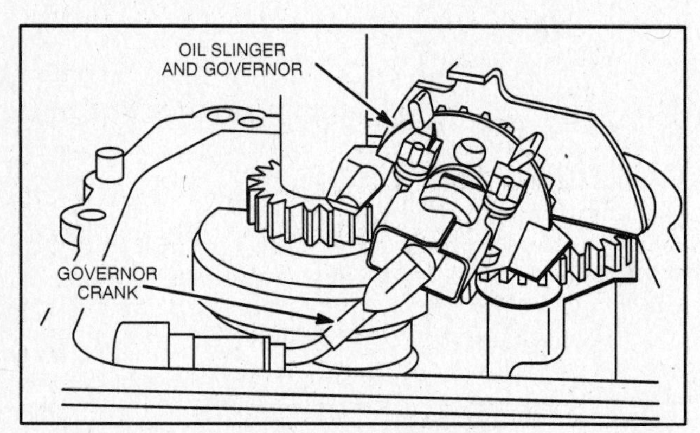

Fig. 46 – Install Governor

5. Snap governor link into retainer on governor lever.
6. Place new gasket(s) same thickness as original gasket(s) on cylinder.
7. Insert Tool #19334, Seal Protector, into seal of oil sump and install oil sump on cylinder.
8. Place non-hardening sealant on screw "A" such as Permatex® II and install sump screws.
9. Torque screws to 90 in. lbs., Fig. 47.
10. Remove seal protector.

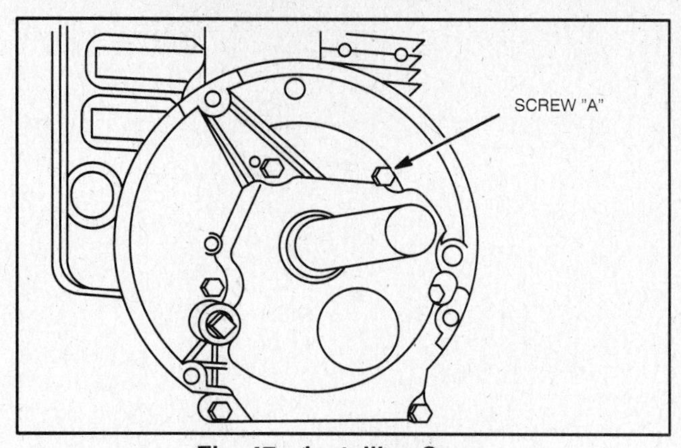

Fig. 47 – Installing Sump

INSTALL GOVERNOR SPRING MODEL SERIES 91700, 111700, 114700

Governor spring should be installed as shown in Fig. 48.

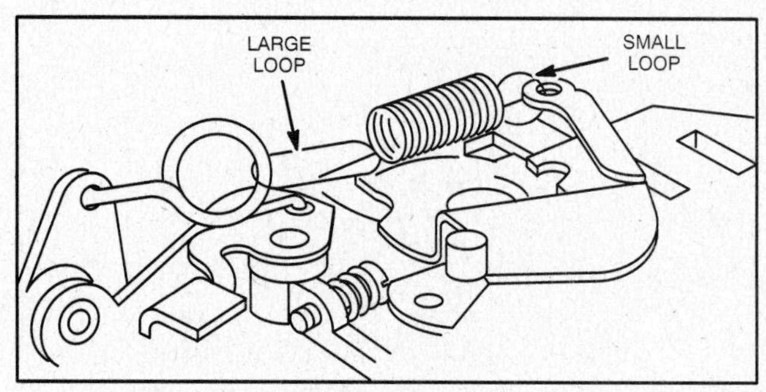

Fig. 48 – Installing Governor Spring

INSTALL GOVERNOR SPRING MODEL SERIES 94500, 94900, 95500, 113900, 114900, (NEW STYLE)

Governor spring should be installed as shown in Fig. 49. Note position of spring loops.

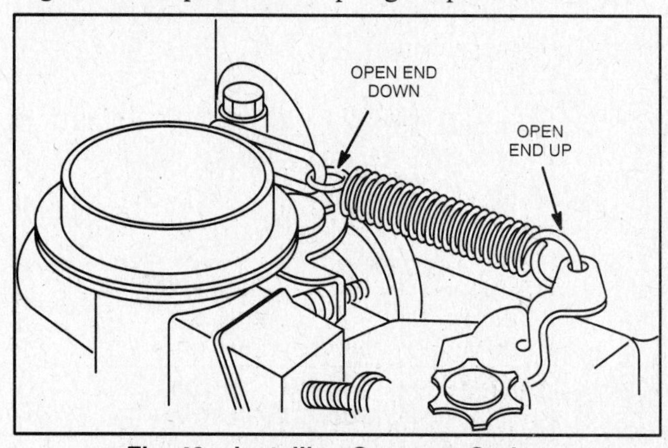

Fig. 49 – Installing Governor Spring

NOTE: METRIC EQUIVALENTS ARE LISTED ON PAGE 28 OF THIS SECTION.

ADJUST GOVERNOR - STATIC

1. Place throttle control in wide open throttle position.
2. With a screwdriver, turn governor crank counter-clockwise as far as it will go and while holding governor crank, torque governor bolt nut 35 to 45 in. lbs., Fig. 50.

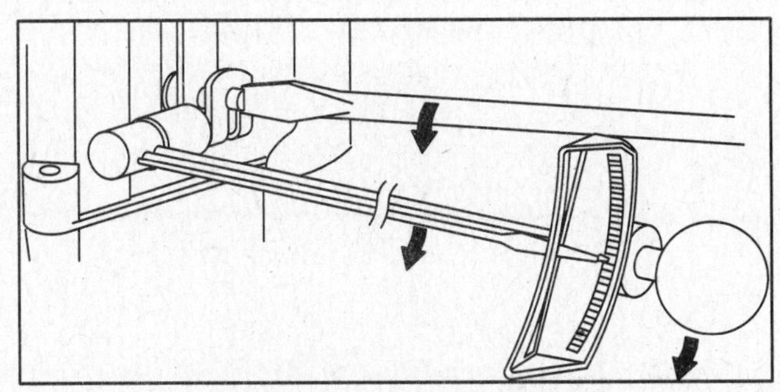

Fig. 50 - Adjusting Governor

MODEL SERIES 91700, 94500, 94900, 95500, 111700, 113900, 114700, 114900, (OLD STYLE)

The mechanical governor for Model Series listed above is illustrated below, Fig. 51.

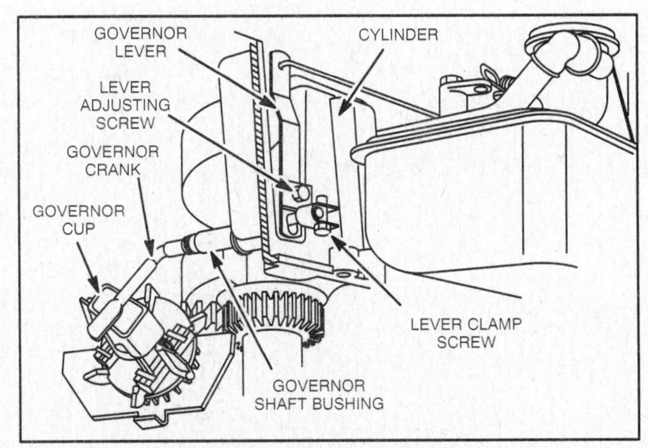

Fig. 51 - Old Style Governor

DISASSEMBLE

1. Before governor can be serviced, the engine sump must be removed.
2. Remove lever adjusting screw and loosen lever clamp screw.
3. Slide off clamp.
4. Lift up on governor lever to release lever from slot in governor crank.
5. Remove any paint or burrs from governor crank. Slide governor crank out of cylinder, Fig. 51.

REPLACE GOVERNOR SHAFT BUSHING

1. Press old bushing out of cylinder.
2. Press new bushing into cylinder until bushing is 1/16 inch above outside surface of cylinder.
3. Ream bushing using Tool #19058, Finish Reamer, using Stanisol or kerosene for lubricant.

ASSEMBLE

1. Slide governor crank into governor bushing from inside cylinder.
2. Then slide governor lever on governor crank and slide lever down onto shaft slot.
3. Slide on lever clamp and start screw in adjusting slot on clamp.
4. Torque lever clamp screw to 15 in. lbs.
5. Install governor gear and oil slinger assembly making sure governor crank is against governor cup.
6. Place Tool #19334, Seal Protector, in seal of sump.
7. Place new gasket(s) on cylinder, same thickness as old gasket(s).
8. Install sump on cylinder. Place non-hardening sealant on screw "A" such as Permatex® II and torque sump screws to 90 in. lbs., Fig. 52.

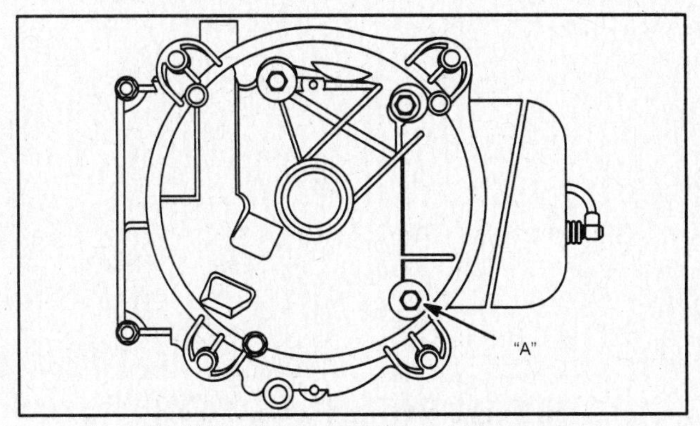

Fig. 52 - Sealant on Screw (Typical)

INSTALL GOVERNOR SPRING MODEL SERIES 91700, 111700, 114700

Governor spring should be installed as shown in Fig. 53.

NOTE: METRIC EQUIVALENTS ARE LISTED ON PAGE 28 OF THIS SECTION.

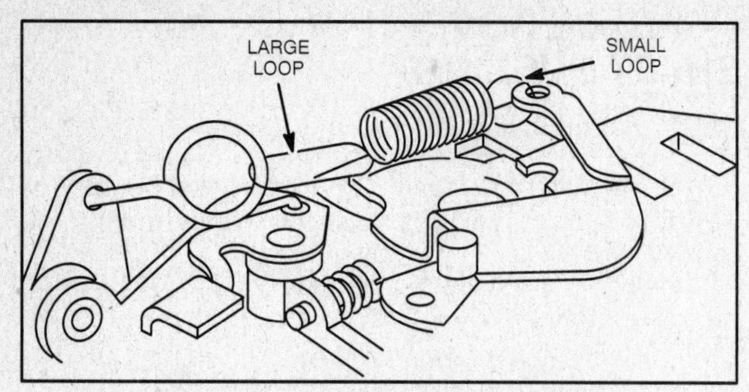

Fig. 53 – Installing Governor Spring

INSTALL GOVERNOR SPRING MODEL SERIES 94500, 94900, 95500, 113900, 114900, (OLD STYLE)

1. Hold governor spring as shown in Fig. 54 with open end of small loop down.
2. Hook large loop in throttle link loop as shown in Fig. 54 and pull loop toward throttle lever until end of spring loop snaps on.
3. Hook small loop in throttle control lever as shown in Fig. 55.

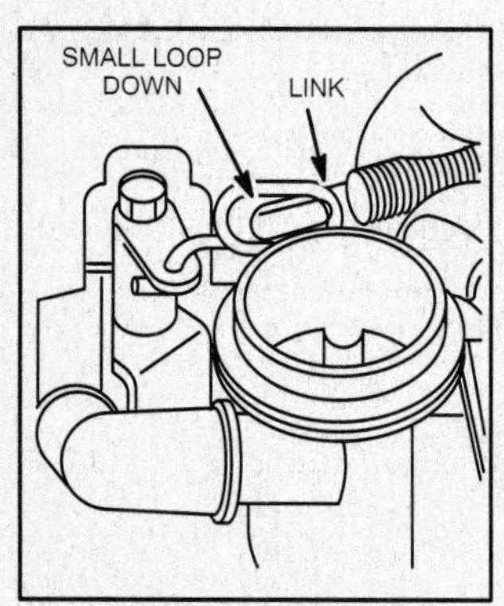

Fig. 54 – Installing Governor Spring

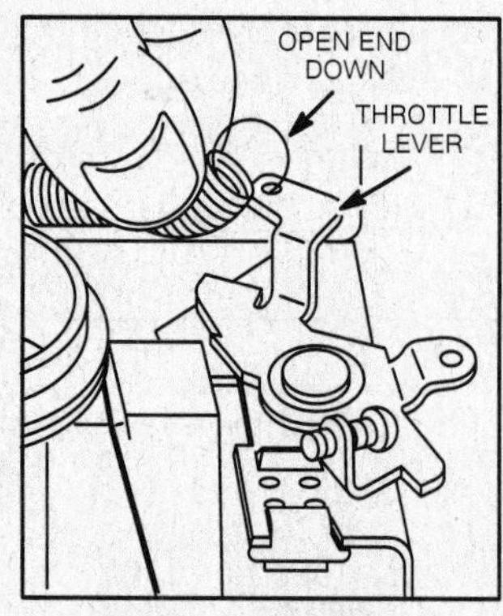

Fig. 55 – Governor Spring Installed

ADJUST GOVERNOR – STATIC

1. Move throttle control to wide open throttle position.
2. Loosen lever adjusting screw, Fig. 51.
3. Turn governor crank counterclockwise and hold.
4. Torque lever adjusting screw to 15 in. lbs., Fig. 51.

MODEL SERIES 120000

The mechanical governor used on Model Series listed above is illustrated in Fig. 56. The governor gear is part of the oil slinger assembly.

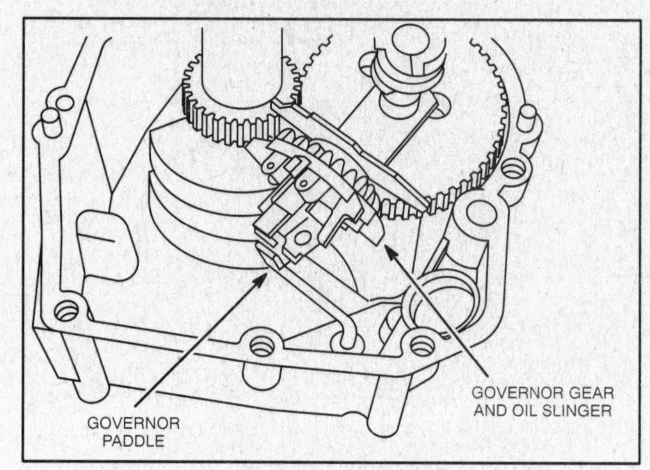

Fig. 56 – Governor, Model Series 120000

DISASSEMBLE

1. Before governor can be serviced, the engine sump must be removed.
2. Loosen governor lever bolt and nut.
3. Slide lever off governor crank and disconnect from governor link.
4. Remove push nut and washer from governor crank, remove burrs from governor crank, and remove crank, Fig. 57.

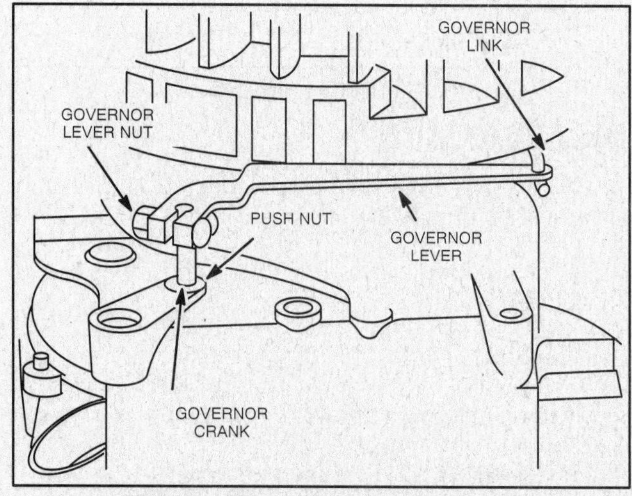

Fig. 57 – Removing Governor Lever

NOTE: METRIC EQUIVALENTS ARE LISTED ON PAGE 28 OF THIS SECTION.

INSPECT GOVERNOR

Check governor gear and oil slinger assembly for worn governor weight pins, worn or damaged governor cup, and chipped or damaged teeth and paddles on oil slinger. Replace any worn or damaged parts.

ASSEMBLE GOVERNOR

1. Install governor crank from inside cylinder.
2. Slide washer onto governor crank and install new push nut on governor crank.
3. Slide governor lever onto governor crank and tighten bolt and nut on lever until governor crank turns with resistance.
4. Turn crank until paddle contacts governor cup on oil slinger, Fig. 56.
5. Place new gasket(s) same thickness as original gasket(s) on cylinder.
6. Insert Tool #19356, Orange Seal Protector, into seal of oil sump and install oil sump on cylinder.
7. Place non-hardening sealant such as Permatex® II, on screw "A" and install sump screws.
8. Torque screws to 85 in. lbs., Fig. 58. Remove seal protector.

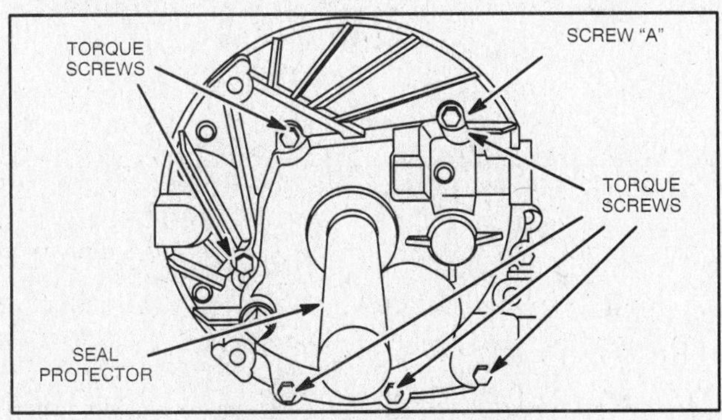

Fig. 58 – Installing Sump

ADJUST GOVERNOR – STATIC

1. Place throttle in fast position and insert a 1/8" rod through holes in carburetor control bracket and lever.

   NOTE: On new style Three-in-One control, there is not a pair of holes for alignment. Move control lever to fast position.

2. With a screwdriver, turn governor crank counter-clockwise as far as it will go and while holding governor crank, torque governor bolt nut to 35 to 45 in. lbs., Fig. 59.

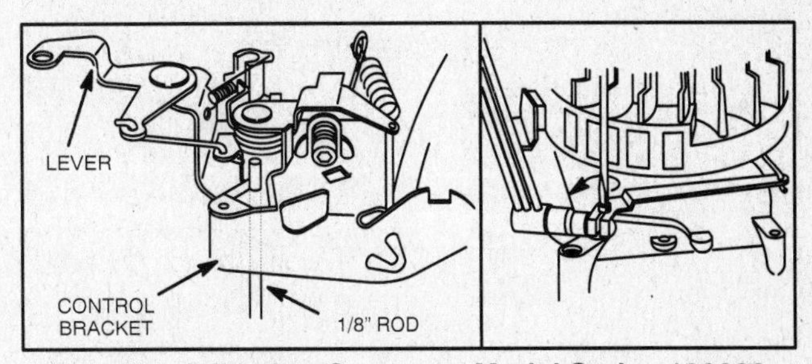

Fig. 59 – Adjusting Governor, Model Series 120000

ADJUST GOVERNOR, NEW STYLE THREE-IN-ONE (TOP NO LOAD) ENGINE RUNNING

1. Place throttle in fast position and insert a 1/8" rod through holes in carburetor control bracket and lever.
2. Start engine and adjust **Top No Load RPM** by turning bending tang to decrease or increase, Fig. 60.

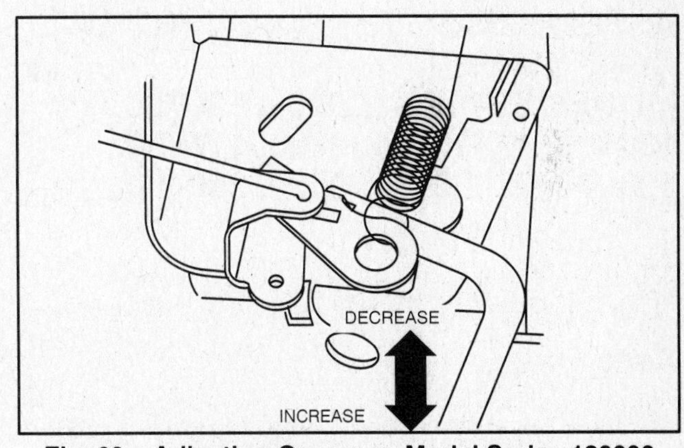

Fig. 60 – Adjusting Governor, Model Series 120000

ADJUST GOVERNOR, OLD STYLE (TOP NO LOAD) ENGINE RUNNING

1. Place throttle in fast position and insert a 1/8" rod through holes in carburetor control bracket and lever.
2. Start engine and adjust **Top No Load RPM** by turning screw clockwise to decrease or counter-clockwise to increase, Fig. 61.

NOTE: METRIC EQUIVALENTS ARE LISTED ON PAGE 28 OF THIS SECTION.

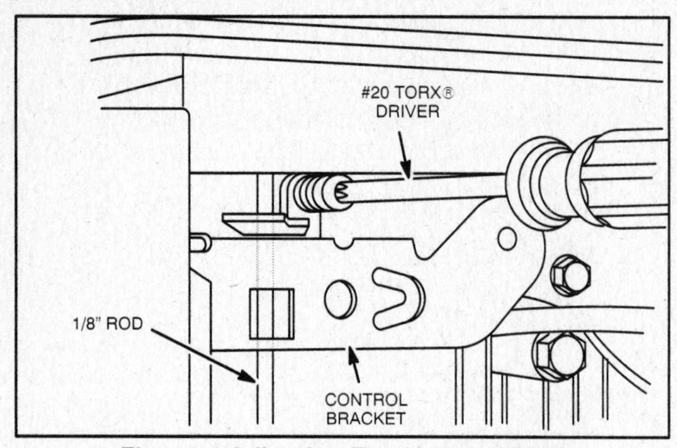

Fig. 61 – Adjusting Top No Load RPM

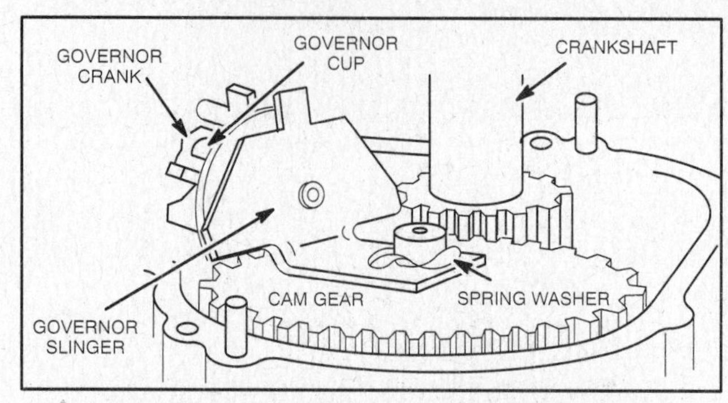

Fig. 62 – Shows Spring on Camshaft after Governor is Installed. Models 100900 and 130700, 130900, 131900, 132900 Only.

NOTE: For correct TOP NO LOAD RPM by model and type, see Engine Sales Manual, MS-4052 or MS-6225, Service Engine Sales Manual microfiche under NOTE column, or MAXIMUM RPM TABLE at end of each manual for the engine model.

ASSEMBLE GOVERNOR, VERTICAL CRANKSHAFT, MODEL SERIES 100900, 130700, 130900, 131900, 132900, 170000, 190000, 220000, 250000, 280000

Assembly

1. On vertical crankshaft models the governor is part of the oil slinger and is installed as shown in Fig. 62.

   NOTE: Models 100900 and 130700, 130900, 131900, 132900 use spring washer as shown in Fig. 62.

2. Before installing sump be sure that governor cup is in line with governor shaft paddle.

3. Install sump and gasket being sure screw "A," Fig. 63 has nonhardening sealant on threads such as Permatex® II.

   NOTE: On Model Series 130700, 130900, 131700 and 132900 equipped with right angle auxiliary drive power take-off, the spring washer is not to be used.

   NOTE: On right angle auxiliary drive power take-off models, screw "A" does not need sealant but the four screws holding the gear sump cover require sealant, Fig. 63.

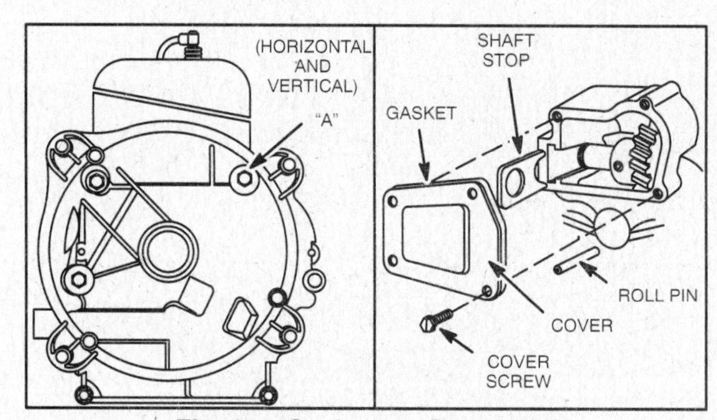

Fig. 63 – Sealant on Screw "A"

4. Complete installation of remaining governor linkages and carburetor. Then adjust governor shaft and lever. See "Adjustments."

NOTE: If governor shaft bushing is replaced, it must be finished reamed with Tool #19333, Governor Bushing Reamer, for 1/4 inch governor crank or with Tool #19058, Governor Bushing Reamer, for 3/16 inch governor crank.

ADJUST GOVERNOR – STATIC

1. Loosen screw holding governor lever to governor crank shaft.

2. Place throttle in high speed position.

3. While holding throttle in this position with a screwdriver, turn governor shaft clockwise as far as it will go.

4. Tighten screw holding governor lever to governor shaft. Torque to 35-45 in. lbs., Fig. 64.

5. Before starting engine, manually move governor linkage to check for any binding.

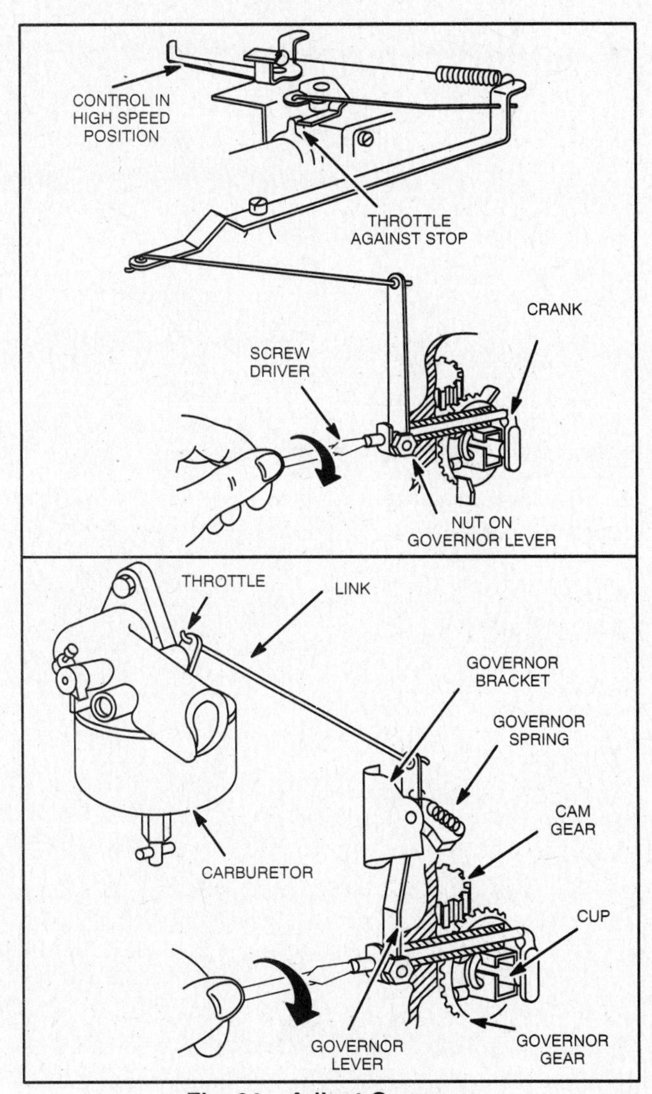

Fig. 64 - Adjust Governor

ADJUST GOVERNOR - ENGINE RUNNING

1. Set control lever to maximum speed position, with engine running.

2. Use Tool #19229, Tang Bending Tool, to bend spring anchor tang to obtain the proper TOP NO LOAD RPM, Fig. 65, swivel and vertical rack and pinion control brackets or Fig. 66, horizontal rack and pinion control bracket. For engines using Top Speed Limit, adjust tang to 4000 RPM, unless otherwise noted in table above figure before installing limit screw.

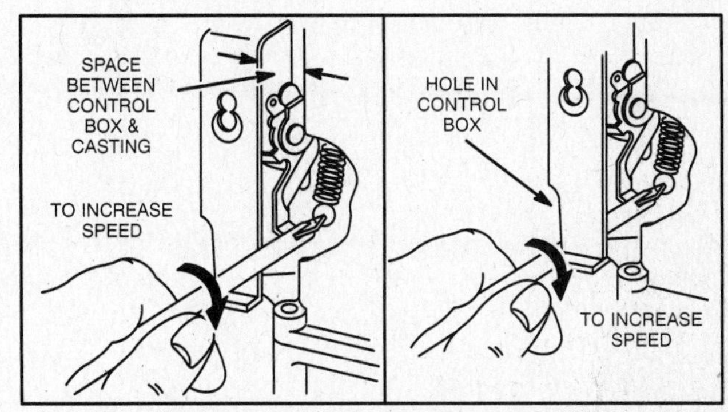

Fig. 65 - Adjusting TOP NO LOAD RPM, Swivel and Vertical Rack and Pinion Control Bracket

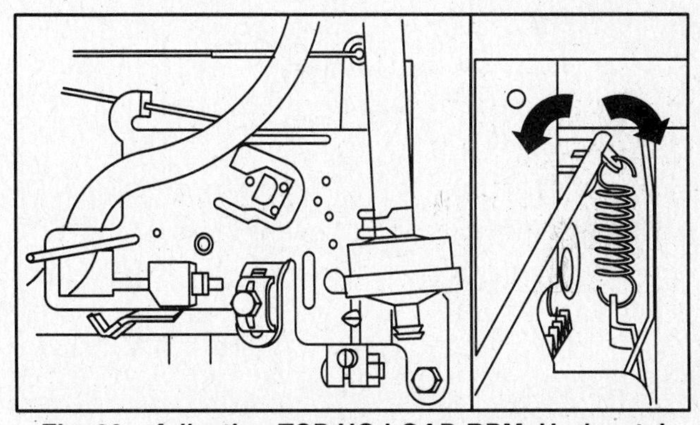

Fig. 66 - Adjusting TOP NO LOAD RPM, Horizontal Rack and Pinion Control Bracket

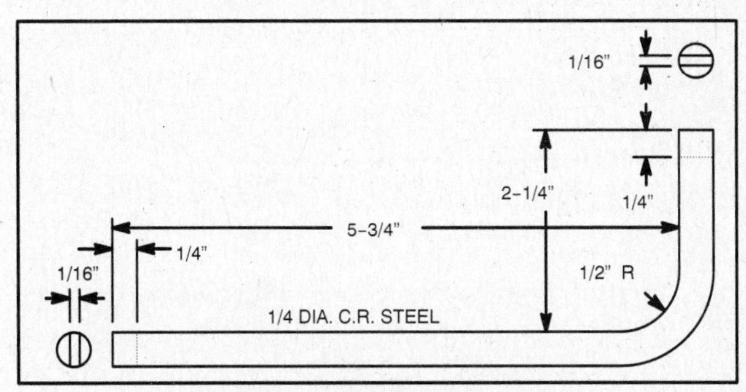

Fig. 67 - Tang Bending Tool

NOTE: If Tool #19229 is not available, make tool, Fig. 67.

NOTE: METRIC EQUIVALENTS ARE LISTED ON PAGE 28 OF THIS SECTION.

NOTE: Refer to Fig.'s 68, 69 and 70 to identify the type of control and refer to table above that figure for correct hole to use after adjusting governor tang, Step 3.

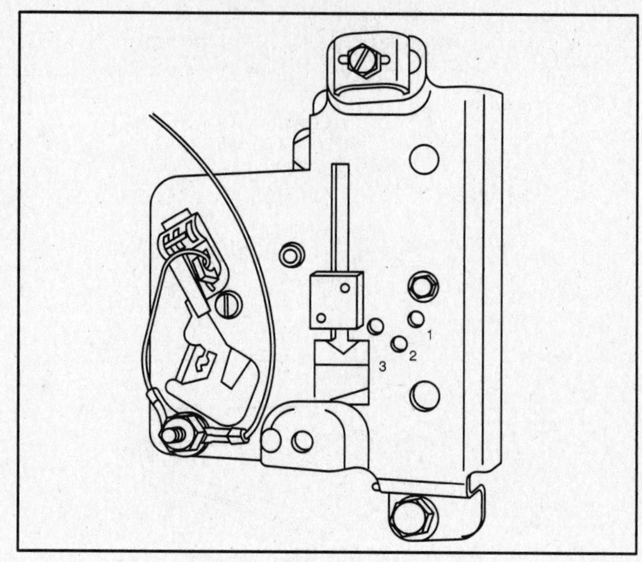

Fig. 69

SETTING TOP SPEED

Top Speed Limit Screw Position	Model Series	No Load Top Speed Range
No. 1 Position with governor tang set to 4000 RPM	194700, 195700, 196700, 254700, 257700, 283700, 286700	3300
No. 1 Position with governor tang set to 3500 RPM	194700, 195700, 196700, 254700, 257700, 283700, 286700	2800
No. 2 Position with governor tang set to 4000 RPM	194700, 195700, 196700, 254700, 257700, 283700, 286700	2850

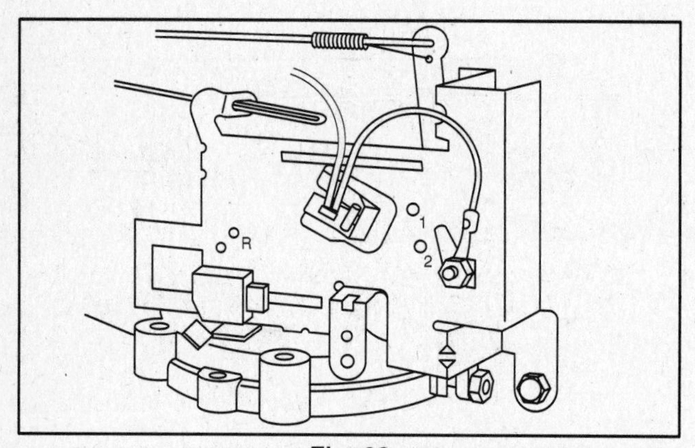

Fig. 68

SETTING TOP SPEED

Top Speed Limit Screw Position	No Load Top Speed Range
None	4000 to 3800 RPM
No. 1 Position	3400 to 2900 RPM
No. 2 Position	2800 to 2400 RPM

SETTING TOP SPEED

Top Speed Limit Screw Position	Model Series	No Load Top Speed Range
None	170000, 190000 220000, 250000 280000	4000
No. 1 Position	170000, 190000 220000, 250000 280000	3300
No. 2 Position	170000, 190000	2800
No. 3 Position	220000, 250000 280000	2800

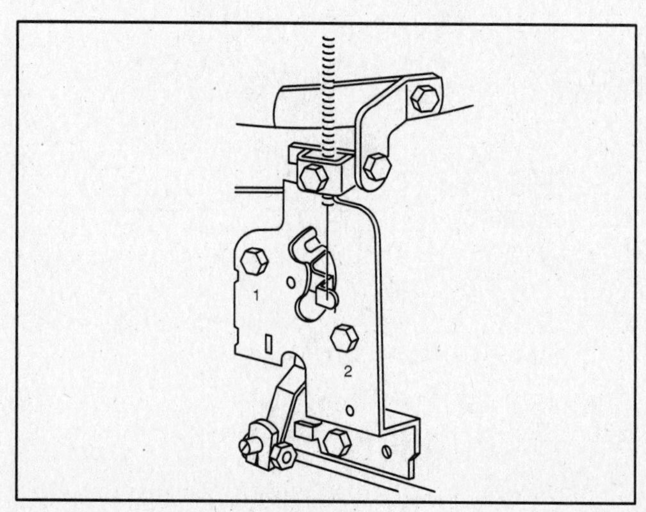

Fig. 70

NOTE: METRIC EQUIVALENTS ARE LISTED ON PAGE 28 OF THIS SECTION.

ADJUST GOVERNED IDLE RACK AND PINION CONTROL HORIZONTAL SLIDE VERTICAL CRANKSHAFT MODELS

1. To adjust, first make final carburetor mixture adjustments.
2. Then place remote control in idle position.
3. Hold throttle shaft in closed position with finger, adjusting idle speed screw to 1200 RPM.
4. Release throttle.
5. Set remote control to 1750 RPM and bend tang until it contacts remote control slide, Fig. 71.

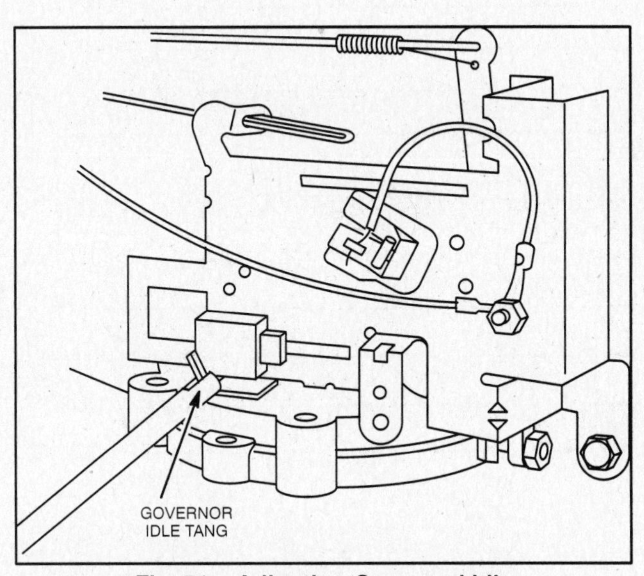

Fig. 71 – Adjusting Governed Idle

ADJUST GOVERNED IDLE RACK AND PINION CONTROL VERTICAL SLIDE

1. To adjust, first make final carburetor mixture adjustment.
2. Then place remote control in idle position.
3. Hold throttle in closed position with finger, adjust idle speed screw to 1550 RPM.
4. Release throttle.
5. Set remote control to 1750 RPM. Turn screw in until it contacts remote control lever, Fig. 72.

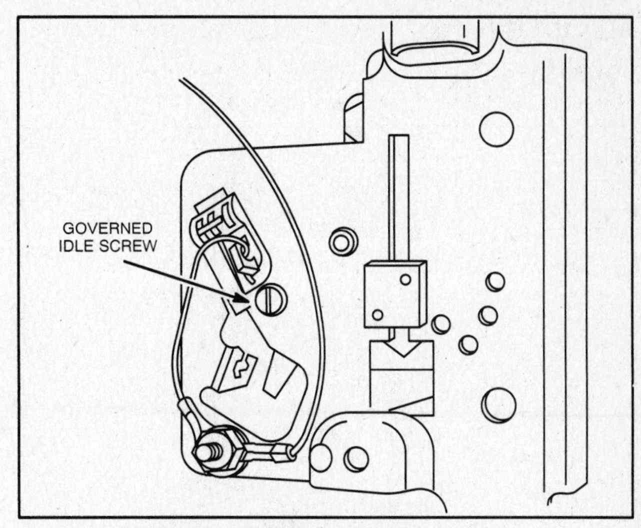

Fig. 72 – Adjusting Governed Idle

ADJUST GOVERNED IDLE, SWIVEL CONTROL HORIZONTAL CRANKSHAFT MODELS

1. To adjust, first make final carburetor mixture adjustment.
2. Then place remote control in idle position.
3. Hold throttle in closed position with finger, adjust idle speed screw to 1550 RPM.
4. Release throttle.
5. Set remote control to 1750 RPM. Turn screw in until it contacts remote control lever, Fig. 73.

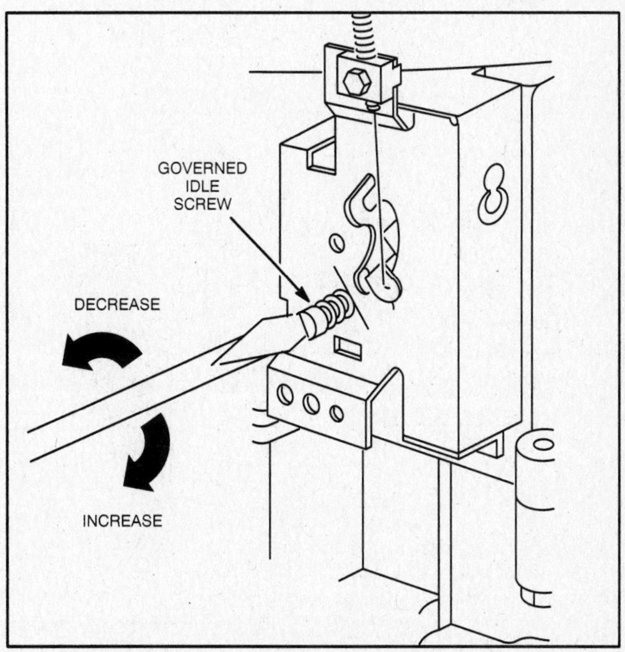

Fig. 73 – Adjusting Governed Idle

NOTE: METRIC EQUIVALENTS ARE LISTED ON PAGE 28 OF THIS SECTION.

ADJUST SPRING LOADED SCREW TYPE

Following steps 1 through 4 above, turn screw until it contacts remote control lever. See Fig. 74.

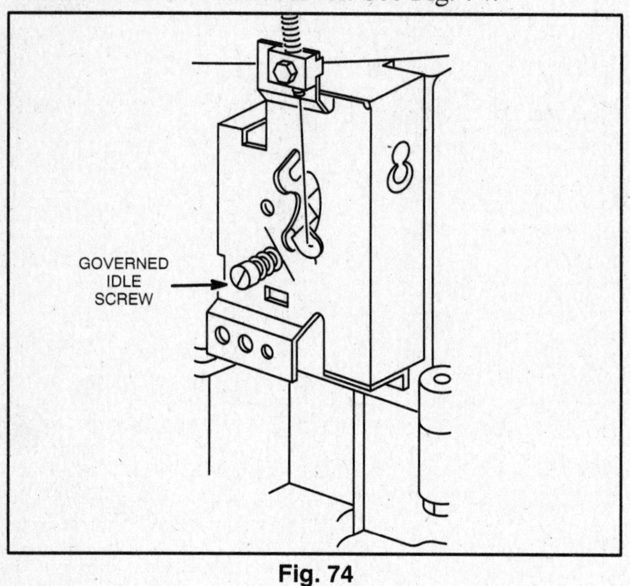

Fig. 74

ADJUST GOVERNED IDLE STOP

1. Set remote control to 1750 RPM.
2. Loosen governed idle stop and place against remote control lever, Fig. 75.
3. Tighten governed idle stop.

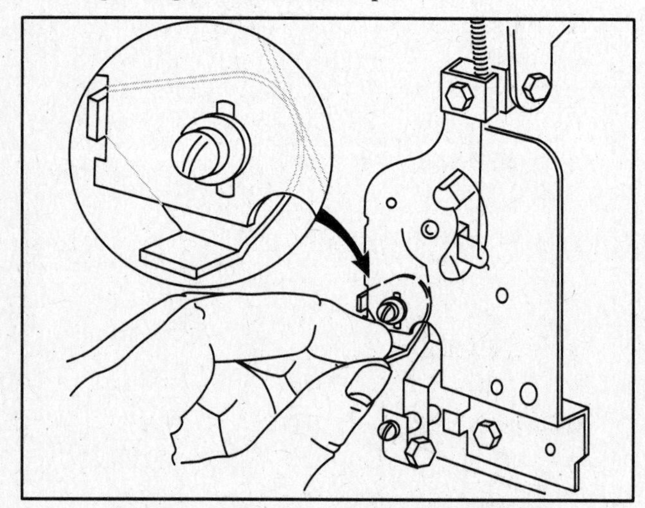

Fig. 75 – Adjusting Governed Idle Stop

METRIC EQUIVALENTS

Inches	Millimeters
1/16	1.57
1/8	3.18
3/16	4.74
1/4	6.35
1/2	12.70
2-1/4	57.15
5-3/4	146.00
18	457
19	483
20	508
21	5.33
22	559
23	584
24	610
25	635

TORQUE

In. Lbs.	Kgcm Kpcm	Nm
15	17.3	1.7
35-45	40-52	4-5.1
85	98	9.6
90	104	10.2

NOTE: METRIC EQUIVALENTS ARE LISTED ON PAGE 28 OF THIS SECTION.

Section 6
COMPRESSION

SECTION INDEX

NOTE: METRIC EQUIVALENTS ARE LISTED ON PAGE 16 OF THIS SECTION.

COMPRESSION

Briggs & Stratton does not publish compression pressures, as it is extremely difficult to obtain an accurate reading without special equipment.

It has been determined through extensive testing, a simple and accurate indication of compression can be made as follows:

Spin the flywheel counterclockwise (flywheel side) against the compression stroke. A sharp rebound indicates satisfactory compression. Slight or no rebound indicates poor compression.

Loss of compression will usually be the result of the following:

1. Cylinder head gasket blown or leaking.
2. Valves sticking or not seating properly.
3. Piston rings not sealing, which would also cause the engine to consume an excessive amount of oil.

Carbon deposits in the combustion chamber should be removed every 100 to 300 hours of use (more often when run at a steady load), or whenever the cylinder head is removed.

Remove Cylinder Head and Shield

Always note the position of the different cylinder head screws so that they may be properly reassembled. If a screw is used in the wrong position, it may be too short and not engage enough threads. It may be too long and bottom on a fin, either breaking the fin, or leaving the cylinder head loose.

CYLINDER HEAD TORQUE PROCEDURE

Assemble the cylinder head with a new head gasket, cylinder head shield, screws and washers in their proper places. (Graphite grease or Valve Guide Lubricant, Part #93963 should be used on cylinder head screws.)

Do not use a sealer of any kind on gasket. Tighten the screws down evenly by hand. Use a torque wrench and tighten head bolts in the sequence shown, Fig. 1, and to the specified torque in Table 1.

Do not turn one screw down completely before the others, as it may cause a warped cylinder head.

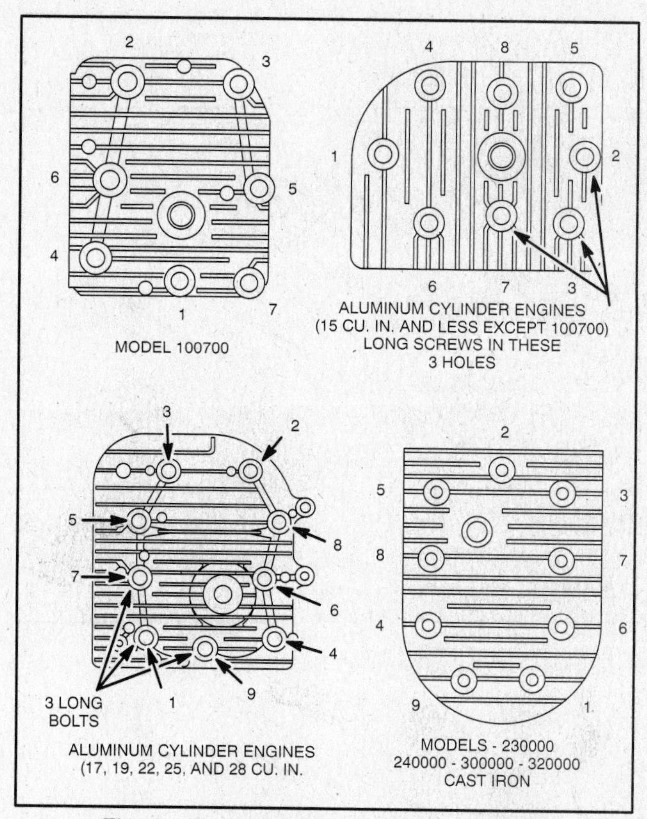

Fig. 1 – Torque Pattern, Cylinder Heads

TABLE NO. 1
CYLINDER HEAD TORQUE

BASIC MODEL SERIES	
ALUMINUM CYLINDER	**Inch Pounds**
60000, 80000, 90000, 100000, 110000, 120000, 130000	140
170000, 190000, 220000, 250000, 280000	165
CAST IRON CYLINDER	**Inch Pounds**
230000, 240000, 300000, 320000	190

NOTE: METRIC EQUIVALENTS ARE LISTED ON PAGE 16 OF THIS SECTION.

VALVES

Remove Valves

Fig. 2 shows three methods used to hold valve spring retainers or rotators.

1. To remove types shown in Illus. 1 and 2, use Valve Spring Compressor, Tool #19063, adjusting jaws until they just touch the top and bottom of the valve chamber.

   NOTE: This will keep the upper jaw from slipping into the coils of the spring.

2. Push the compressor in until the upper jaw slips over the upper end of the spring.

3. Tighten the jaws to compress the spring, Fig. 3.

4. Remove collars or pin and lift out valve. Pull out compressor and spring, Fig. 4.

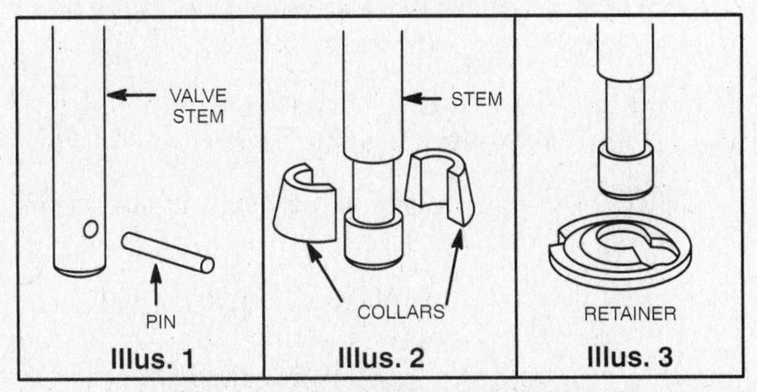

Fig. 2 – Valve Spring Retainers

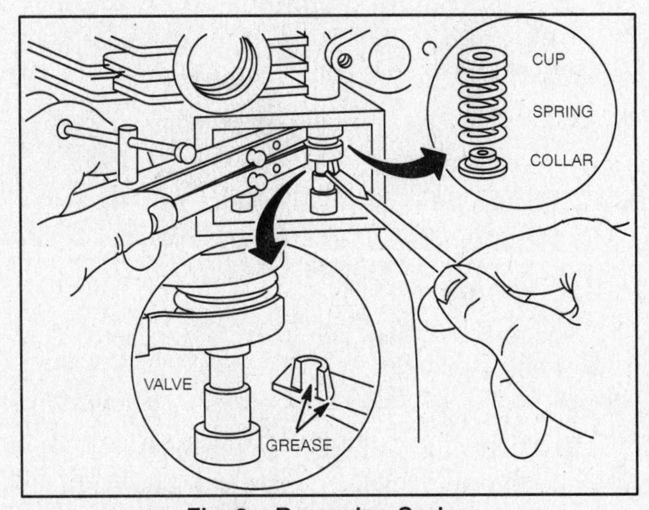

Fig. 3 – Removing Spring

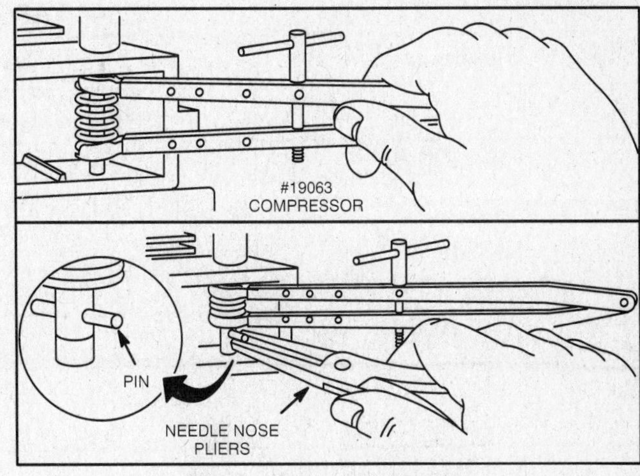

Fig. 4 – Removing Spring

1. To remove valves using retainers, Fig. 2, Illus. 3 slip the upper jaw of Tool #19063, Valve Spring Compressor, over the top of the valve chamber and lower jaw between spring and retainer.

2. Compress spring. Remove retainer.

3. Pull out valve.

4. Remove compressor and spring, Fig. 5.

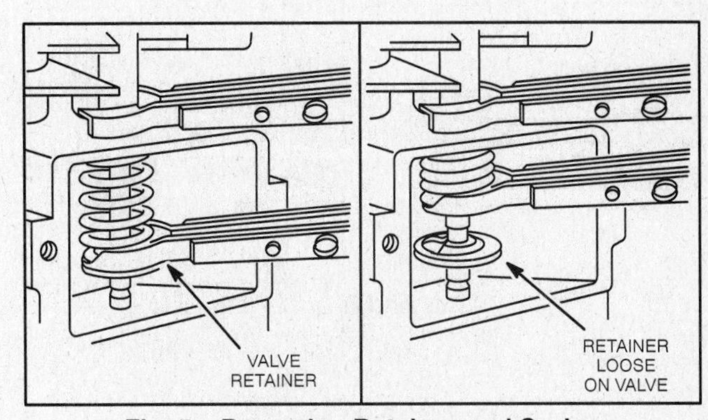

Fig. 5 – Removing Retainer and Spring

NOTE: METRIC EQUIVALENTS ARE LISTED ON PAGE 16 OF THIS SECTION.

TABLE NO. 2
VALVE TAPPET CLEARANCE

BASIC MODEL SERIES	INTAKE		EXHAUST	
ALUMINUM CYLINDER**	**MIN.**	**MAX.**	**MIN.**	**MAX.**
60000, 80000, 90000*, 100000, 110000, 120000	.005	.007	.007*	.009*
130000, 170000, 190000, 220000, 250000●, 280000***	.005	.007	.009	.011
CAST IRON CYLINDER				
230000, 240000, 300000, 320000	.007	.009	.017	.019

* Some Model Series System 2®, System 3®, and System 4® have been built with .005 to .007" exhaust valve clearance. The breathers on these engines are stamped on the inside surface.

● On Model Series 253400, 255400 engines equipped with "**both**" electric start and rewind start, set **VALVE TAPPET clearance** to "Rewind Start" specifications as listed in Table No. 2. For **Electric Start Only** engines, set intake valve clearance to .009 to .011".

** Includes Cylinders with Cast Iron sleeves.

*** Model Series 286700 engines, set **INTAKE VALVE TAPPET clearance** to .004 to .006".

6

Reface Valves and Seats

Valve faces should be resurfaced on a valve grinder. Valve seats are cut using Tool #19237 or #19343, Neway Valve Seat Cutter Kit, to 45° on exhaust and some intake seats. Other intake seats are cut to 30°. Valve and seat are lapped in using Tool #19258, Valve Lapping Tool, and Part #94150,Valve Lapping Compound, to assure a good seal between the valve face and the seat.

Valve seat width should be 3/64 to 1/16 inch, Fig. 6. If the seat is wider, a narrowing cutter should be used. If valve face or seat are badly burned, the burned part should be replaced. Replace valve if margin is damaged, 1/64 inch or less, Fig. 6.

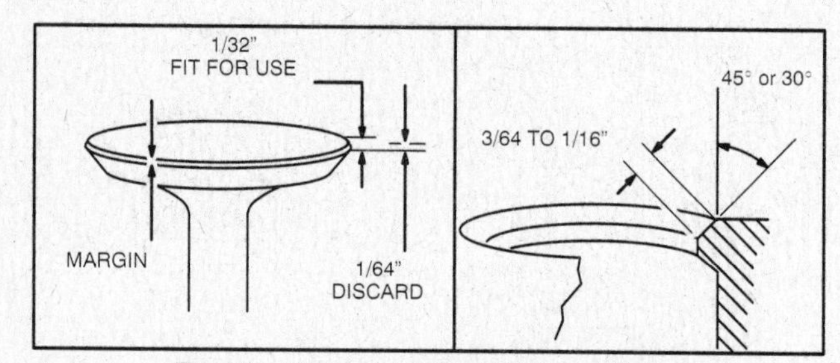

Fig. 6 - Valve and Seat Dimensions

Check and Adjust Tappet Clearance

1. Place valves in their correct guides in cylinder.
2. Turn crankshaft until piston comes to top dead center, compression stroke. Both valves should be closed.
3. Turn crankshaft past top dead center until piston is 1/4 inch down from top of cylinder.

   NOTE: Turn crankshaft counterclockwise as viewed from PTO.
4. Check clearance of intake and exhaust valves to tappets with feeler gauge, Table No. 2.
5. If there is not enough clearance, grind ends of valves square until correct clearance is obtained.
6. If clearance is too much, cut valve seat until correct clearance is obtained.
7. Narrow the seat, if required, to maintain 3/64 to 1/16 inch seat width.

NOTE: Check valve clearances while engine is cold.

Install Valves

Some engines use the same spring for intake and exhaust side, while others use a heavier spring on the exhaust side. Compare springs before installing.

NOTE: Apply "LED-PLATE" or Part #93963, Valve Guide Lubricant, to valve stems and guides before installing. Be sure that no "LED-PLATE" or Part #93963 is on the ends of the valve stems or tappets.

NOTE: METRIC EQUIVALENTS ARE LISTED ON PAGE 16 OF THIS SECTION.

Install Valves, Pin or Collar Retainers
Fig. 2, Illus. 1 and 2

1. If retainers are held by a pin or collars, Fig. 2, Illus. 1 and 2, place valve spring and retainer (and cup on Model Series 230000, 240000, 300000 and 320000) into Tool #19063, Valve Spring Compressor.

2. Compress spring until it is solid.

3. Insert the compressed spring and retainer (and cup when used) into valve chamber.

4. Then drop the valve into place, pushing the stem through the retainer.

5. Hold the spring up in the chamber, and the valve down.

6. Insert the retainer pin with a needle nose pliers or place the collars in the groove in the valve stem.

7. Lower the spring until the retainer fits around the pin or collars, then pull out the spring compressor, Fig. 3.

8. Be sure pin or collars are in place.

Install Valves, Self-Lock Retainers
Fig. 2, Illus. 3

1. If self-lock retainer, Fig. 2, Illus. 3 is used, compress retainer and spring with Valve Spring Compressor, Tool #19063, until spring is solid.

2. Large hole of retainer should face toward opening in Tool #19063, Valve Spring Compressor, Fig. 7.

3. Insert compressed spring and retainer into valve chamber.

4. Lower valve stem through large hole of retainer slot and then push down and in on compressor until retainer bottoms on valve stem shoulder.

5. Release valve spring compressor until it is just free of spring tension and withdraw compressor, Fig. 7.

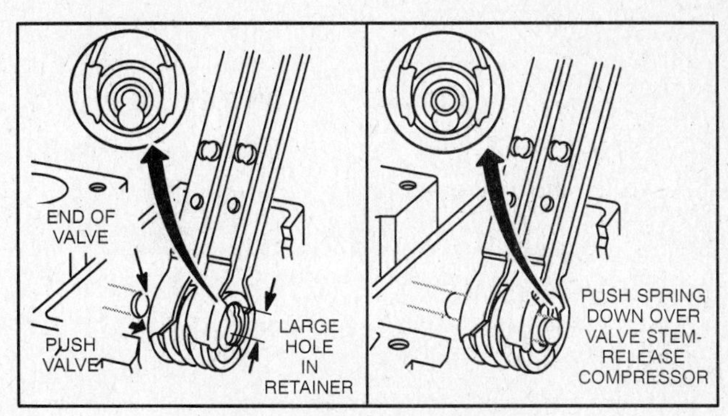

Fig. 7 - Installing Valves

VALVE GUIDES

Service 1/4 Inch Valve Guides

Model Series 60000, 80000, 90000, 100000, 110000, 120000, 130000

If flat end of Valve Guide Plug Gauge, Tool #19122, can be inserted into valve guide a distance of 5/16 inch, Fig. 8, Illus. 1, the valve guide is worn and should be rebushed.

Rebush Worn Aluminum Guides

1. Place pilot of Tool #19064, Counterbore Reamer, in valve guide.

2. Slide Tool #19191, Pilot Bushing, down over counterbore reamer until bushing rests on valve seat.

3. Hold replacement guide bushing, Part #63709 on top of pilot bushing and mark reamer 1/16 inch above top of bushing, Fig. 8, Illus. 2.

4. Ream worn valve guide until mark on counterbore reamer is even with top of pilot bushing. Use kerosene or equivalent to lubricate reamer.

5. After guide is counterbored, continue to turn reamer in same direction used to ream guide while withdrawing reamer, Fig. 8, Illus 3.

6. Position bushing in counterbored guide.

7. Press bushing with Tool #19065 or #19274, Valve Guide Bushing Driver, until bushing is flush with top of guide, Fig. 8, Illus. 4.

NOTE: METRIC EQUIVALENTS ARE LISTED ON PAGE 16 OF THIS SECTION.

8. Finish ream bushing with Tool #19066, Finish Reamer, using kerosene or equivalent to lubricate reamer, Fig. 8, Illus. 5. Finish ream through to breather chamber.
9. Before removing reamer, flush all chips away.
10. Remove reamer by turning it in the same direction used to ream while pulling up on reamer.

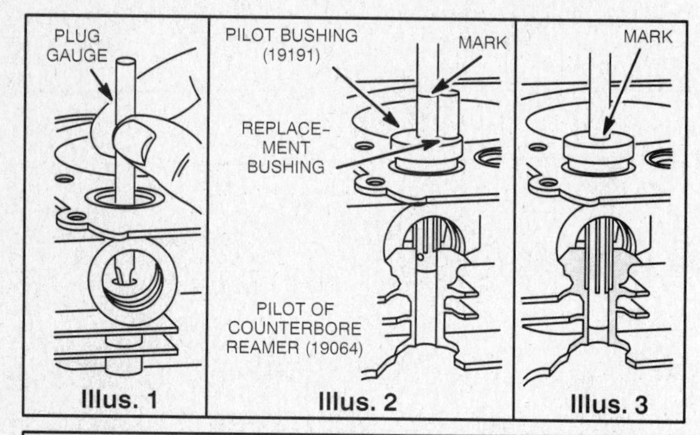

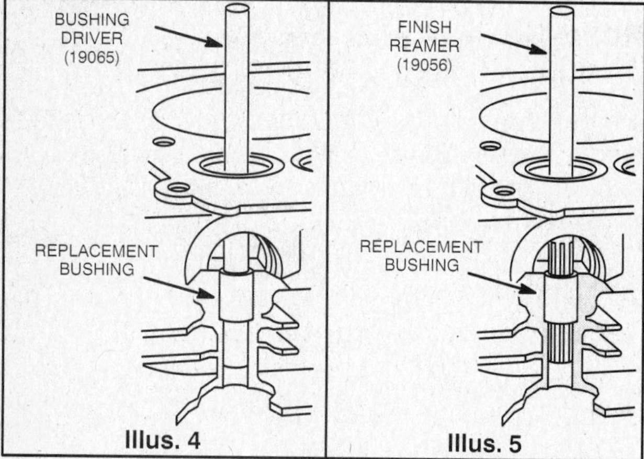

Fig. 8 - Bushing Valve Guides

NOTE: Tool #19191, Pilot Bushing, can be modified to provide more accurate alignment with the valve seat. Counterbore with Tool #19191, Counterbore and Tool #19064, Counterbore Reamer, press in bushing Part #63709 and finish ream with Tool #19066, Finish Reamer, Fig. 9.

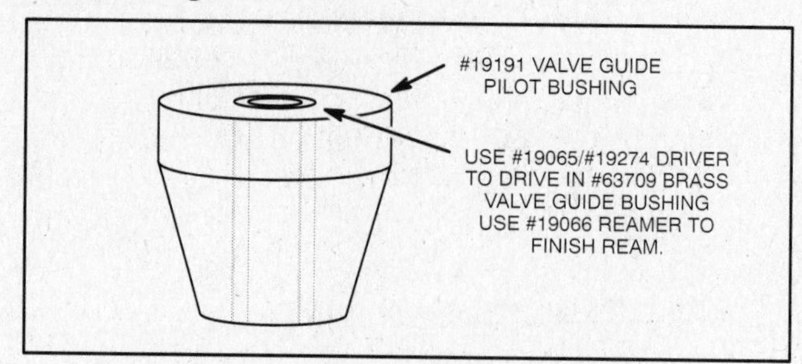

Fig. 9 - Modified Pilot Tool #19191

Replace Worn Brass or Sintered Iron Guides

NOTE: To assure accurate alignment of 7 mm Tap, Tool #19273, Reamer Guide Bushing, Tool #19191 may need to be modified. Measure shank of Tool #19273, 7 mm Tap, and either drill or bush Tool #19191 to assure that tap will be square to the bushing to be pulled.

1. Lubricate Tool #19273, 7 mm Tap, and bushing with engine oil or kerosene.
2. With a tap wrench and Tool #19191 Pilot Guide Bushing, (modified), turn tap into bushing clockwise until tap is 1/2 inch deep. DO NOT tap more than 3/4 inch deep.
3. Remove tap and flush chips out of bushing.
4. Rotate Tool #19272, Puller Nut, up to head of Tool #19271, Puller Screw, and insert puller screw down through Tool #19270 Puller Washer.
5. Thread puller screw into tapped bushing until screw bottoms in tapped hole.
6. Back off screw 1/8 to 1/4 turn and place a drop of engine oil on threads of puller screw, Fig. 10.

NOTE: METRIC EQUIVALENTS ARE LISTED ON PAGE 16 OF THIS SECTION.

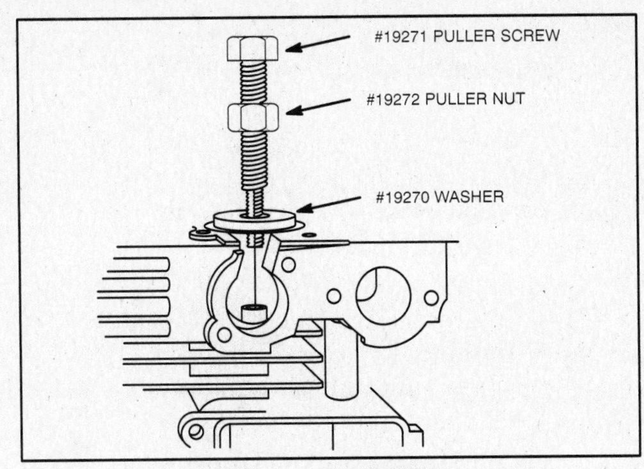

Fig. 10 - Pulling Bushing

7. Hold puller screw stationary and turn puller nut down on washer until valve guide bushing is removed, Fig. 10.
8. Use Table No. 3 to select correct service valve guide bushing.

TABLE NO. 3
GUIDE BUSHING IDENTIFICATION

BUSHING REMOVED FROM CYLINDER				
Sintered Guide Gray or Copper Colored	Brass Guide 1 or 2 Grooves	Brass Guide 1 or 2 Grooves	Brass Guide No Grooves	Alum. Guide or Cast Iron Cylinder
3/4"	3/4"	1-1/16"	3/4"	3/4"
REPLACEMENT BUSHING				
Use Part #262001	Use Part #231348	Use Part #231349	Use Part #63709	Use Part #63709

9. Place grooved or tapered end of new bushing into cylinder valve guide.
10. Press bushing into cylinder with Tool #19065* or #19274, Bushing Driver, until bushing bottoms. Rotate driver while pressing in bushing.

    * 19065 drivers purchased before October 1983 must be modified by reducing driver's tip to .240 inches when used to press in sintered bushings.

11. Finish ream bushing with Tool #19066, Finish Reamer, and Tool #19191, Reamer Guide Bushing, (modified), Fig. 9.
12. Finish ream entire guide. Before removing reamer, flush all chips away.
13. Remove reamer by turning reamer in same direction used to ream bushing while pulling up on reamer, Fig. 8.

Service 5/16 Inch Valve Guides

Model Series 170000, 190000 220000, 230000, 240000, 250000, 280000, 300000, 320000

If flat end of Valve Guide Plug Gauge, Tool #19151, can be inserted into guide a distance of 5/16 inch, the guide is worn and should be rebushed.

6

Rebush Worn Aluminum Guides and Worn Cast Iron Guides (Cast Iron Cylinders)

1. Place pilot of Tool #19231, Counterbore Reamer, in valve guide.
2. Slide Tool #19234, Reamer Guide Bushing, down over counterbore reamer until bushing rests on valve seat.
3. Hold replacement valve guide bushing, Part #231218, on top of pilot bushing and mark reamer 1/16 inch above top of bushing, Fig. 11.

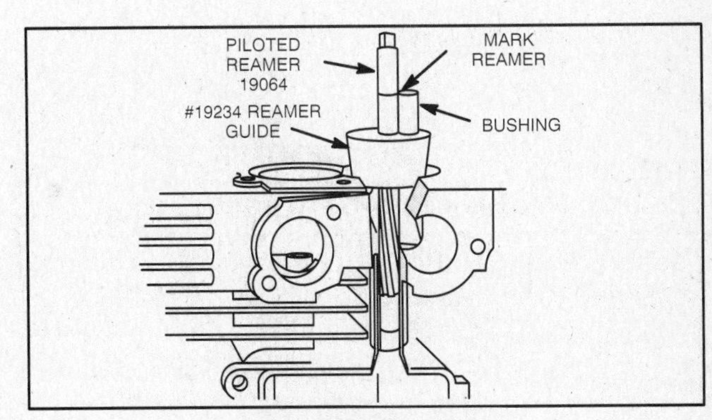

Fig. 11 - Rebushing

4. Ream worn valve guide until mark on counterbore reamer is even with top of reamer guide bushing. Use kerosene or equivalent to lubricate reamer.
5. After guide is counterbored, continue to turn reamer in same direction used to ream guide while withdrawing reamer, Fig. 11.

NOTE: METRIC EQUIVALENTS ARE LISTED ON PAGE 16 OF THIS SECTION.

6. Position bushing in counterbored guide. Press bushing with Tool #19204, Bushing Driver, until bushing is flush with top of guide, Fig. 11.
7. Finish ream bushing with Tool #19233, Finish Reamer, using kerosene or equivalent to lubricate reamer, Fig. 11.
8. Before removing reamer, flush all chips away.
9. Remove reamer by turning it in same direction used to ream bushing while pulling up on reamer.

Replace Worn Brass or Sintered Iron Guides

1. Lubricate Tool #19264, 9 mm Tap, and bushing with engine oil or kerosene.
2. With a tap wrench, turn tap into bushing clockwise until tap is 1/2 inch deep. DO NOT tap more than 1 inch deep. Remove tap and flush chips out of bushing.
3. Rotate Tool #19239, Puller Nut, up to head of Tool #19238, Puller Screw, and insert puller screw down through Tool #19240, Puller Washer.
4. Thread puller screw into tapped bushing until screw bottoms in tapped hole.
5. Back off screw 1/8 to 1/4 turn. Place a drop of engine oil on threads of puller screw, Fig. 11.
6. Hold puller screw stationary and turn puller nut down on washer until valve guide bushing is removed, Fig. 10.

TABLE NO. 4
GUIDE BUSHING IDENTIFICATION

BUSHING REMOVED FROM CYLINDER			
Sintered Guide Gray or Copper Colored	Brass Guide 1 or 2 Grooves	Brass Guide No Grooves	Alum. Guide or Cast Iron Cylinder
REPLACEMENT BUSHING			
Use Part #261961	Use Part #231218	Use Part #230655	Use Part #231218

7. Place grooved or tapered end of new bushing into cylinder valve guide.
8. Press bushing into cylinder with Tool #19204, Bushing Driver, until bushing bottoms. Rotate driver while pressing in bushing, Fig. 11.
9. Finish ream bushings, Part #261961 and #231218 with Finish Reamer, Tool #19233, and Reamer guide Bushing, Tool #19234 until reamer goes through entire guide, Fig. 11.

NOTE: Bushing, Part #230655 does not need to be reamed.

10. Before removing finish reamer, flush all chips away.
11. Remove reamer by turning reamer in same direction used to ream bushing while pulling up on reamer, Fig. 11.

NOTE: Valve seating should be checked after bushing the guide, and corrected if necessary by refacing the seat.

VALVE SEAT INSERTS

Cast iron cylinder engines are equipped with an exhaust valve seat insert which can be removed and a new insert installed. The intake side must be counter-bored to allow installation of an intake valve seat insert Figs. 12, 13, & 14.

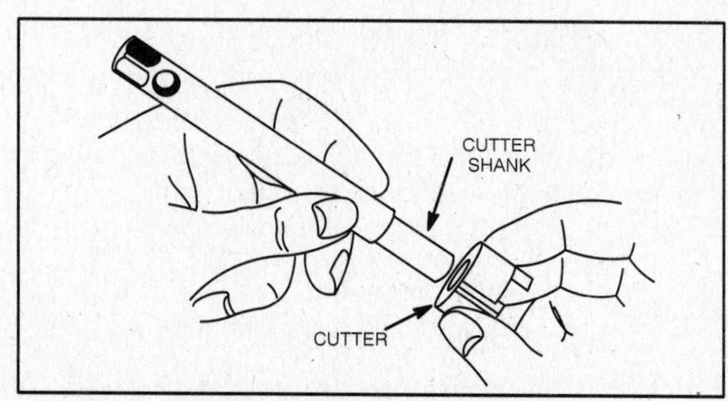

Fig. 12 - Inserting Cutter Shank

NOTE: METRIC EQUIVALENTS ARE LISTED ON PAGE 16 OF THIS SECTION.

TABLE NO. 5
VALVE SEAT INSERTS

BASIC MODEL SERIES	INTAKE STANDARD	EXHAUST STANDARD	EXHAUST COBALITE™	INSERT* PULLER ASSEMBLY	PULLER NUT
ALUMINUM CYLINDER					
60000, 80000	210879• ♦ 211172•	211291	210452	19138	19140 Ex. 19182 In.
90000, 110000	210879• 211172•	211291	210452	19138	19140 Ex. 19182 In.
100200, 100900, 130000	211787	211172	211436	19138	19182 Ex. 19139 In.
120000	213512	213513	None	None	None
170000, 190000	211661	211661	210940▪	19138	19141
220000, 250000, 280000	261463	211661	210940	19138	19141 Ex.
CAST IRON CYLINDER					
230000	21880	21880	21612	19138	19141
240000	21880	None	21612	19138	19141
300000, 320000	None	None	21612	19138	19141 Ex.

♦ 211291 used before Serial No. 5810060; 210808 used from Serial No. 5810060 to No. 6012010.
* Includes puller and No. 19182, 19140 and 19139 nuts.
▪ Before Code No. 7101260 replace cylinder.
• Use 210879 if seat is 1.097" O.D.; Use 211172 if seat is 1.079" O.D.

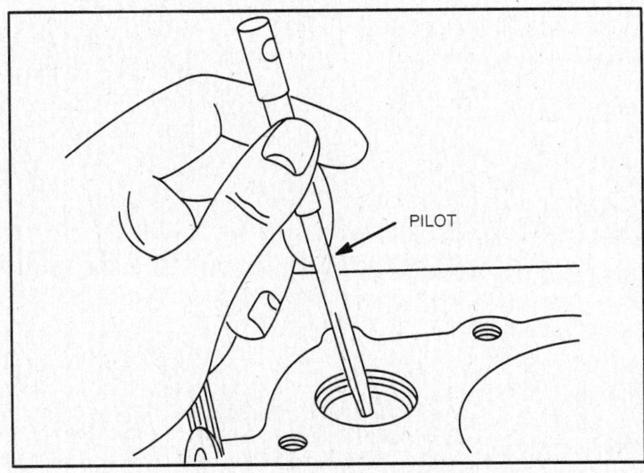

Fig. 13 - Inserting Pilot

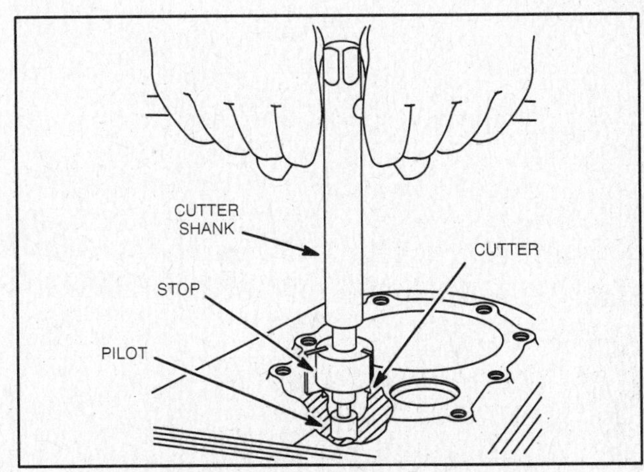

Fig. 14 - Counterboring for Valve Seat

Aluminum alloy cylinder models are equipped with inserts on exhaust and intake side. See Table No. 5.

NOTE: METRIC EQUIVALENTS ARE LISTED ON PAGE 16 OF THIS SECTION.

To Remove Valve Seat Insert

1. Use Tool #19138, Valve Seat Puller, as shown in Fig. 15, and select the proper puller nut. See Table 5.

2. Be sure the puller body does not rest on the valve seat insert, Fig. 16.

3. Turn the 5/16" bolt with a wrench until insert is pulled out of the cylinder, Fig. 16.

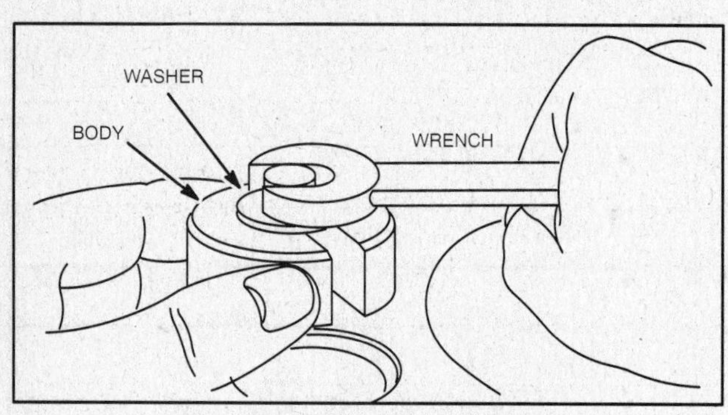

Fig. 15 - Removing Valve Seat

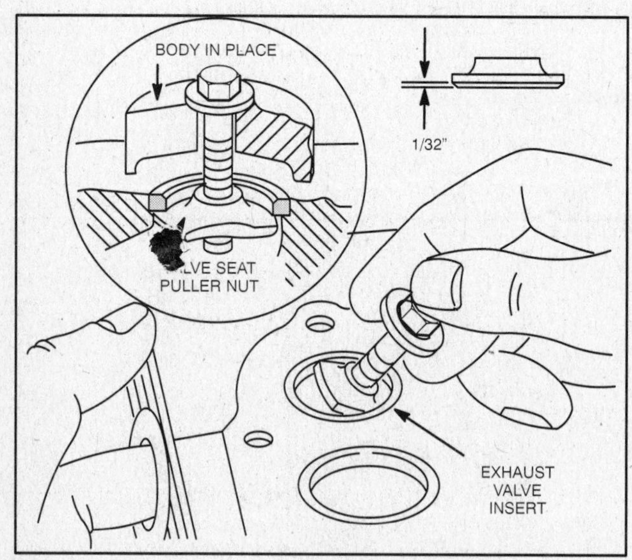

Fig. 16 - Inserting Valve Seat Puller

NOTE: On aluminum alloy cylinder models, it may be necessary to grind the puller nut until the edge is 1/32" thick in order to get the puller nut under the valve insert, Fig. 16.

Drive in New Valve Seat Insert

1. Select the proper valve seat insert and the correct pilot and driver according to Table 5 and 6. You will note that one side of the seat insert is chamfered at the outer edge. This side should go down into the cylinder.

2. Insert the pilot into the valve guide.

3. Then drive the valve insert into place with the driver, as shown in Fig. 17.

4. Reface seat using Tool # #19237 or #19343, Neway Valve Seat Cutter Kit. Then valves and seat are lapped lightly with grinding compound. Clean thoroughly.

NOTE: For aluminum alloy cylinder models only use the old valve seat insert as a spacer between the driver and the new insert, Fig. 17

1. Drive new insert until it bottoms. Top of insert will be slightly below cylinder head gasket surface.

2. Using a flat punch, peen around the insert as shown in Fig. 18.

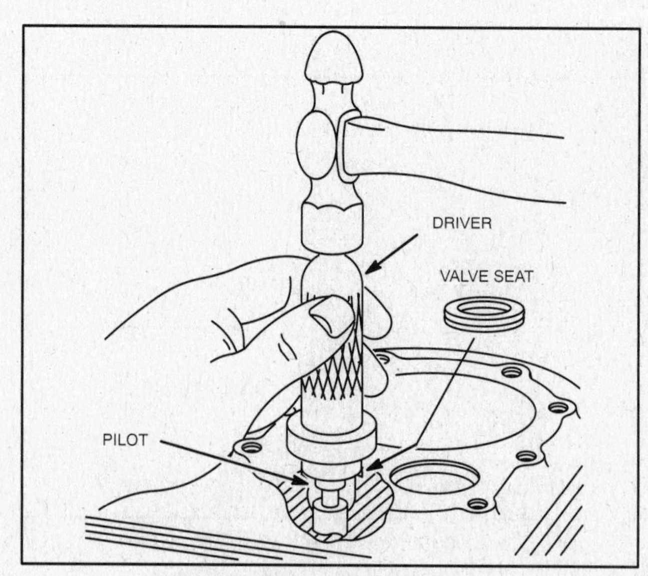

Fig. 17 - Driving in Valve Seat

NOTE: METRIC EQUIVALENTS ARE LISTED ON PAGE 16 OF THIS SECTION.

TABLE NO. 6
VALVE SEAT INSERT AND COUNTERBORE TOOLS

BASIC MODEL SERIES	COUNTER-BORE CUTTER	SHANK	CUTTER & DRIVER PILOT	INSERT DRIVER
ALUMINUM CYLINDER				
60000, 80000	NONE	NOT USED	19126	19136
90000	NONE	NOT USED	19126	19136
100000, 130000	NONE	NOT USED	19126	19136
170000, 190000	NONE	NOT USED	19127	19136
CAST IRON CYLINDER				
230000, 240000	19131	19129	19127	19136
300000, 320000	NONE	NOT USED	19127	19136

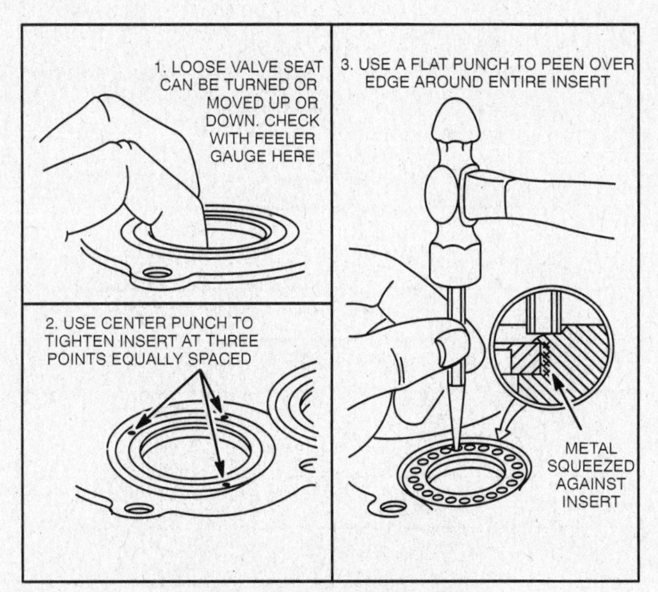

Fig. 18 - Peening Valve Seat

To Counterbore Cylinder for Intake Valve Seat Cast Iron Cylinder Models

NOTE: Replace cylinder if a .005" feeler gauge enters between valve seat and cylinder.

Cast iron cylinder models must be counterbored to allow installation of the intake valve seat insert.

1. Select proper seat insert, cutter shank, counter-bore cutter, pilot and driver according to Table 6.

NOTE: The Model Series 320000 intake valve seat is part of the cylinder. There is no replacement valve seat.

2. Insert pilot in intake valve guide, Fig. 19.

3. Assemble correct counterbore cutter to cutter shank as shown in Fig. 20.

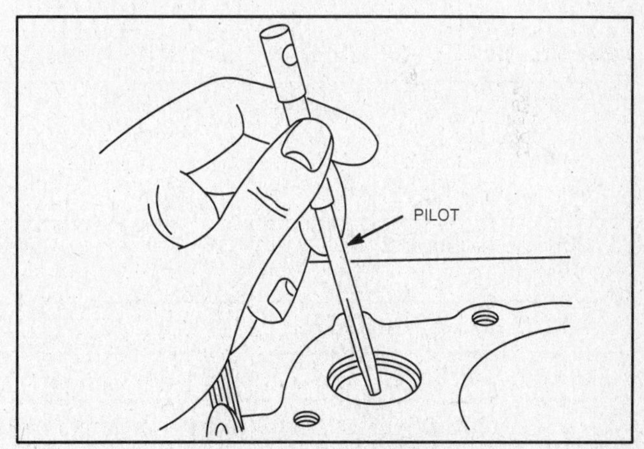

Fig. 19 - Inserting Pilot

4. Counterbore cylinder by hand until stop on cutter touches top of cylinder, Fig. 21.

   Do not force the cutter to one side or it will cut oversize.

5. Blow out all chips.

6. Use Knockout Pin, Tool #19135, to remove cutter from cutter shank.

NOTE: METRIC EQUIVALENTS ARE LISTED ON PAGE 16 OF THIS SECTION.

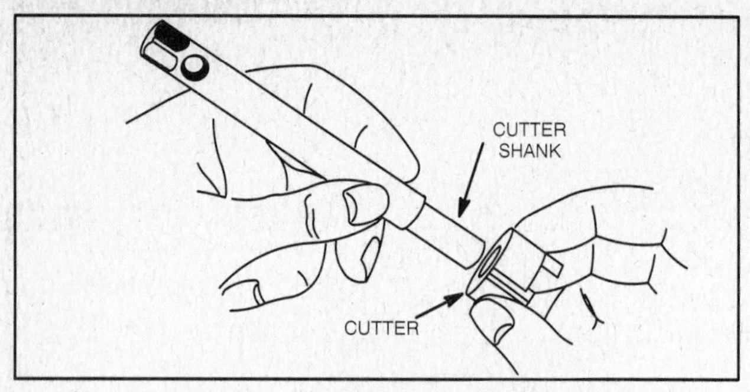

Fig. 20 - Inserting Cutter Shank

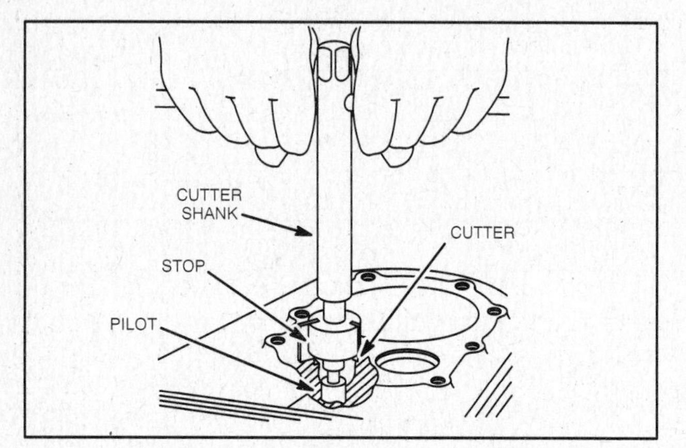

Fig. 21 - Counterboring for Valve Seat

VALVE CONVERSIONS

The life of a valve is considered to be the period of time the valve will operate before repair or replacement is necessary. The life of a standard exhaust valve is often shortened because of burning, which occurs when pieces of combustion deposit lodge between the valve seat and valve face, preventing the valve from closing completely. This is most likely to occur on engines which are operated at constant speed and constant load, for long periods of time. Exhaust valve life can be extended by using:

A. A valve rotator turns the exhaust valve a slight bit on each lift, wiping away any deposits which tend to lodge between the valve face and seat, Table No. 7 and Fig. 22 or,

B. A Cobalite™ exhaust valve which has a greater resistance to heat, Table 8 or,

C. Or a combination of both the rotator and Cobalite™ valve, Table No. 9, or,

D. For LP or Natural gas, use a Cobalite™ valve without rotator, see Table Nos. 10 or 11, using Fig. 23 or Fig. 24 to determine type of retainer being used.

TABLE NO. 7

TO CONVERT FROM STANDARD EXHAUST VALVE (WITHOUT ROTATOR) TO STANDARD EXHAUST VALVE WITH (ROTATOR)

	REMOVE		ADD			
BASIC MODEL SERIES	SPRING	RETAINER	SPRING	Rotator	RETAINER	PIN
60000, 80000, 90200, 92000, 93000, 94000, 95000, 96000	26478	93312	26826	292259	230127	230126
100200, 100900, 130000	26478	93312	26826	292259	230127	230126
170000, 190000, 200000, 250000	Reuse	221596	26828	292260	93630	
CAST IRON CYLINDER						
230000	65906	Reuse	26828	292260	68283	

NOTE: Rotator not to be used with LP fuel or natural gas.

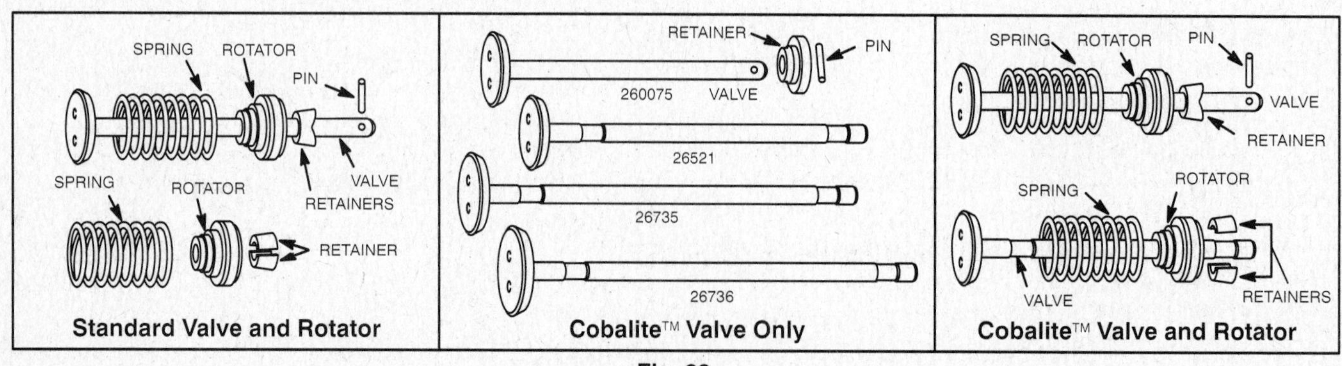

Fig. 22

NOTE: METRIC EQUIVALENTS ARE LISTED ON PAGE 16 OF THIS SECTION.

TABLE NO. 8

TO CONVERT FROM STANDARD EXHAUST VALVE TO COBALITE™ EXHAUST VALVE (WITHOUT ROTATOR)								
	REMOVE			ADD				
Model Series	**Standard Exhaust Valve**	**Retainer or Rotator**	**Spring**	**Cobalite™ Exhaust Valve**	**Retainer Collar**	**Retainer**	**Spring**	**Pin**
60000▪ 80000▪ 90000▪	296676	93312	26478	262580		224450	26478	
100200▪ 100900▪ 130000▪	211119	93312	26478	262464		224450	26478	Not Used
170000•▪ 190000•▪	390419	Reuse Split Retainers (93630)	Reuse Spring (26828)	390420	68293	Reuse Split Retainers (93630)	Reuse Spring (26828)	Not Used
220400* 221400* 250000* 280000*		**Cobalite™ Exhaust Valve and Seat with Rotator Standard**						
		292260	Reuse Spring (26828)	Reuse 261185	68293	Reuse Split Retainers (93630)	Reuse Spring (26828)	Not Used
280000		**Cobalite™ Exhaust Valve and Seat with Rotator Standard**						
		292260	Reuse Spring 26828	Reuse 262246	68293	Reuse Split Retainers 93630	Reuse Spring (26828)	Not Used
233000	23923	69293 (Collar Type)	65906	394436 Includes Retainers	68293	Reuse Split Retainers (68283)	26828	Not Used
243000* 300000* 320000*		**Cobalite™ Exhaust Valve and Seat with Rotator Standard**						
		Reuse Split Retainers (93630)	Reuse Spring (26828)	Reuse 394436	68293	Reuse Split Retainers (93630)	Reuse Spring (26828)	Not Used

▪ Some standard with Cobalite™ exhaust valve and seat with Rotator. Cobalite™ valves are usually marked "TXS," "XS" or "PP-XS" on head.

• Valve Rotator standard with standard exhaust valve.

* Standard with Cobalite™ exhaust valve and seat with Rotator.

NOTE: Apply Briggs & Stratton "Valve Guide Lubricant," Part #93963 to valve stems and guides before installing valves especially when operating with LP fuel or natural gas. Rotator should not be used with LP fuel or natural gas.

NOTE: METRIC EQUIVALENTS ARE LISTED ON PAGE 16 OF THIS SECTION.

6

6

TABLE NO. 9

TO CONVERT FROM STANDARD EXHAUST VALVE TO COBALITE™ EXHAUST VALVE (WITH ROTATOR)								
	REMOVE			ADD				
Model Series	Standard Exhaust Valve	Retainer	Spring	Cobalite™ Exhaust Valve	Rotator	Retainer	Spring	Pin
60000▪ 80000▪ 90000▪	296676	93312	26478	260443	292259	230127 (Sleeve Type)	26826	230126
110000▪	212004 or 261913	93312	Reuse 260552	261912	292259	230127 (Sleeve Type)	Reuse 260552	230126
100200▪ 100900▪ 130000▪	211119	93312	26478	494191	Part of 494191		Part of 494191	Not Used
170000•▪ 190000•▪	390419	Reuse Split Retainers (93630)	Reuse Spring (26828)	390420	Reuse Rotator (292260)	Reuse Split Retainers (93630)	Reuse Spring (26828)	Not Used
220400* 221400* 250000* 280000*	Cobalite™ Exhaust Valve and Seat with Rotator Standard							
233000	23923	69293 (Collar Type)	65906	394436 Includes Retainers	292260	Reuse Split Retainers (68283)	26828	Not Used
243000* 300000* 320000*	Cobalite™ Exhaust Valve and Seat with Rotator Standard							

▪ Some standard with Cobalite™ exhaust valve and seat with Rotator. Cobalite™ valves are usually marked "TXS," "XS" or "PP-XS" on head.

• Valve Rotator standard with standard exhaust valve.

* Standard with Cobalite™ exhaust valve and seat with Rotator.

NOTE: Apply Briggs & Stratton "Valve Guide Lubricant," Part #93963 to valve stems and guides before installing valves especially when operating with LP fuel or natural gas. Rotator should not be used with LP fuel or natural gas.

NOTE: METRIC EQUIVALENTS ARE LISTED ON PAGE 16 OF THIS SECTION.

TABLE NO.10

TO CONVERT FROM COBALITE™ EXHAUST VALVE (WITH ROTATOR AND PIN OR SPLIT RETAINERS) TO COBALITE™ EXHAUST VALVE (WITHOUT ROTATOR)							
	REMOVE				ADD		
Model Series	Rotator	Retainer	Spring	Pin	Retainer	Spring	Pin
60000▪ 80000▪ 90000▪	292259	230127 (Sleeve Type)	26826	230126	23184 (Collar Type)	26478	23187
110000▪	292259	230127 (Sleeve Type)	Reuse Spring (260552)	230126	23184 (Collar Type)	Reuse Spring (260552)	23187
100200▪ 100900▪ 130000▪	292259	230127 (Sleeve Type)	26826	230126	23184 (Collar Type)	26478	23187
170000•▪ 190000•▪	292260	Reuse Split Retainers (93630)	Reuse Spring (26828)	Not Used	68293 (Collar Type)	Reuse Spring (26828)	Not Used
220400* 221400* 250000* 280000*	292260	Reuse Split Retainers (93630)	Reuse Spring (26828)	Not Used	68293 (Collar Type)	Reuse Spring (26828)	Not Used
233000	292260	Reuse Split Retainers (68283)	26826	Not Used	68293 (Collar Type)	65906	Not Used
243000* 300000* 320000*	292260	Reuse Split Retainers (68283)	26826	Not Used	68293 (Collar Type)	65906	Not Used

▪ Some standard with Cobalite™ exhaust valve and seat with Rotator. Cobalite™ valves are usually marked "TXS," "XS" or "PP-XS" on head.

• Valve Rotator standard with standard exhaust valve, not to be used with LP fuel or natural gas.

* Standard with Cobalite™ exhaust valve and seat with Rotator.

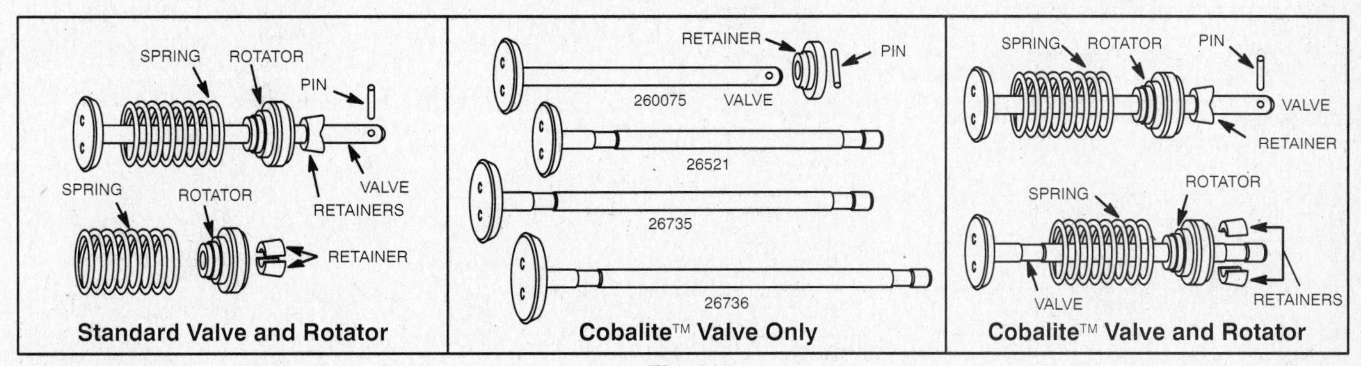

Fig. 23

NOTE: METRIC EQUIVALENTS ARE LISTED ON PAGE 16 OF THIS SECTION.

TABLE NO.11

TO CONVERT FROM COBALITE™ EXHAUST VALVE (WITH KEYHOLE ROTATOR) TO COBALITE™ EXHAUST VALVE (WITHOUT ROTATOR)							
	REMOVE				ADD		
Model Series	Rotator	Retainer	Spring	Pin	Retainer	Spring	Pin
60000▪ 80000▪ 90000▪	491442	Not Used	262750	Not Used	224450	26478	Not Used
110000▪	491442	Not Used	262750	Not Used	224450	26478	Not Used
100200▪ 100900▪ 130000▪	491442	Not Used	262750	Not Used	224450	26478	Not Used

▪ Some standard with Cobalite™ exhaust valve and seat with Rotator. Cobalite™ valves are usually marked "TXS," "XS" or "PP-XS" on head.

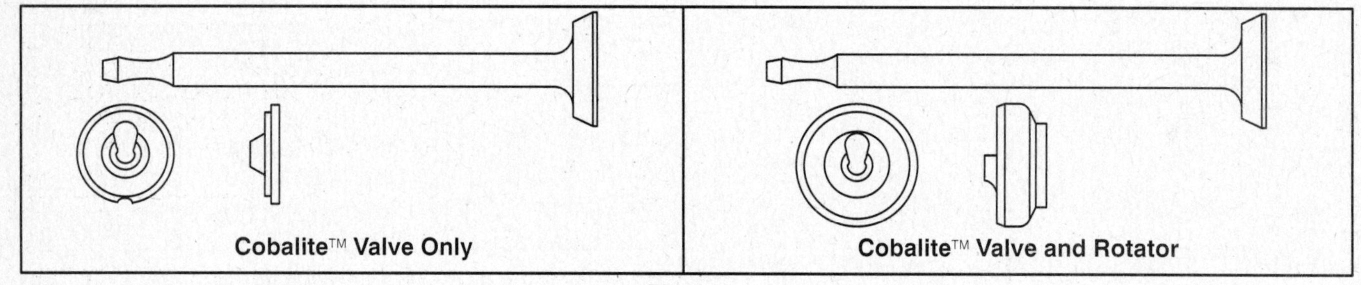

Fig. 24

METRIC EQUIVALENTS

DIMENSIONS			
DECIMAL		FRACTIONAL	
Inches	Millimeters	Inches	Millimeters
.004	.10	1/64	.40
.005	.13	1/32	.80
.006	.15	3/64	1.17
.007	.18	1/16	1.57
.009	.23	1/4	6.40
.011	.28	5/16	7.92
.017	.43	1/2	13.00
.019	.48	3/4	19.00
.240	6.09	1	25.40
1.079	27.41	1-1/16	26.97
1.097	27.80		

TORQUE		
In. Lbs.	Kgcm Kpcm	Nm
140	160	1580
165	190	1860
190	220	2150

NOTE: METRIC EQUIVALENTS ARE LISTED ON PAGE 16 OF THIS SECTION.

Section 7A
REWIND STARTERS

INDEX, REWIND STARTERS

INDEX, REWIND STARTERS, CONT'D

Various rewind starter assemblies are illustrated below and on the next page.

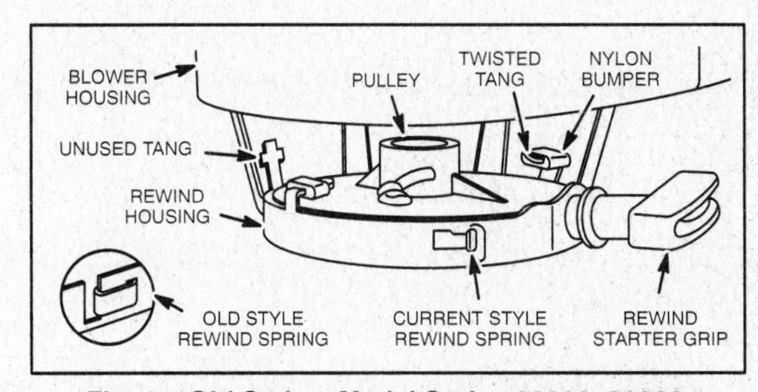

Fig. 1 – Old Style – Model Series 60000, 80000, 90000, 100200, 100900 and 110000

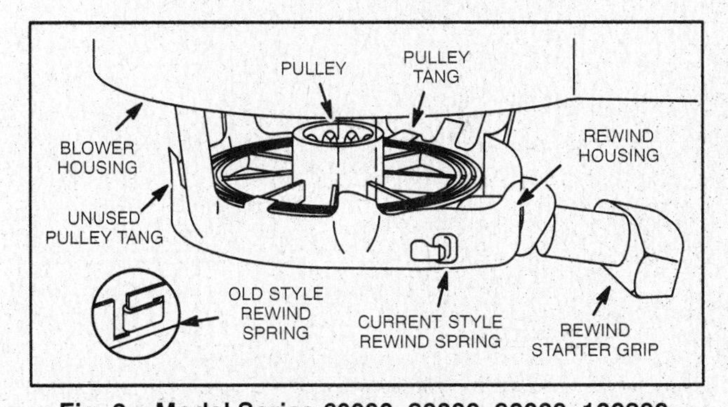

Fig. 2 – Model Series 60000, 80000, 90000, 100200, 100900 and 110000

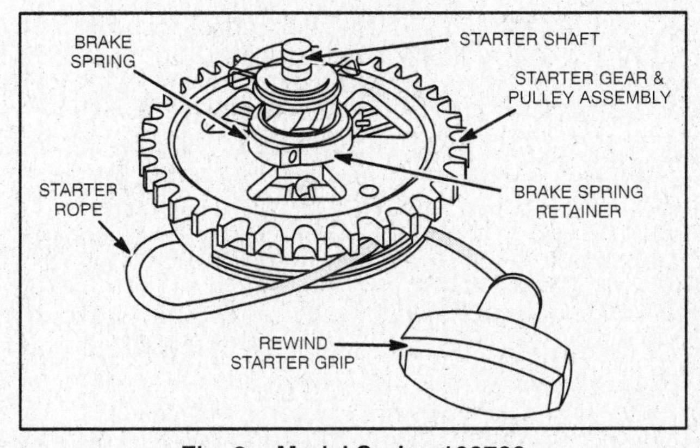

Fig. 3 – Model Series 100700

NOTE: METRIC EQUIVALENTS ARE LISTED ON PAGE 16 OF THIS SECTION.

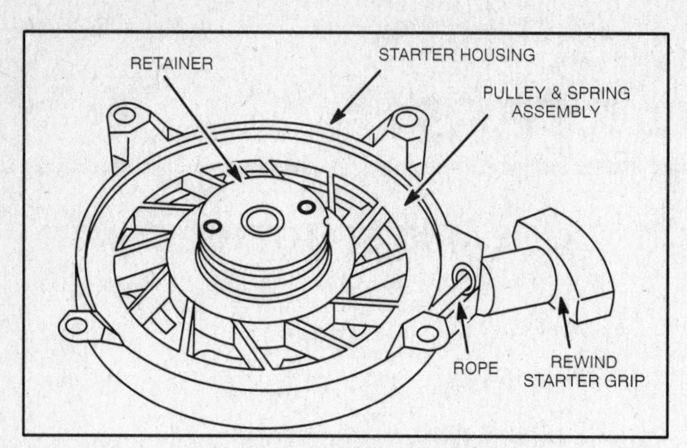

Fig. 4 - Model Series 120000

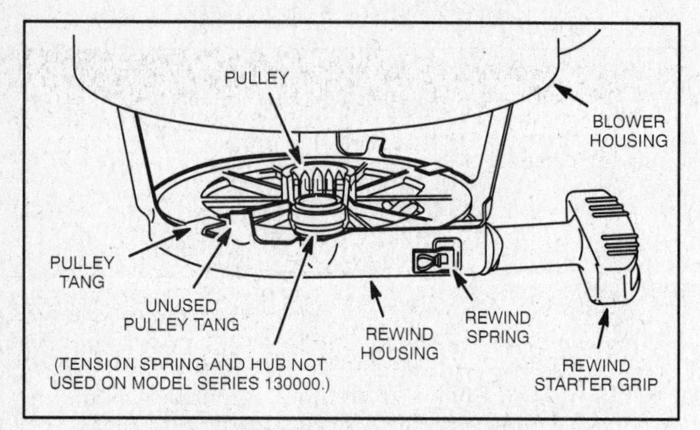

Fig. 5 - Model Series 130000,170000, 190000, 220000, 250000 and 280000

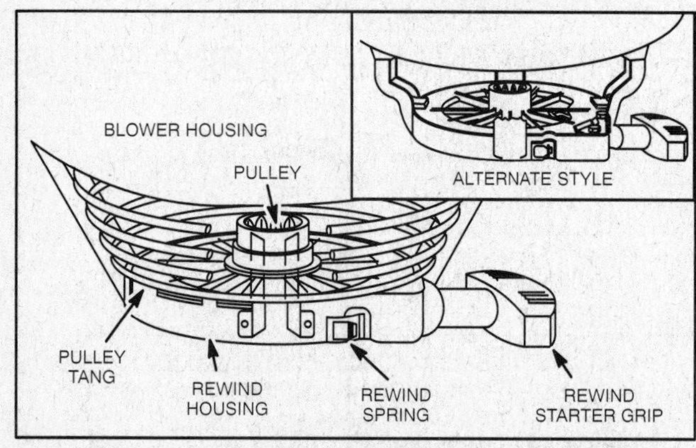

Fig. 6 - Model Series 170000, 190000, 250000 300000 and 320000

Repair procedure is similar except as indicated.

Remove Rope or Spring, Except Model Series 100700 & 120000

1. Cut knot at starter pulley and remove rope.
2. With rope removed, grasp outer end of rewind spring with pliers, Fig. 7, and pull out of housing as far as possible.
3. Turn spring 1/4 turn and remove from pulley or bend one of the tangs with Tang Bender, Tool #19229, up and lift out starter pulley to disconnect spring.

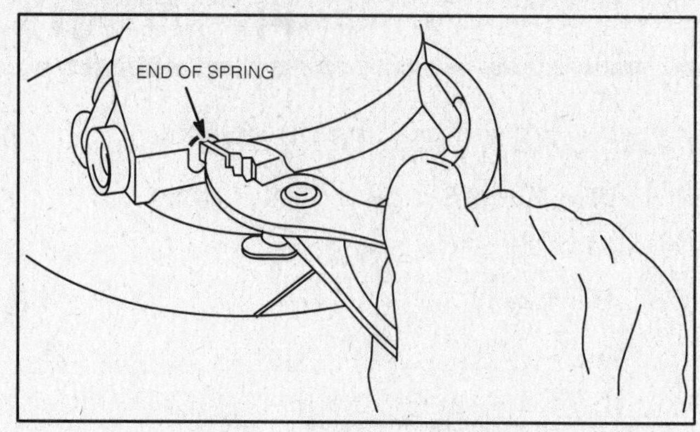

Fig. 7 - Remove Spring

Install Spring

1. Clean rewind housing, pulley and rewind spring in solvent.
2. Wipe clean with cloth.
3. Straighten spring to allow easier installation and restore tension.
4. Oil spring.
5. Insert either end of spring into blower housing slot and hook into pulley, Fig. 8.

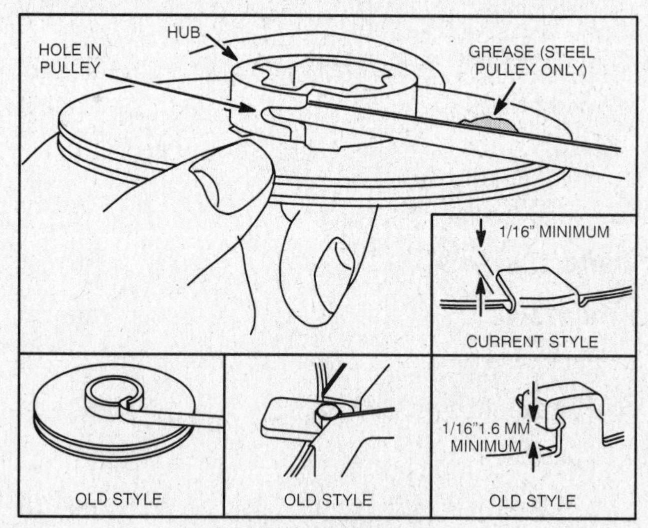

Fig. 8 - Install Spring

6. Place a dab of grease on pulley.
7. Set pulley into housing and bend tang down, Fig. 8. Adjust tang gap as shown. Pulley must be depressed fully into rewind housing when measuring tang gap.

NOTE: Do not remove nylon bumper from old style tang when replacing metal pulley with nylon pulley. Replace nylon bumpers if worn.

NOTE: METRIC EQUIVALENTS ARE LISTED ON PAGE 16 OF THIS SECTION.

Wind Spring

1. Place a 3/4” square piece of stock into center of pulley hub or make rewind tool similar to one shown in Fig. 9.
2. GRASPING STOCK WITH A WRENCH, WIND PULLEY COUNTERCLOCKWISE UNTIL SPRING IS WOUND TIGHTLY and end of spring is located in smaller portion of tapered hole, Fig. 10.
3. Then back off pulley one turn or until hole in pulley for rope knot and eyelet in blower housing are in alignment, Figs. 13 and 14.

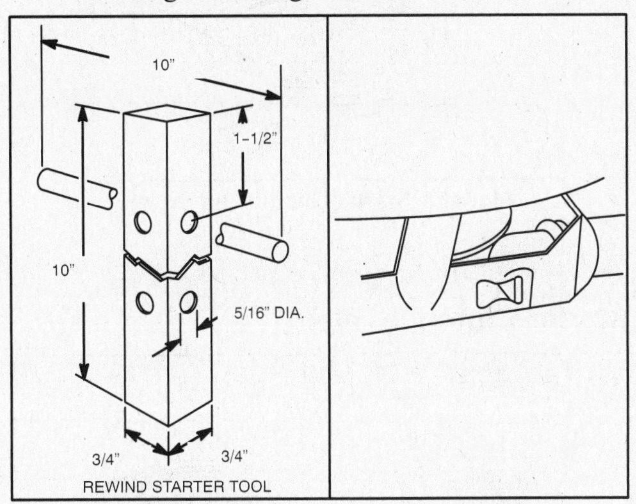

Fig. 9 - Rewind Starter Tool

Fig. 10 - Spring in Retainer Slot or Separate Retainer

Install Rope

1. Inspect rope. Replace if frayed.
2. Insert rope through handle and tie a figure eight knot.
3. Insert pin through knot and pull tightly into handle, Fig. 11. ALWAYS SEAL BOTH ENDS OF KNOT.

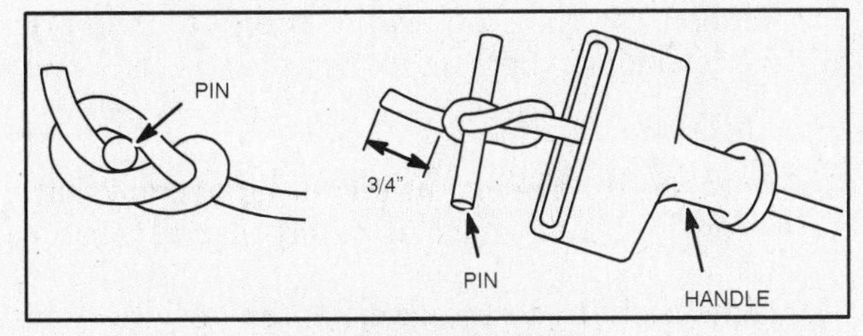

Fig. 11 - Install Rope

4. If re-using old rope, burn pulley end of rope with a match.
5. Wipe with waste cloth, using caution while it is still hot, to prevent swelling and unraveling.

NOTE: WHEN INSTALLING A NEW ROPE, CHECK PARTS LIST TO BE SURE CORRECT DIAMETER AND LENGTH ROPE ARE USED.

A rope inserter tool may be made by using a piece of music wire or spring wire, and forming it as shown in Fig. 12.

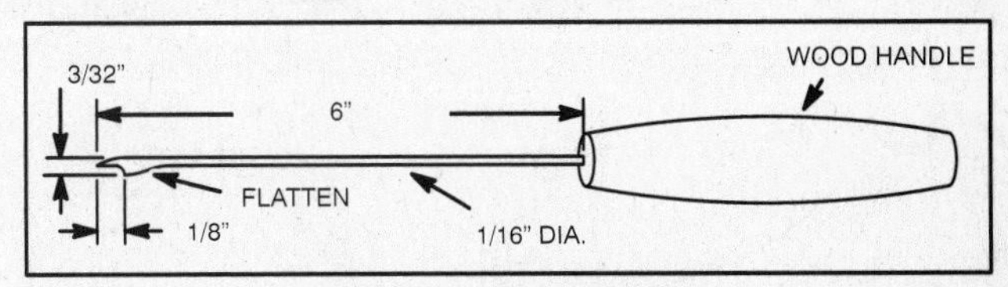

Fig. 12 - Rope Inserter

6. Thread wire and rope through rope eyelet in housing and out pulley hole. (NOTE: Rope must pass inside a guide lug on metal pulley.) Fig. 13.

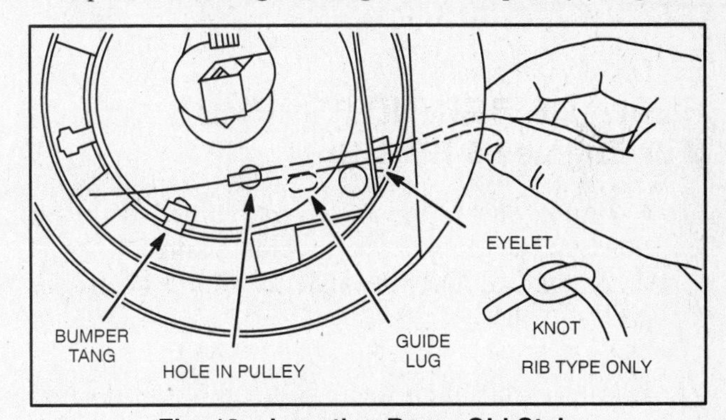

Fig. 13 - Inserting Rope, Old Style

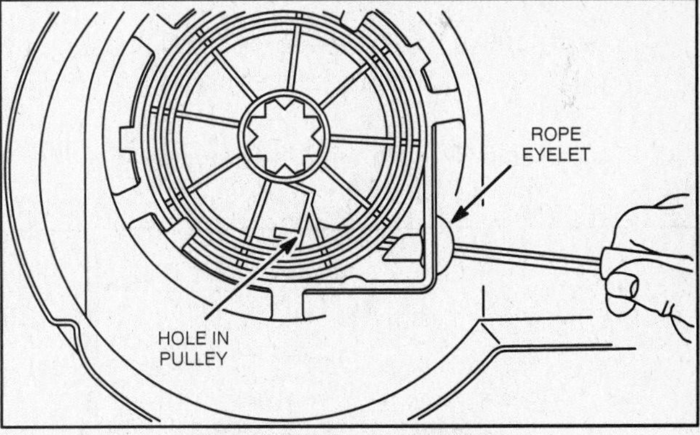

Fig. 14 - Inserting Rope

Old Style with Guide Lug

Tie a knot in rope and pull tight. Make sure knot in pulley does not contact bumper tangs, Fig. 13.

Current Style without Guide Lug

Tie a knot in rope and pull tight. Manipulate knot so it can be pulled down into knot cavity, Fig. 15.

NOTE: METRIC EQUIVALENTS ARE LISTED ON PAGE 16 OF THIS SECTION.

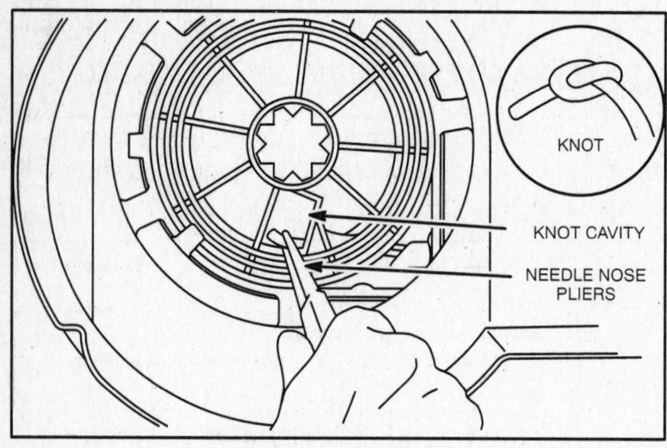

Fig. 15 - Tie Knot

REPLACE REWIND ASSEMBLY
(For Engines 5 HP & Up)

1. If original starter housing is spot welded to blower housing, drill out spot welds using a 3/16" diameter drill. Drill deeply enough to loosen spot welds ONLY.

2. Locate replacement rewind assembly in desired position.

3. Install screws from inside blower housing up through starter housing mounting leg.

4. Fasten securely with nuts as shown in Fig. 16.

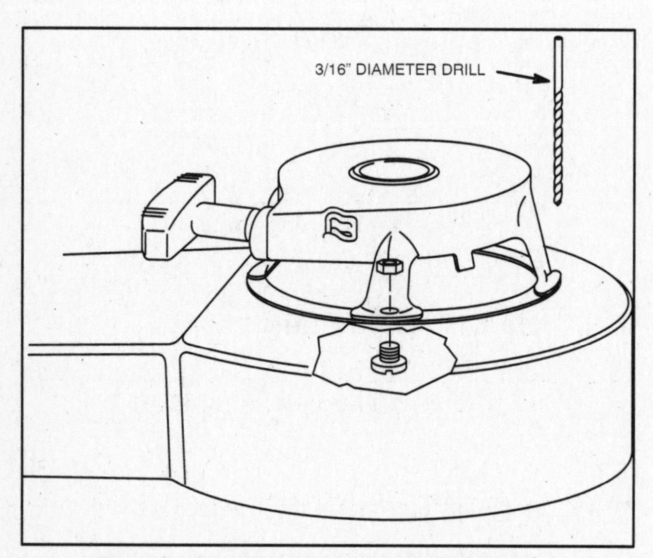

Fig. 16 - Removing and Installing Rewind

STARTER CLUTCH (OLD STYLE)

Inspect and clean starter clutch assembly as necessary, Figs. 17 and 18. Do not oil ball cavity area.

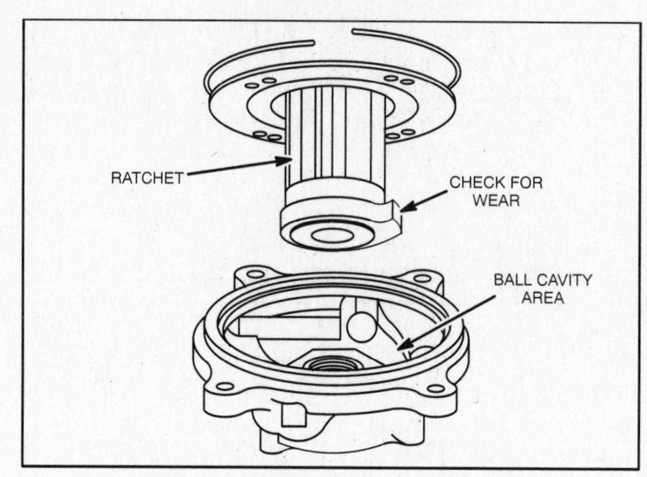

Fig. 17 - Starter Clutch (Old Style)

Starter Clutch (Sealed)

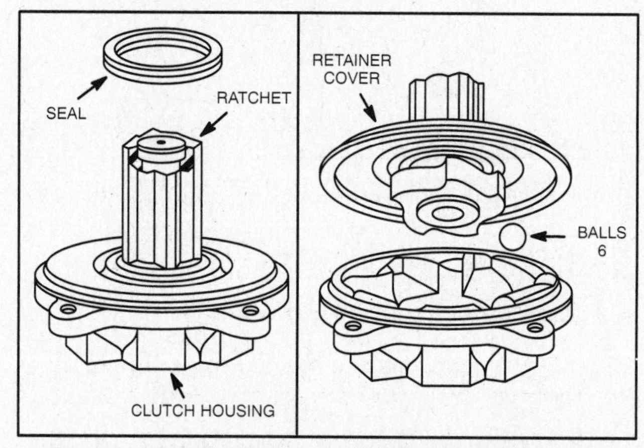

Fig. 18 - Sealed Clutch Assembly (Current Style)

1. If necessary, the sealed clutch can be disassembled by using a screwdriver or wedge to pry the retainer cover from the housing, as shown in Fig. 19.

2. Place one drop of engine oil on end of crankshaft before replacing clutch assembly on crankshaft.

3. Tighten clutch to torque noted on specification sheet for your model engine.

NOTE: DO NOT run engine without screen screws assembled to clutch.

NOTE: Clean ratchet by wiping with cloth only.

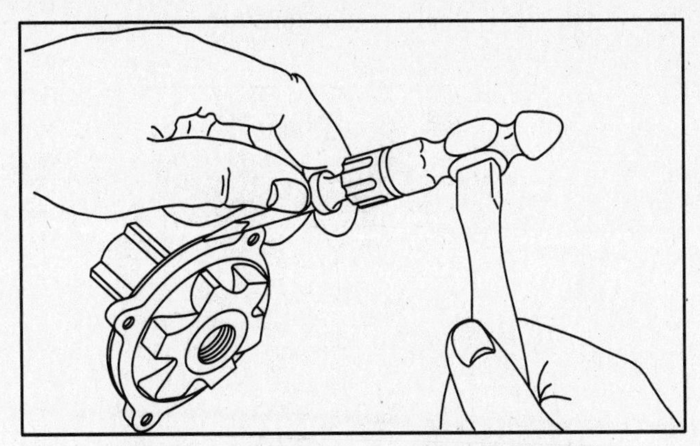

Fig. 19 - Disassembling Sealed Clutch

NOTE: The sealed clutch may be installed on older model engines, by modifying the starter pulley and crankshaft. The old pulley can be made to fit the new clutch by cutting off the hub to a dimension of 1/2" as shown in Fig. 20.

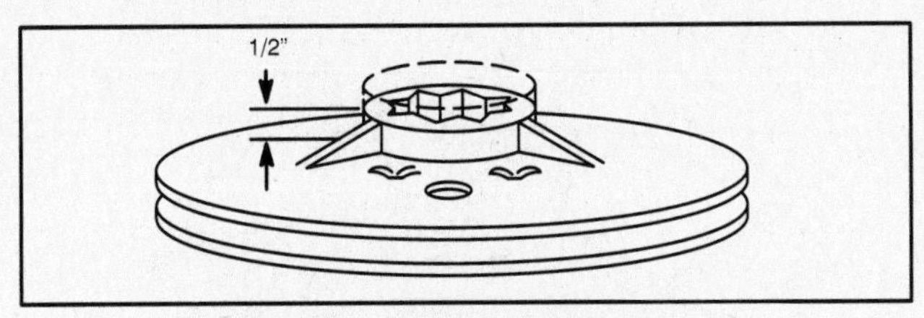

Fig. 20 - Pulley Modification

The crankshaft must be shortened 3/8" and the end chamfered as shown in Fig. 21. A new screen #221661 is required with the new clutch.

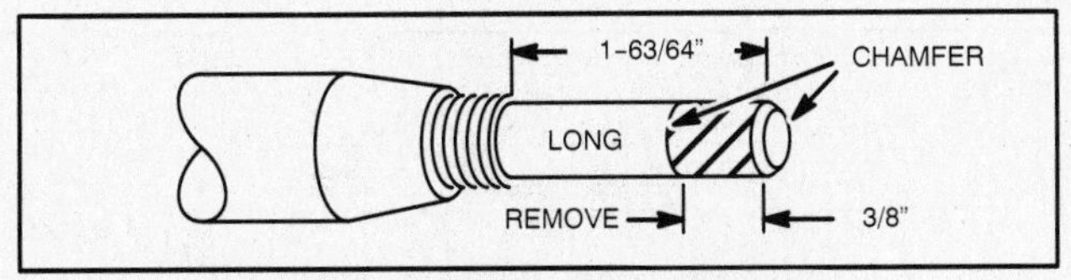

Fig. 21 - Crankshaft Modification

MODEL SERIES 100700 (QUANTUM) STARTER

Disassemble Side Mount Starter

1. Loosen starter mounting screw and remove starter, Fig. 22.

NOTE: To remove the starter, it may be necessary to remove or raise the fuel tank.

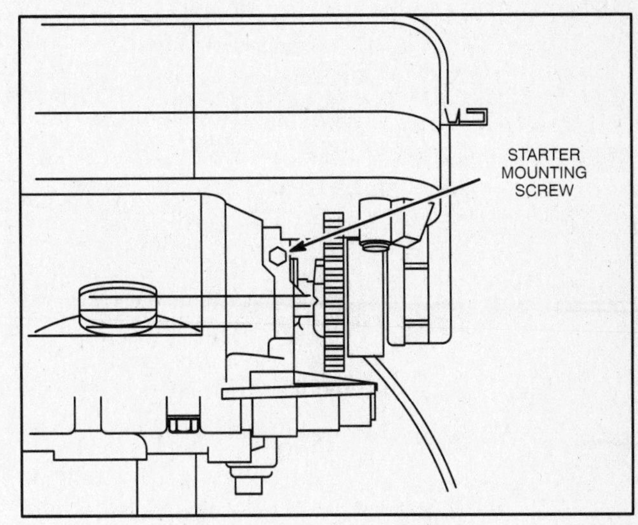

Fig. 22 - Removing Starter

2. Pull rope out as far as it will go and while holding pulley and cover, remove rope from pulley.

3. Then slowly relieve spring tension by releasing cover or pulley.

4. Remove and save decal.

5. Remove cover screw by turning screw clockwise (left hand thread).

6. Remove screw and washer, Fig. 23.

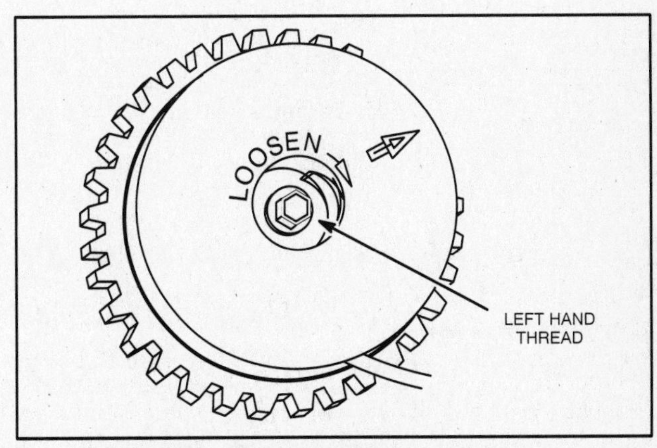

Fig. 23 - Removing Screw and Cover

7. Bend anchor tang out and turn cover counter-clockwise to disengage spring hook from cover notch.

8. Lift cover off assembly, Fig. 24.

NOTE: METRIC EQUIVALENTS ARE LISTED ON PAGE 16 OF THIS SECTION.

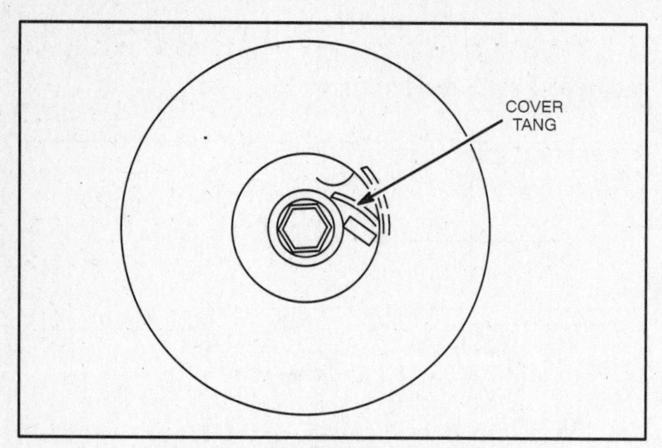

Fig. 24 - Bending Cover Tang

NOTE: On early production starters, the tang was bent in to retain the spring hook.

9. With a pair of needle nose pliers grasp spring as close to spring hook on outside edge of pulley and lift out spring.

10. While still gripping spring with pliers, slowly relieve spring tension, Fig. 25.

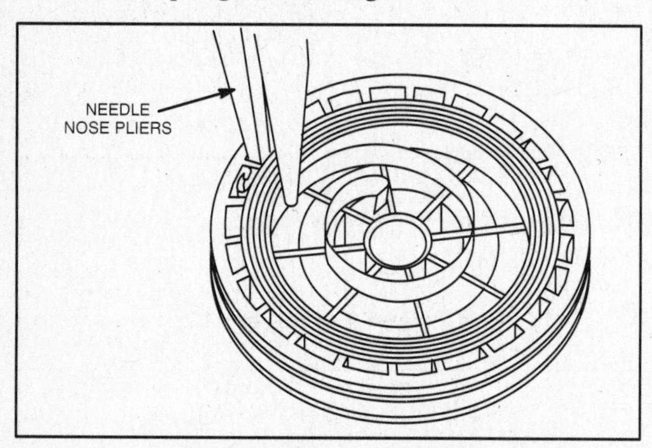

Fig. 25 - Removing Spring

11. Remove plastic washer, pulley and gear from starter shaft.

12. Remove steel washer and plastic washer from starter shaft.

Inspect Starter

Inspect pulley for cracks, sharp edges and cracks. Inspect gear for broken or cracked teeth. Inspect washers for cracks and sharp edges. Inspect spring for kinks, cracks and nicks. Replace all damaged parts.

Assemble Starter

1. Clamp starter shaft in vise with vise jaw protectors or a shop rag to protect shaft.

2. Place dab of grease under steel washer.

3. Then place steel washer and plastic washer on shaft, Fig. 26.

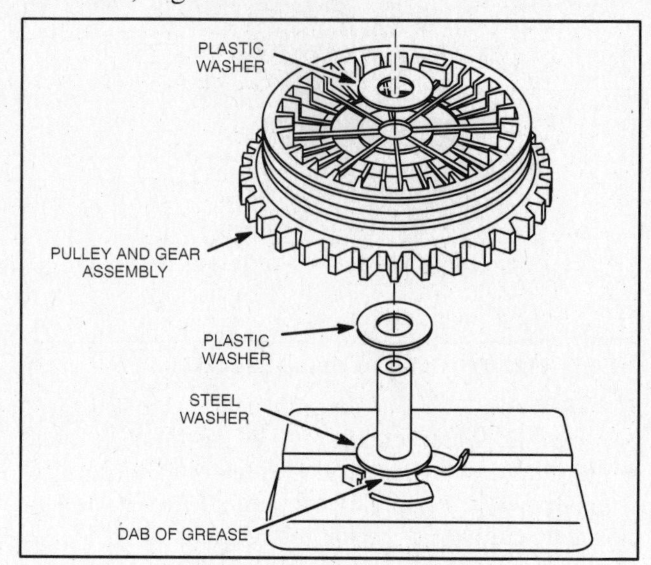

Fig. 26 - Assembling Starter

4. Assemble pulley to gear with gear hub and brake spring toward end of helix, Fig. 27.

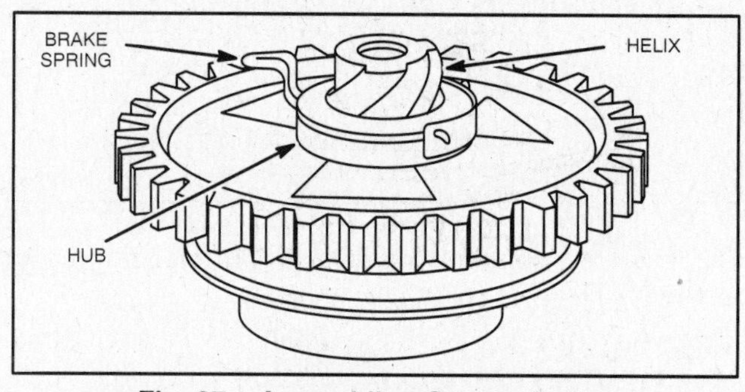

Fig. 27 - Assembling Gear to Pulley

5. Place gear and pulley assembly on shaft with brake spring between two posts on shaft, Fig. 28.

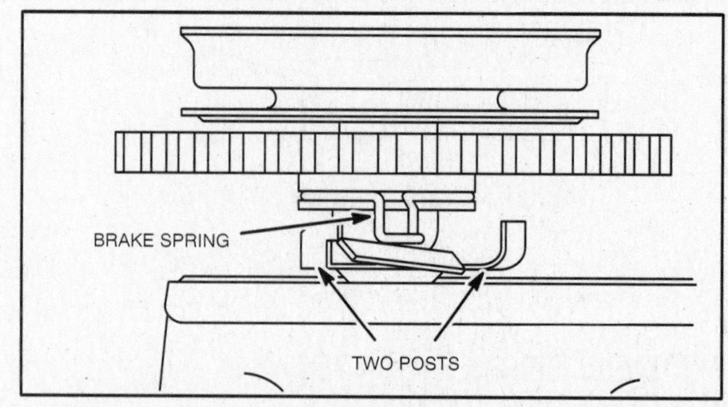

Fig. 28 - Assembling Pulley and Gear Assembly

6. Place plastic washer in center of pulley, Fig. 26.

NOTE: Service springs are held in a retainer. For ease of assembly outer hook of spring should be against end of retainer, Fig. 29. If not, rotate spring until hook is against retainer.

NOTE: METRIC EQUIVALENTS ARE LISTED ON PAGE 16 OF THIS SECTION.

7. Place spring and retainer on pulley with hook over spring notch in pulley, Fig. 30.

8. Push spring down into pulley, Fig. 30.

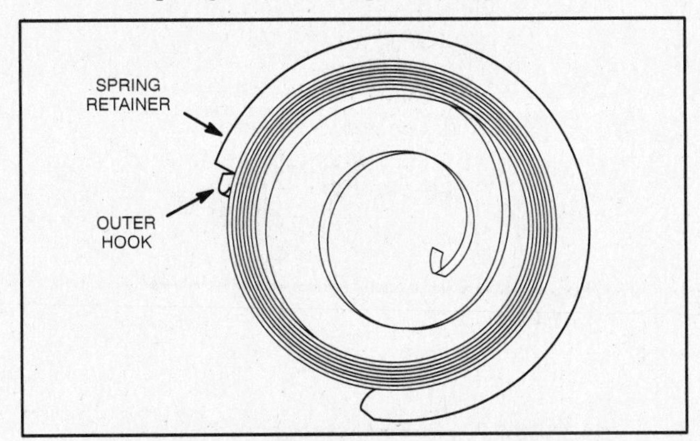

Fig. 29 - Positioning Spring in Retainer

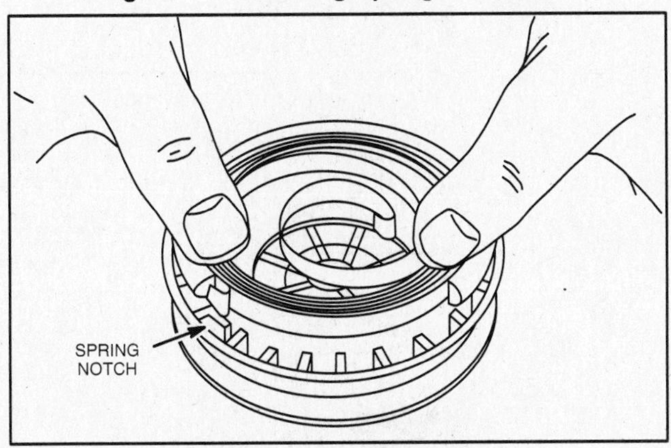

Fig. 30 - Installing Spring

9. When reusing original spring, straighten spring. Hook outer end of spring in spring notch and wind spring into pulley, Fig. 31.

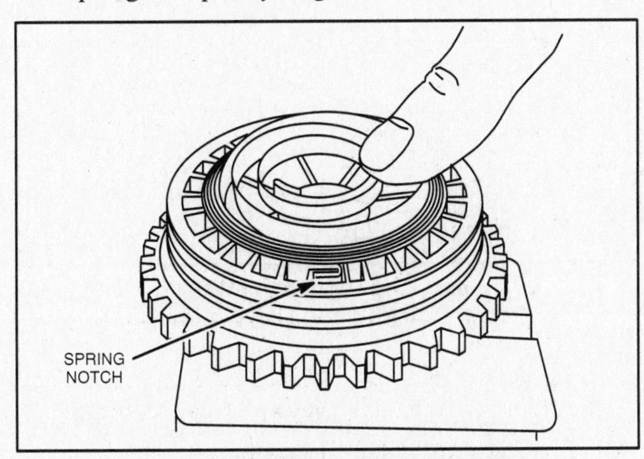

Fig. 31 - Installing Original Spring

10. Place a dab of grease in pulley, Fig. 26.

11. Lay cover over pulley and start cover screw and washer.

12. Turn screw counterclockwise (left hand thread) until finger tight.

Locate Cover (Starter Handle on Top)

1. Continue to turn cover clockwise until "O" or "Arrow" on cover is in line with starter shaft cam, Fig. 32.

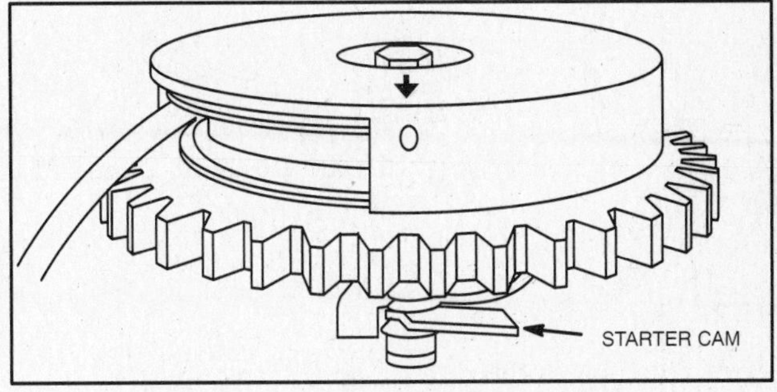

Fig. 32 - Locating Cover on Shaft

Locate Cover (Starter Handle and Rope Come Out Rope Guide on Cylinder Head)

1. Continue to turn cover clockwise until "O" or "Arrow" is 90° from cam on starter shaft, Fig. 33.

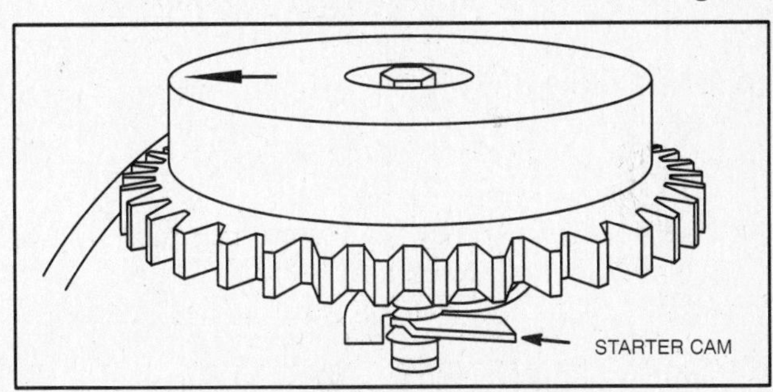

Fig. 33 - Locating Cover on Shaft

Complete Assembly, Both Styles

2. Hold cover in correct position and torque screw to 55 in. lbs.

3. Install decal over cover hole.

4. Hold starter cover and turn gear and pulley assembly clockwise until spring is tight.

5. Turn gear and pulley back 1/2 to 1-1/2 turns until rope knot pocket is in line with cover opening.

6. Insert unknotted end on rope thru rope pocket and pull rope thru until knot is seated in rope pocket, Fig. 34.

NOTE: METRIC EQUIVALENTS ARE LISTED ON PAGE 16 OF THIS SECTION.

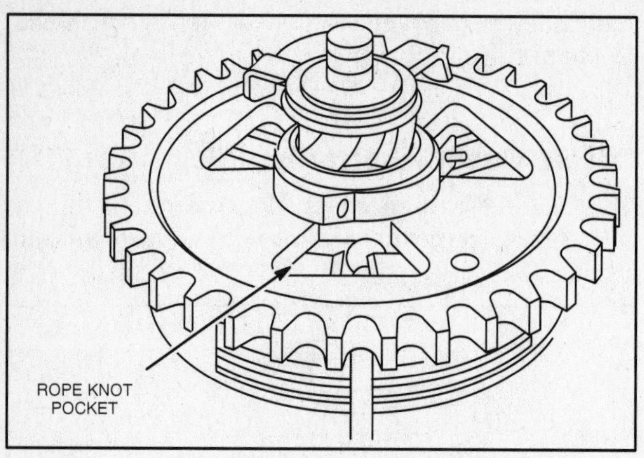

Fig. 34 – Installing Rope

7. While holding pulley and cover assembly, tie a slip knot in rope and slowly let rope wind into pulley.

8. Install starter assembly on engine with "O" or "Arrow" pointing at rope eyelet.

9. Torque starter mounting screw to 80 in. lbs

10. Thread rope thru eyelet(s), handle and rope handle insert.

11. Tie a single overhand knot in rope. Tail on knot should not be more than 1/4 inch long.

12. Pull knot into insert and insert into handle.

REWIND STARTER
Model Series 120000 Quantum Power

Disassemble Starter

1. Remove spark plug wire, finger guard and fuel tank, Fig. 35.

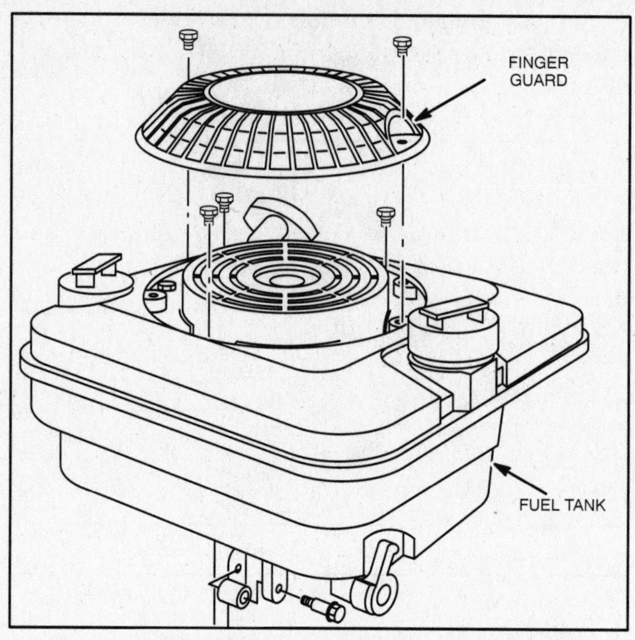

Fig. 35 – Removing Finger Guard and Fuel Tank

2. Remove dipstick and oil fill tube. Remove blower housing and rewind starter, Fig. 36.

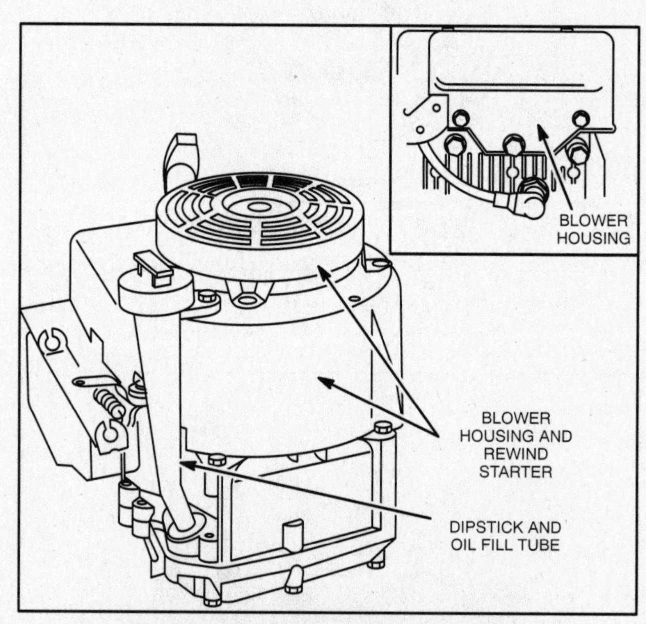

Fig. 36 – Removing Dipstick and Oil Fill Tube, Blower Housing and Rewind Starter

3. Pull starter rope out as far as it will go.

4. While holding the pulley and starter housing, pull pulley end of rope out and untie knot at end of rope.

5. Remove rope and handle from starter.

6. Slowly release pulley to release spring tension.

NOTE: METRIC EQUIVALENTS ARE LISTED ON PAGE 16 OF THIS SECTION.

NOTE: On some models it may be necessary to remove the label before center pin can be removed. Support blower housing on Tool #19227, Cylinder Support, and drive out center pin with 5/16" dia. pin punch, Fig. 37.

NOTE: On early engines the starter housing must be removed from the blower housing by drilling out the four pop rivets holding the starter on the blower housing. Service rewind starters include mounting hardware to replace pop rivets.

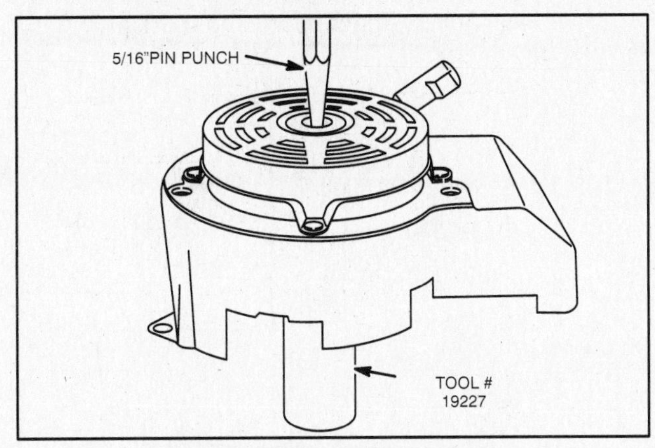

Fig. 37 – Removing Center Pin

7. Remove starter housing from support tool while holding rewind starter retainer and starter housing.
8. Place starter upside down on work bench.
9. Lift off retainer. Remove starter pawls and springs.
10. Lift off pulley and spring assembly. Note plastic washer on pulley, Fig. 38.

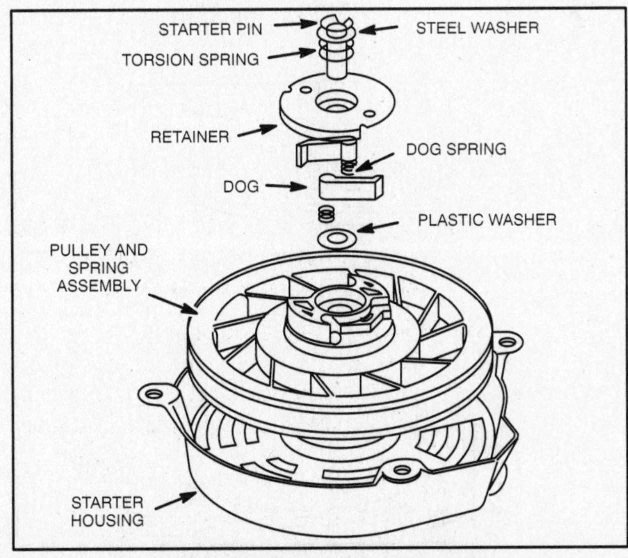

Fig. 38 – Starter Components

WARNING: The starter spring is still under tension when the rope has been removed and the pulley has no spring pressure against it. Wear eye protection to prevent eye injury while disassembling and reassembling starter pulley and spring.

CAUTION: Pulley and spring with retainer are serviced as an assembly. DO NOT ATTEMPT TO REMOVE SPRING RETAINER FROM PULLEY.

Inspect Starter Housing and Pulley

Inspect pulley for cracks, rough edges, or burrs in pulley groove, wear or cracks in center hole or loose spring retainer, Fig. 39. Replace pulley if damaged or worn.

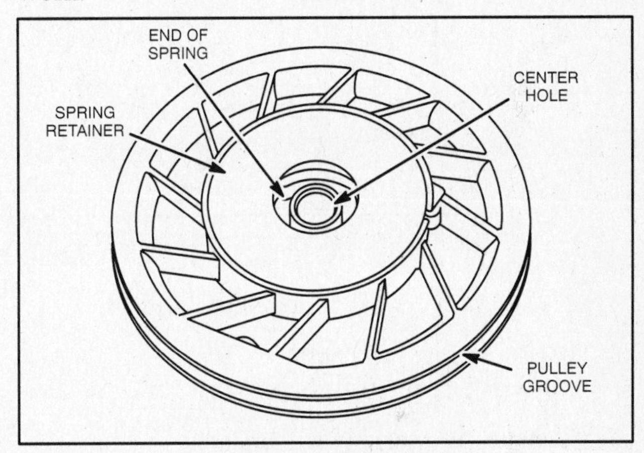

Fig. 39 – Inspecting Pulley

Inspect starter housing for wear or burrs at rope eyelet, center pivot post, and at inner spring retainer, Fig. 40. Replace if worn.

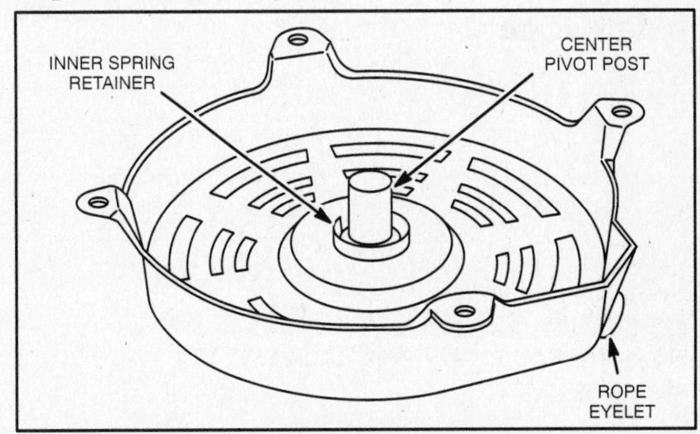

Fig. 40 – Inspecting Starter Housing

Assemble Starter Housing and Pulley

1. Note location of free end of spring in pulley assembly and location of spring retainer in starter housing.

NOTE: METRIC EQUIVALENTS ARE LISTED ON PAGE 16 OF THIS SECTION.

2. Line up free end of spring, Fig. 39 with spring retainer in housing and assembly pulley in housing, Fig. 40.
3. Rotate pulley counterclockwise until spring engages retainer.
4. Install dogs and dog springs in pulley assembly, Fig. 41.

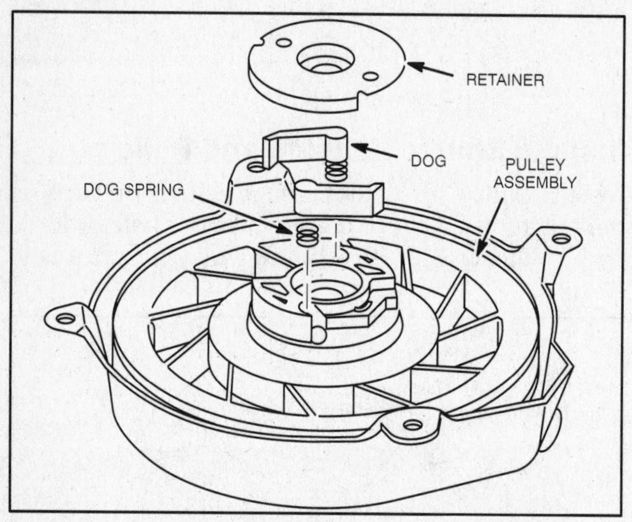

Fig. 41 – Installing Dogs, Dog Springs and Retainer

5. Place plastic washer in center of pulley hub.
6. Place retainer on pulley with pierced holes between dogs and stops on pulley, Fig. 41.
7. Place metal washer and brake spring on new starter pin and start pin in center hole.
8. Press or drive pin in until pin is flush with retainer.

Install Rope

1. Wind spring and pulley counterclockwise until spring is tight.
2. Back pulley off until rope eyelet in housing and rope hole in pulley are in line.
3. Install end of rope through eyelet and pulley hole and tie a single overhand knot.
4. Slowly let pulley and spring unwind.

Install Rewind Starter on Blower Housing

1. If rewind starter housing was removed from blower housing use four (4) Part #92987 nuts and four (4) Part #94128 screws to attach rewind starter to blower housing.

Install Blower Housing and Rewind Starter

1. Place blower housing on engine and start one (1) screw in extruded hole.
2. Hold blower housing with extruded hole in recess of cylinder block, Fig. 42.
3. Tighten screw and then install three remaining screws. Install dipstick tube and dipstick.
4. Install fuel tank, finger guard and spark plug wire.

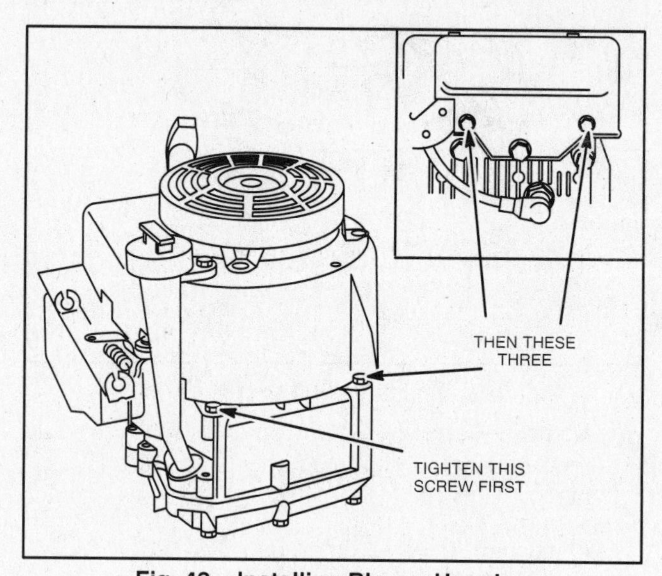

Fig. 42 – Installing Blower Housing

VERTICAL PULL STARTER

Vertical pull starters have been made in two versions, Figs. 43 and 44.

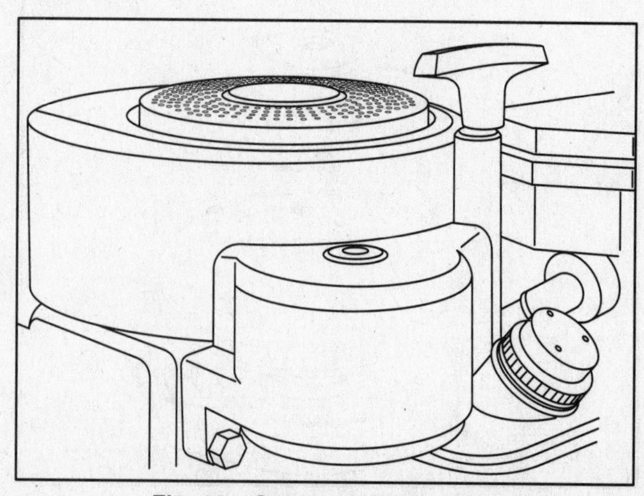

Fig. 43 – Standard Vertical Pull

NOTE: METRIC EQUIVALENTS ARE LISTED ON PAGE 16 OF THIS SECTION.

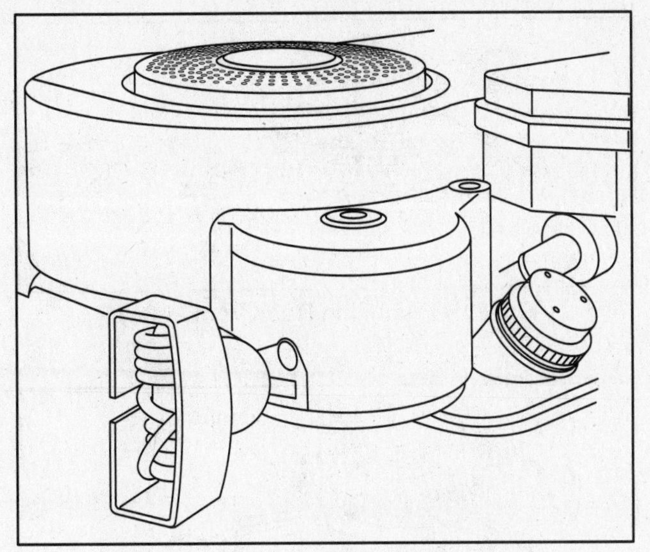

Fig. 44 – Alternate Style Vertical Pull

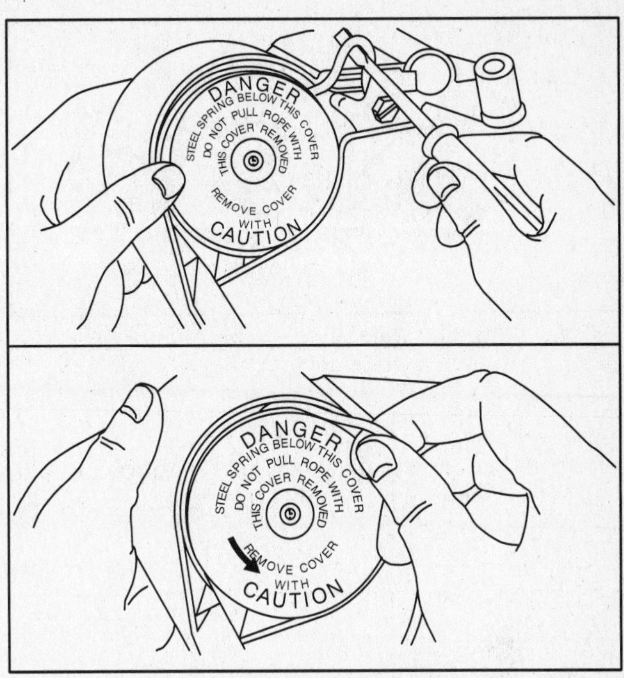

Fig. 45 – Providing Slack

NOTE: Before removing alternate style starter, measure length of rope from starter housing to rope handle at equipment handle bar.

DISASSEMBLE STARTER

Remove Rope or Spring

1. Before servicing starter, all tension must be removed from rope and spring.

2. Use a screwdriver to lift the rope up approximately one foot.

3. Wind rope and pulley counterclockwise 4 turns, as shown in Fig. 45. This will completely release tension from the starter spring.

4. Note the warning on the plastic cover, then use a screwdriver as shown in Fig. 46 to remove the cover.

CAUTION: Do not pull rope with the pulley cover removed, unless the spring is detached from spring anchor.

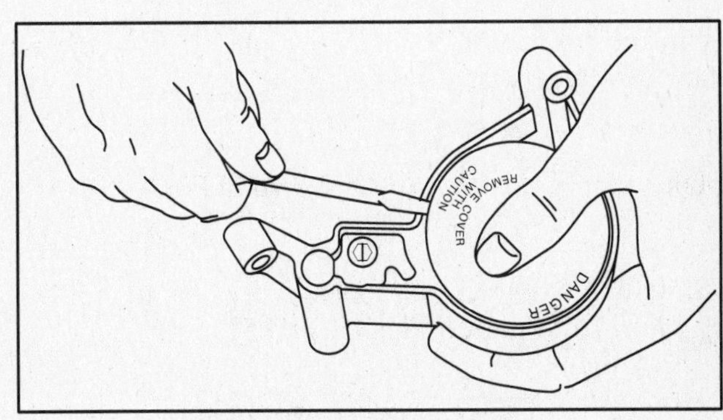

Fig. 46 – Removing Cover

5. Remove anchor bolt and anchor, Fig. 47.

   Inspect starter spring for kinks or damaged ends. If the starter spring is to be replaced, carefully remove it from the housing.

6. Replace cover to keep spring in housing.

NOTE: METRIC EQUIVALENTS ARE LISTED ON PAGE 16 OF THIS SECTION.

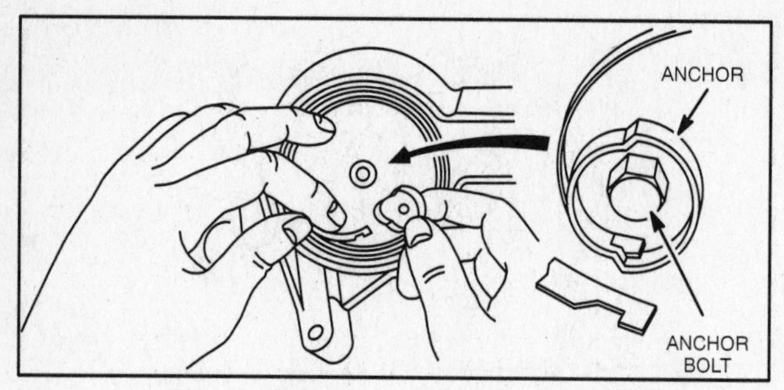

Fig. 47 - Removing Spring Anchor

7. Remove rope guide and note position of link before removing assembly from housing, Fig. 48.

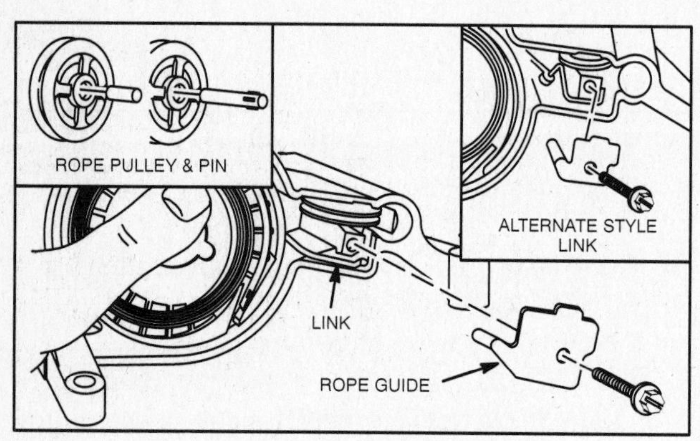

Fig. 48 - Removing Rope Guide

Rope pulley and pin may be replaced if worn or damaged, when used.

Make a rope inserter tool, as shown in Fig. 49.

8. Use the rope inserter tool and/or pliers to remove rope from pulley, Figs. 50 and 51.

9. Untie knot and remove rope from pulley.

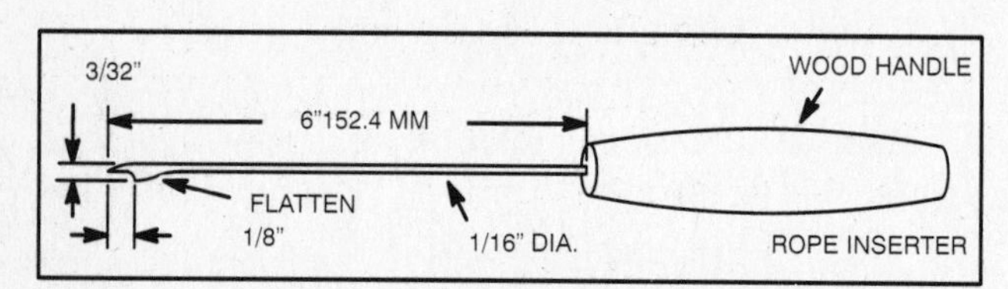

Fig. 49 - Rope Inserting Tool

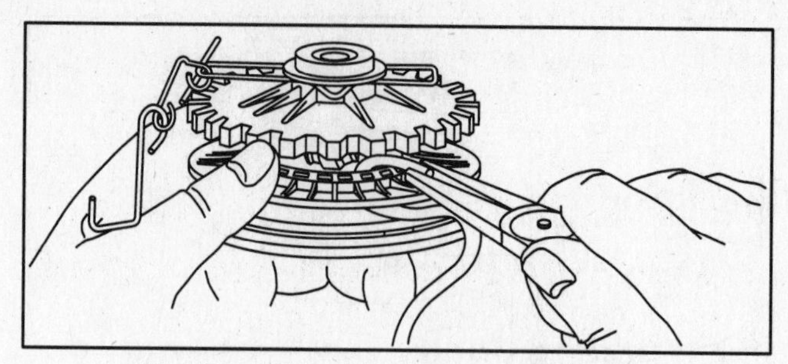
Fig. 50 - Removing Rope from Pulley

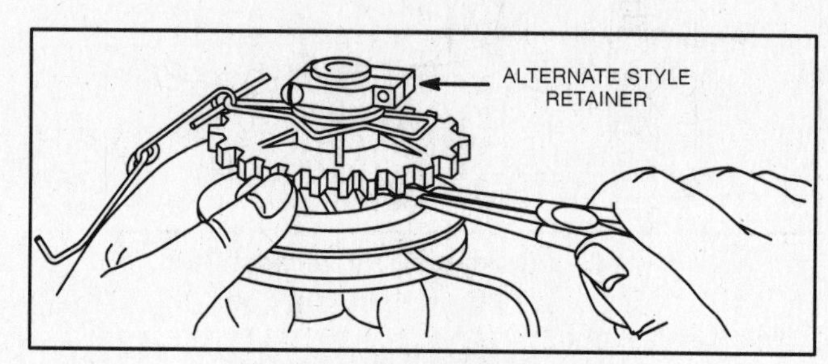

Fig. 51 - (Alternate Style) Removing Rope from Pulley

10. Remove rope from grip, as shown in Fig. 52.

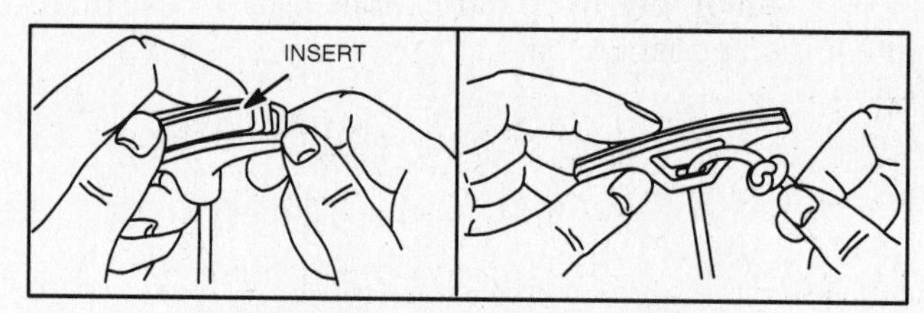

Fig. 52 - Removing Rope from Grip

If pulley or gear is damaged, replace with new assembly.

Clean all dirty or oily parts and check link for proper friction. Link should move gear to both extremes of its travel. If not, replace link assembly, Fig. 53.

Fig. 53 - Checking Friction Link

NOTE: To repair vertical pull starters with INTERLOCK SYSTEM, follow equipment manufacturers interlock repair procedure.

NOTE: METRIC EQUIVALENTS ARE LISTED ON PAGE 16 OF THIS SECTION.

ASSEMBLE STARTER

Install Spring

1. Place pulley and gear assembly in starter housing.

2. Hook end of spring into spring retainer on outside diameter of pulley, Fig. 54.

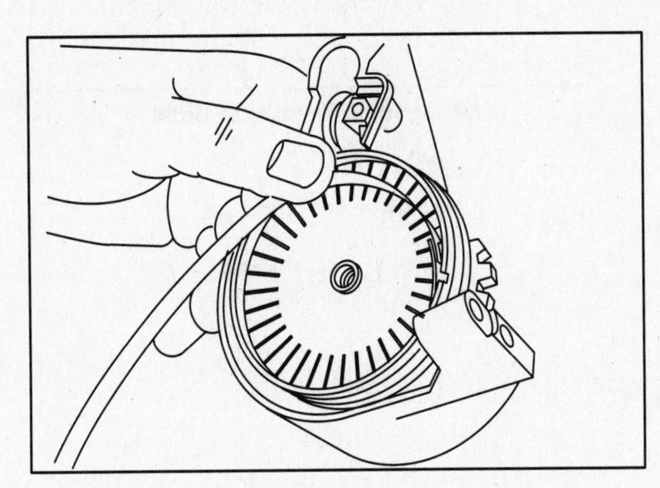

Fig. 54 - Installing Spring in Outer Retainer

3. Rotate pulley clockwise to wind spring into pulley while holding end of spring in outer spring retainer, Fig. 55.

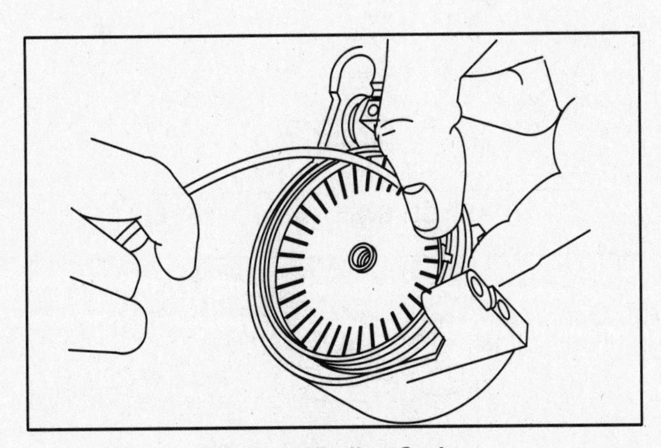

Fig. 55 - Winding Spring

4. Install spring anchor on free end of spring and install pulley cover, Fig. 56. Do not install anchor screw at this time.

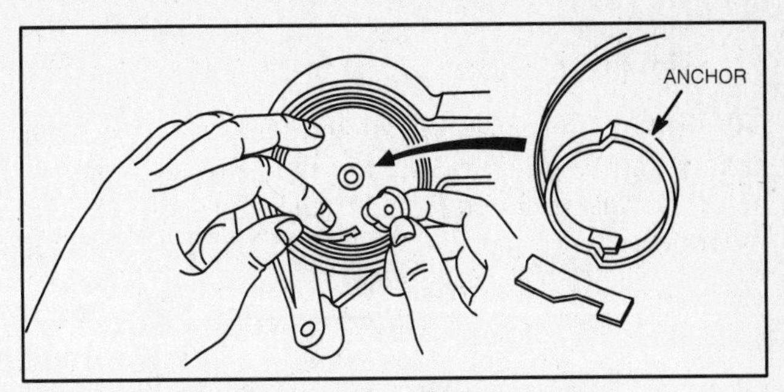

Fig. 56 - Installing Spring Anchor

Install Rope

NOTE: When installing a new rope, check parts list to be sure correct diameter and length rope is used.

1. Insert rope through housing and into pulley, using rope inserter tool.

2. Tie a small knot, heat seal and pull tight into recess in rope pulley. Rope must not interfere with gear motion, Fig. 57.

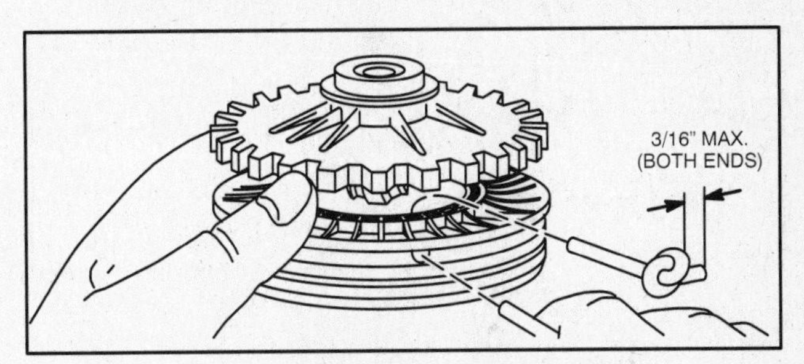

Fig. 57 - Starting Rope in Pulley

3. Install pulley and gear assembly in housing, with link in pocket or hole of casting, as shown.

4. Install small pulley, rope pulley pin, and rope guide, Fig. 58.

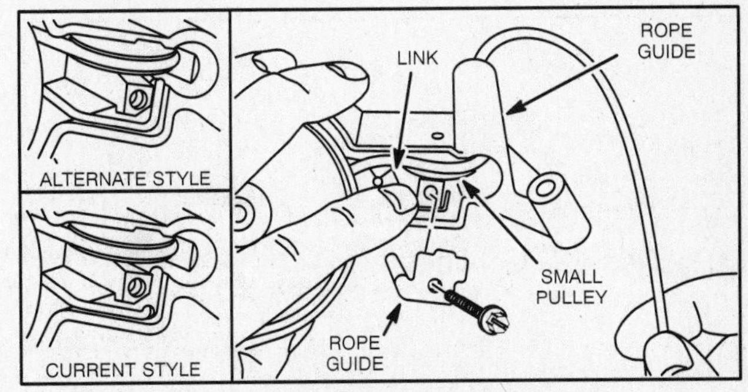

Fig. 58 - Installing Pulley Assembly

5. Thread rope through grip and into insert.

6. Tie a small, tight knot.

7. Heat seal the knot to prevent loosening.

NOTE: METRIC EQUIVALENTS ARE LISTED ON PAGE 16 OF THIS SECTION.

8. Pull knot into insert pocket and snap insert into grip, Fig. 59.

NOTE: On alternate style starter, measure rope from handle end to guide on starter, the same distance as before it was removed from engine. Tie a slip knot in the rope at this point. DO NOT INSTALL HANDLE AND INSERT AT THIS TIME.

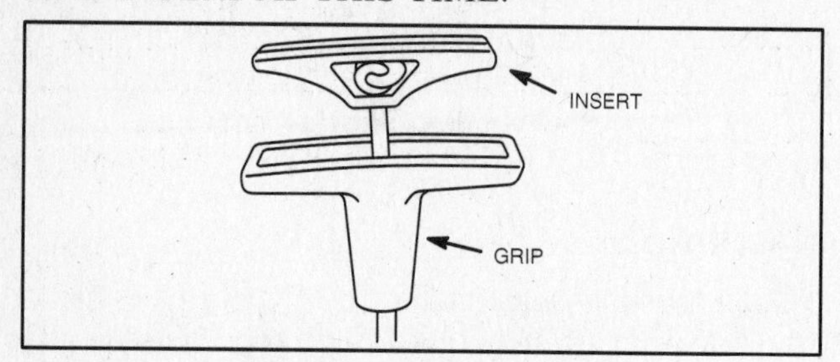

Fig. 59 - Installing Rope

9. Rotate pulley in a counterclockwise direction until rope is fully retrieved, Fig. 60.

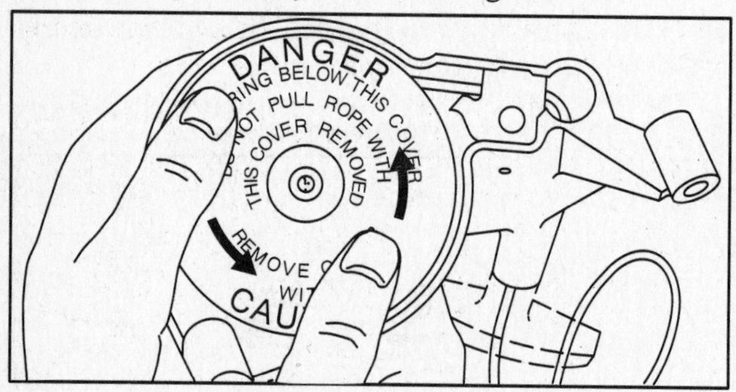

Fig. 60 - Retracting Rope

10. Remove cover from pulley.
11. If not already done, hook free end of spring to spring anchor, and install screw.
12. Torque to 75 to 90 in. lbs.
13. Lubricate spring with a small quantity of engine oil or lubricant, Fig. 61.

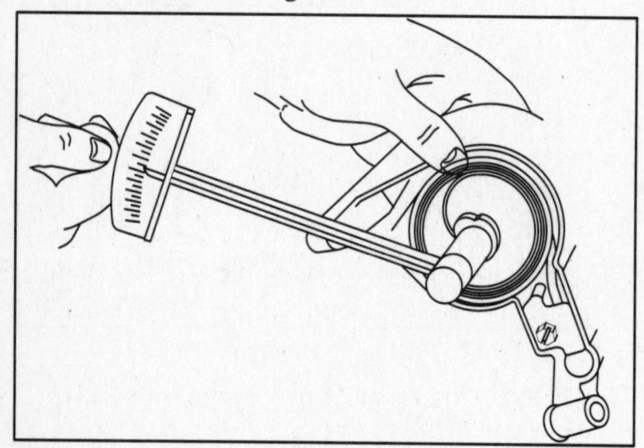

Fig. 61 - Tightening Screw

14. Snap cover in place.
15. Wind starter spring by pulling rope out approximately one foot.
16. Wind rope and pulley 2 or 3 turns clockwise to achieve proper rope tension, Fig. 62.

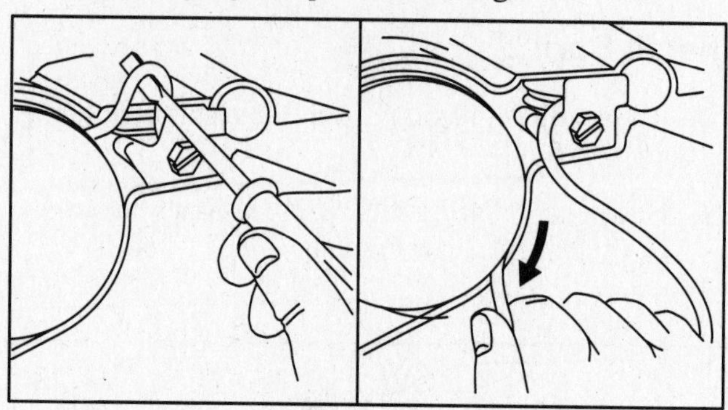

Fig. 62 - Adding Tension to Rope

17. Install starter on engine
18. After installing alternate style starter on engine, route rope up to equipment control handle and install handle and insert, Fig. 59.

WIND-UP STARTERS

Two types of windup starters have been used. The control knob release, Fig. 63, was used with the unsealed four ball clutch. The control lever release, Fig. 64, can only be used with a sealed six ball clutch.

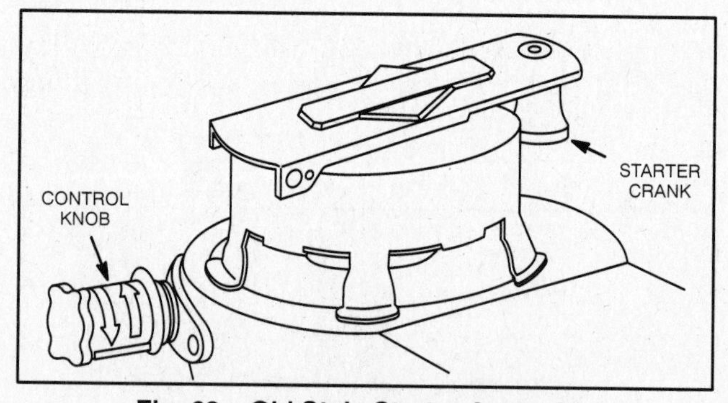

Fig. 63 - Old Style Starter Assembly

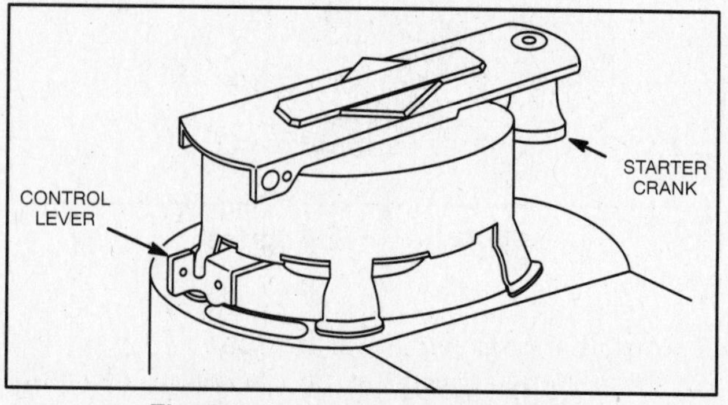

Fig. 64 - Lever Starter Assembly

NOTE: METRIC EQUIVALENTS ARE LISTED ON PAGE 16 OF THIS SECTION.

NOTE: Before working on equipment, remove spark plug from engine. Make sure starter spring is not wound. This can be determined by attempting to turn starter crank clockwise.

1. If wound tight, release tension by placing control knob or lever to "START" position.
2. If starter spring does not release, place control at "CRANK" position.
3. To prevent injury, hold crank handle with one hand while removing Phillips head screw and handle assembly from starter housing. This will release spring, Fig. 65.

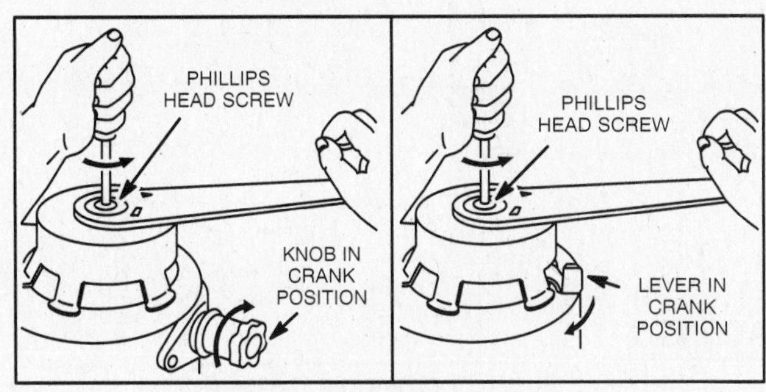

Fig. 65 – Releasing Spring

Check for Broken Spring, Wind-up Starter

1. To check starter for a broken spring, while unit is still on engine, place control knob or lever to "START" position.
2. Turn cranking handle ten turns clockwise.
3. If engine does not turn over, either the spring is broken or the starter clutch balls are not engaged.
4. While turning the cranking handle, watch the starter clutch ratchet.
5. If it does not move the starter spring is probably broken.

Disassemble Wind-up

1. Remove blower housing.
2. Remove screw holding cranking handle to housing, Fig. 65.
3. Bend tangs holding starter spring and housing assembly upward and lift retainer plate, spring and housing assembly out of blower housing, Fig's. 65 and 66.

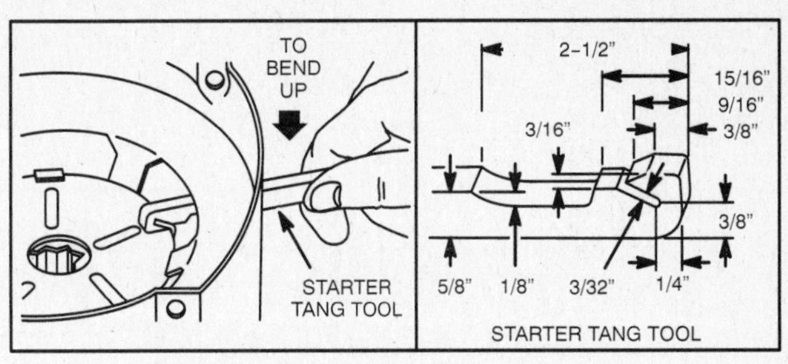

Fig. 66 – Removing Spring Housing

CAUTION: Do not attempt to remove starter spring from its housing.

Inspect Starter Parts

Inspect spring and housing assembly for spring breakage or other damage. Inspect ratchet gear on outside of blower housing for wear or damage.

DO NOT remove retaining plate from spring and cup assembly.

Check movement of control knob or control lever for ease of operation and damage or wear. (Clean and oil.) Fig. 67.

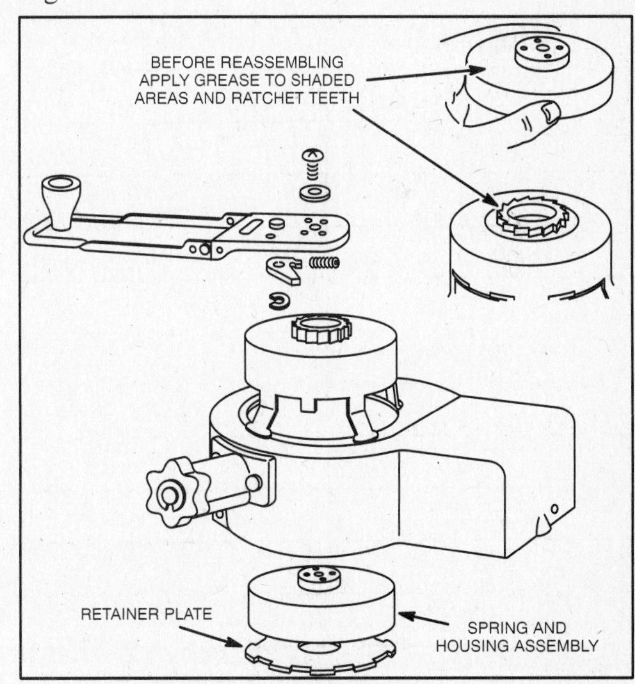

Fig. 67 – Inspecting Parts & Replacing Spring Cup

Assemble

1. When re-assembling, be sure to re-install spring washer in housing before placing cup, spring and release assembly into housing.
2. Bend retaining tangs down securely, Fig. 68.

NOTE: METRIC EQUIVALENTS ARE LISTED ON PAGE 16 OF THIS SECTION.

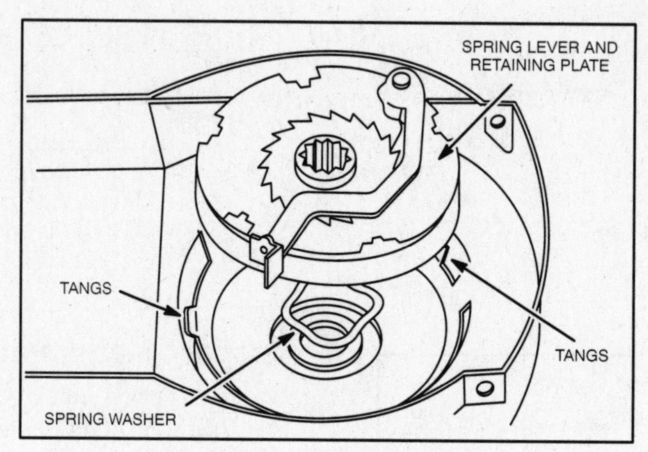

Fig. 68 - Replace Spring Lever and Retaining Plate

METRIC EQUIVALENTS

DIMENSIONS, FRACTIONAL	
Inches	**Millimeters**
1/16	1.6
3/32	2.4
1/8	3.2
3/16	4.8
1/4	6.4
5/16	7.9
3/8	9.5
1/2	12.7
9/16	14.3
5/8	15.9
3/4	19.1
15/16	23.8
1/2	38.1
1-63/64	50.4
2-1/2	63.5
6	152.4
10	254.0

TORQUE		
In. Lbs.	**Kgcm Kpcm**	**Nm**
55	63	6.2
75	85	8.5
80	92	9
90	105	10.2

NOTE: METRIC EQUIVALENTS ARE LISTED ON PAGE 16 OF THIS SECTION.

Section 7B
ELECTRIC STARTER SYSTEMS

INDEX, SECTION 7B

NOTE: METRIC EQUIVALENTS ARE LISTED ON PAGE 63 OF THIS SECTION.

Electric Starters
Index, cont'd

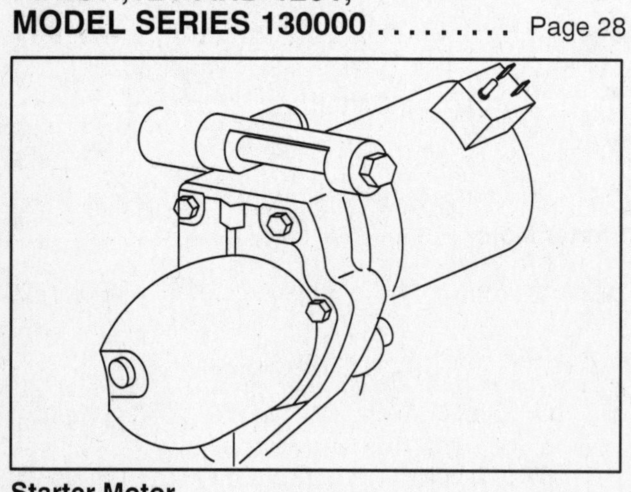

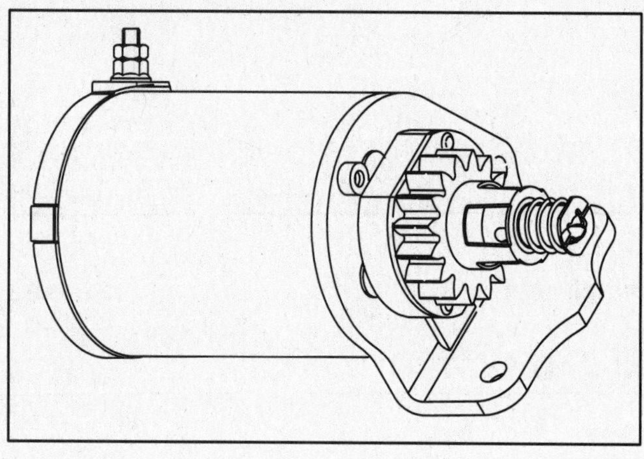

NOTE: METRIC EQUIVALENTS ARE LISTED ON PAGE 63 OF THIS SECTION.

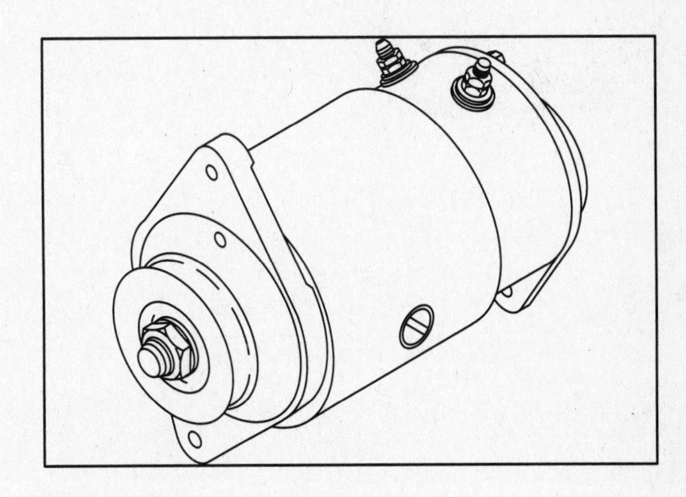

NOTE: METRIC EQUIVALENTS ARE LISTED ON PAGE 63 OF THIS SECTION.

EQUIPMENT TO TEST STARTER MOTORS

The following is a list of equipment recommended to test and repair starter motors.

Digital Multimeter

The Digital Multimeter is available from your Briggs & Stratton source of supply. Order as Tool #19390. The meter may be used to read volts, ohms or amperes, and test diodes (rectifiers) when test leads are inserted in the appropriate receptacle, Fig. 1.

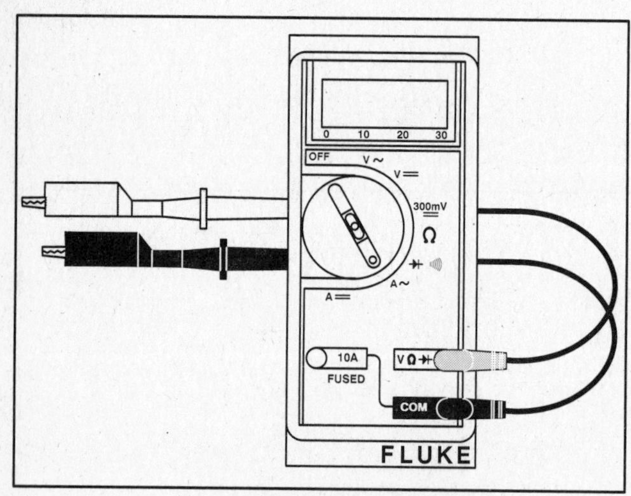

Fig. 1 - Digital Multimeter

DC Shunt

Use with Digital Multimeter. The DC Shunt may be used to read starter motor current draw on 12 volt starter motors. Order as Tool #19359, Fig. 2.

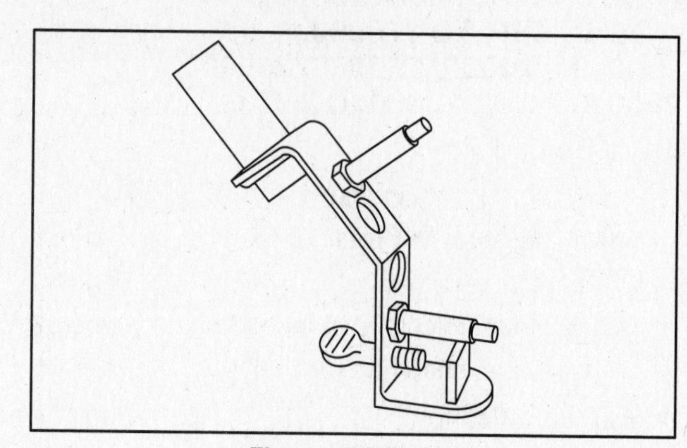
Fig. 2 - DC Shunt

AC Shunt

Use with Digital Multimeter. The AC Shunt may be used to read starter motor current draw on 120 volt starter motors. Order as Tool #19358, Fig. 3.

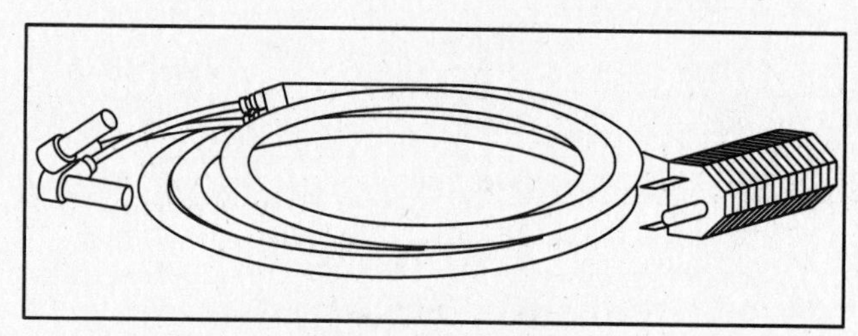
Fig. 3 - AC Shunt

A Trysit Sirometer (Tachometer) is available from your Briggs & Stratton source of supply. Order as Part #19200. The Sirometer measures from 800 to 25,000 revolutions per minute (RPM), Fig. 4.

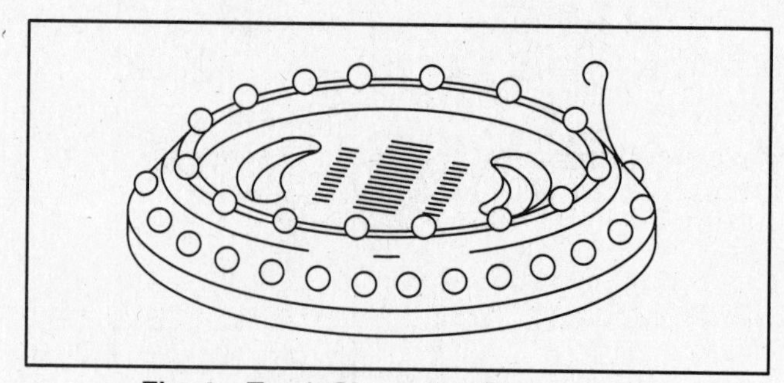
Fig. 4 - Trysit Sirometer (Tachometer)

A starter motor test bracket may be made as shown in Fig. 5.

NOTE: METRIC EQUIVALENTS ARE LISTED ON PAGE 63 OF THIS SECTION.

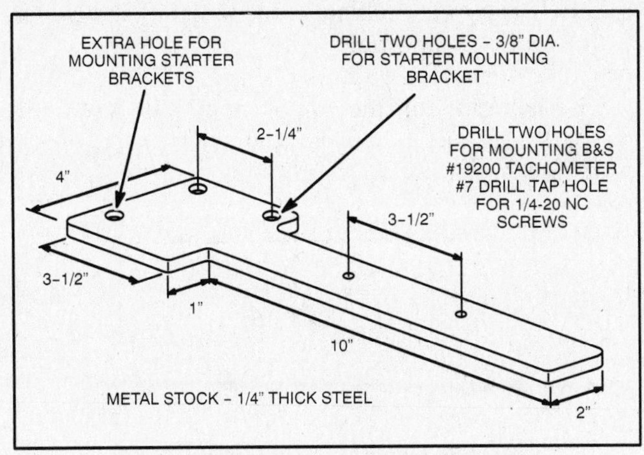

Fig. 5 - Starter Mounting Test Bracket

A growler or armature tester is available from an Automobile Diagnostic Service supplier.

A known good 6 volt or 12 volt battery is required when testing 6 or 12 volt starting systems.

Brush retainers may be made from scrap pieces of rewind starter spring as shown in Fig. 6. Select the retainer required.

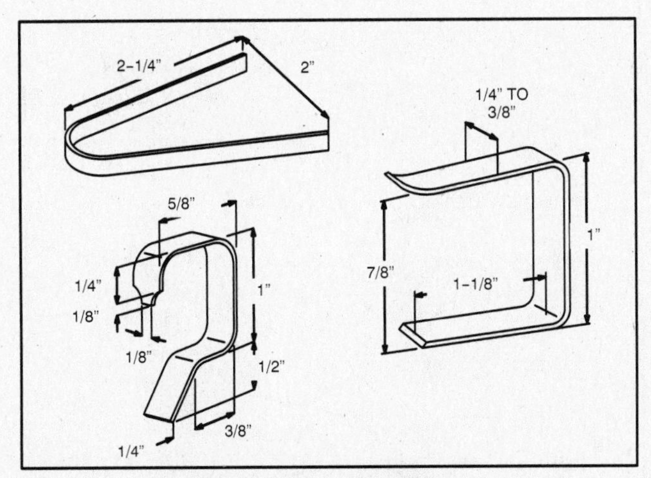

Fig. 6 - Brush Retainers

TROUBLESHOOTING 6, 12, AND 120 VOLT STARTING SYSTEMS

The following list is given to aid in diagnosing problems for 6, 12, and 120 volt starting systems.

NOTE: If a starting problem is encountered, the engine itself should be thoroughly checked to eliminate it as the cause of starting difficulty. It is a good practice to check the engine for freedom of rotation by removing the spark plug and turning the crankshaft over by hand, to be sure it rotates freely.

1. **Cranks Engine Slowly -**
   - A. Additional load affecting performance (see note above).
   - B. Discharged battery (also, see alternators).
   - C. Faulty electrical connection (battery circuit).
   - D. Dirty or worn starter motor commutator, bearing, weak magnets, etc.
   - E. Worn brushes or weak brush springs.
   - F. Wrong oil viscosity for temperature expected.
   - G. Battery leads too long or wire diameter too small.
   - H. Incorrect AMP capacity battery (too small).
   - I. Extension cord longer than 25 feet. (120 volt AC only)
2. **Engine Will Not Crank -**
   - A. Faulty safety interlocks.
   - B. Discharged or defective battery.
   - C. Faulty electrical connections.
   - D. Faulty starter motor switch (open circuit).
   - E. Open circuit in starter motor.
   - F. Defective rectifier assembly (120 Volt AC only).
   - G. Brushes sticking, etc.
   - H. Faulty solenoid.
   - I. Power source inoperative (wall outlet - 120 Volt AC only).
3. **Starter Motor Spins; But Does Not Crank Engine -**
   - A. Sticking pinion gear due to dirt.
   - B. Damaged pinion or ring gear.
   - C. Starter motor clutch slipping.
   - D. Battery faulty or damaged.
   - E. Incorrect rotation due to reversed motor polarity - all motors rotate counterclockwise viewed from pinion gear.
4. **Starter Motor Blows Fuses - (120 Volt Starter Motor Only)**
   - A. Shorted starter motor switch.
   - B. Shorted rectifier assembly.
   - C. Shorted 120 volt extension cord to starter motor.
   - D. Armature shorted.
   - E. Overloaded circuit.
5. **Starter Motor Spins; Will Not Stop**
   - A. Defective starter switch.

NOTE: METRIC EQUIVALENTS ARE LISTED ON PAGE 63 OF THIS SECTION.

NICKEL-CADMIUM STARTER SYSTEM MODEL SERIES 92000 AND 110900 ENGINES

This Briggs & Stratton starter system consists of a starter motor and a starter switch, a wiring harness and a nickel-cadmium rechargeable battery and battery charger. When the ignition key is turned to "START," the battery supplies power to the starter motor, cranking the engine similar to the system used in an automobile. Under normal conditions, the battery will provide 40 to 60 starts before recharging is necessary.

NOTE: Some equipment manufacturers use a battery and charger of a different style than illustrated. In such cases, follow the equipment manufacturer's recommendations.

When the battery needs recharging, the charger is plugged into a 120 volt AC household outlet, and then connected to the battery. The battery will be fully charged within a 14 to 16 hour period. It is not recommended the battery be recharged if temperatures are below 40° F. Continual charging may be harmful to this battery.

For best results, charge the battery within temperature limits of 40° F to 105° F and after each use of equipment. When long periods of storage are encountered, the battery should be charged overnight every two months. This type of battery will lose its charge when not in use. This will shorten battery life.

NOTE: The battery is shipped in a discharged state and must be charged 14 to 16 hours prior to its initial use.

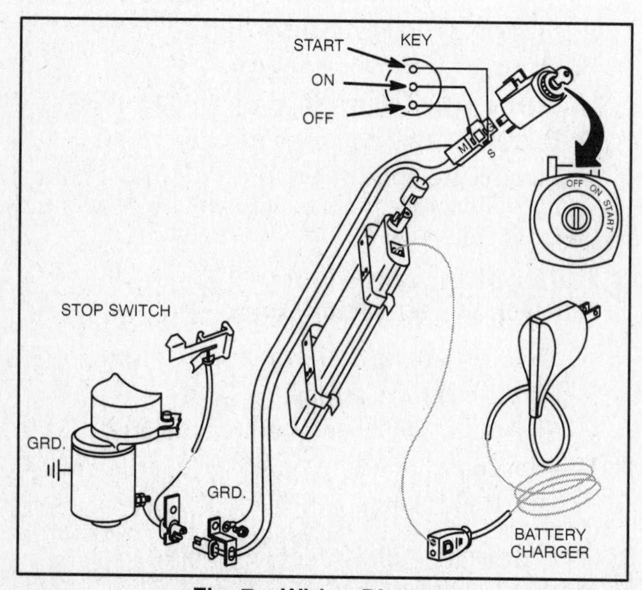

Fig. 7 - Wiring Diagram

NOTE: If a starting problem is encountered, the engine itself should be thoroughly checked to eliminate it as the cause of starting difficulty. It is a good practice to check the engine for freedom of rotation by removing the spark plug and turning the crankshaft over by hand, to be sure it rotates freely.

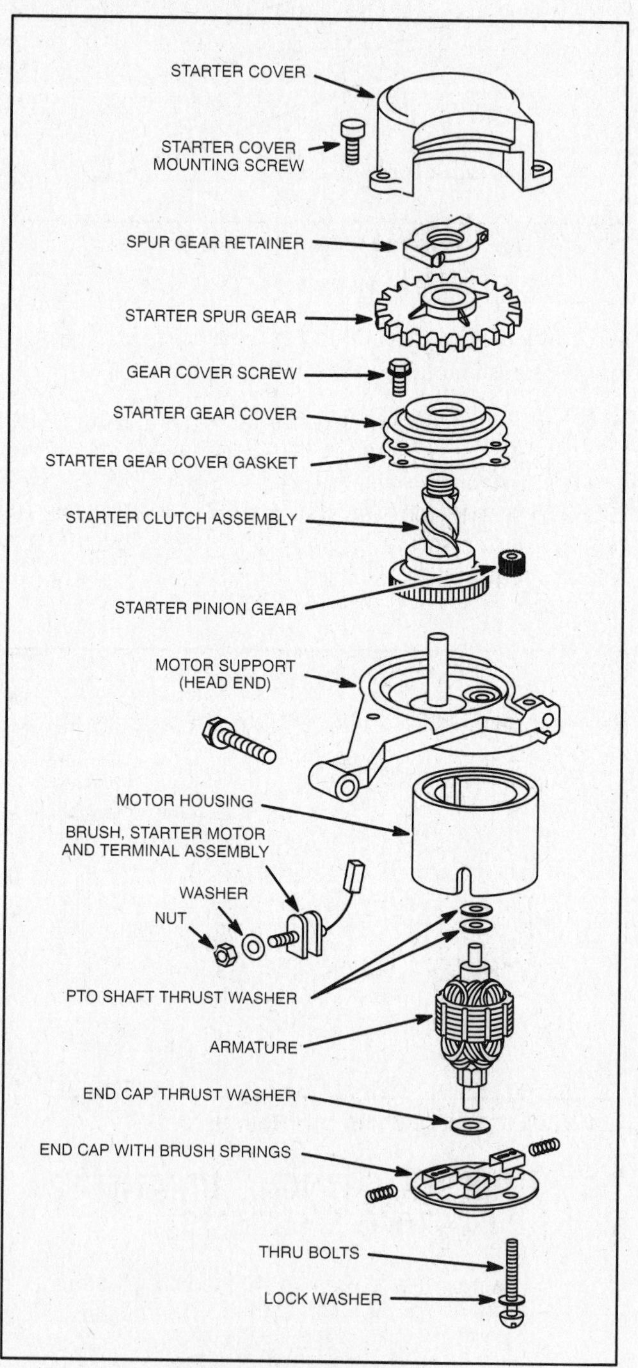

Fig. 8 - Exploded View

Use "Troubleshooting" list on page 3 to aid in diagnosing problems.

NOTE: METRIC EQUIVALENTS ARE LISTED ON PAGE 63 OF THIS SECTION.

Nickel-Cadmium Battery and Charger

NOTE: The battery must be in a fully charged condition for this test. If the battery is not fully charged, it will require charging for a 14 to 16 hour period before proceeding with this test.

The following paragraphs describe an inexpensive battery load tester and a battery charger tester which may be easily constructed.

Battery Tester

Equipment Needed

1. Briggs & Stratton Digital Multimeter (#19357 or #19390) or VOA meter (#19236).
2. Two GE sealed beam headlight bulbs #4001.
3. Make two test leads, approximately 12 inches long, using 16 gauge wire, with two #70 Miller alligator clips and two #62 insulators.

Solder the two headlights together along with test lead wires as shown in Fig. 9.

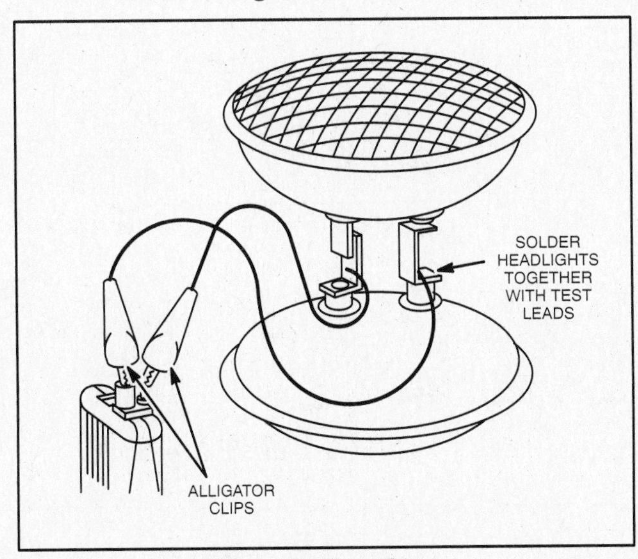

Fig. 9 - Battery Tester

Battery Test

Connect Digital Multimeter as shown in Fig. 10.

- or -

Connect VOA meter as shown in Fig. 11.

NOTE: Positive (+) battery terminal has male connector. Negative (-) battery terminal has female connector.

Headlight test leads may be attached to either battery terminal. Meter test leads must be attached in series; RED lead to positive (+) battery terminal, BLACK lead to negative (-) battery terminal, as shown.

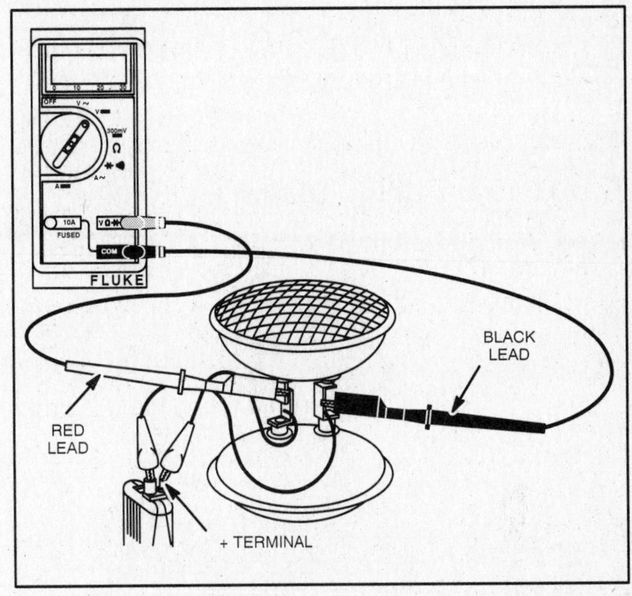

Fig. 10 - Testing Battery with Digital Multimeter

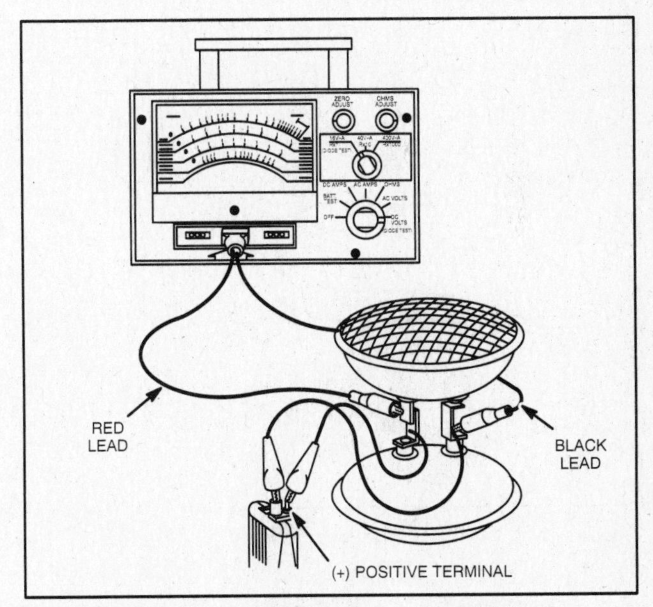

Fig. 11 - Testing Battery - VOA Meter

A fully charged battery, when connected to this headlight set-up will light the bulbs brightly for at least five minutes. The voltmeter reading should be 13.5 volts minimum after one minute, using the headlight load. A voltmeter reading of 13 volts or less, within a one minute period indicates a defective cell in the battery. Replace battery.

NOTE: METRIC EQUIVALENTS ARE LISTED ON PAGE 63 OF THIS SECTION.

Battery Charger Test

The battery charger may be tested using the Digital Multimeter or the VOA meter. The test is performed with the meter in the "Diode Test" position.

DO NOT PLUG CHARGER INTO AC OUTLET WHILE TESTING.

Test Charger Using Digital Multimeter

1. Set Digital Multimeter to "Diode Test" position.
2. Insert RED meter test lead probe into the small plug receptacle in charger plug, Fig. 12.
3. Insert BLACK meter test lead probe into the large plug receptacle in charger plug.
4. Meter should "Beep" once.
   A. If meter makes continuous tone or displays "OL," charger is defective. Replace charger.

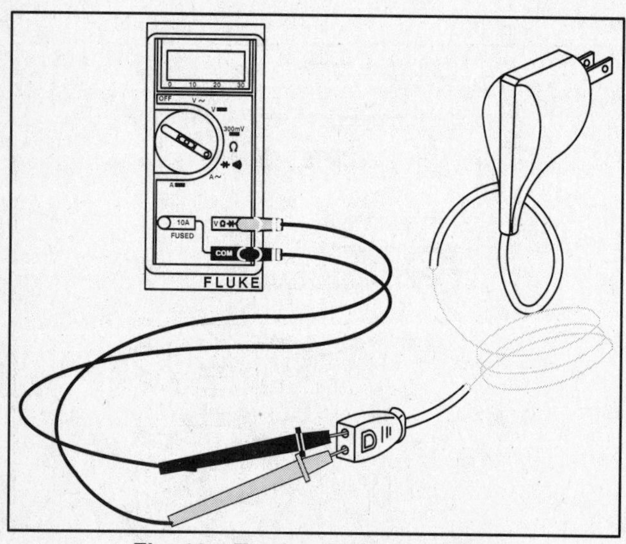

Fig. 12 - Testing Charger - DMM

Test Charger Using VOA Meter

1. Set VOA meter to "Diode Test" position.
2. Insert RED meter test lead probe into the small plug receptacle in charger plug, Fig. 13.
3. Insert BLACK meter test lead probe into the large plug receptacle in charger plug.
4. Meter should display a reading (approximately half scale).
   A. If meter displays a reading, charger is defective. Replace charger.
5. Reverse test leads. Meter should display no reading.
   A. If meter displays no reading, charger is defective. Replace charger.

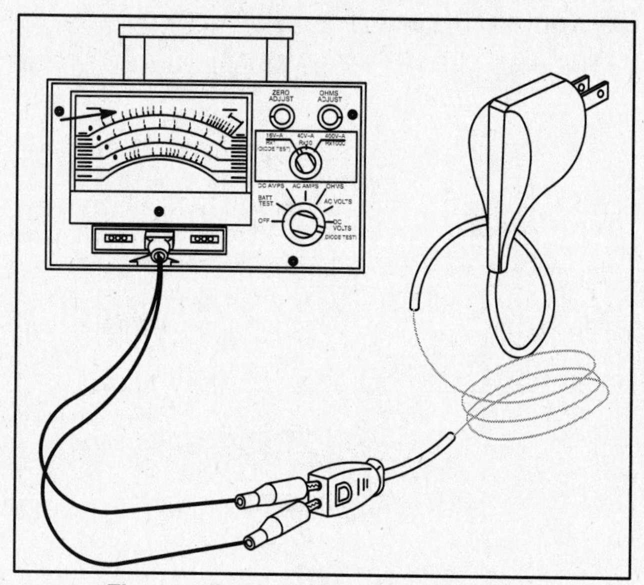

Fig. 13 - Testing Charger - VOA Meter

Key Switch Test

To test the key switch, use the Briggs & Stratton Digital Multimeter or VOA meter.

Set the multimeter to the "Diode Test" position. In the "Diode Test" position the meter will emit a continuous tone, indicating continuity (complete circuit). No continuity (incomplete circuit) is displayed as "OL" and no tone will be heard.

Set the VOA meter to Ohms position and set selector to Rx1 scale. Zero the meter.

Test key switch as shown in Fig. 14. Replace switch if test results differ from chart.

NOTE: METRIC EQUIVALENTS ARE LISTED ON PAGE 63 OF THIS SECTION.

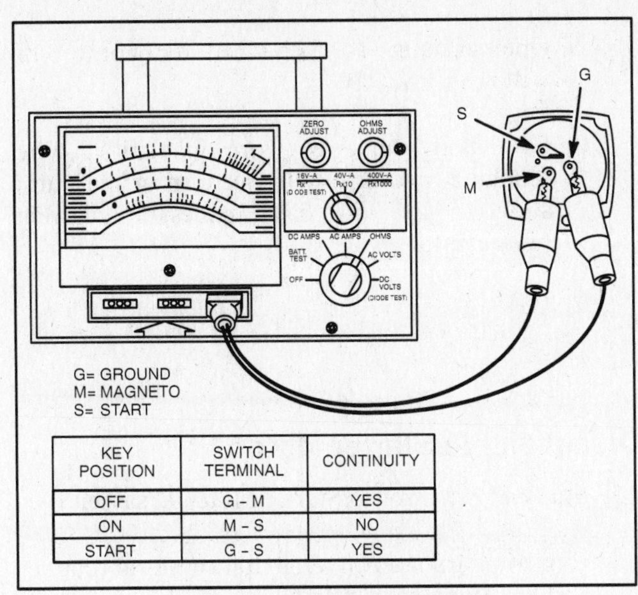

KEY POSITION	SWITCH TERMINAL	CONTINUITY
OFF	G - M	YES
ON	M - S	NO
START	G - S	YES

Fig. 14 - Testing Key Switch

Check Starter Motor Drive and Clutch

When the starter switch is activated, the nylon spur gear should rise, engage the flywheel ring gear, and crank the engine. This can be observed by removing the starter cover. If the starter motor drive does not react properly, inspect the helix and the nylon spur gear for freeness of operation. The nylon spur gear must move freely on the helix for correct starter operation, Fig. 15. If any sticking occurs, this must be corrected.

NOTE: Do not oil nylon spur gear or clutch helix.

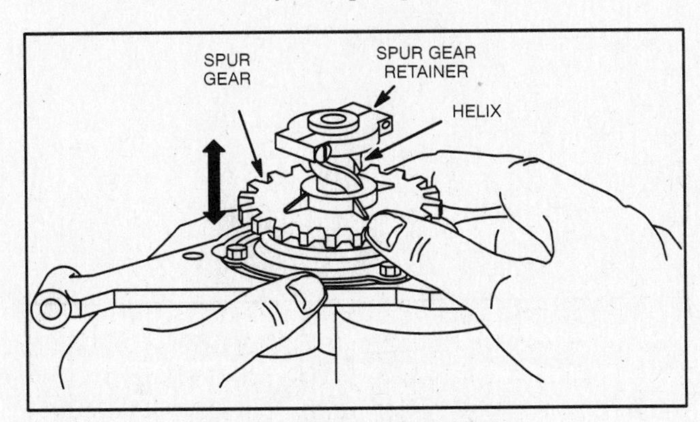

Fig. 15 - Starter Motor Drive

The starter motor clutch is designed to prevent damage from shock loads such as an engine backfire. The clutch should not slip during normal engine cranking. This can be checked by blocking the mower blade and engaging the starter motor. If the clutch assembly slips at this time, it should be replaced.

CAUTION: Ground spark plug wire using Ignition Tester, Tool #19051 or #19368, before this test.

Checking the Starter Motor

A performance test of the starter motor may be made in the following manner.

Equipment Needed

Digital Multimeter, Tool (#19357 or 19390) or VOA Meter, Tool #19236.

A tachometer capable of reading 10,000 RPM.

A fully charged battery.

To Test

1. Set the meter to read DC amps.
2. Connect the starter motor, battery and meter, as shown in Figs. 16 or 17.
3. Place the sirometer on the starter motor and activate the starter motor.

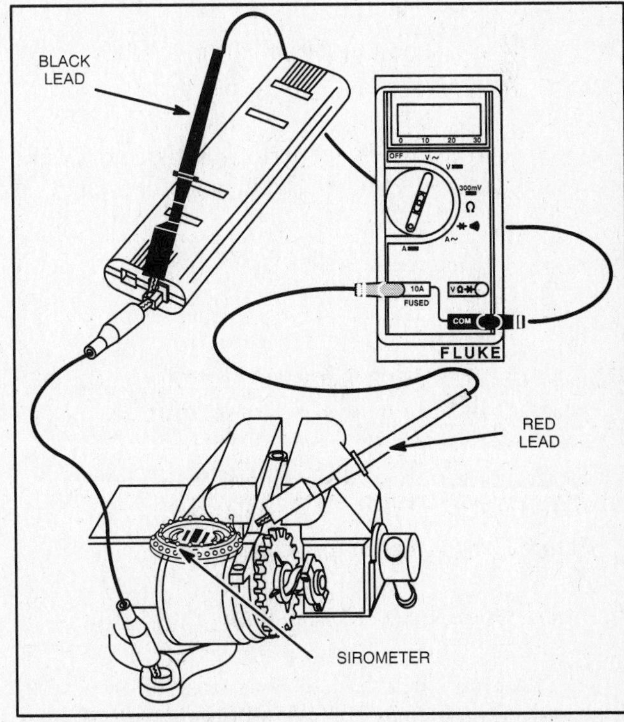

Fig. 16 - Testing Starter Motor -with Digital Multimeter

7B

NOTE: METRIC EQUIVALENTS ARE LISTED ON PAGE 63 OF THIS SECTION.

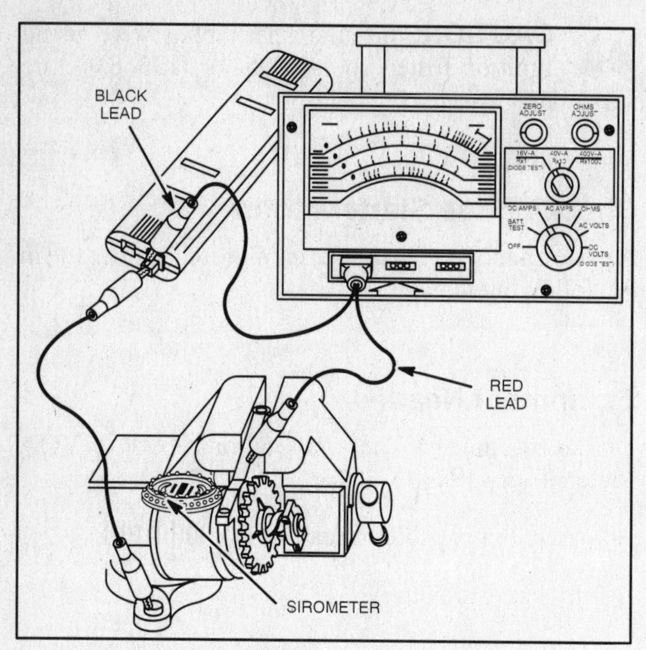

Fig. 17 – Testing Starter Motor – VOA Meter

A starter motor in good condition will be within the following specifications.

Minimum RPM – 1000
Maximum Amps – 3-1/2

If the starter motor does not perform satisfactorily, the following should be checked, and corrected if necessary.

1. A binding condition between the pinion and clutch gear or misalignment of motor bearings.
2. Starter motor brushes sticking in brush holders.
3. A dirty or worn armature commutator.
4. A shorted, open or grounded armature.
   A. Shorted armature (worn insulation, wires touching each other) will be indicated by slow speed and high current.
   B. Open armature (broken wire) may not turn or will have low RPM.
   C. Grounded armature (worn insulation, wire touching armature) will not turn or may turn slowly and will have excessive current (amperes).
5. Weak magnets.

Disassemble Starter Motor

1. Study Fig. 8 prior to Starter Motor Disassembly.
2. Remove the starter cover, nylon spur gear retainer and the nylon spur gear.
3. The three screws holding the gear cover and the gear itself may now be removed.
4. Lift the clutch assembly and the pinion gear off their respective shafts.
5. Remove the starter motor thru bolts, Fig. 18.
6. Separate motor end head from motor housing.
7. Push motor armature out through bottom of starter housing, taking care to slide rubber mounted terminal out of motor housing along with end cap, Fig. 19.

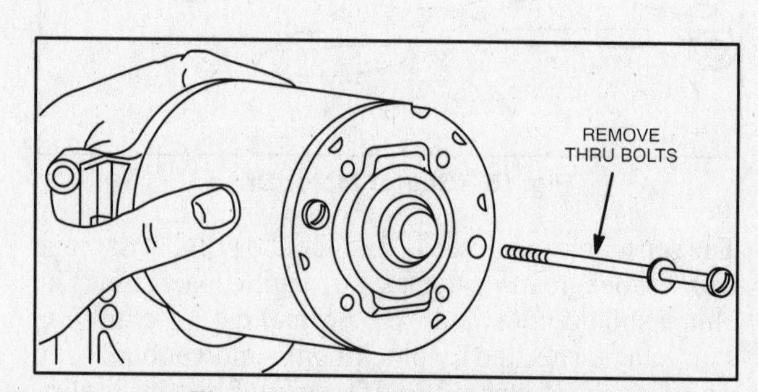

Fig. 18 – Removing Thru Bolts

NOTE: METRIC EQUIVALENTS ARE LISTED ON PAGE 63 OF THIS SECTION.

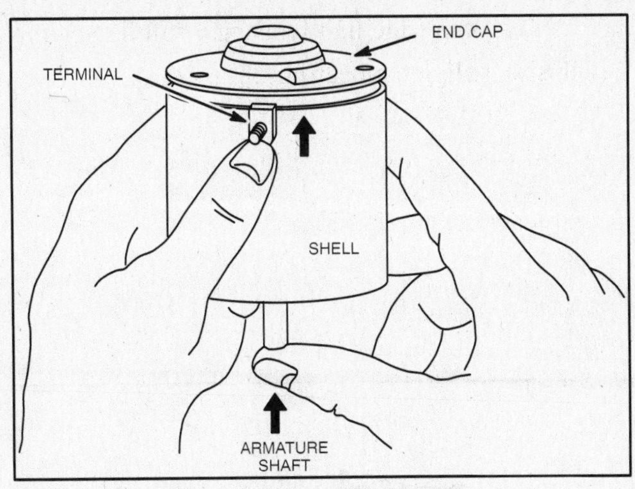

Fig. 19 - Removing Armature

8. Before removing armature from end cap, check brushes for freedom of movement. If brushes are found to be sticking in their retainers, this must be corrected, or poor starter motor performance will result, Fig. 20.

9. If brushes are worn to a length of 1/4" or less, the brushes should be replaced.

10. Check brush springs for proper tension (sufficient force to keep brush in firm contact with commutator).

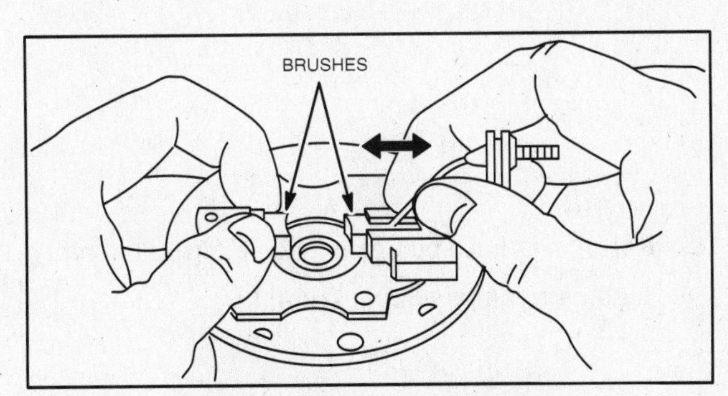

Fig. 20 - Checking Brushes

11. Clean all dirt from armature, end cap, motor support, gears, etc. The end cap bearings and armature should not be soaked in a solvent.

12. The armature commutator may be cleaned with a fine sandpaper or commutator paper.

    NOTE: DO NOT USE ALUMINUM OXIDE PAPER OR EMERY CLOTH, AS EMERY WILL BECOME EMBEDDED IN THE COMMUTATOR CAUSING RAPID BRUSH WEAR.

13. If the armature is suspected to be defective, a new armature should be tried in the motor. If proper testing equipment is available, check the suspected armature to determine if it is defective.

14. Starter motor armatures have very low resistance, usually below detection on available multimeters. To check for shorted armatures, a piece of equipment known as a "growler" may be used. If this equipment is not available, a known good armature should be tried and performance rechecked.

15. If the magnets appear to be weak, a new motor housing should be tried.

Assemble Starter Motor

When all parts have been thoroughly inspected, lightly lubricate bearings with a #20 oil and reassemble in the following manner.

1. Insert brush springs and brushes in holders as far as possible, and hold them in this position with tool shown in Fig. 21.

2. Place thrust washers on armature shaft, using care to ensure brushes clear commutator.

3. Slide armature shaft into end cap bearing, Fig. 21.

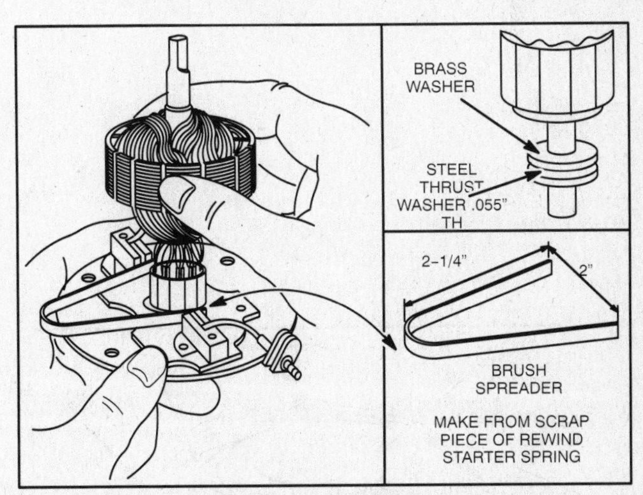

Fig. 21 - Assembling Armature to End Cap

4. Support armature shaft and slide it slowly into starter housing, as shown in Fig. 22.

5. Insert rubber mounted terminal into starter housing at this time.

7B

NOTE: METRIC EQUIVALENTS ARE LISTED ON PAGE 63 OF THIS SECTION.

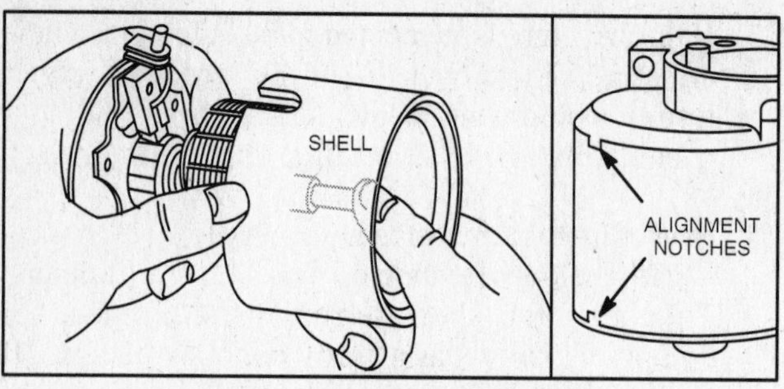

Fig. 22 - Inserting Armature

6. Place remaining thrust washers on motor PTO shaft, install end head cover and thru bolts.
7. Notches in end cap, housing and end head must be aligned, Fig. 22.
8. Notches in end cap, housing and end head must be aligned, Fig. 22.
9. Check for end play to be sure armature is free.
10. Slip pinion and starter motor clutch gear on shaft, add a small amount of gear lubricant to gears and install gear cover and gasket, Fig. 23.

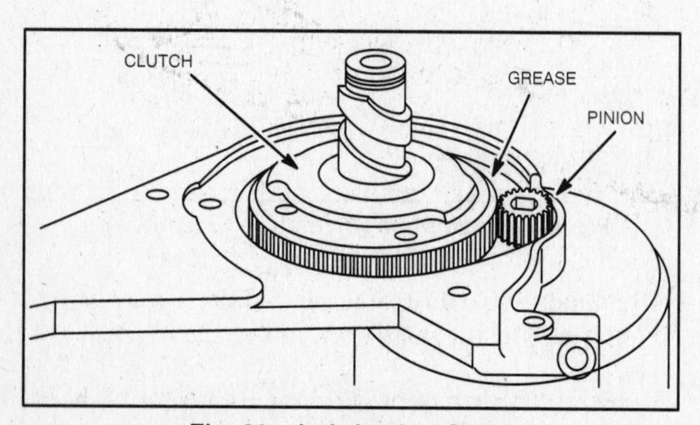

Fig. 23 - Lubricating Gears

11. Tap end cap edge lightly using a soft hammer as this will align the bearings, Fig. 24.

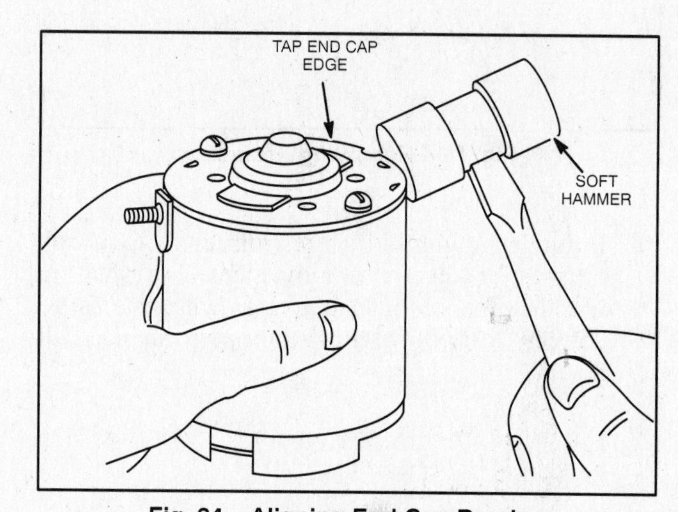

Fig. 24 - Aligning End Cap Bearing

12. Replace nylon spur gear and retainer assembly. Tighten retainer screws securely.

NOTE: Do not oil nylon spur gear or clutch helix.

13. Install starter cover and torque screws to 25 in. lbs..

14. Install starter motor on engine. Torque rear starter mounting screw (5/16"- 18) to 140 in. lbs. Torque front mounting screw (1/4"- 20) to 90 in. lbs.

NOTE: METRIC EQUIVALENTS ARE LISTED ON PAGE 63 OF THIS SECTION.

Electric Starter Key Switch And Wiring Recommendations For 12 Volt Nickel-Cadmium Battery Starter System - Series 92000 and 110900 Engines

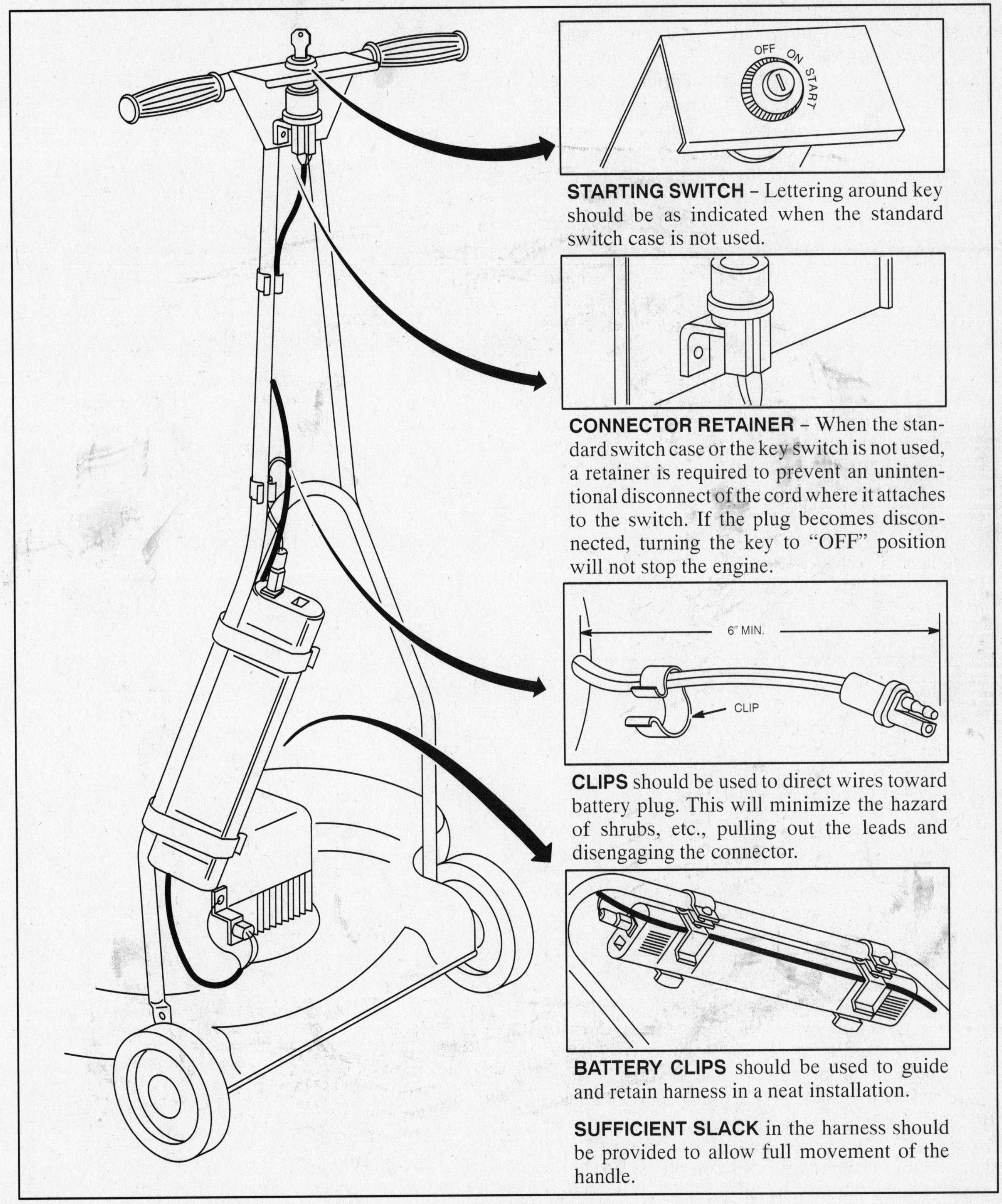

STARTING SWITCH - Lettering around key should be as indicated when the standard switch case is not used.

CONNECTOR RETAINER - When the standard switch case or the key switch is not used, a retainer is required to prevent an unintentional disconnect of the cord where it attaches to the switch. If the plug becomes disconnected, turning the key to "OFF" position will not stop the engine.

CLIPS should be used to direct wires toward battery plug. This will minimize the hazard of shrubs, etc., pulling out the leads and disengaging the connector.

BATTERY CLIPS should be used to guide and retain harness in a neat installation.

SUFFICIENT SLACK in the harness should be provided to allow full movement of the handle.

Fig. 25

NOTE: METRIC EQUIVALENTS ARE LISTED ON PAGE 63 OF THIS SECTION.

SYSTEM 3®, SYSTEM 4®

The Briggs & Stratton System 3® and System 4® consist of a starter motor, starter switch and/or starter solenoid, wiring harness, 6 or 12 volt battery (rechargeable), alternator and separate trickle type battery charger. When the starter switch and/or solenoid is actuated, the battery supplies power to the starter motor, cranking the engine similar to the system used on an automobile, Fig. 26. When the engine is running, the alternator recharges the battery.

NOTE: Some equipment manufacturers use a battery and trickle charger of a different style than illustrated. In such cases, follow the equipment manufacturer's recommendations.

Should the battery need additional recharging, the trickle charger is plugged into a 120 volt AC household outlet, and then connected to the battery. The battery will be fully charged within a 72 hour period. It is not recommended that the battery be recharged if temperatures are below 40° F. For best results, charge the battery within temperature limits of 40° F to 105° F. When long periods of storage are encountered, the battery should be charged overnight every two months. This type of battery will lose its charge when not in use. This may shorten battery life.

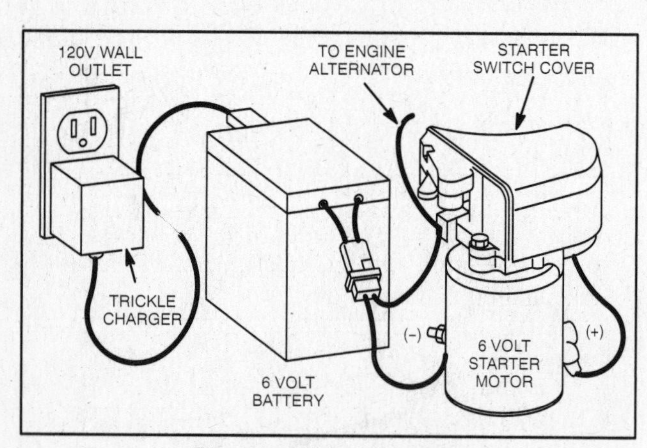

Fig. 26 - Wiring Diagram

NOTE: The 6 volt battery is shipped in a partially charged state and must be charged at least 72 hours before being used for the first time. If the equipment manufacturer did not supply a trickle charger for the Briggs & Stratton 6 volt battery, order Part #395569 for use with 120 volt 60 cycle (Hertz) power. Order Part #395585 for use with 240 volt 50 cycle (Hertz) power. Contact equipment manufacturer for 12 volt trickle chargers.

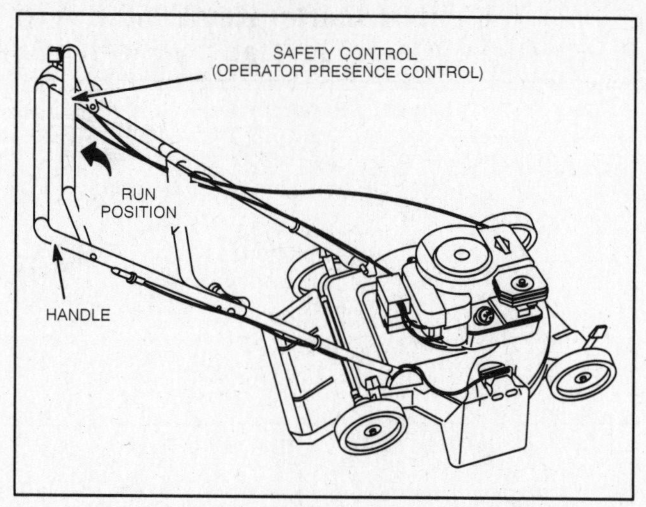

Fig. 27 - Typical Mower/System 4® Engine

NOTE: If a starting problem is encountered, the engine itself should be thoroughly checked to eliminate it as the cause of starting difficulty. It is a good practice to check the engine for freedom of rotation by removing the spark plug, releasing brake, and turning the engine over by hand, to be sure it rotates freely. The equipment itself should be similarly inspected to eliminate possible parasitic load or other damage such as loose blade or mounting screws which contribute to hard starting. A typical mower equipped with a System 4® electric starter engine is shown in Fig. 27. A typical System 3® or System 4® engine is shown in Fig. 28.

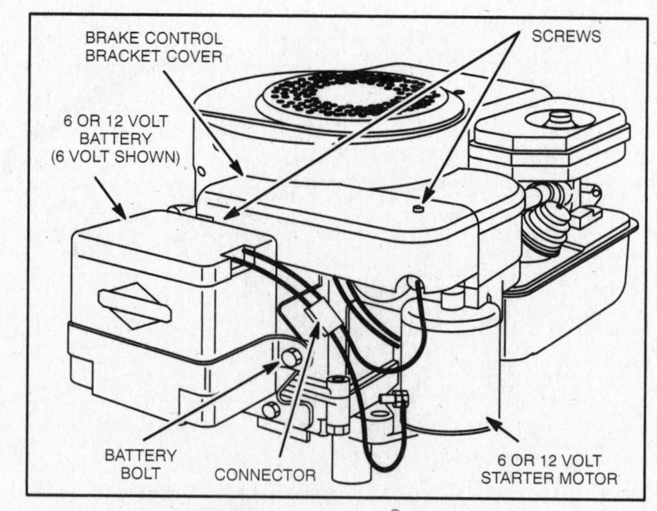

Fig. 28 - System 4® Engine

Troubleshooting 6 or 12 Volt Starting System

The following list is provided to aid in diagnosing problems for the 6 or 12 volt system.

NOTE: METRIC EQUIVALENTS ARE LISTED ON PAGE 63 OF THIS SECTION.

1. Cranks Engine Slowly (Below 500 RPM) -

A. Additional load affecting performance, such as: grass or debris obstructing cutter blade.

B. Faulty electrical connection (battery circuit, connector and wiring harness).

C. Discharged or defective battery (also, see alternators and charger).

D. Dirty or worn starter motor commutator, bearing, weak magnets, etc.

E. Worn brushes or weak brush springs.

F. Wrong engine oil viscosity for starting temperature expected.

G. Defective clutch.

H. Band brake misadjusted.

2. Engine Will Not Crank -

A. Faulty equipment safety interlocks.

B. Discharged or defective battery.

C. Faulty electrical connections.

D. Faulty starter motor switch (open circuit or high resistance).

E. Open circuit in starter motor.

F. Brushes sticking, etc.

G. Faulty solenoid.

H. Drive and clutch.

3. Starter Motor Spins; But Does Not Crank Engine -

A. Sticking pinion gear due to dirt.

B. Damaged starter or ring gear.

C. Battery faulty or damaged.

D. Incorrect rotation due to reversed motor polarity – all motors rotate counterclockwise viewed from pinion gear.

E. Starter clutch slipping.

4. Starter Motor Spins; Will Not Stop

A. Defective starter switch.

NOTE: The following test procedures apply only to the Briggs & Stratton 6 volt battery. For test procedures for 12 volt batteries, contact the battery manufacturer or the original equipment manufacturer.

Testing the 6 Volt Charger and Battery

The following describes a four step test for the 6 volt trickle charger and battery using Battery and Charger Tester, Tool #19257.

NOTE: Tester needle must align with NEEDLE ADJUST line, Fig. 29. If required, turn the needle adjust screw to obtain proper alignment.

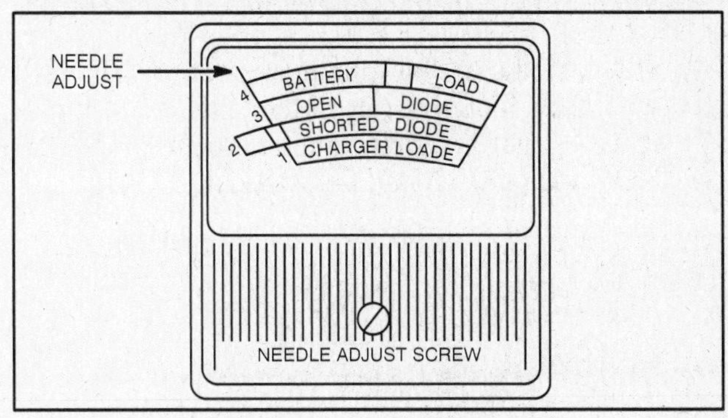

Fig. 29 – Meter Scale

Trickle Charger Load Test (Gates and Globe Union Batteries)

1. To test charger, place rotary switch in position number 1.
2. With charger plugged into wall outlet and tester, press button marked 1, Fig. 30.
3. Meter needle must remain in green area on scale 1. If meter needle falls to red area, output is insufficient and the charger must be replaced.

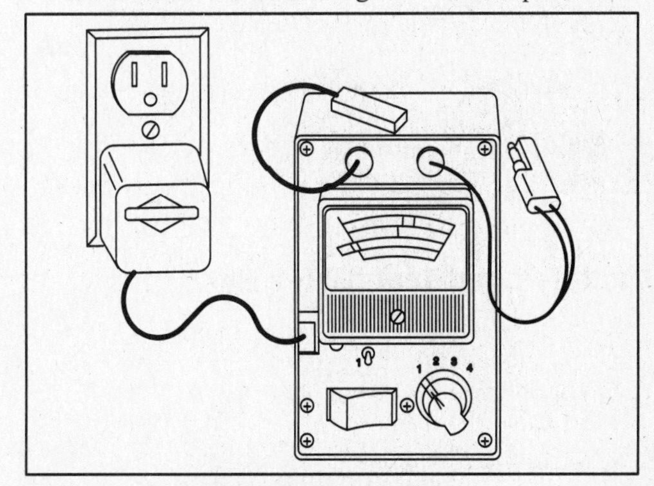

Fig. 30 – Charger Test

Charger Lead Diode Test (Gates Battery Only)

NOTE: See next page for Globe Union battery test.

Diode Short Test

1. With charger still plugged into wall outlet and tester, connect battery charger lead to tester lead "A." Slot in charger lead and lead "A" must be lined up, Fig. 31.

7B

NOTE: METRIC EQUIVALENTS ARE LISTED ON PAGE 63 OF THIS SECTION.

2. Turn rotary switch to position 2.

3. Connect battery to other end of charger lead.

4. Meter needle MUST remain in green area of meter scale 2. If meter needle enters either red area of scale 2, diode is shorted and must be replaced. **DO NOT PERFORM OPEN DIODE TEST.**

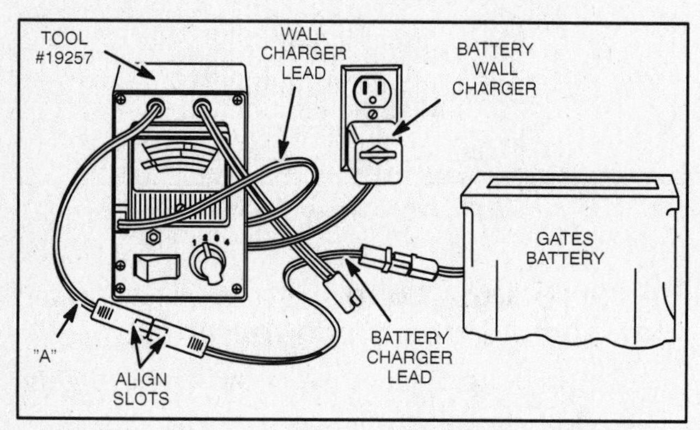

Fig. 31 – Charger Diode Lead Test (Gates Battery)

Diode Open Test

1. If charger lead passed **DIODE SHORT TEST**, turn rotary switch to position 3.

2. Meter needle must move into green area of scale 3. If needle stays in red area, diode is open and charger lead must be replaced.

Battery Load Test (Gates Battery)

1. Disconnect charger lead from battery.

2. Plug battery into tester lead "B."

3. Turn rotary switch to position 4.

4. Press rocker switch and HOLD for 10 SECONDS. Release switch. Meter needle must remain in green area of scale 4 for FULL 10 SECOND test, Fig. 32.

CAUTION: Do not hold rocker switch down over 20 seconds. Allow 5 minutes between tests.

5. If meter needle drops into yellow area – or remains in red area of scale, charge battery as described in "Battery – Fast Charge." (Battery may also be charged 72 hours using Trickle Charger.)

6. Remove battery from charger and allow to normalize for two hours.

7. Repeat test.

8. If meter needle drops into or remains in red area of scale 4, replace battery.

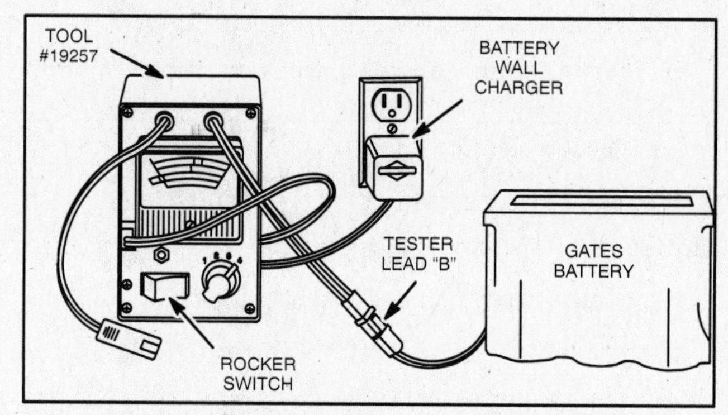

Fig. 32 – Battery Load Test (Gates Battery)

Battery Diode Test (Globe Union Battery)

Trickle charger, Part #395569 (120 V) or 395585 (240 V) must be plugged into a wall outlet and tester. Connect both tester leads to battery, Fig. 33.

Diode Short Test

1. Place rotary switch in position number 2.

2. Attach tester connectors to battery, Fig. 33.

3. Meter needle MUST remain in green area of meter scale 2. A meter needle which enters red area of scale 2, indicates that battery diode has failed and battery must be replaced.

Diode Open Test

1. Place rotary switch in position number 3. Meter needle must enter green area of scale 3.

2. If meter needle remains in red area of scale 3, check connectors for cleanliness and tight fit.

3. If meter needle still remains in red area, replace battery.

NOTE: METRIC EQUIVALENTS ARE LISTED ON PAGE 63 OF THIS SECTION.

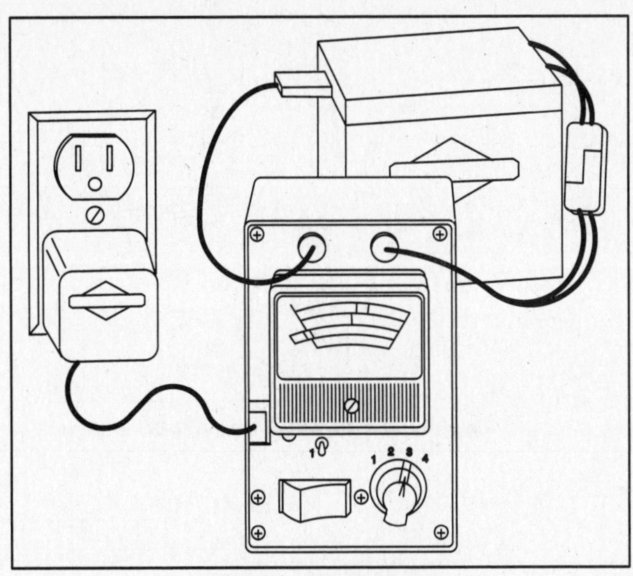

Fig. 33 - Battery Test

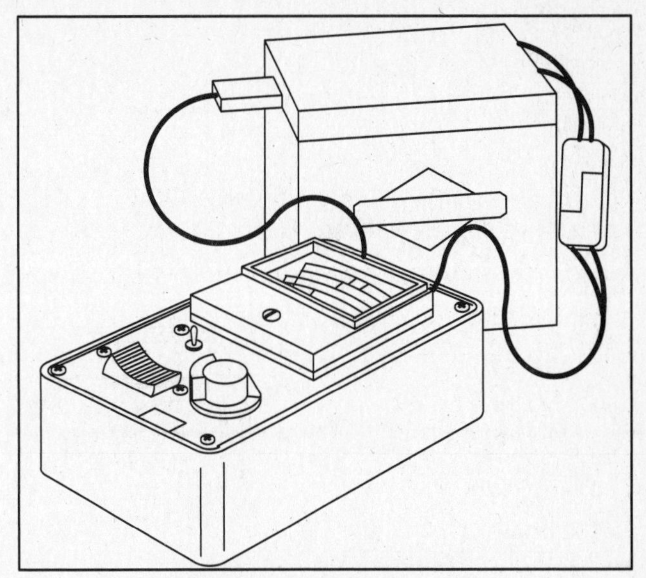

Fig. 34 - Battery Load Test

Battery Load Test (Globe Union Battery)

1. Place rotary switch in position number 4, Fig. 34.

2. Press rocker switch and HOLD for 10 SECONDS test. Release switch. Meter needle must remain in green area of scale 4 for FULL 10 SECOND test.

CAUTION: Do not hold rocker switch down over 20 seconds. Allow 5 minutes between tests.

3. If meter needle drops into yellow area – or remains in red area of scale, charge battery as described in "Battery - Fast Charge." (Battery may also be charged 72 hours using Trickle Charger.)

4. Remove battery from charger and allow to normalize for two hours.

5. Repeat test.

6. If meter needle drops into or remains in red area of scale 4, replace battery.

(Alternate) Battery Load Test

The following describes an alternate battery load test.

Parts required are listed as follows:

A. 14 AWG stranded wire with #70 alligator clips (test lead).

B. Resistor - 0.15 ohms x 240 watts (minimum)

C. Briggs & Stratton Digital Multimeter, Tool (#19357 or 19390) or VOA Meter, Tool #19236.

D. Briggs & Stratton Part #396473 wire harness.

1. Set Multimeter or VOA meter to DC volts as shown in Fig. 35.
2. Place Part #396473, red harness wire terminal on resistor lead.
3. Hold harness wire on resistor lead with alligator clip on RED test lead wire from DMM or VOA meter.
4. Place black harness wire terminal on other resistor lead (side opposite from red wires).
5. Hold harness wire on resistor lead with alligator clip on BLACK test lead wire from DMM or VOA meter.
6. Assemble connector from wire harness to battery. At the end of ONE MINUTE, battery should read 5.5 volts DC, minimum.
7. If at the end of one minute, test voltage reads less than 5.5 volts DC, charge battery as described in "Battery - Fast Charge." (Battery may also be charged 72 hours with trickle charger.)

NOTE: METRIC EQUIVALENTS ARE LISTED ON PAGE 63 OF THIS SECTION.

8. Remove battery from charger and allow to normalize for two hours.

9. Retest battery.

NOTE: A meter reading of 4.5 volts DC or less after charging and retest indicates a failed battery cell. Replace battery.

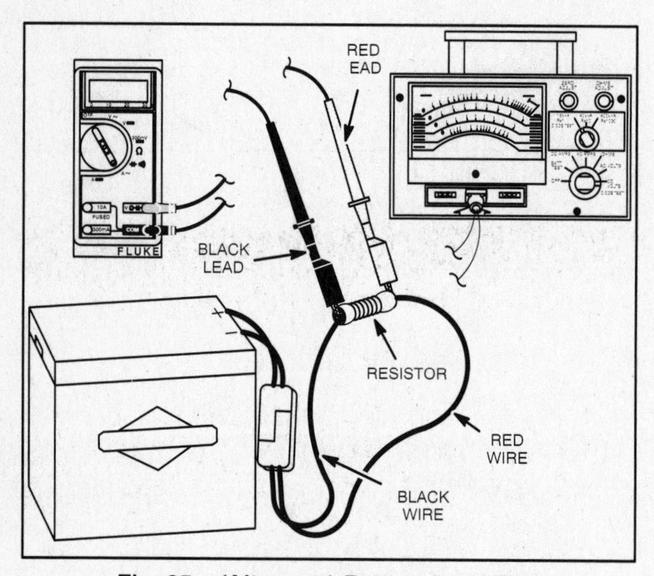

Fig. 35 – (Alternate) Battery Load Test

Battery – Fast Charge

A fully charged battery will have a minimum NO-LOAD reading of 6.4 volts DC. During normal engine use, the alternator will keep the battery charged. During storage, the battery should be recharged 72 hours every two months using Part #395569 or 395585 trickle charger. The following describes a Fast Charge procedure using a 6 or 12 volt charger to provide a faster battery charging method.

Charge Battery – 6 Volt Charger

1. Attach positive charger lead to positive battery connector terminal, Fig. 36.

2. Attach negative charger lead to negative battery connector terminal.

3. Charge battery at a rate not to exceed 1 ampere for 12 hours.

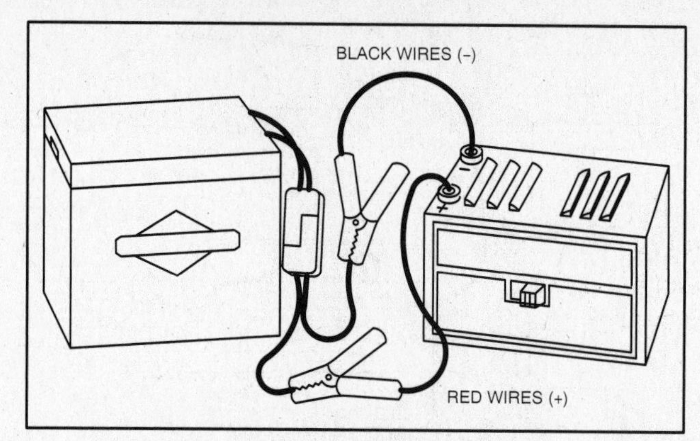

Fig. 36 – 6 Volt Battery Charger

Charge Battery – 12 Volt Charger

1. Attach positive charger lead to a #4001 sealed beam headlight terminal as shown in Fig. 37.
2. Connect alligator clips of test lead from other terminal of headlight to positive terminal of battery connector.
3. Attach negative charger lead to negative battery connector terminal.
4. Attach harness to battery connector. Charge battery at a rate not to exceed 1 ampere for 12 hours.

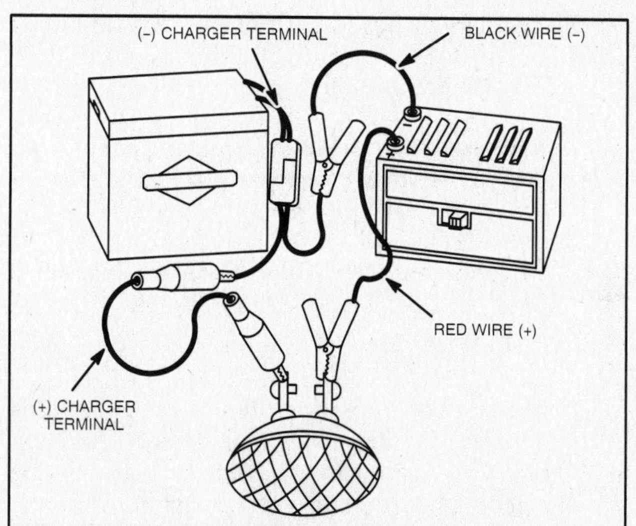

Fig. 37 – 12 Volt Battery Charger

CAUTION:

Handling Instructions

Like all batteries, these units contain corrosive fluids and toxic materials and should be handled with care.

- Do not puncture, disassemble, mutilate or incinerate.

- As with all rechargeable batteries, explosive gases could be vented during charge or discharge. Use in a well ventilated area, away from sources of ignition.
- Battery should be recharged by adults only.
- Use only the battery charger specified. Do not make direct contact between the positive and negative terminals as this could cause high current to flow, creating high heat and the possibility of a fire in the connecting part.
- Avoid any direct connection of battery terminals that will cause the battery to short out.

Switch Test

To test the switch, use the Briggs & Stratton Digital Multimeter or VOA meter.

1. Set the Multimeter to the "Diode Test" position. In the "Diode Test " position the meter will emit a continuous tone, indicating continuity (complete circuit). No continuity (incomplete circuit) is displayed as "OL" and no tone will be heard.
2. Set the VOA meter to Ohms position and set selector to Rx1 scale.
3. Zero the meter.
4. Test switch as shown in Fig. 38. With switch lever in "RUN" or "STOP" (brake) position, there should be NO continuity.
5. Place lever in "START" position, meter should indicate a continuity reading.

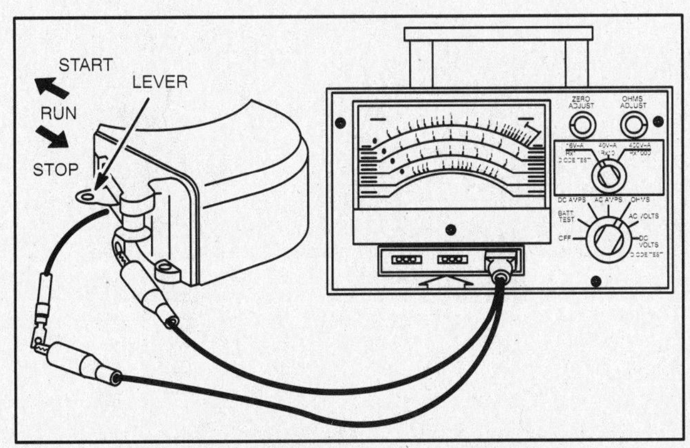

Fig. 38 - Testing Starter Switch

6. If there is NO continuity in "START" position, the wire and brush assembly may be serviced as shown in Fig's. 39 and 40, by removing 3 screws.

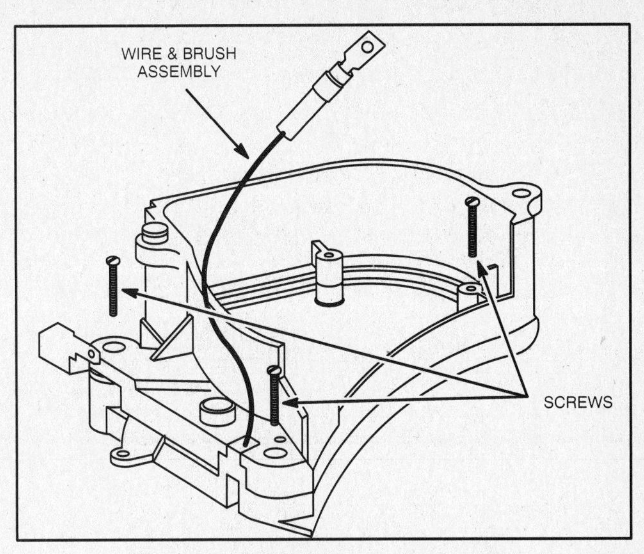

Fig. 39 - Switch Cover Assembly

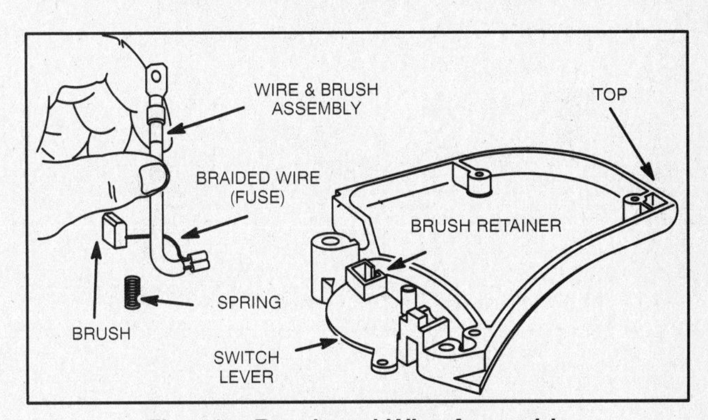

Fig. 40 - Brush and Wire Assembly

Check Interlock Switch, Model Series 120000

1. Disconnect interlock switch wires from spade terminals on switch.
2. Set meter to read Ω ohms.
3. Connect meter test leads or continuity light to two spade terminals of switch. Light should not be on or meter should read no continuity.
4. Push switch lever in until switch clicks. The light should be on and the meter should read low resistance.

Check Interlock Switch Wiring, Model Series 120000

1. Disconnect interlock switch wires from spade terminals on switch and at starter motor connector.
2. Set meter to read Ω ohms.

NOTE: METRIC EQUIVALENTS ARE LISTED ON PAGE 63 OF THIS SECTION.

3. Connect one meter test lead to end of one wire inside connector and other test lead to second connector terminal for the same wire. Light should be on or meter should read low or no resistance. Move wire inside connector. Light should stay constant or meter should not change value. Replace or repair wiring if there is no continuity or intermittent. Repeat for each wire in harness.

NOTE: Some equipment manufacturers provide a key operated ignition switch. For servicing, contact equipment manufacturer.

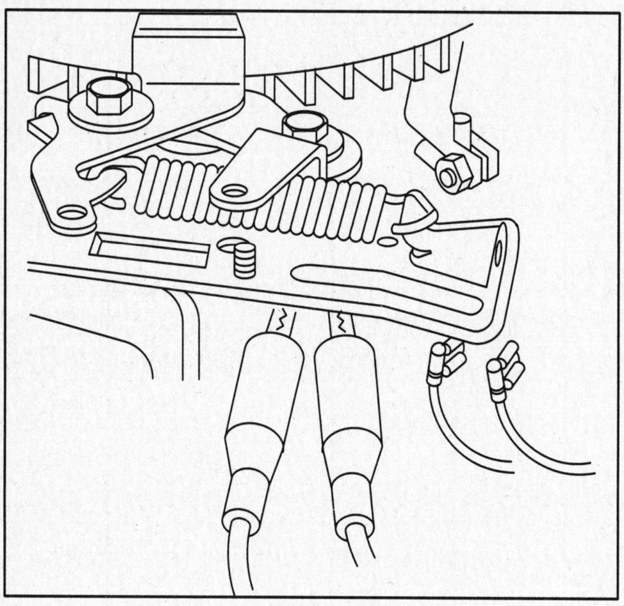

Fig. 41 – Testing Interlock Switch

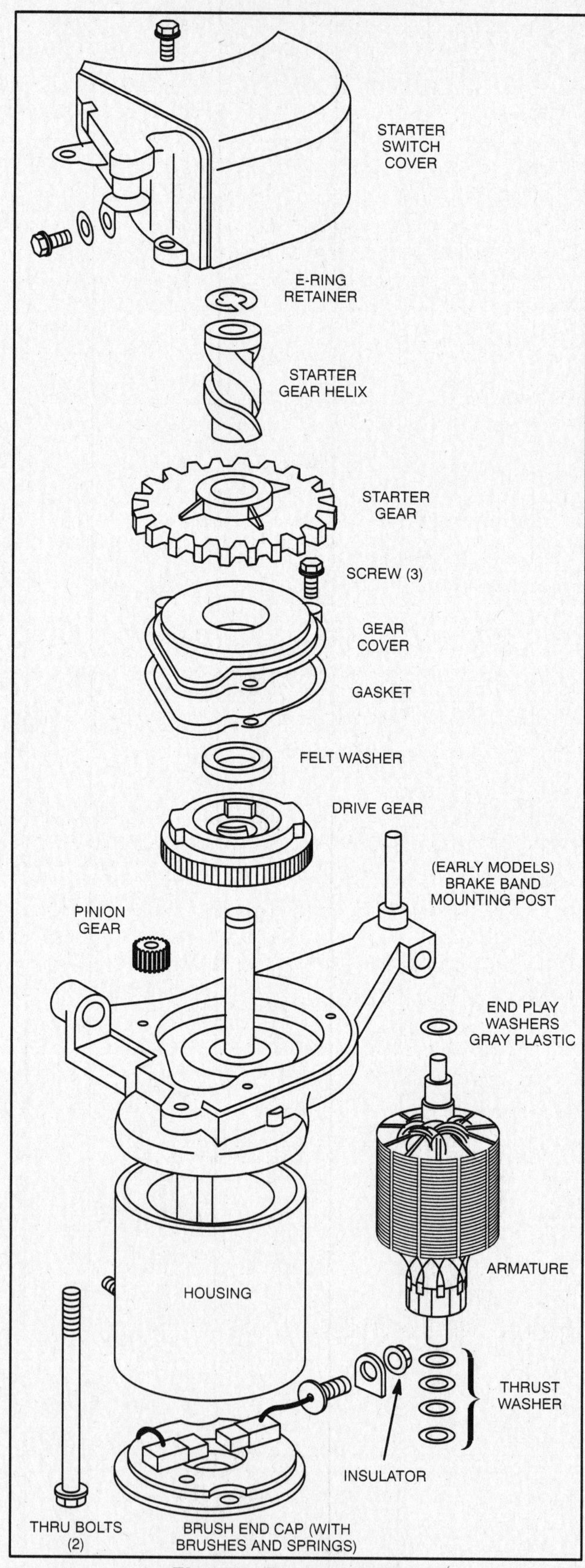

Fig. 42 – Exploded View

NOTE: METRIC EQUIVALENTS ARE LISTED ON PAGE 63 OF THIS SECTION.

Checking the Starter Motor Drive and Clutch

When the starter switch is activated, the nylon spur gear should rise, engage the flywheel ring gear, and crank the engine. This should be observed. If the starter motor drive does not react properly, inspect the helix and the nylon spur gear for freeness of operation. The nylon spur gear must move freely on the helix for correct starter operation. If any sticking occurs, this must be corrected, Fig. 43.

NOTE: Do not oil nylon spur gear on clutch helix.

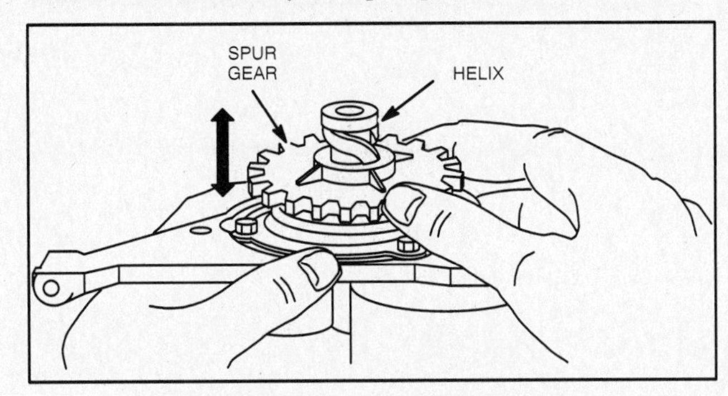

Fig. 43 - Starter Motor Drive

The starter motor clutch is designed to prevent damage from shock loads such as an engine backfire. The clutch should not slip during normal engine cranking. This can be checked by blocking the mower blade and engaging the starter motor. If the clutch assembly slips at this time, it should be replaced.

CAUTION: Ground spark plug wire using Ignition Tester, Tool #19051 or #19368, before this test. DO NOT engage starter motor more than five seconds.

Check 6 or 12 Volt Starter Motor

A performance test of the starter motor may be made in the following manner.

Equipment Needed

1. Digital Multimeter, Tool (#19357 or 19390) or VOA Meter, Tool #19236.
2. A tachometer capable of reading 10,000 RPM.
3. A fully charged 6 or 12 volt battery.

To Test

1. Set the meter to read DC amps.
2. Connect the starter motor, battery and meter as shown in Fig's. 44 or 45.
3. Place the sirometer on the starter motor and activate the starter motor as shown, Fig's. 44 or 45.

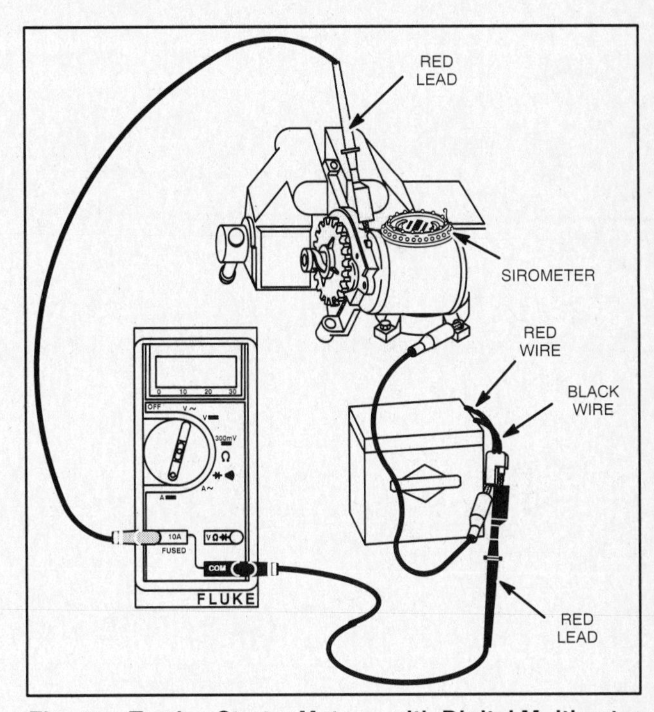

Fig. 44 - Testing Starter Motor - with Digital Multimeter

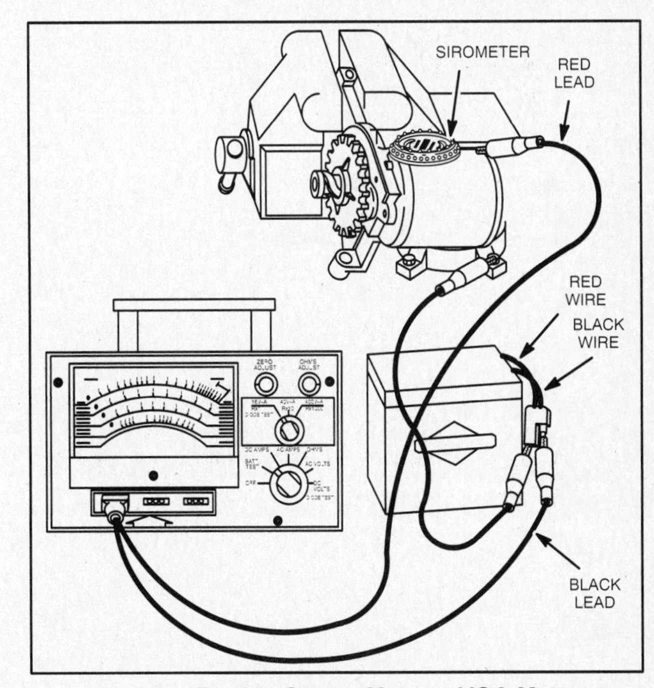

Fig. 45 - Testing Starter Motor - VOA Meter

4. A starter motor in good condition will be within the following specifications, TABLE NO. 1.

NOTE: METRIC EQUIVALENTS ARE LISTED ON PAGE 63 OF THIS SECTION.

TABLE NO. 1
6 & 12 VOLT SPECIFICATIONS

Voltage	Minimum Motor RPM	Maximum Amps
6	800	18 (Disregard surge current)
12	1400	9 (Disregard surge current)

If the starter motor does not perform satisfactorily, the following should be checked, and corrected if necessary.

1. A binding condition between the pinion and clutch gear or misalignment of motor bearings.
2. Starter motor brushes sticking in brush holders.
3. A dirty or worn armature commutator.
4. A shorted, open or grounded armature.
   A. Shorted armature (worn insulation, wires touching each other) will be indicated by slow speed and high current (amps).
   B. Open armature (broken wire) may not turn or will have low RPM.
   C. Grounded armature (worn insulation, wire touching armature) will not turn or may turn slowly and will have excessive current (amps).
5. Weak or damaged magnets.
6. Armature end play.

Disassemble Starter Motor

1. Study Fig. 42 prior to Starter Motor Disassembly.
2. Remove the starter switch housing, nylon spur gear "E" ring and the nylon spur gear.
3. The three screws holding the gear cover and the gear itself may now be removed.
4. Lift the clutch assembly and the pinion gear off their respective shafts.
5. Remove the starter motor thru bolts, Fig. 46.
6. Separate motor end cap from motor housing.

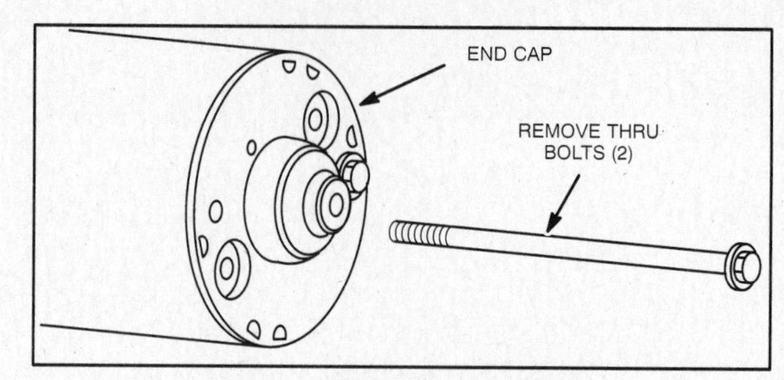

Fig. 46 - Removing Thru Bolts

7. Push motor armature out through bottom of starter housing, taking care to slide plastic mounted terminal out of motor housing along with end cap, Fig. 47.

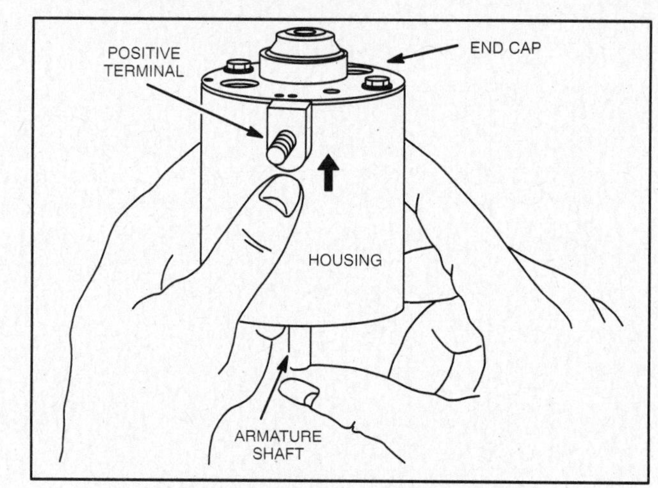

Fig. 47 - Removing Armature

8. Before removing armature from end cap, check brushes for freedom of movement. If brushes are found to be sticking in their retainers, this must be corrected, or poor starter motor performance will result, Fig. 48.
9. If brushes are worn to a length of 5/64" or less, the brushes should be replaced.
10. Check brush springs for proper tension (sufficient force to keep brush in firm contact with commutator).

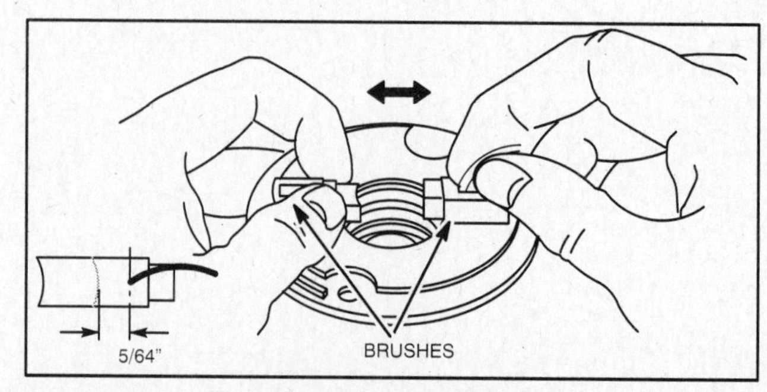

Fig. 48 - Checking Brushes

NOTE: METRIC EQUIVALENTS ARE LISTED ON PAGE 63 OF THIS SECTION.

11. Clean all dirt from armature, end cap, motor support, gears, etc. The end cap bearings and armature should not be soaked in a solvent.

12. The armature commutator may be cleaned with a fine sandpaper or commutator paper.

NOTE: DO NOT USE ALUMINUM OXIDE PAPER OR EMERY CLOTH, AS EMERY WILL BECOME EMBEDDED IN THE COMMUTATOR CAUSING RAPID BRUSH WEAR.

13. If the armature is suspected to be defective, a new armature should be tried in the motor. If proper testing equipment is available, check the suspected armature to determine if it is defective.

NOTE: Starter motor armatures have very low resistance, usually below detection on available multimeters. To check for shorted armatures, a piece of equipment known as a "growler" may be used.

14. If this equipment is not available, a known good armature should be tried and performance rechecked.

15. If the magnets appear to be weak, a new motor housing should be tried.

Assemble Starter Motor

1. When all parts have been thoroughly inspected, lightly lubricate bearings with an oil made for use in electric motors and reassemble in the following manner.

2. Insert brush springs and brushes in holders as far as possible, and hold them in this position with tool shown in Fig. 49.

3. Place thrust washers on armature shaft in sequence shown.

4. Add gray plastic washers to obtain dimension shown in Fig. 49 inset.

5. Using care to ensure brushes clear commutator, slide armature shaft into end cap bearing.

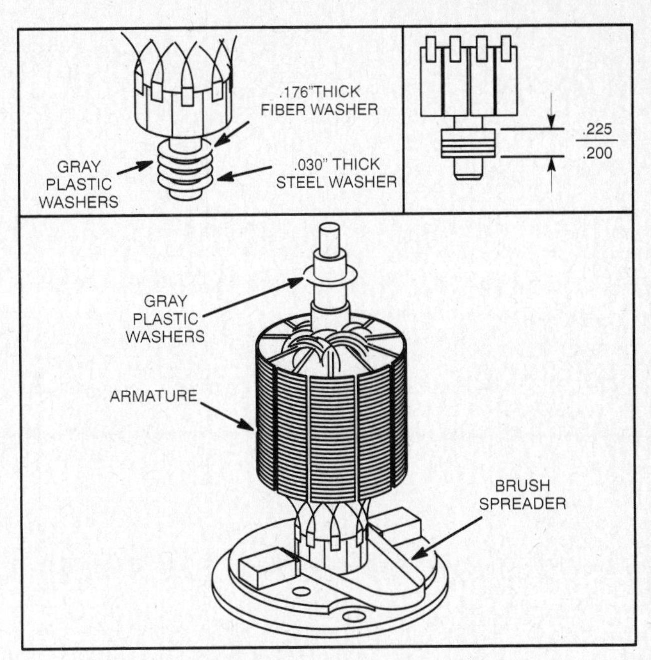

Fig. 49 - Armature Assembly to End Cap

6. Support armature shaft and slide it slowly into starter housing, as shown in Fig. 50.

7. Insert plastic insulator terminal into starter housing at this time.

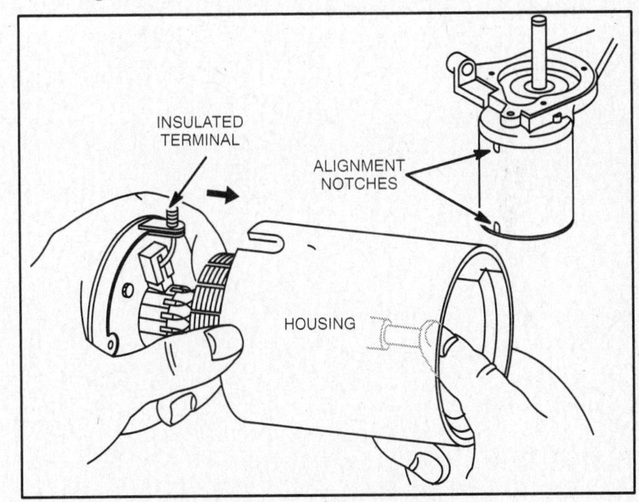

Fig. 50 - Inserting Armature

8. Place remaining thrust washers on motor PTO shaft.

9. Install end head cover and thru bolts.

10. Torque bolts to 25 in. lbs. Notches in end cap, housing and end head must be aligned, Fig. 50.

11. Check for end play to obtain .005" to .025" armature movement.

12. If required, install or remove gray plastic washers between armature and end head to obtain end play.

NOTE: METRIC EQUIVALENTS ARE LISTED ON PAGE 63 OF THIS SECTION.

13. Slip pinion and starter motor clutch gear on shaft.
14. Add approximately 3/4 ounce of gear lubricant under large gear and on gear teeth.
15. Oil felt washer with electric motor oil.
16. Install washer, gasket and cover, Fig. 51.

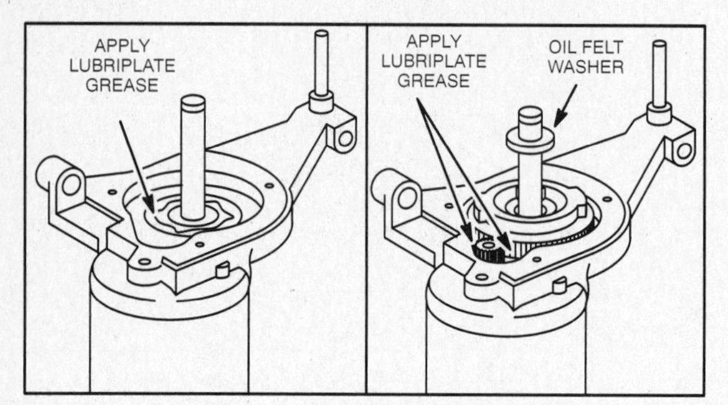

Fig. 51 - Lubricating Gears

17. Tap end cap edge lightly using a soft hammer as this will align the bearings, Fig. 52.
18. Retorque screws to 25 in. lbs.

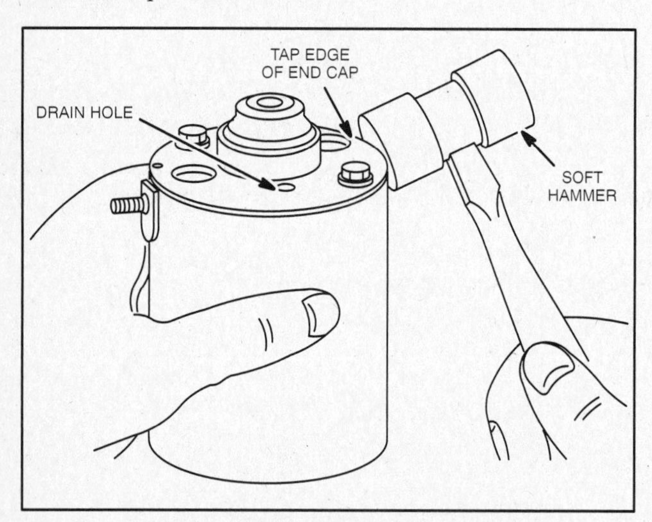

Fig. 52 - Aligning End Cap Bearing

19. Replace nylon spur gear and "E" ring assembly.

NOTE: Do not oil nylon spur gear or clutch helix.

20. Install starter cover and torque screws to 25 in. lbs.
21. Install starter motor on engine.
22. Torque rear starter mounting screw (5/16"- 18) to 140 in. lbs.
23. Torque front mounting screw (1/4"- 20) to 90 in. lbs.

12 VOLT DC GEAR DRIVE STARTER MOTOR, NYLON DRIVE PINION

Model Series 130000

This starting system uses a permanent magnet motor and gear type engagement method similar to an automobile starter. When the starter motor is activated, the pinion gear engages a ring gear attached to the engine flywheel and cranks the engine, Fig. 53.

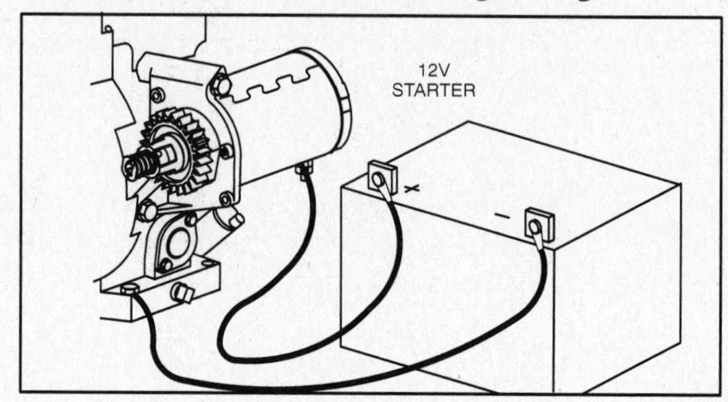

Fig. 53 - Typical Starter Motors

A list is given to aid you in diagnosing problems for 12 volt systems. See page 3.

Fig. 54 shows an exploded view of the 12 volt nylon drive starter

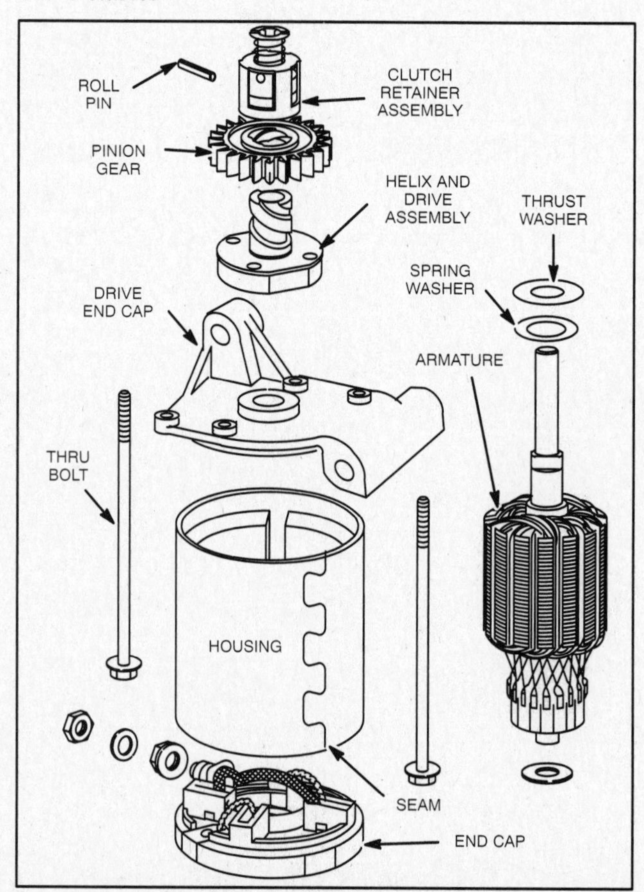

Fig. 54 - Exploded View of 12 Volt Starter

NOTE: METRIC EQUIVALENTS ARE LISTED ON PAGE 63 OF THIS SECTION.

Check Starter Motor Drive

When the starter motor is activated, the pinion gear should engage the flywheel ring gear and crank the engine. This can be observed by removing the starter shield. If the starter motor drive does not react properly, inspect the helix and pinion gear for freeness of operation. The pinion must move freely on the helix for correct starter motor operation, Fig. 55. If any sticking occurs, this must be corrected.

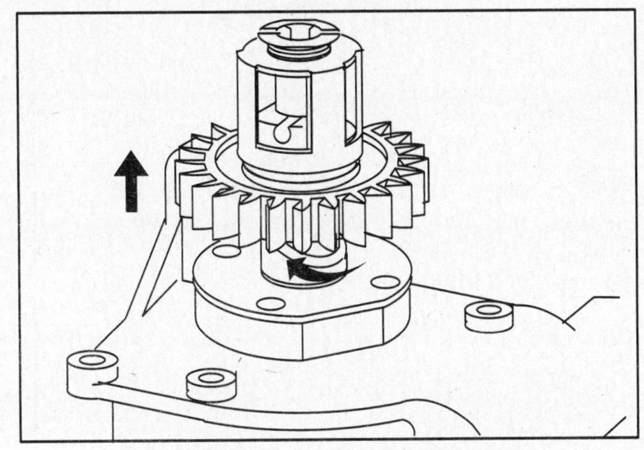

Fig. 55 - Checking Starter Motor Drive

Disassemble Starter Motor Drive

1. To remove the drive assembly for cleaning or replacement, disconnect and remove starter from engine.
2. Place in "V" block as shown in Fig. 56.
3. Drive the roll pin out with a hammer and 1/8" diameter punch to remove the retainer.

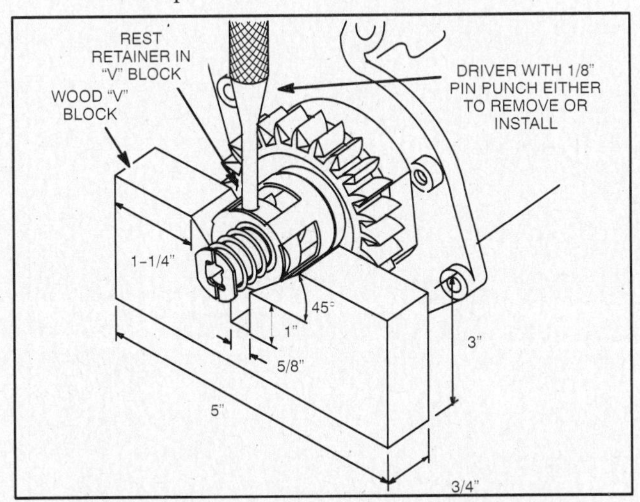

Fig. 56 - Disassembling Starter Motor Drive

The pinion gear should be inspected for damaged teeth. If a sticking condition exists between the pinion gear and the helix, this must be corrected. The parts may be washed in a solvent such as Stanisol® or Varsol®. The gear, retainer, roll pin and clutch assembly are available from your Briggs & Stratton source of supply.

Assemble Starter Motor Drive

1. Reverse disassembly procedure for assembling. Assemble the pinion gear with beveled edge on the gear up as shown in Fig. 57.
2. Assemble cup and spring on gear if original assembly was so equipped.
3. Press or drive new roll pin through retainer slot and armature shaft hole with roll pin slot positioned as shown. The roll pin should be centered in shaft within 1/32."

NOTE: ASSEMBLE WITH NEW ROLL PIN ONLY.

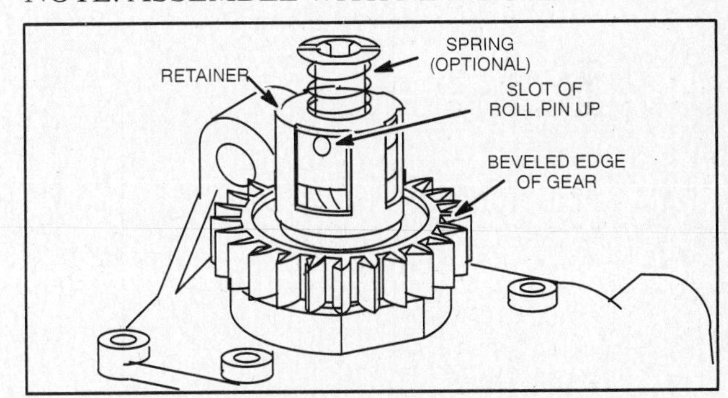

Fig. 57 - Assembling Starter Motor Drive

Test Starter Motor

A performance test of the 12 volt DC starter motors may be made in the following manner.

Equipment Needed

See page 3 for a starter mounting test bracket that can be made.

Digital Multimeter, Tool (#19357 or 19390) and Tool #19359, DC Shunt or Tool #19236, VOA Meter, and DC Shunt.

See Instruction Manual MS-6574 (Digital Multimeter) or Instruction Manual MS-7585 (VOA Meter) for installation procedure.

A tachometer capable of reading 10,000 RPM.

A 12 volt battery fully charged.

To Test

1. Connect the starter motor, battery and meter as shown in Fig. 58.

NOTE: METRIC EQUIVALENTS ARE LISTED ON PAGE 63 OF THIS SECTION.

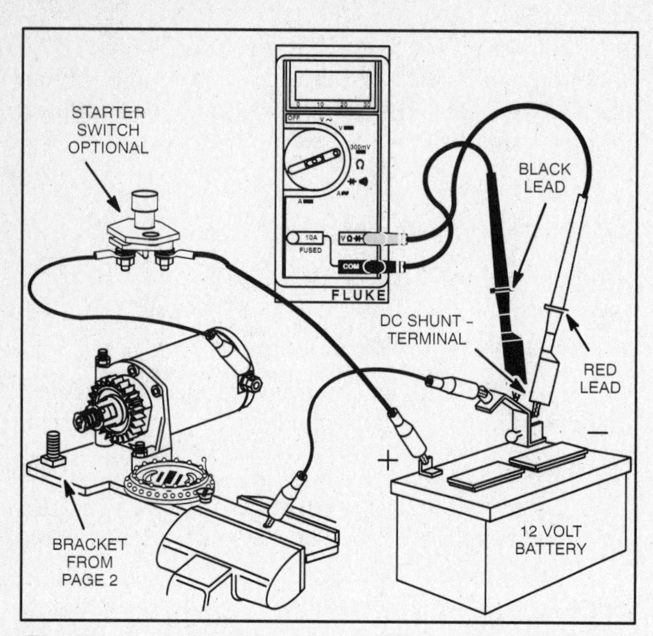

Fig. 58 - Testing 12 Volt Starter Motor Digital Multimeter

CAUTION: DO NOT clamp motor housing in a vise or strike with a steel hammer. Starter motors contain two powerful magnets which can be broken or cracked if the motor housing is deformed or dented.

2. Activate the starter motor and note readings of meter and tachometer (RPM). A starter motor in good condition will be within specifications as listed in TABLE NO. 2. If starter motor is not within specifications shown, see list on page 41 for possible causes.

TABLE NO. 2
12 VOLT DC STARTER SPECIFICATIONS

Minimum RPM	Maximum Amps
5250	14 (Disregard surge current)

If the 12 volt starter motor does not perform satisfactorily, the following should be checked and corrected if necessary:

1. A binding or seizing condition in the starter motor bearings.
2. Starter motor brushes sticking in brush holders.
3. A dirty or worn armature commutator or brushes.
4. A shorted, open or grounded armature.
   A. Shorted armature (wire insulation worn and wires touching one another). Will be indicated by low or no RPM.
   B Open armature (wire broken) will be indicated by low or no RPM.
   C. Grounded armature (wire insulation worn and wire touching armature lamination or shaft). Will be indicated by excessive current or no RPM.
5. A defective starter motor switch.
6. Weakened magnets.

Disassemble Starter Motor

CAUTION: DO NOT clamp motor housing in a vise or strike with a steel hammer. Starter motors contain two powerful ceramic magnets which can be broken or cracked if the motor housing is hit, deformed, dented or dropped.

1. Study Fig. 54 prior to starter motor disassembly. Notice location of housing seam to drive end mounting bracket.
2. Remove thru bolts.
3. The drive head end may now be removed. Inspect bushing for wear. If worn, replace drive head end mounting bracket, Fig. 59.

NOTE: MATCH MARKS AND THRU BOLTS MUST BE PLACED IN THE SAME POSITION AS WHEN REMOVED OR INTERFERENCE MAY RESULT.

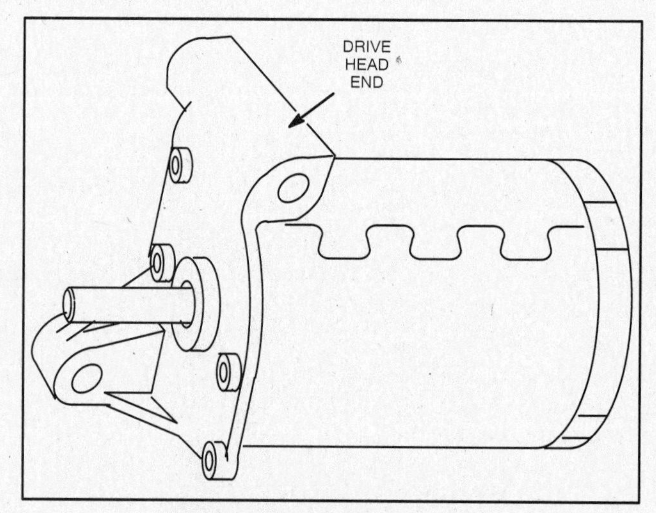

Fig. 59 - Removing Thru Bolts

4. Hold the armature and commutator end cap against a work surface while sliding housing off the armature. This allows the armature to remain in the end cap for inspection of brush contact to armature, Fig. 60.

NOTE: METRIC EQUIVALENTS ARE LISTED ON PAGE 63 OF THIS SECTION.

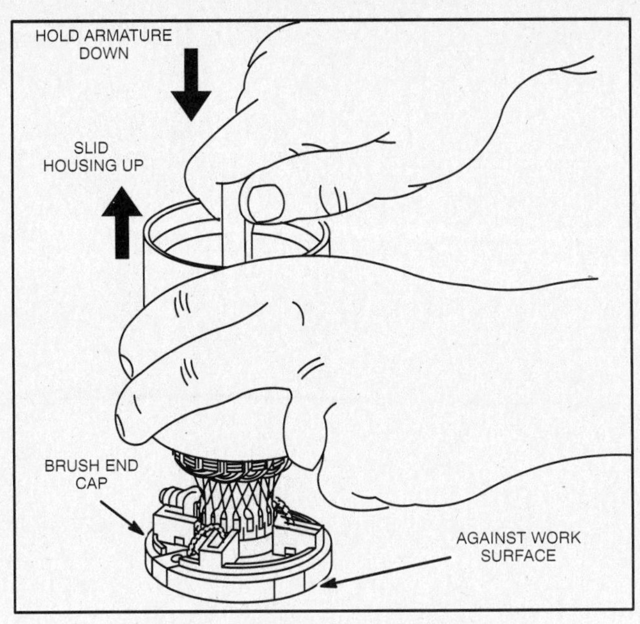

Fig. 60 - Removing Motor Housing

Remove Armature from Brush End Cap

1. Clean all dirt or corrosion from the armature, end cap, motor support, etc.

   NOTE: The bearings, housing and armature should not be soaked in a cleaning solution.

2. The armature commutator may be cleaned with a fine sand paper.
3. NOTE: DO NOT USE EMERY CLOTH, AS EMERY WILL BECOME EMBEDDED IN THE COMMUTATOR CAUSING RAPID BRUSH WEAR.
4. The commutator may also be machined with the use of a diamond cutting tool to no less than 1.23" - 12 volt, 1.32" - 120 volt, outside diameter.
5. Slots between commutator bars should be cleaned as shown in Fig. 61, after cleaning or machining.
6. If it is suspected that the armature field coil, magnets or motor housing is defective, a new part should be tried in the motor.
7. If proper testing equipment is available, check the suspected armature or field coil to determine if it is defective (opens or grounds).

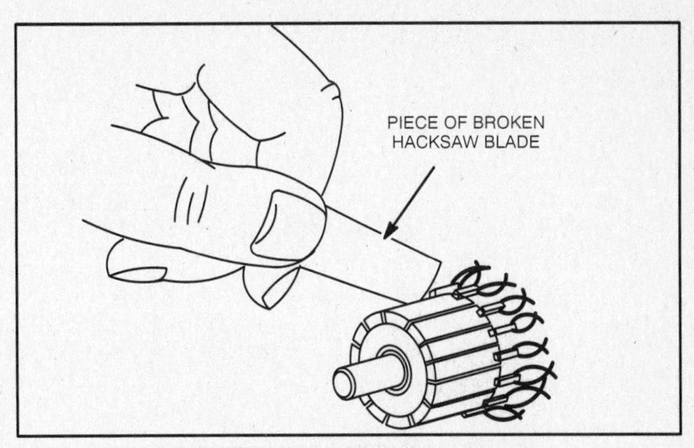

Fig. 61 - Cleaning Commutator

8. The brushes should be checked for poor seating, weak brush springs, dirt, oil or corrosion.
9. Brush spring pressure should be strong enough to ensure good brush contact with armature.
10. If brushes are worn to dimension shown in Fig. 62, replace.
11. Check to be sure brushes are not sticking in their holders.
12. Use holders to retain brushes and spring during assembly.

BRUSHES MUST MOVE FREELY IN HOLDERS!

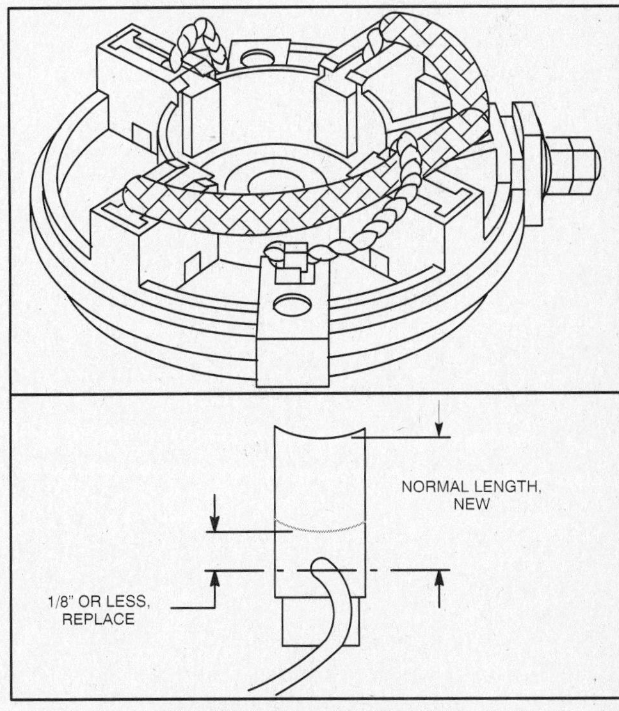

Fig. 62 - Checking Brushes

NOTE: METRIC EQUIVALENTS ARE LISTED ON PAGE 63 OF THIS SECTION.

Assemble Starter Motor

1. When all parts have been thoroughly inspected, lightly lubricate the bearings with #20 oil and reassemble in the following manner.

2. Insert brushes and springs in their respective holders.

NOTE: A brush holding tool as shown in Fig's. 6, page 5 or Fig. 63, below, should be used to hold the brushes clear of the armature commutator during assembly.

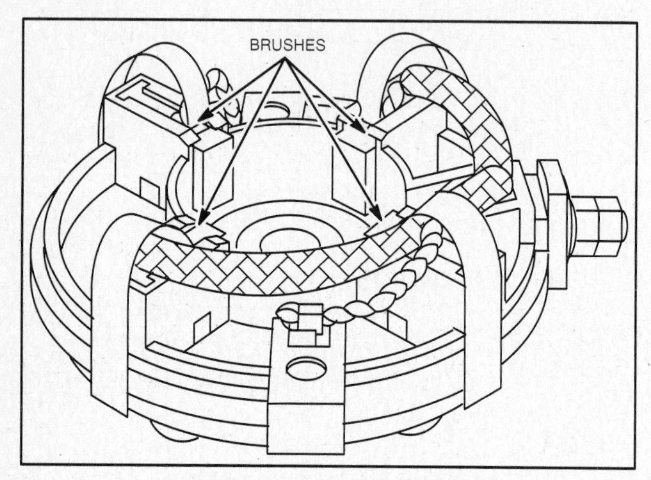

Fig. 63 - Positioning Brushes

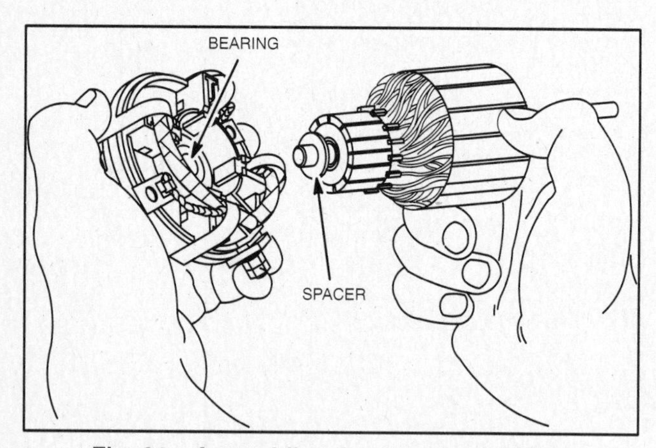

Fig. 64 - Assembling Armature to End Cap

Assemble Housing

1. Slide motor housing over armature with the notch toward commutator end cap.

2. Match notch in housing with boss on brush end cap, Fig. 59. Remove brush holders, if used and rotate armature to be sure brushes are making full contact with commutator.

3. Care should be used to prevent damage to magnets in motor housing during assembly.

4. Assemble spacers and drive head end bracket, aligning seam in housing with drive end mounting bracket.

5. Assemble thru bolts and torque to 35 in. lbs.

6. Armature end play is .006" to .038" after assembly.

Assemble starter drive as described on page 25, this section.

Install starter on engine and torque mounting screws to 140 in. lbs..

12 VOLT DC & 120 VOLT AC GEAR DRIVE STARTER MOTOR, STEEL DRIVE PINION
Model Series 130000

This starting system uses a permanent magnet motor and gear type engagement method similar to an automobile starter. When the starter motor is activated, the pinion gear engages a ring gear attached to the engine flywheel and cranks the engine.

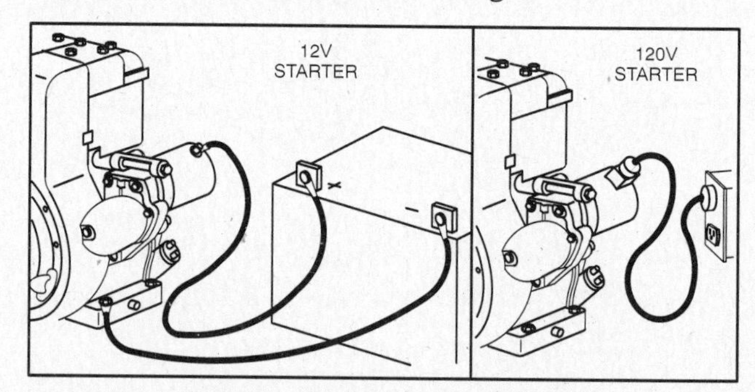

Fig. 65 - Typical Starter Motors

A list is given to aid you in diagnosing problems for 12 volt and 120 volt systems. See page 3.

The 120 volt electric starter is equipped with a three-prong plug for safety. The longer prong in this plug is connected to the starter motor housing. When the starter motor is plugged into the three-wire cord supplied, and the cord is plugged into a properly grounded receptacle, it will protect the user from shock should the starter-motor insulation fail for any reason. If a longer extension cord is used with this starter, it should also have three prong sockets and three hole plugs, Fig. 66.

NOTE: METRIC EQUIVALENTS ARE LISTED ON PAGE 63 OF THIS SECTION.

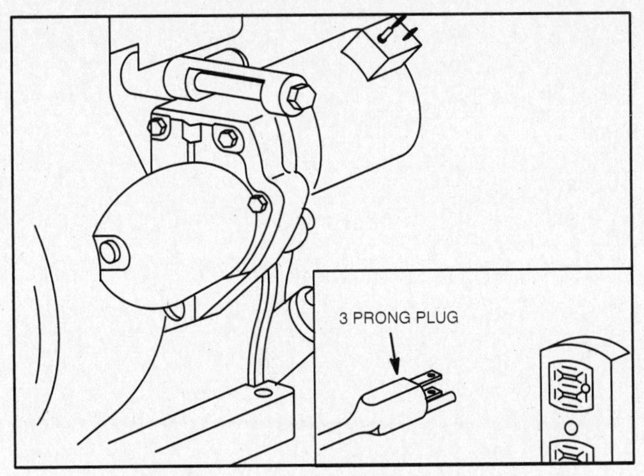

Fig. 66 - 120 Volt Gear Drive Starter

NOTE: DO NOT run starter motor for more than one minute without cooling 15 minutes.

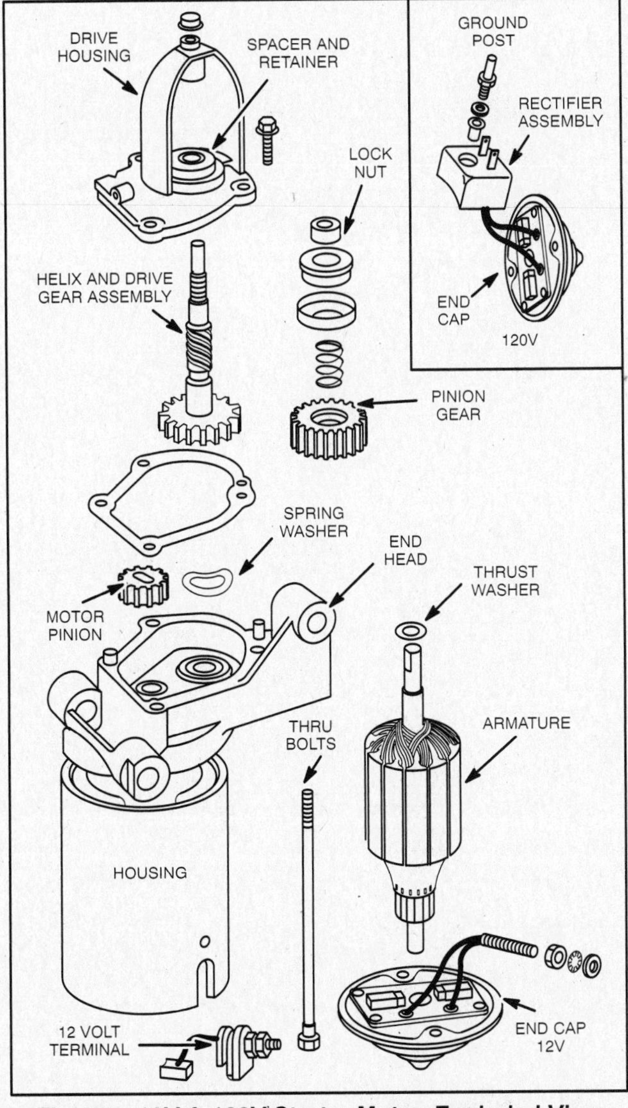

Fig. 67 - 12V & 120V Starter Motor, Exploded View

NOTE: If a starting problem is encountered, the engine itself should be thoroughly checked to eliminate it as the cause of starting difficulty. It is a good practice to check the engine for freedom of rotation by removing the spark plug and turning the crankshaft over by hand, to be sure it rotates freely.

A 12 ampere hour battery is suggested for warm temperature operation. For cold temperature operation, use no less than a 24 ampere hour battery.

Check Starter Motor Drive

The service procedure for the 12 volt and 120 volt starter motor drive is the same.

When the starter motor is activated, the pinion gear should engage the flywheel ring gear, and crank the engine. This action can be observed by removing the starter motor. If the starter motor drive does not react properly, inspect the helix and pinion gear for freeness of operation. The pinion gear must move freely on the helix for correct starter motor operation. If any sticking occurs, this must be corrected, Fig. 68.

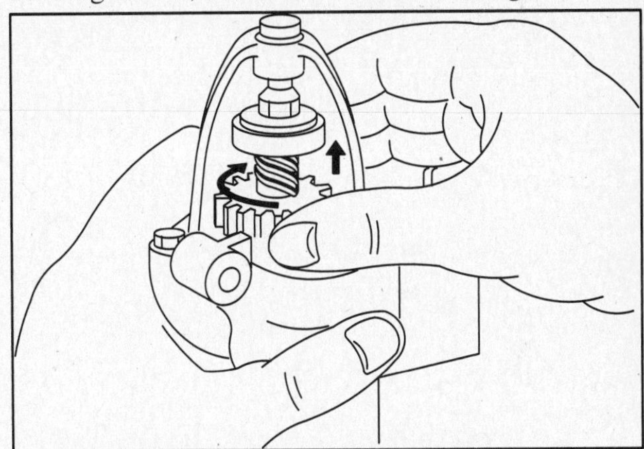

Fig. 68 - Checking Starter Motor Drive

Disassemble Starter Motor Drive

1. Remove drive housing from end head, Fig. 67.
2. To remove the drive gear assembly for cleaning or replacement, clamp the drive gear in a vise having brass jaws, to prevent damage to the gear teeth.
3. The lock nut may then be removed and the starter drive disassembled for cleaning or replacement.

The pinion gear should be inspected for damaged teeth. If a sticking condition exists between the pinion gear and the helix, the parts may be washed in a solvent such as Stanisol® or Varsol®. If the sticking condition cannot be corrected by cleaning, the complete drive assembly must be replaced. Individual parts of the drive assembly are not available.

NOTE: METRIC EQUIVALENTS ARE LISTED ON PAGE 63 OF THIS SECTION.

Assemble Starter Motor Drive

Reverse disassembly procedure for assembling, Fig. 69. Be sure drive spacer and retainer are correctly positioned in drive housing.

NOTE: Do not lubricate drive assembly. A dry silicone spray may be used if necessary.

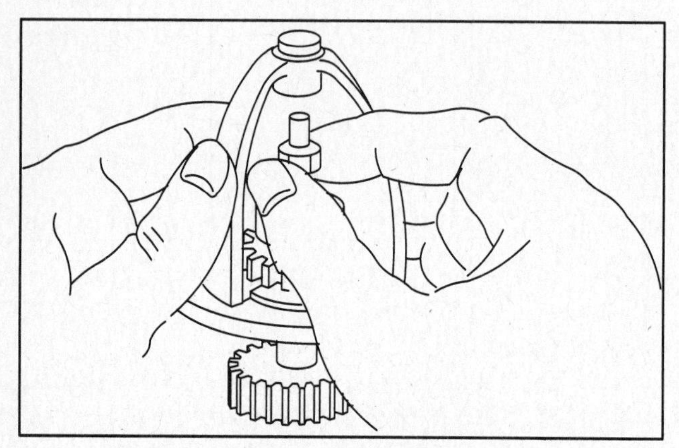

Fig. 69 – Assembling Starter Motor Drive

Testing 12 Volt DC Starter Motor

A performance test of the 12 volt starter motor may be made in the following manner:

Equipment Needed

Digital Multimeter, Tool (#19357 or 19390) or VOA Meter, Tool #19236.

A tachometer capable of reading 10,000 RPM.

A 12 volt battery ± 0.3 volts.

To Test

1. Set the meter to read DC amps.

2. Connect the starter motor, battery and meter as shown in Fig's. 70 or 71.

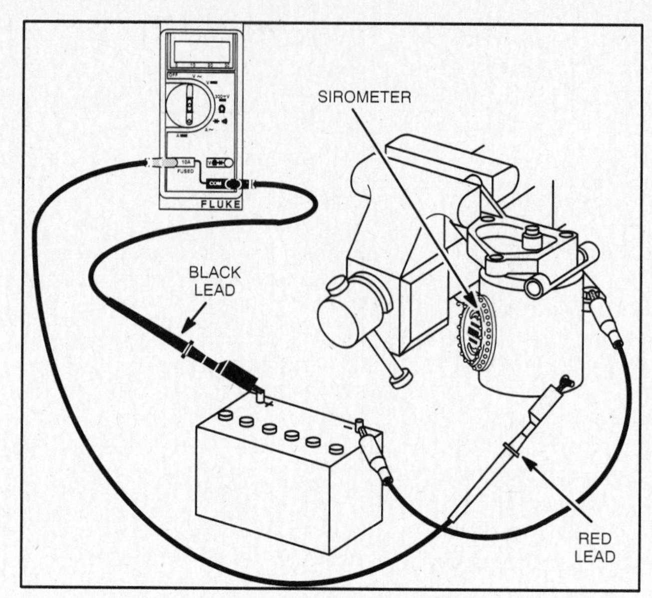

Fig. 70 – Testing 12 Volt Starter Motor with Digital Multimeter

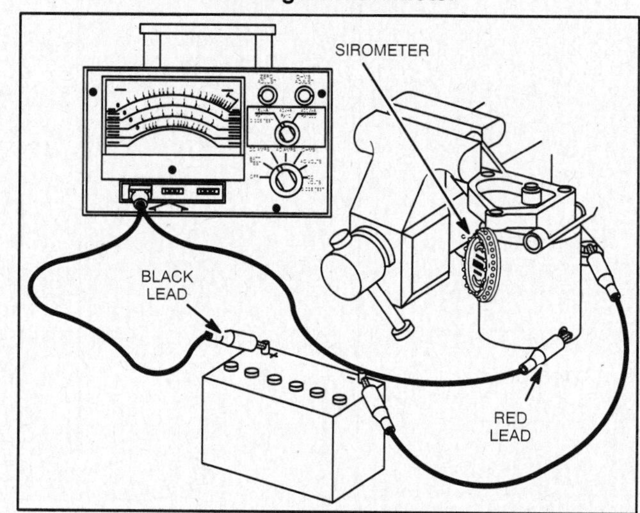

Fig. 71 – Testing 12 Volt Starter Motor VOA Meter

3. Place the sirometer on the starter motor and activate the starter motor. A starter motor in good condition will be within the following specifications:

TABLE NO. 3
12 VOLT SPECIFICATIONS

Minimum Motor RPM	Maximum Amps
5600	6 (Disregard surge current)

4. If the starter motor does not meet the specifications listed, the following should be checked and corrected if necessary.

   A. Binding condition between the pinion gear, helix and drive gear assembly.

NOTE: METRIC EQUIVALENTS ARE LISTED ON PAGE 63 OF THIS SECTION.

B Misalignment or binding between motor bearings.

C. Starter motor brushes sticking in brush holders.

D. Dirty or worn commutator.

5. Shorted, open or grounded armature.

A. Shorted armature (wire insulation worn and wires touching one another) will be indicated by slow speed and high current.

B. Open armature (wire broken) will be indicated blow or no RPM.

C. Grounded armature (wire insulation worn and wire touching armature lamination or shaft) will be indicated by excessive current or no RPM.

6. Weakened magnets.

Disassemble Starter Motor

1. Study Fig. 67 prior to starter motor disassembly.

NOTE: END HEAD, END CAP AND HOUSING MUST BE PLACED IN THE SAME POSITION AS WHEN REMOVED, OR INTERFERENCE MAY RESULT, Fig. 72.

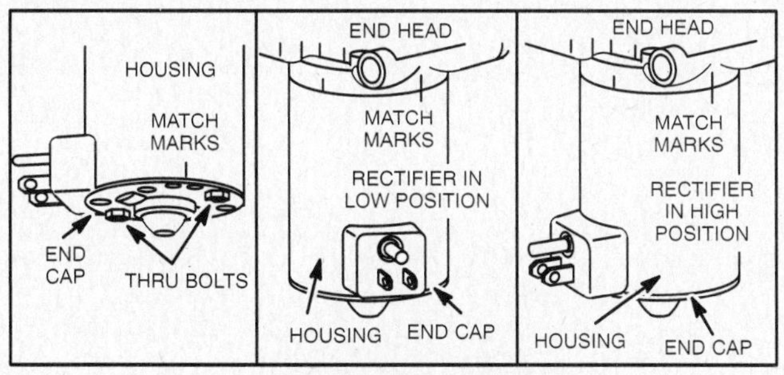

Fig. 72 - Match Marks

2. Remove thru bolts, Fig. 73.

3. The end head may then be removed.

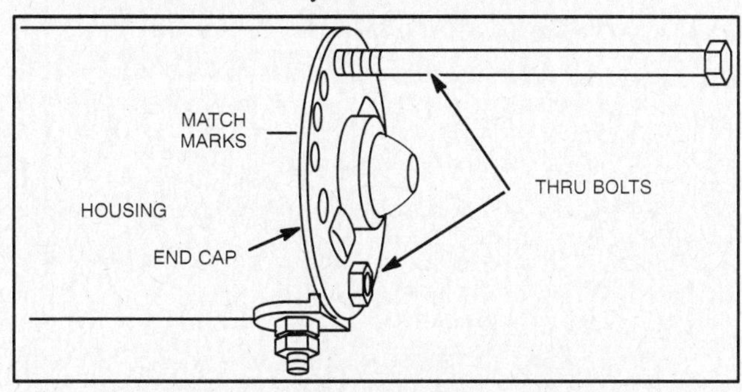

Fig. 73 - Removing Thru Bolts

4. Remove armature and end cap as shown in Fig. 74.

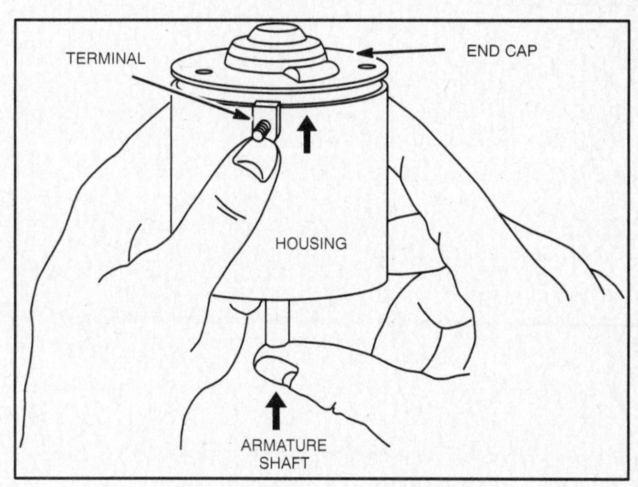

Fig. 74 - Removing Armature

5. Clean all dirt or corrosion from the armature, end cap, end head, etc.

6. The bearings, motor housing and armature should not be soaked in a cleaning solution.

7. The armature commutator may be cleaned with a fine sand paper or commutator paper.

NOTE: Do not use emery cloth, as emery will become embedded in the commutator causing rapid brush wear.

8. If it is suspected that the armature is defective, a new armature should be tried in the motor. If proper testing equipment is available, check the suspected armature to determine if it is defective.

NOTE: Starter motor armatures have very low resistance, usually below detection on available multimeters. To check for shorted armatures, a piece of equipment known as a "growler" may be used.

9. The brushes should be checked for poor seating, weak brush springs, dirt, oil or corrosion, Fig. 75.

10. If brushes are worn less than 1/4", replace the end cap assembly.

11. If the magnets appear to be weak , a new motor housing should be tried.

NOTE: METRIC EQUIVALENTS ARE LISTED ON PAGE 63 OF THIS SECTION.

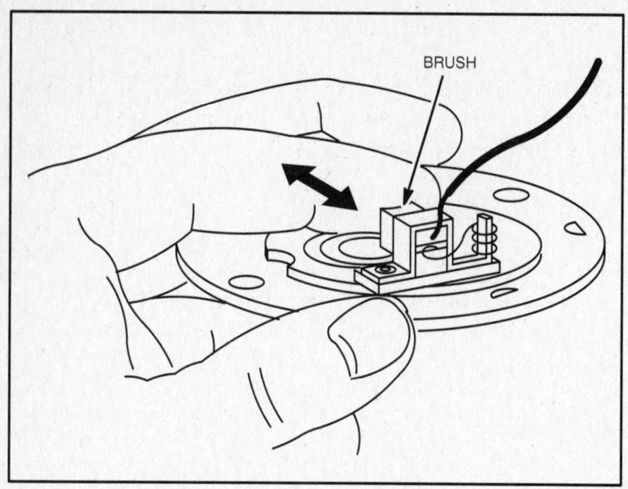

Fig. 75 - Check Brushes

Assemble Starter Motor

1. When all parts have been thoroughly inspected, lightly lubricate the bearings with #20 oil, and reassemble in the following manner.
2. Insert the brushes in their respective holders.

   NOTE: Tools such as shown in Fig's. 6, page 5, and 76, this page, should be used to hold the brushes clear of the armature commutator when assembling the armature to end cap.

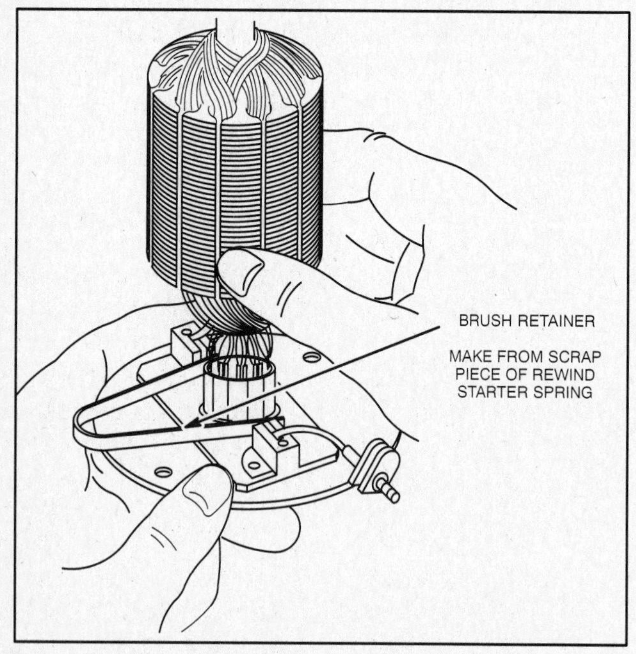

Fig. 76 - Assembling Armature to End Cap

3. Support armature shaft and slide it slowly into housing, as shown in Fig. 77.
4. Insert rubber mounted terminal into housing at this time.

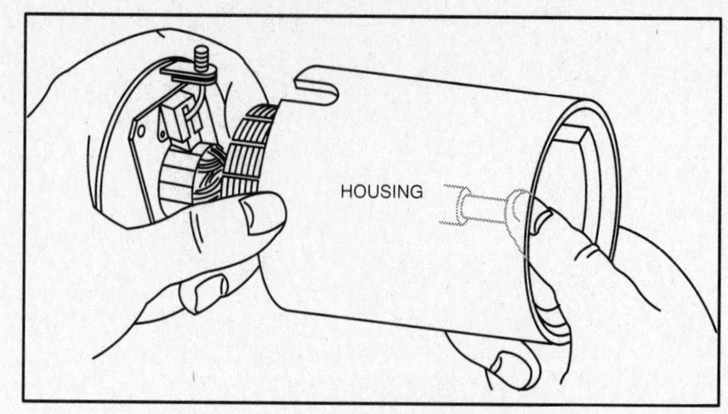

Fig. 77 - Inserting Armature

5. Place thrust washer on motor PTO shaft.
6. Install end head and thru bolts.
7. Align end cap and end head match marks correctly, Fig. 72.
8. Tighten screws.
9. Tap edge of end cap using a soft hammer to align motor bearings if required, Fig. 78.
10. Check armature shaft for end play. Armature should rotate freely.

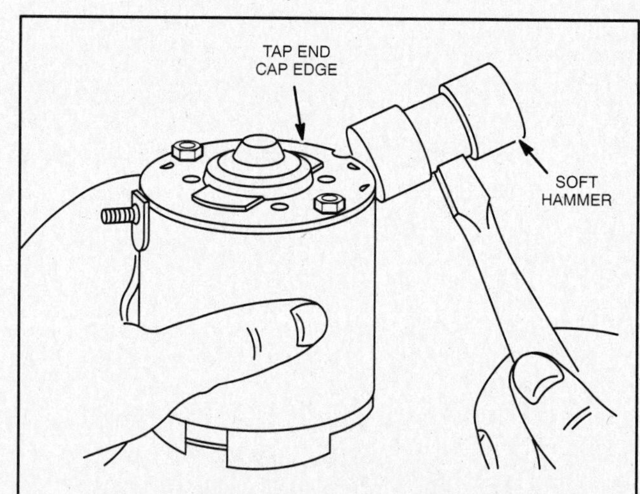

Fig. 78 - Aligning Bearings

11. Test performance of starter motor, Page 20. If starter motor tests as specified, continue assembly.
12. Slip motor pinion gear on armature shaft.
13. Add a small amount of gear lubricant to gear teeth. Position gasket, spring washer and drive housing assembly, Fig. 67.
14. Fasten drive housing to end head securely with three screws. The starter motor assembly is now ready to be installed on the engine.

NOTE: METRIC EQUIVALENTS ARE LISTED ON PAGE 63 OF THIS SECTION.

Test the 120 Volt AC Starter Motor

A performance test of the 120 volt starter motor may be made in the following manner:

Equipment Needed

Digital Multimeter, Tool (#19357 or 19390) with AC Shunt, Tool #19358 or VOA Meter, Tool #19236 with 120 Volt Adapter, Tool #19242.

A tachometer capable of reading 10,000 RPM.

WARNING: Extreme care should be used in making this test to minimize the hazard of electrical shock.

CAUTION: Starter motor housing contains two powerful ceramic magnets that may crack if motor housing is clamped in a vise or struck with a hammer or hard object.

To Test

1. Clamp the starter motor in a vise as shown in Fig's. 79 or 80.
2. Set meter to AC amps.
3. Insert leads into meter and plug starter motor cord into AC adapter.
4. Then connect AC adapter to a 120 volt outlet.
5. Refer to specifications and note the maximum allowable amperage.

TABLE NO. 4
120 VOLT SPECIFICATIONS

Minimum Motor RPM	Maximum Amps
8300	1-1/2 (Disregard surge current)

6. Depress starter switch button. When meter reading stabilizes (approximately 3 seconds), amperage should not exceed the specification shown.

CAUTION: If amperage is higher than specification shown, immediately stop the test! An amperage reading higher than number in chart indicates a shorted starter motor, which could be dangerous.

7. If amperage is within specification, check RPM of starter motor using Tool #19200, tachometer.

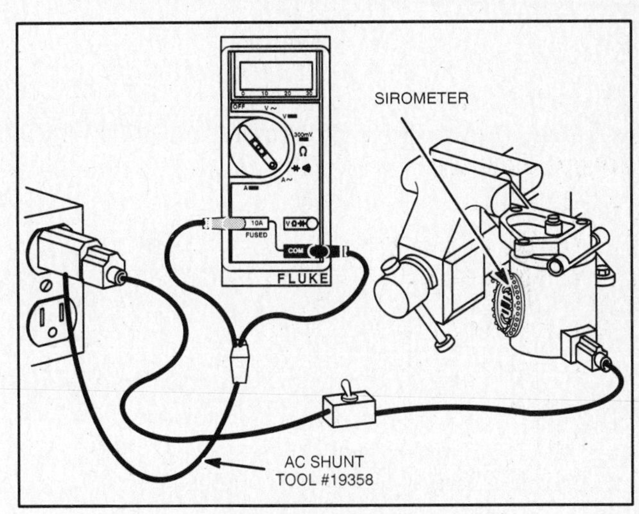

Fig. 79 – Testing 120 Volt Starter Motor – Digital Multimeter

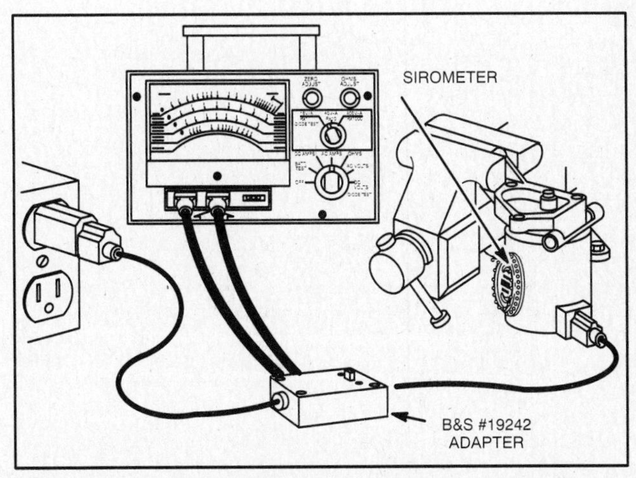

Fig. 80 – Testing 120 Volt Starter Motor – VOA Meter

If the 120 volt AC starter motor does not meet the specifications listed, the motor must be replaced.

NOTE: METRIC EQUIVALENTS ARE LISTED ON PAGE 63 OF THIS SECTION.

Briggs & Stratton Gear Drive Starter Motors

120 Volt AC; 12 Volt DC with Housings 3-1/16" to 4-9/16" long Model Series 170000, 190000, 220000, 240000, 250000, 280000 and 320000

All 120 volt electric starters are equipped with a three prong plug for safety. The longer prong in this plug is connected to the starter motor housing. When the starter motor is plugged into the three wire cord supplied, and the cord is plugged into a properly grounded receptacle, it will protect the user from shock should the starter motor insulation fail for any reason. If a longer extension cord is used with this starter, it should also have three prongs and a three hole plug. DO NOT USE extension cords longer than 25 feet.

Both starter motors use a gear type engagement method, similar to an automobile starter. When the starter motor is activated, the pinion gear engages a ring gear attached to the engine flywheel and cranks the engine.

CAUTION: After servicing, the120 volt starter motor should be Hi-Pot tested before reinstalling on engine to determine if a shock hazard exists.

TABLE NO. 5
Briggs & Stratton
Starter Motor Identification

Housing Length	Motor Voltage
3-1/16"	12
3-1/2"	120
3-21/32"	12
3-3/4"	12
3-13/16"	12
4-3/8"	12
4-9/16"	12

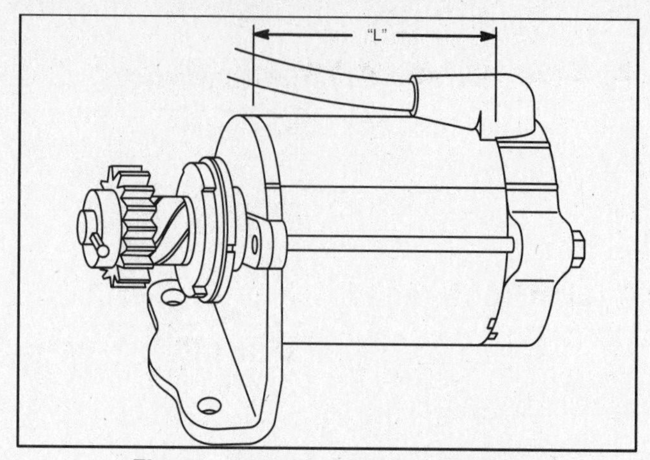

Fig. 81 - 120 Volt AC Starter Motor

CAUTION: DO NOT run starter motors for more than one minute without cooling 15 minutes.

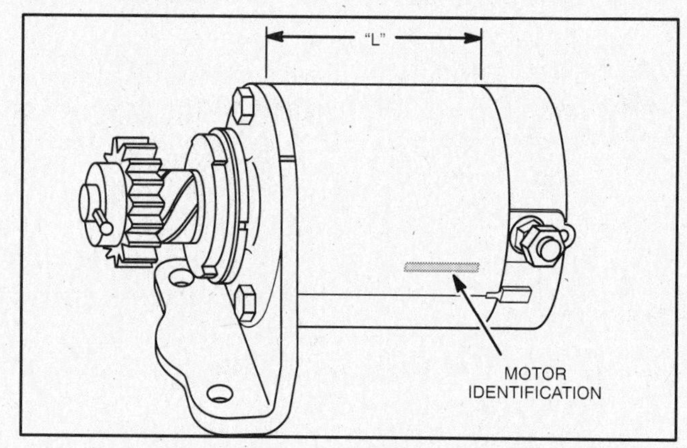

Fig. 82 - Typical 12 Volt DC Starter Motor

Battery Recommendations

These battery size recommendations are based on minimum temperature expected and correct weight of oil being used. See Section 8.

30 Amp. Hr. +20° F or higher
40 Amp. Hr. -5° F or higher
50 Amp. Hr. -15° F or higher

Battery Cable Recommendations

These cable sizes are based on total length of cable from battery positive post to starter switch or solenoid, and to starter plus ground return to battery negative post.

#6 AWG - 4 ft. or less
#5 AWG - 5 ft. or less
#4 AWG - 6 ft. or less

NOTE: A battery of higher amperage may be required for extremely cold weather starting conditions.

NOTE: METRIC EQUIVALENTS ARE LISTED ON PAGE 63 OF THIS SECTION.

Replace Ring Gear

Briggs & Stratton starter motors use either an aluminum or plastic ring gear on the flywheel.

To replace a worn or damaged flywheel ring gear, proceed as follows:

WARNING: DO NOT strike flywheel with a hard object or metal tool as this may cause flywheel to shatter in operation, causing personal injury or property damage.

1. Mark the center of the rivets holding the ring gear to flywheel, with a center punch.
2. Drill out the rivets using a 3/16" drill.
3. Clean holes after drilling, Fig. 83.

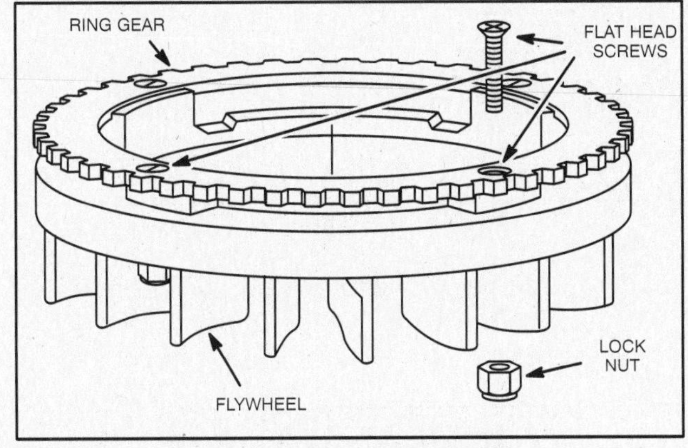

Fig. 83 - Replacing Ring Gear

4. Attach new gear to flywheel using four screws and lock nuts provided with gear.

Check Engine

If a starting problem is encountered, check the engine thoroughly to be sure it is not the cause of starting difficulty. It is a good practice to remove the spark plug and rotate the crankshaft by hand, to be sure it rotates freely. Any belt, clutch or other parasitic load will affect cranking performance.

A list is provided to aid in diagnosing problems for 12 volt DC and 120 volt AC systems. See page 3.

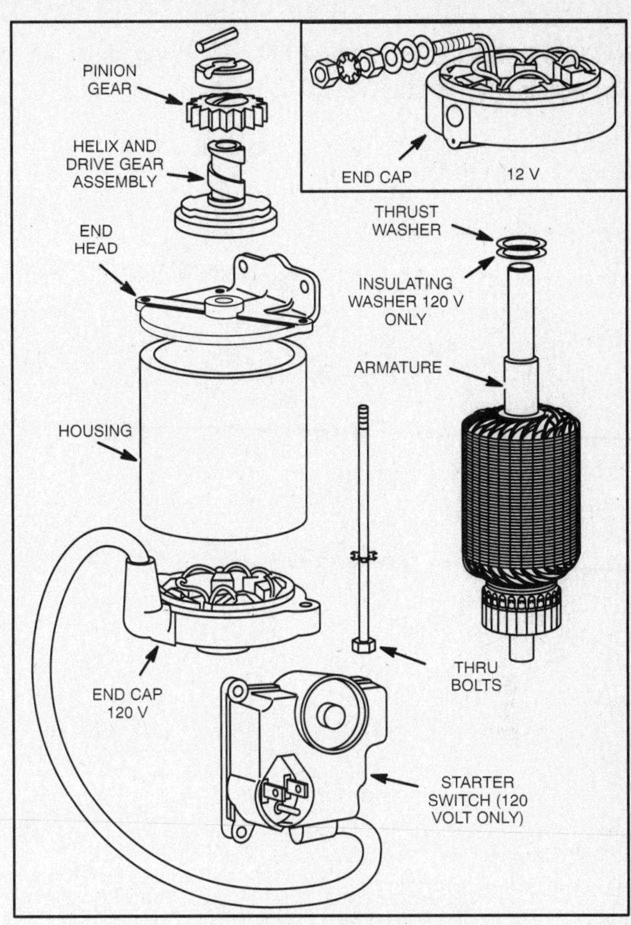

Fig. 84 - 12 Volt & 120 Volt Starter Motor - Exploded View

Check Starter Motor Drive

When the starter motor is activated, the pinion gear should engage the flywheel ring gear and crank the engine. This can be observed by removing the starter shield. If the starter motor drive does not react properly, inspect the helix and pinion gear for freeness of operation. The pinion must move freely on the helix for correct starter motor operation, Fig. 85. If any sticking occurs, this must be corrected.

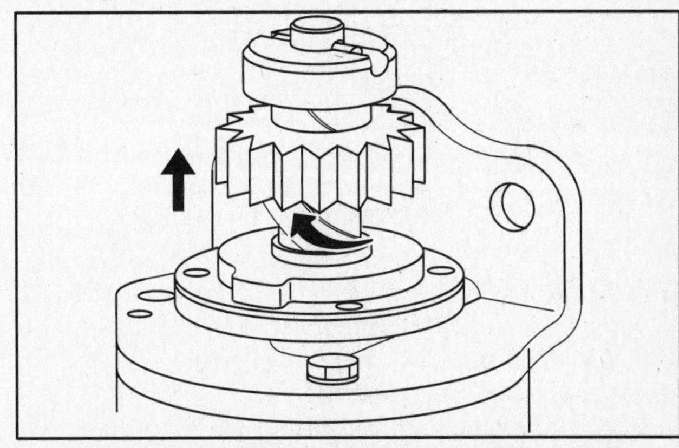

Fig. 85 - Checking Typical Starter Motor Drive

NOTE: METRIC EQUIVALENTS ARE LISTED ON PAGE 63 OF THIS SECTION.

Disassemble Starter Motor Drive, Snap Ring Retainer Type/Style

1. Depress retainer and pry off snap ring, Fig. 86. Discard old snap ring.

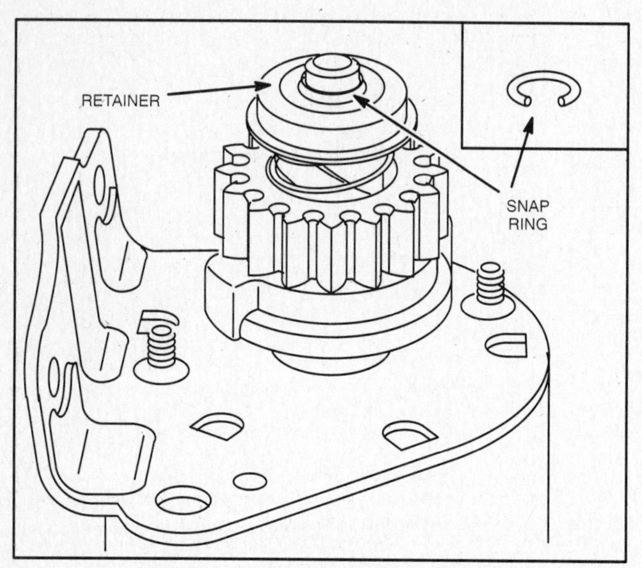

Fig. 86 - Removing Snap Ring

2. Remove retainer, return spring, flat washer, wave washer, pinion gear, and starter clutch, Fig. 87.

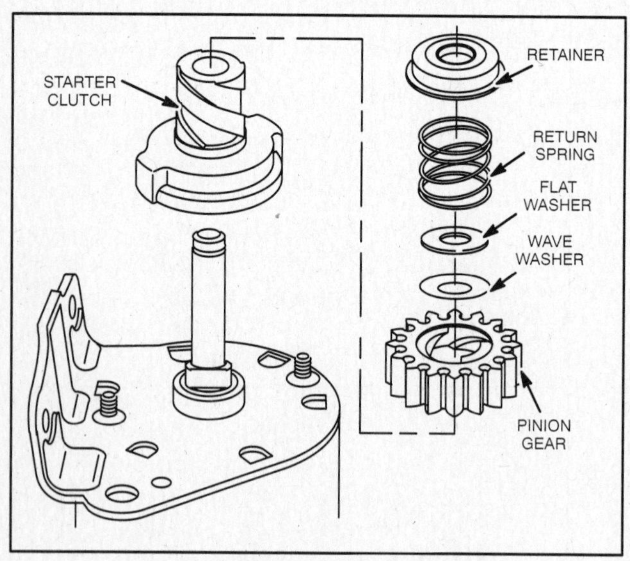

Fig. 87 - Removing Starter Drive

The pinion gear should be inspected for damaged teeth. If a sticking condition exists between the pinion gear and the helix, this must be corrected. The parts may be washed in a solvent such as Stanisol® or Varsol®. The gear, return spring, wave washer, flat washer, retainer, retainer ring and clutch assembly are available from your Briggs & Stratton source of supply.

Assemble Starter Motor Drive, Snap Ring Retainer

1. Place starter clutch on starter shaft, Fig. 88A. Rotate clutch until it drops into place, Fig. 88B.

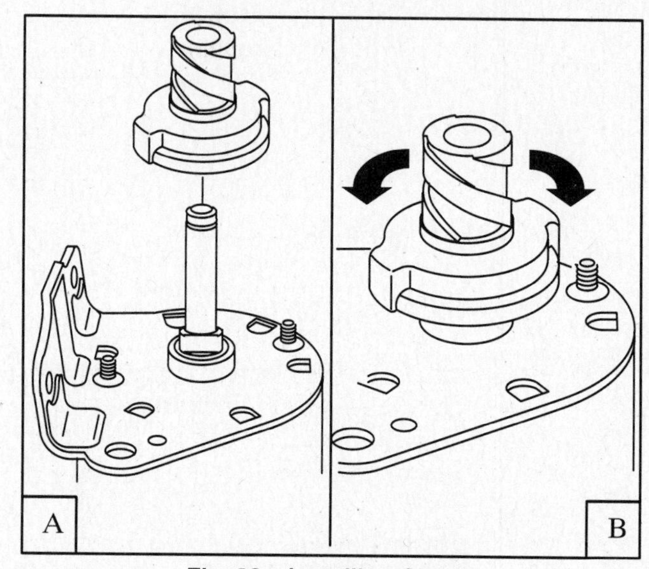

Fig. 88 - Installing Clutch

2. Install starter gear with beveled side of teeth up, Fig. 89. Then install return spring making sure spring is in recess of starter gear, Fig. 89.

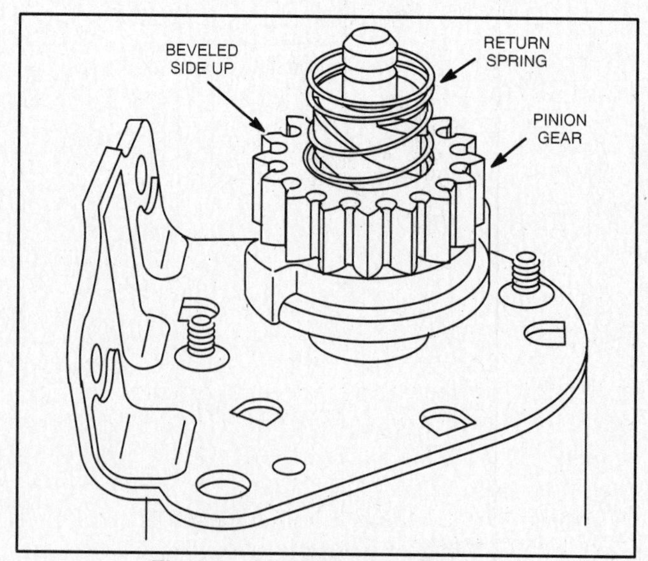

Fig. 89 - Installing Starter Gear

3. Place wave washer with concave side up and then place flat washer on starter clutch spline, Fig. 90.

NOTE: METRIC EQUIVALENTS ARE LISTED ON PAGE 63 OF THIS SECTION.

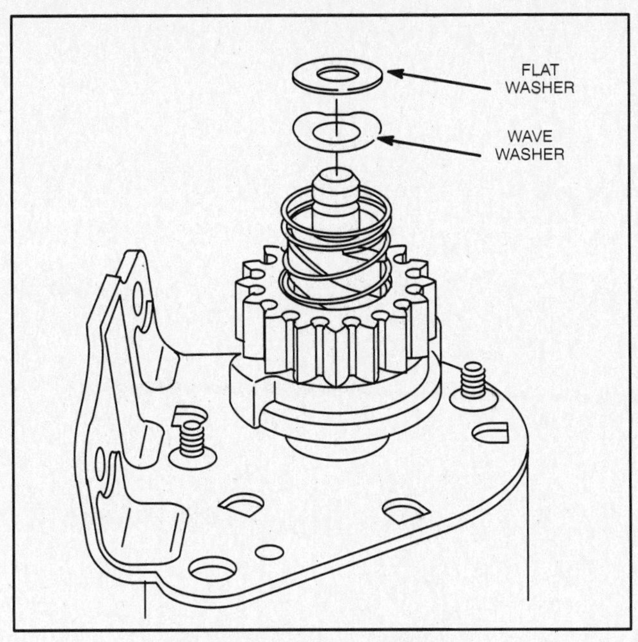

Fig. 90 - Installing Washers

4. Place retainer and new snap ring on starter shaft. Using a 6 point socket and hammer, drive snap ring down until it engages groove in starter shaft, Fig. 91. Then make sure retainer is all the way up against the snap ring.

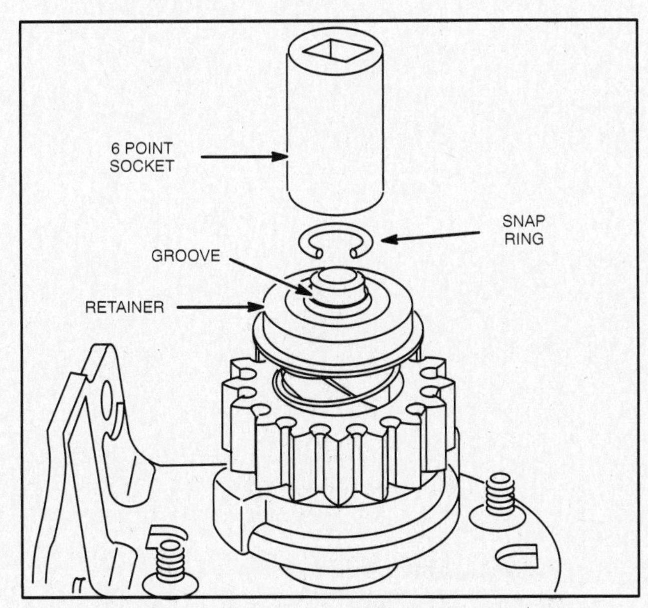

Fig. 91 - Installing Snap Ring and Retainer

Disassemble Starter Motor Drive, Roll Pin Retainer Type/Style

1. To remove the drive assembly for cleaning or replacement, disconnect and remove starter from engine.
2. Place in "V" block as shown in Fig. 92.
3. Drive the roll pin out with a hammer and 1/8" diameter punch to remove the retainer.

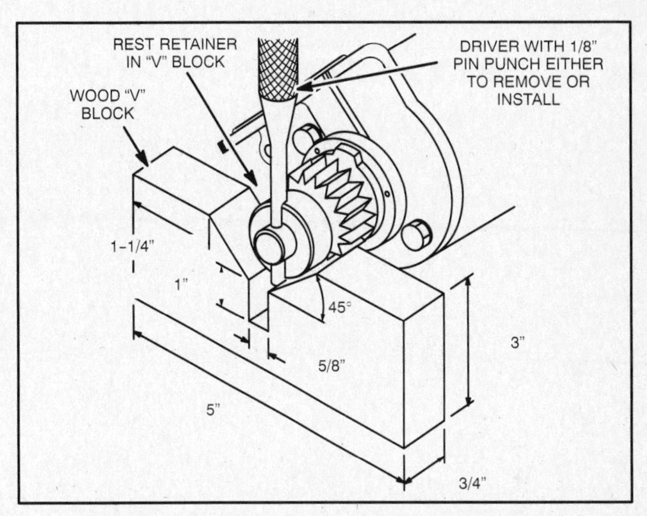

Fig. 92 - Disassembling Starter Motor Drive

NOTE: Some starter drive assemblies utilize a gear return spring. Two (2) styles of returns have ben used, current style, Fig. 93 and early style, Fig. 94. The current style is removed after removing the roll pin, Fig. 92.

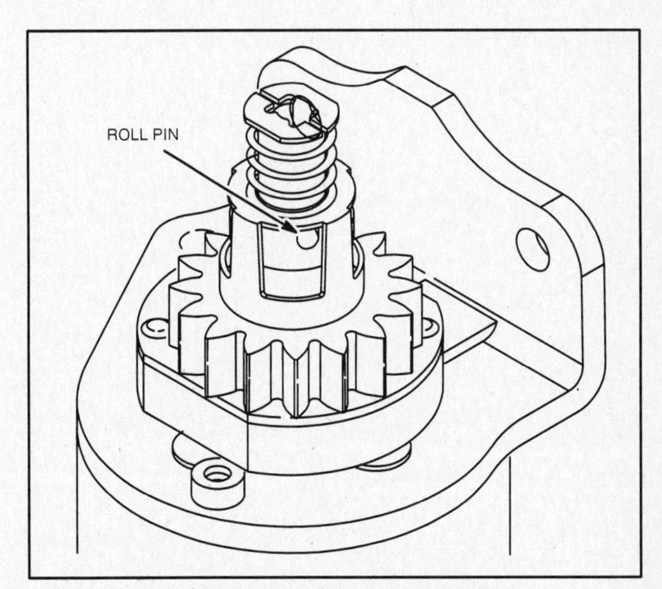

Fig. 93 - Current Style Spring Return

The early style is protected by a plastic cap over the drive assembly. Carefully remove the plastic cap from the cup using two screwdrivers, Fig. 94.

NOTE: METRIC EQUIVALENTS ARE LISTED ON PAGE 63 OF THIS SECTION.

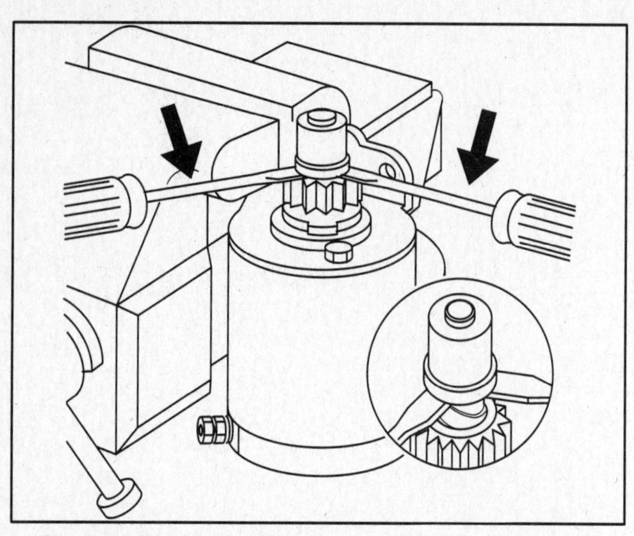
Fig. 94 - Removing Cap Assembly (Some Models)

The pinion gear should be inspected for damaged teeth. If a sticking condition exists between the pinion gear and the helix, this must be corrected. The parts may be washed in a solvent such as Stanisol® or Varsol®. The gear, retainer, roll pin and clutch assembly are available from your Briggs & Stratton source of supply.

Assemble Starter Motor Drive, Roll pin Retainer

1. Reverse disassembly procedure for assembling. Assemble the pinion gear with beveled edge on the gear up as shown in Fig. 95.
2. Assemble cup and spring on gear if original assembly was so equipped.
3. Press or drive new roll pin through retainer slot and armature shaft hole with roll pin slot positioned as shown. The roll pin should be centered in shaft within 1/32."

   NOTE: ASSEMBLE WITH NEW ROLL PIN ONLY.

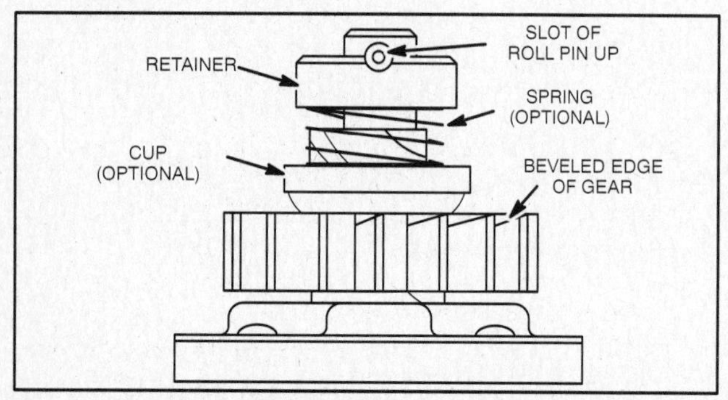

Fig. 95 - Assembling Starter Motor Drive

4. If the original assembly is equipped with a spring cap assembly, assemble cap as follows:
5. To install plastic cap, use a socket approximately the same diameter as the plastic cap, for a driver as shown in Fig. 96.
6. Press cap in position. Cap should lock in position when properly assembled.

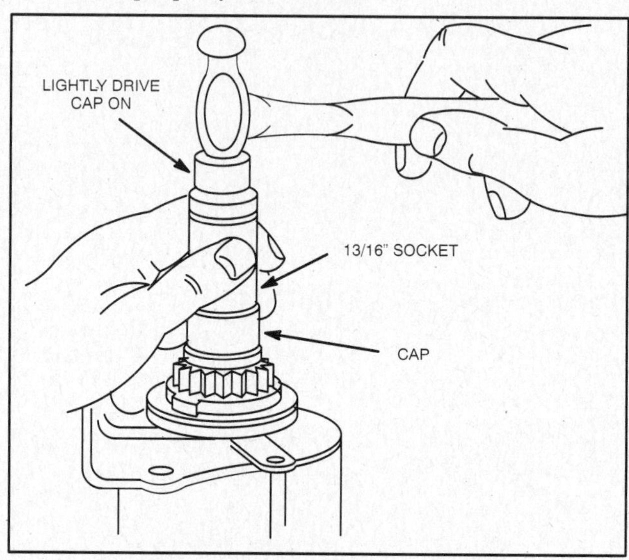

Fig. 96 - Installing Plastic Cap

Test Starter Motor

A performance test of the 12 volt DC and 120 volt AC starter motors may be made in the following manner.

12 Volt DC Starter Motor

Equipment Needed

See page 3 for a starter mounting test bracket that can be made.

Digital Multimeter, Tool (#19357 or 19390) and Tool #19359, DC Shunt or Tool #19236, VOA Meter, and DC Shunt.

See Instruction Manual MS-6574 (Digital Multimeter) or Instruction Manual MS-7585 (VOA Meter) for installation procedure.

A tachometer capable of reading 10,000 RPM.

A 12 volt battery fully charged.

To Test

1. Connect the starter motor, battery and meter as shown in Fig's. 97 or 98.

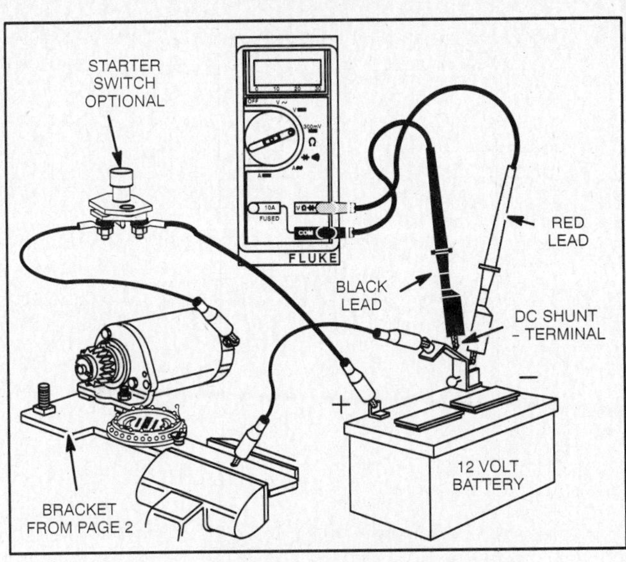

Fig. 97 - Testing 12 Volt Starter Motor Digital Multimeter

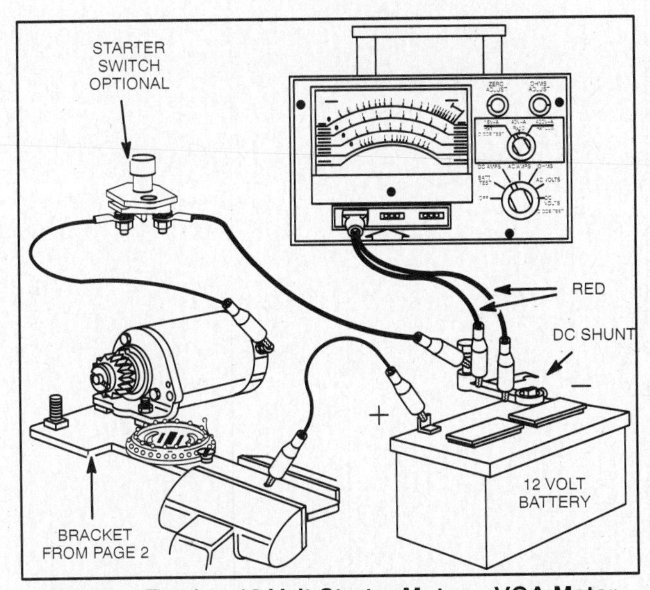

Fig. 98 - Testing 12 Volt Starter Motor - VOA Meter

CAUTION: DO NOT clamp motor housing in a vise or strike with a steel hammer. Starter motors contain two powerful magnets which can be broken or cracked if the motor housing is deformed or dented.

2. Note length of starter motor housing as shown in Fig. 68 and refer to TABLE NO. 6 for specifications for motor being tested.

3. Activate the starter motor and note readings of meter and tachometer (RPM). A starter motor in good condition will be within specifications listed. If starter motor is not within specifications shown, see list on page 41 for possible causes.

TABLE NO. 6
12 VOLT DC STARTER SPECIFICATIONS

Motor Housing Length	Minimum RPM	Maximum Amps
3-1/16"	6500	18 (Disregard surge current)
93.0 mm	6500	18 (Disregard surge current)
3-3/4"	6900	19 (Disregard surge current)
3-13/16"	6900	19 (Disregard surge current)
4-3/8"	6500	20 (Disregard surge current)
4-9/16"	6500	35 (Disregard surge current)

Test 120 Volt AC Starter Motor

Equipment Needed

See page 3 for a starter mounting test bracket that can be made.

Digital Multimeter, Tool (#19357 or #19390) with AC Shunt, Tool #19358 or VOA Meter, Tool #19236 with 120 Volt Adapter, Tool #19242.

A tachometer capable of reading 10,000 RPM,

CAUTION: The following test procedure must be used to avoid any accidental shock hazard to the service technician.

To Test

1. Set meter to AC amps position.
2. Insert leads into meter and plug starter motor cord into AC shunt, Fig. 99 (Digital Multimeter) or Fig. 100 (VOA meter).
3. Then connect AC shunt to a 120 volt outlet.
4. Refer to TABLE NO. 7 and note the maximum allowable amperage draw.
5. Depress starter switch button. When meter reading stabilizes, (approximately 3 seconds) amperage should not exceed the specification shown in TABLE NO. 7.

NOTE: METRIC EQUIVALENTS ARE LISTED ON PAGE 63 OF THIS SECTION.

CAUTION: If amperage is higher than specification shown, immediately stop the test! An amperage reading higher than number in chart indicates a shorted starter motor, which could be dangerous.

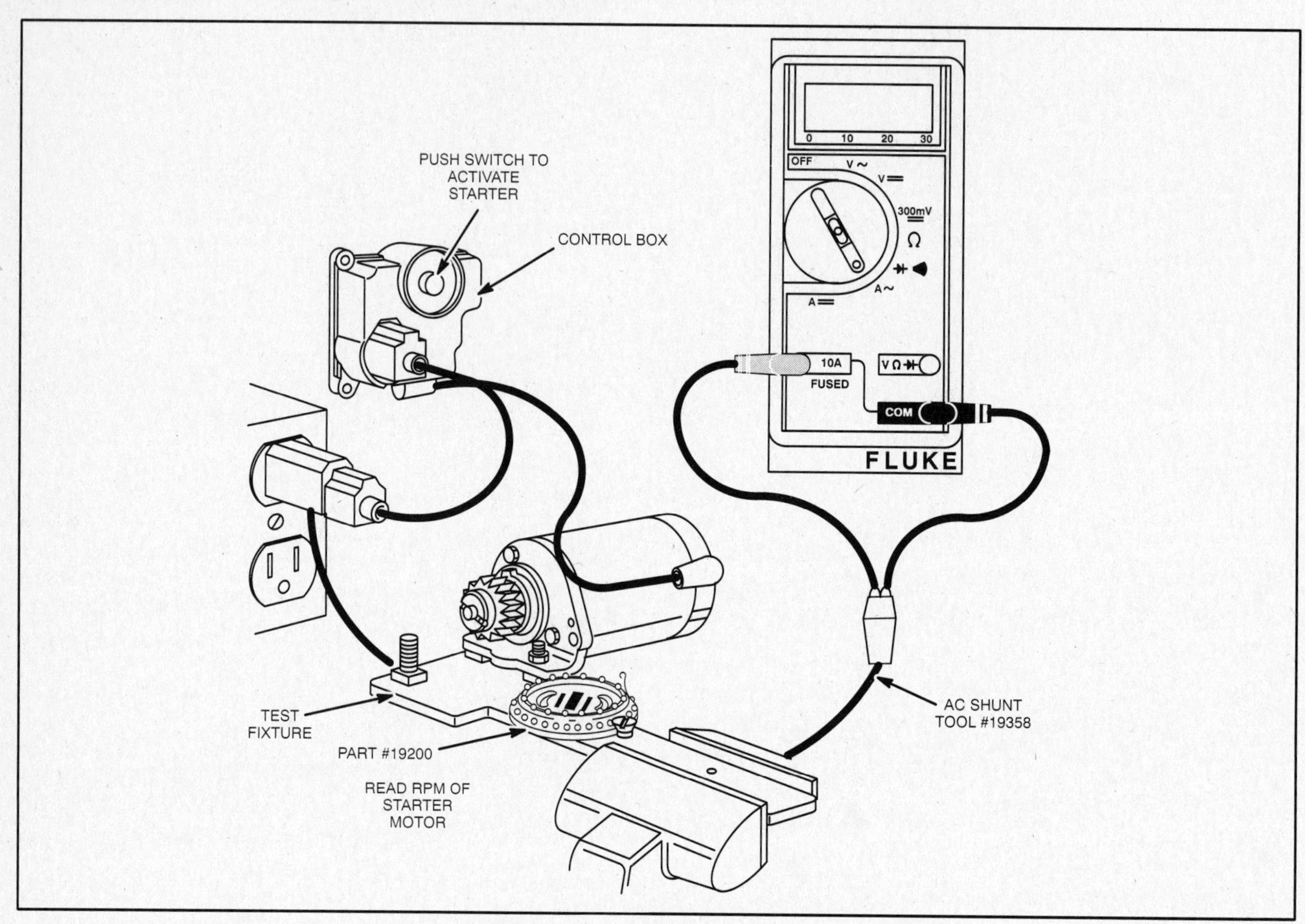

Fig. 99 - Testing 120 Volt AC Starter - Digital Multimeter

NOTE: METRIC EQUIVALENTS ARE LISTED ON PAGE 63 OF THIS SECTION.

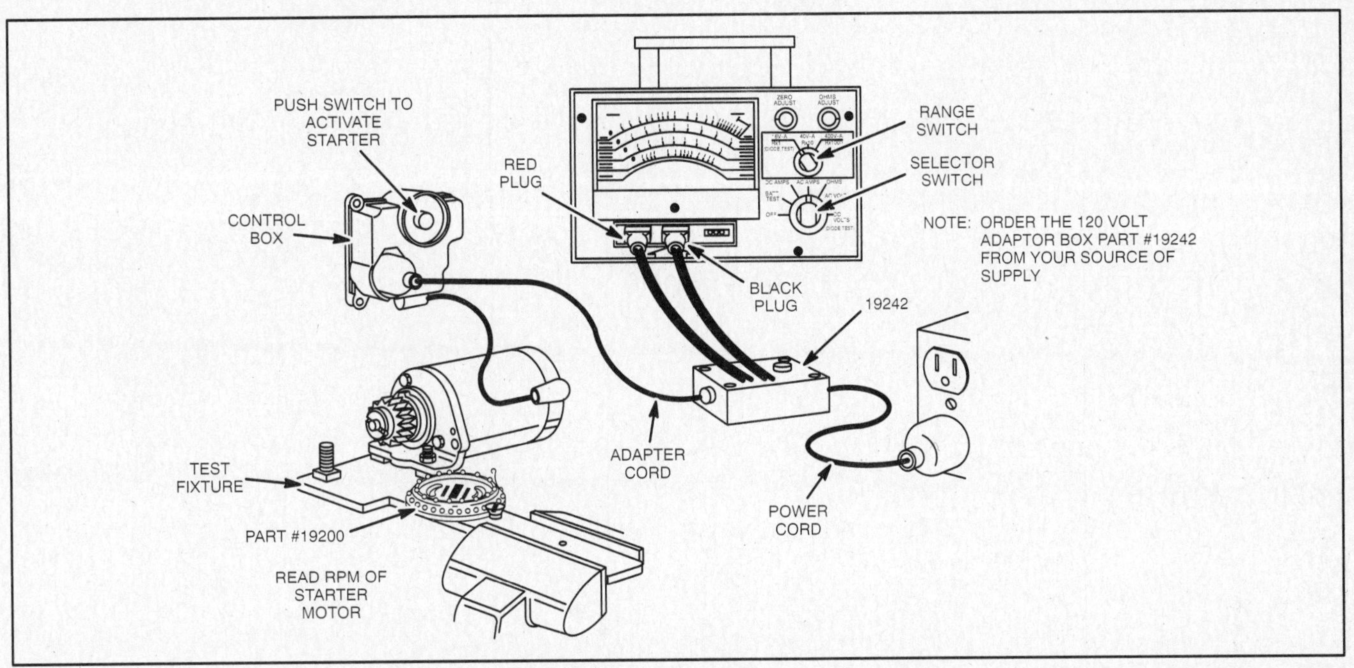

Fig. 100 - Testing 120 Volt AC Starter - VOA Meter

6. If starter motor amperage is within specification, check RPM with Tachometer Tool #19200.

TABLE NO. 7
120 VOLT AC STARTER SPECIFICATIONS

Motor Housing Length	Minimum RPM	Maximum Amps
3-1/2"	6500	2.7 (Disregard surge current)

If either the 12 or the120 volt starter motor does not perform satisfactorily, the following should be checked and corrected if necessary:

1. A binding or seizing condition in the starter motor bearings.
2. Starter motor brushes sticking in brush holders.
3. A dirty or worn armature commutator or brushes.
4. A shorted, open or grounded armature.

   A. Shorted armature (wire insulation worn and wires touching one another). Will be indicated by low or no RPM.

   B. Open armature (wire broken) will be indicated by low or no RPM.

   C. Grounded armature (wire insulation worn and wire touching armature lamination or shaft). Will be indicated by excessive current or no RPM.

5. A defective starter motor switch.
6. A defective starter motor control box rectifier assembly (120 volt AC only).
7. Weakened magnets.

Disassemble Starter Motor, Snap Ring Retainer

CAUTION: DO NOT clamp motor housing in a vise or strike with a steel hammer. Starter motors contain two powerful ceramic magnets which can be broken or cracked if the motor housing is hit, deformed, dented or dropped.

Remove drive assembly as described on Page 36.

1. Study Fig. 101 prior to starter motor disassembly. Remove thru bolts.

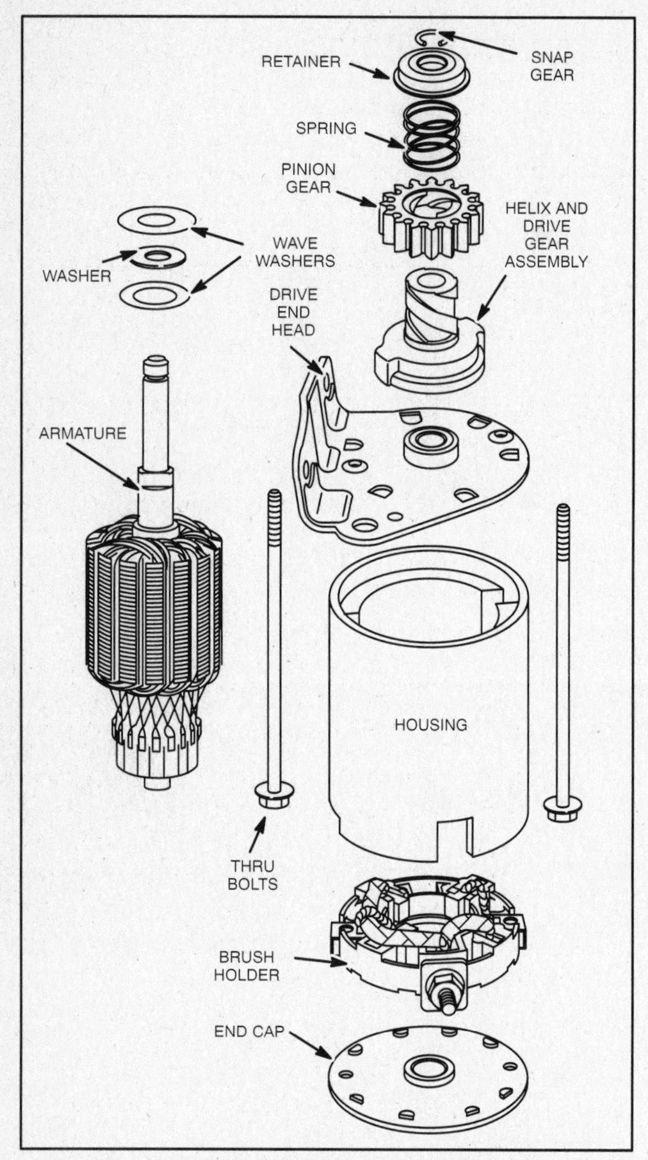

Fig. 101 - 12 Volt Volt Starter Motor - Exploded View

2. The drive head end may now be removed. Inspect bushing for wear. If worn, replace drive head end assembly, Fig. 102.

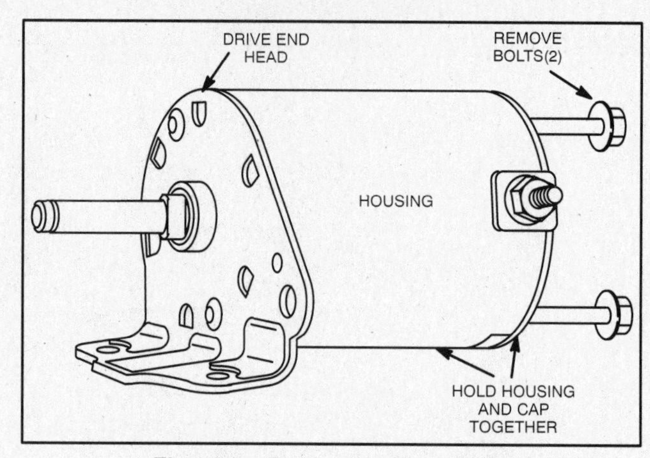

Fig. 102 - Removing Thru Bolts

3. Hold the armature and bearing end cap against a work surface while sliding housing off the armature. This allows the armature to remain in the bearing end cap and brush holder for inspection of brush contact to armature, Fig. 103.

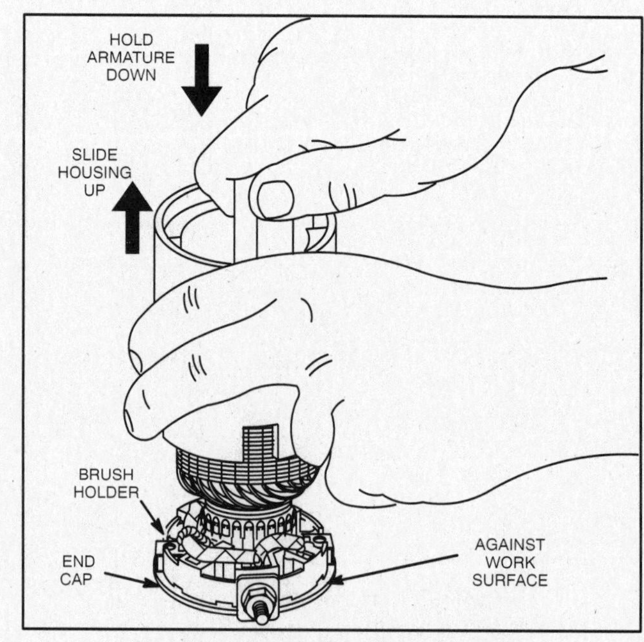

Fig. 103 - Removing Motor Housing

4. While holding brush holder and armature, remove bearing end cap from armature, Fig. 104.

NOTE: METRIC EQUIVALENTS ARE LISTED ON PAGE 63 OF THIS SECTION.

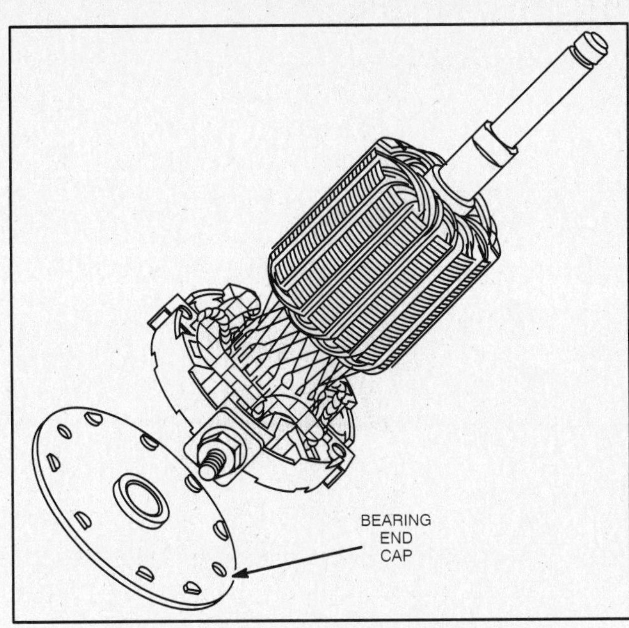

Fig. 104 - Removing Bearing End Cap

5. Remove brush holder from armature commutator, Fig. 105.

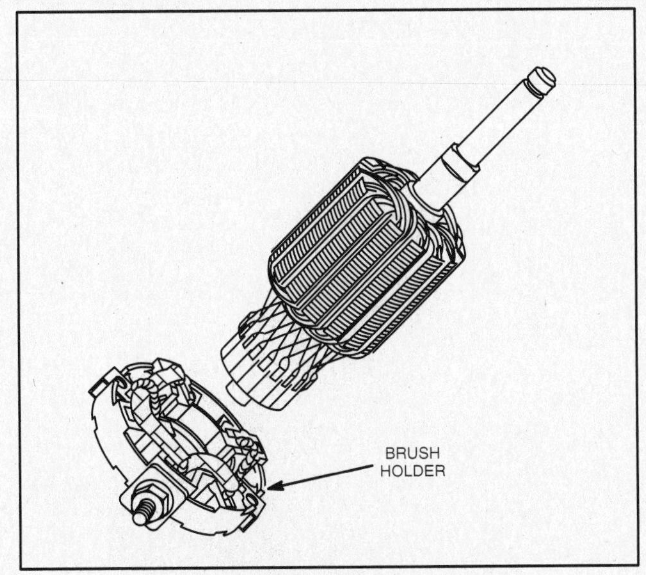

Fig. 105 - Removing Brush Holder

6. The bearings, housing and armature should not be soaked in a cleaning solution.

7. The armature commutator may be cleaned with a fine sand paper.

   NOTE: DO NOT USE EMERY CLOTH, AS EMERY WILL BECOME EMBEDDED IN THE COMMUTATOR CAUSING RAPID BRUSH WEAR.

8. The commutator may also be machined with the use of a diamond cutting tool to no less than 1.23" outside diameter.

9. Slots between commutator bars should be cleaned as shown in Fig. 106, after cleaning or machining.

10. If it is suspected that the armature field coil, magnets or motor housing is defective, a new part should be tried in the motor. If proper testing equipment is available, check the suspected armature or field coil to determine if it is defective (opens or grounds).

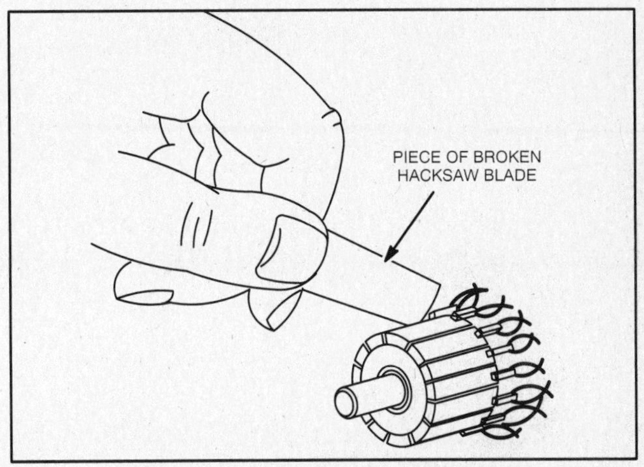

Fig. 106 - Cleaning Commutator

11. The brushes should be checked for poor seating, weak brush springs, dirt, oil or corrosion.

12. If brushes are worn to dimension shown in Fig. 107, replace.

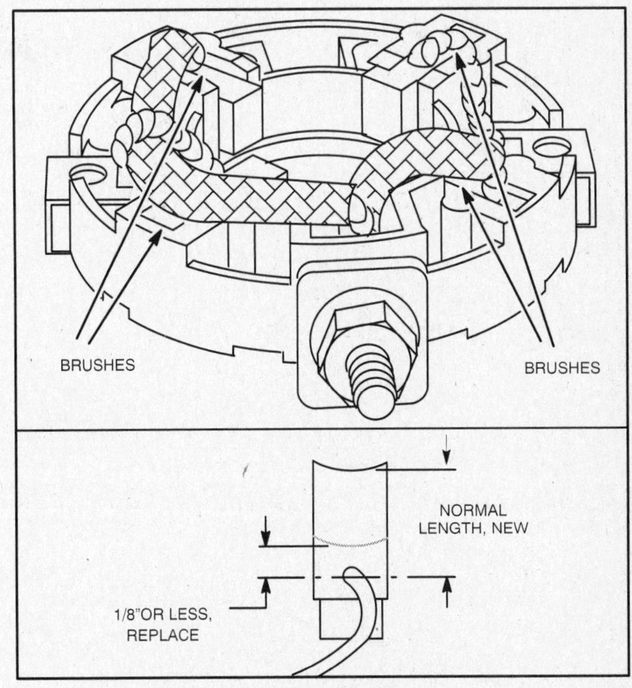

Fig. 107 - Checking Brushes

13. Check to be sure brushes are not sticking in their holders.

NOTE: METRIC EQUIVALENTS ARE LISTED ON PAGE 63 OF THIS SECTION.

Assemble Starter Motor, Snap Ring Retainer

1. When all parts have been thoroughly inspected, lightly lubricate the bearings with #20 oil and reassemble in the following manner.

2. Place brushes in their slots and hold brushes with brush retainers, Fig. 108. Dimensions for making brush retainers from annealed rewind starter springs are shown in Fig. 109.

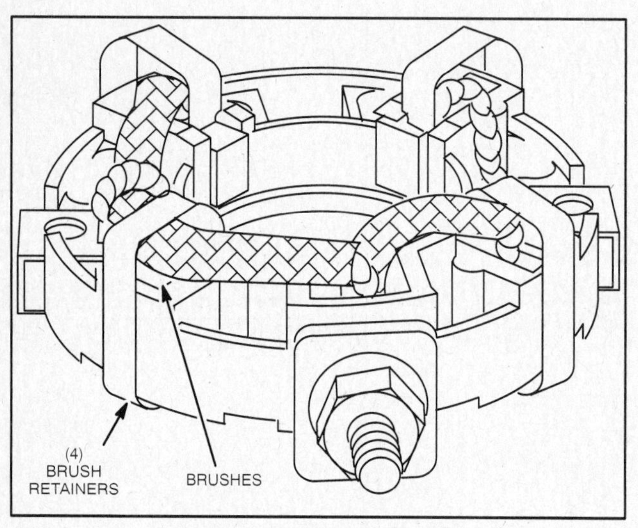

Fig. 108 - Installing Brushes

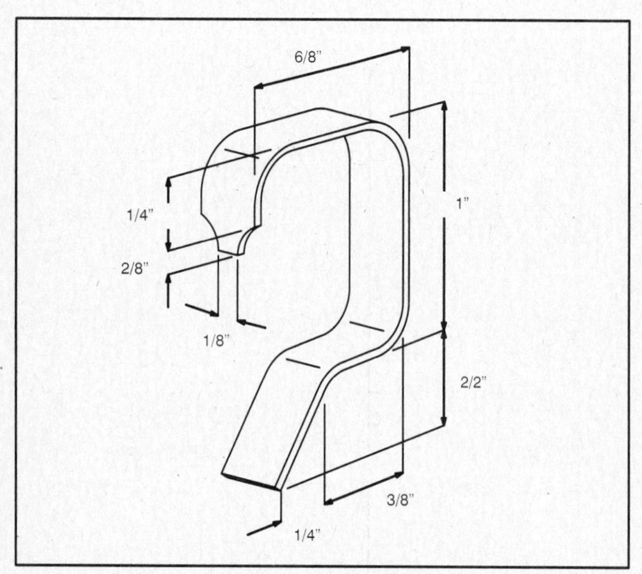

Fig. 109 - Brush Retainer

3. Place armature commutator in brush holder and remove brush retainers, Fig. 110.

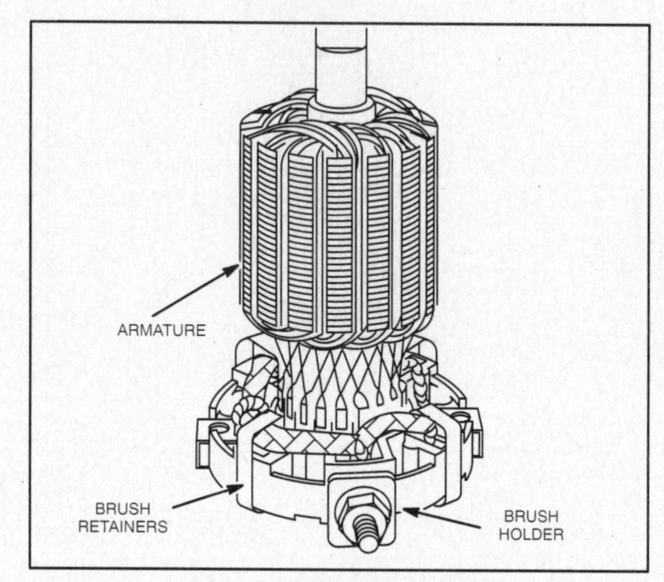

Fig. 110 - Installing Armature

4. install bearing end plate on armature commutator journal making sure plate indexes with brush holder, Fig. 111.

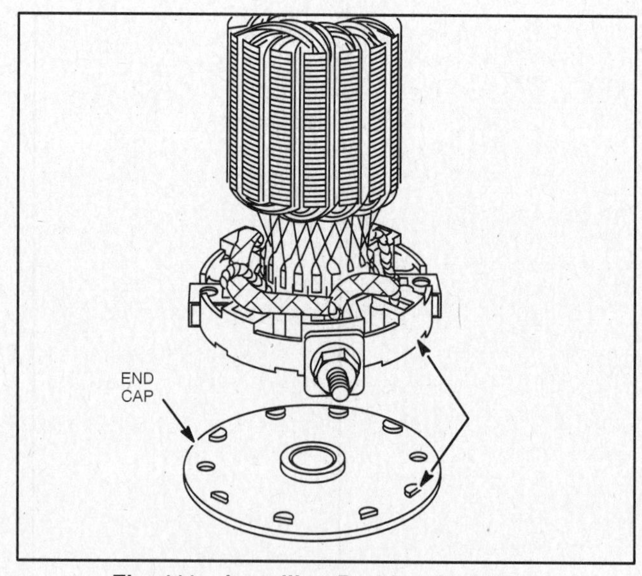

Fig. 111 - Installing Bearing End Plate

5. Slide motor housing over armature with the notch toward brush holder, Fig. 113.

NOTE: METRIC EQUIVALENTS ARE LISTED ON PAGE 63 OF THIS SECTION.

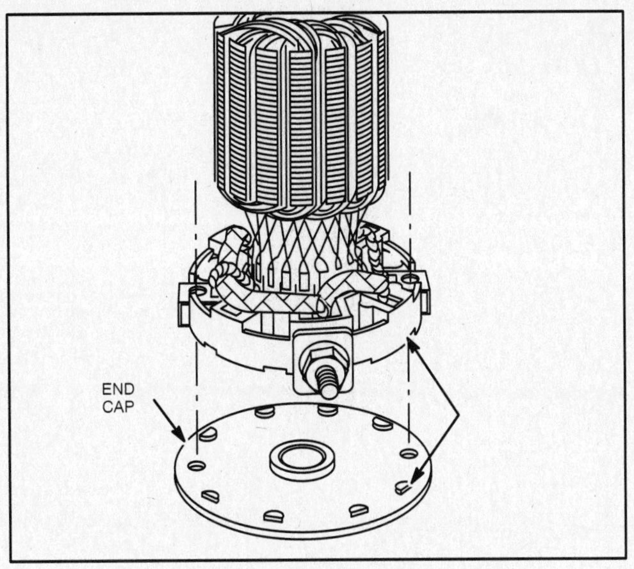

Fig. 112 - Installing Bearing End Plate

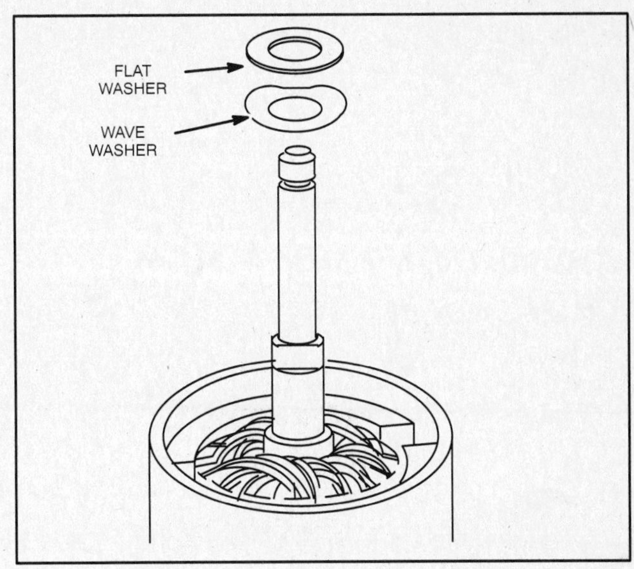

Fig. 114 - Installing Thrust Washers

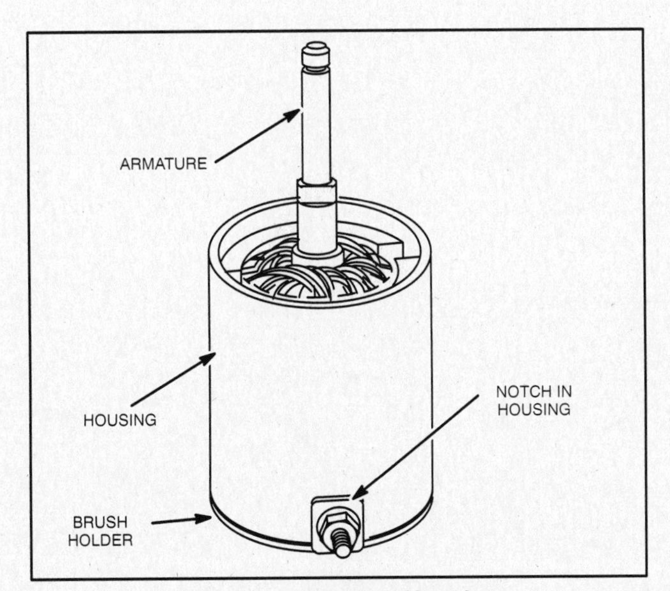

Fig. 113 - Installing Housing

6. Place wave washer on armature shaft with concave side up, Fig. 114. Then place flat washer on armature.

7. Place drive end cap on starter housing making sure that mark on cap line up with housing seam, Fig. 115.

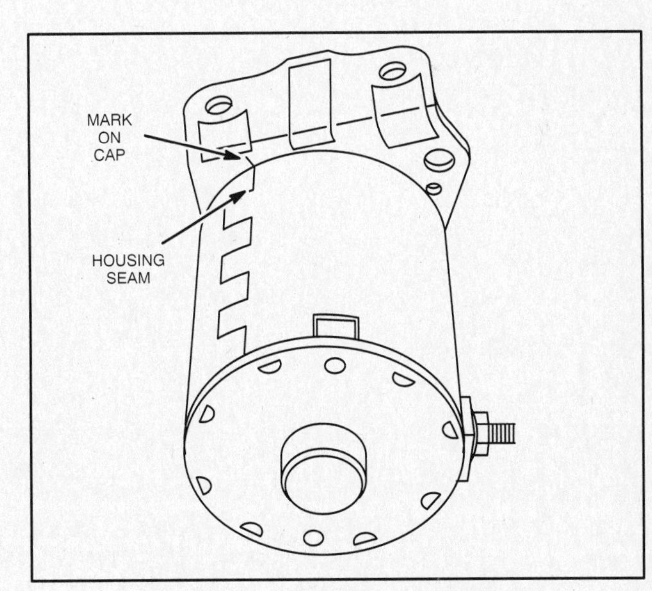

Fig. 116 - Installing Drive End Cap

8. Install through bolts in starter, Fig. 117. Use starter clutch to check for binding of armature shaft and correct if it binds.

NOTE: METRIC EQUIVALENTS ARE LISTED ON PAGE 63 OF THIS SECTION.

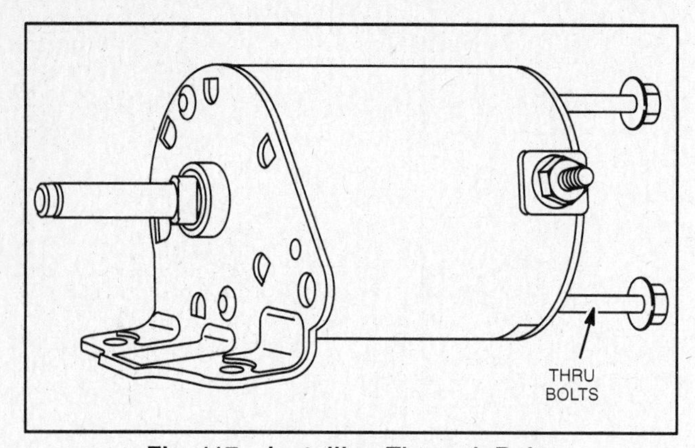

Fig. 117 - Installing Through Bolts

9. Install starter drive as described on page 36 of this section.

10. Install starter on engine and start mounting screws. While holding starter against locating lugs on cylinder, Fig. 118, torque mounting screws to 140 in. lbs.

11. Reinstall starter guard, when used.

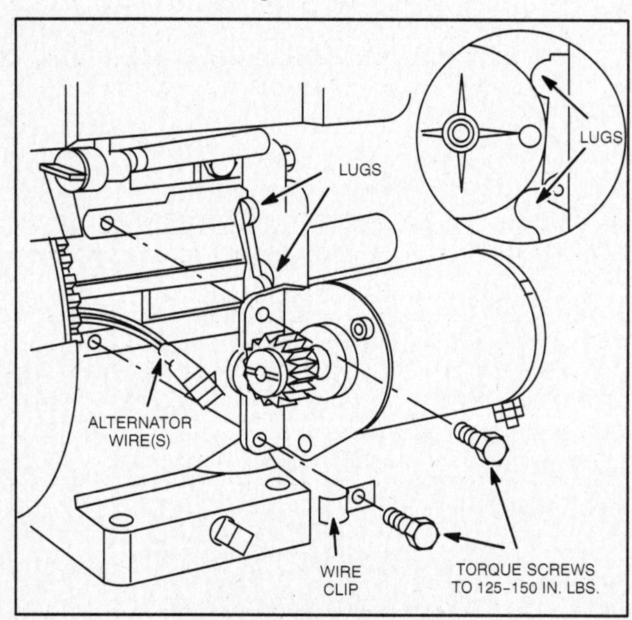

Fig. 118 - Installing Starter

Disassemble Starter Motor, Roll Pin Retainer

CAUTION: DO NOT clamp motor housing in a vise or strike with a steel hammer. Starter motors contain two powerful ceramic magnets which can be broken or cracked if the motor housing is hit, deformed, dented or dropped.

1. Study Fig. 84 prior to starter motor disassembly.

2. Mark drive end cap at seam on housing. Remove thru bolts.

3. The drive head end may now be removed. Inspect bushing for wear. If worn, replace drive head end assembly, Fig. 119.

NOTE: MATCH MARKS AND THRU BOLTS MUST BE PLACED IN THE SAME POSITION AS WHEN REMOVED OR INTERFERENCE MAY RESULT.

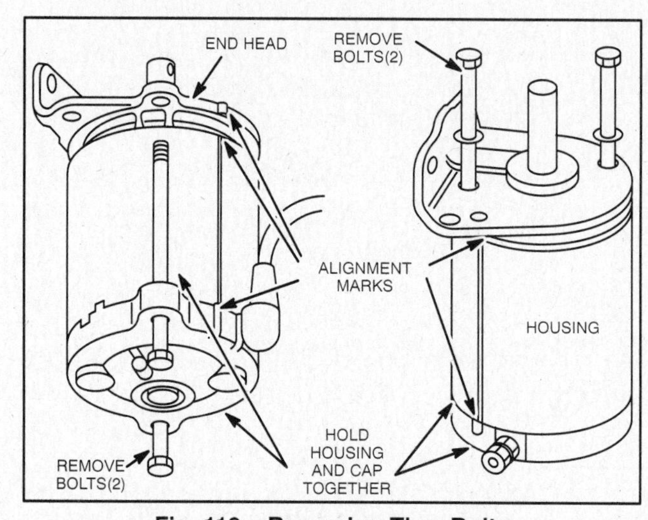

Fig. 119 - Removing Thru Bolts

4. Hold the armature and commutator end cap against a work surface while sliding housing off the armature. This allows the armature to remain in the end cap for inspection of brush contact to armature, Fig. 120.

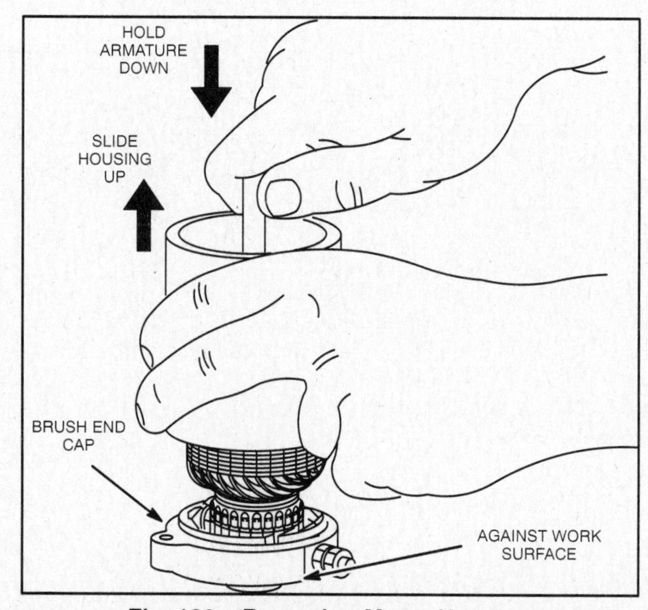

Fig. 120 - Removing Motor Housing

NOTE: METRIC EQUIVALENTS ARE LISTED ON PAGE 63 OF THIS SECTION.

Remove Armature from Brush End Cap

1. Clean all dirt or corrosion from the armature, end cap, motor support, etc. The bearings, housing and armature should not be soaked in a cleaning solution. The armature commutator may be cleaned with a fine sand paper.

   NOTE: DO NOT USE EMERY CLOTH, AS EMERY WILL BECOME EMBEDDED IN THE COMMUTATOR CAUSING RAPID BRUSH WEAR.

2. The commutator may also be machined with the use of a diamond cutting tool to no less than 1.23" - 12 volt, 1.32" - 120 volt, outside diameter.

3. Slots between commutator bars should be cleaned as shown in Fig. 121, after cleaning or machining.

4. If it is suspected that the armature field coil, magnets or motor housing is defective, a new part should be tried in the motor. If proper testing equipment is available, check the suspected armature or field coil to determine if it is defective (opens or grounds).

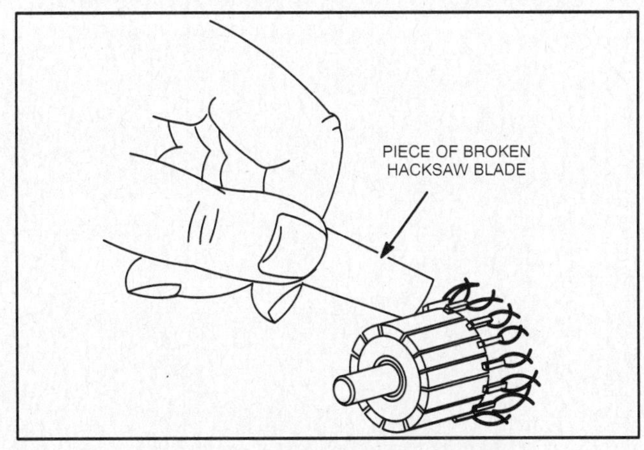

Fig. 121 - Cleaning Commutator

5. The brushes should be checked for poor seating, weak brush springs, dirt, oil or corrosion.

6. Brush spring pressure should be strong enough to ensure good brush contact with armature.

7. If brushes are worn to dimension shown in Fig. 122, replace.

8. Check to be sure brushes are not sticking in their holders.

9. Use holders to retain brushes and spring during assembly.

BRUSHES MUST MOVE FREELY IN HOLDERS!

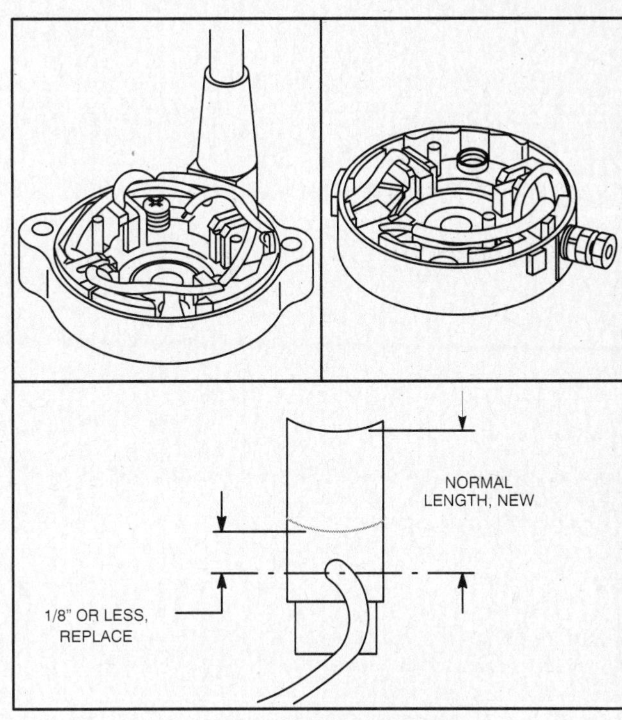

Fig. 122 - Checking Brushes

Testing Rectifier Control Assembly Briggs & Stratton 120 Volt Starter Motor

The AC control assembly housing contains a spring loaded starter button, cord assembly and rectifier. It is equipped with a three wire grounded receptacle. Fig. 123. The test procedure for checking the rectifier control assembly is as follows:

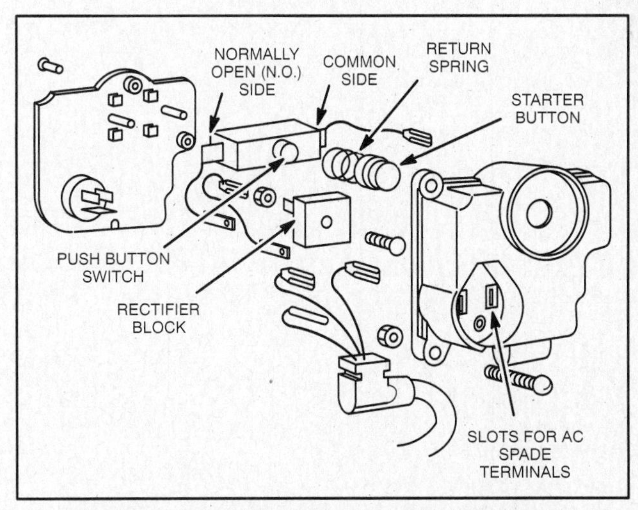

Fig. 123 - Exploded View - Control Assembly

NOTE: METRIC EQUIVALENTS ARE LISTED ON PAGE 63 OF THIS SECTION.

Disassemble Control Assembly

CAUTION: Disconnect extension cord from AC outlet and control assembly before disassembling.

1. With control assembly removed from mounting surface, remove three screws holding backplate to housing, Fig. 124.

2. Note position of wires, page 50.

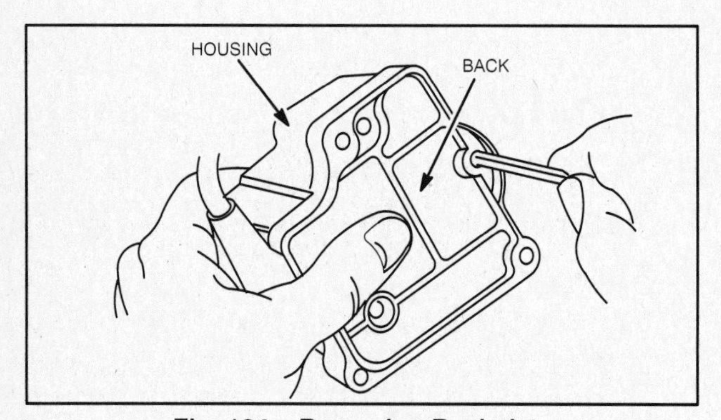

Fig. 124 - Removing Backplate

Test Rectifier (Shorts or Opens)

3. Remove all wires from rectifier before checking.

4. Use Digital Multimeter, Tool (#19357 or #19390) or VOA Meter, Tool #19236.

5. Set meter to "Diode Test."

6. Using test leads, place RED test lead and BLACK test lead on rectifier terminals in sequence shown in Fig. 125, and TABLE NO. 8 or TABLE NO. 9.

Test results must be as indicated in TABLE NO. 8 if Digital Multimeter is used.

Test results must be as indicated in TABLE NO. 9 if VOA meter is used.

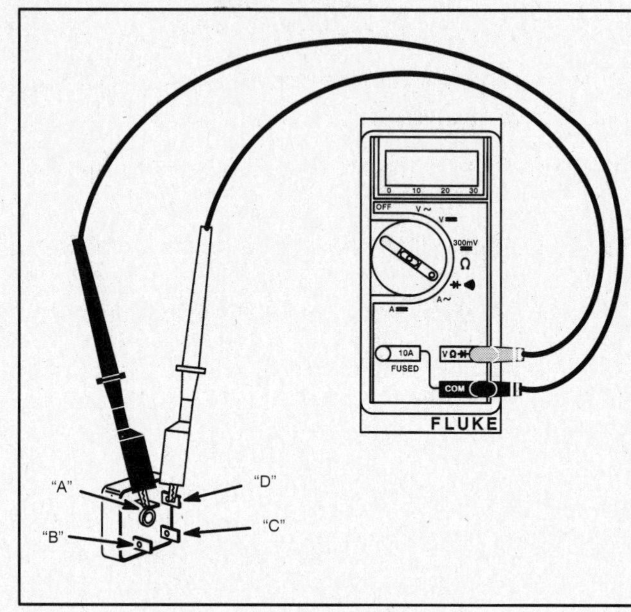

Fig. 125 - Testing Rectifier

TABLE NO. 8
DIGITAL MULTIMETER

Red Test Lead (+) Positive	Black Test Lead (-) Negative	"Beep" (Continuity)
A	B	NO
B	A	YES
B	C	NO
C	B	YES
C	D	YES
D	C	NO
D	A	YES
A	D	NO

NOTE: METRIC EQUIVALENTS ARE LISTED ON PAGE 63 OF THIS SECTION.

TABLE NO. 9
VOA METER

Red Test Lead (+) Positive	Black Test Lead (-) Negative	Meter Reading (Continuity)
A	B	NO
B	A	YES
B	C	NO
C	B	YES
C	D	YES
D	C	NO
D	A	YES
A	D	NO

7. If test results differ from those shown, the rectifier is defective and must be replaced.

Test Rectifier (Grounded)

1. Leave Digital Multimeter in Diode Test position.

2. With BLACK meter test lead contacting metal rectifier case, touch RED meter test lead to each rectifier terminal, Fig. 126.

3. Meter should display "OL" at each terminal. If meter makes a continuous tone when any terminal is contacted, the rectifier is grounded and must be replaced.

4. Set VOA meter to Ohms Position.

5. With one lead contacting metal rectifier case, touch other lead to each rectifier terminal, Fig. 126. There should be no continuity from any terminal to case.

6. Replace rectifier if grounded.

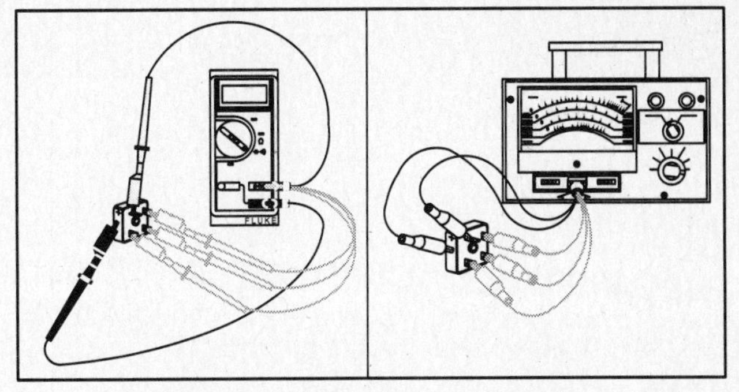

Fig. 126 - Checking for Grounds

7. To replace rectifier assembly, remove retainer spring washer.

   NOTE: If rectifier post should break, drill a 3/16" diameter hole in post location.

8. Attach rectifier with plastic screw and nut. Assemble as shown in Fig. 127.

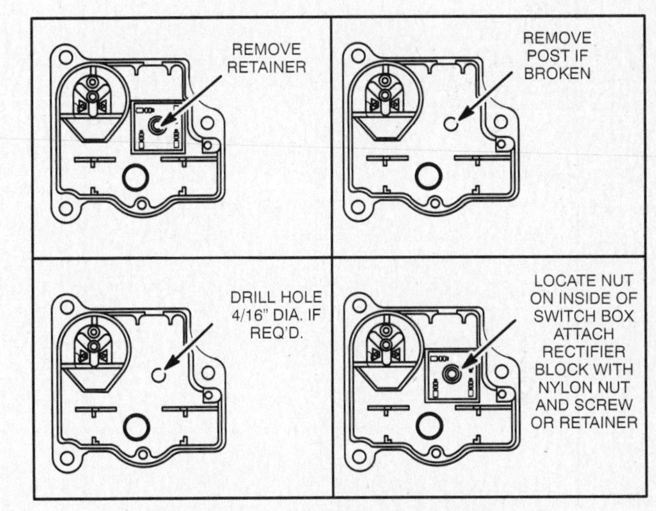

Fig. 127 - Replacing Rectifier

Test Switch

1. To test the switch assembly using the Digital Multimeter, leave meter in the Diode Test position.

2. Attach meter test leads to switch terminals, Fig. 128.

3. Meter should display "OL," indicating no continuity.

4. When button is depressed, the meter should make a continuous tone, indicating continuity. Meter should indicate continuity only when button is depressed.

NOTE: METRIC EQUIVALENTS ARE LISTED ON PAGE 63 OF THIS SECTION.

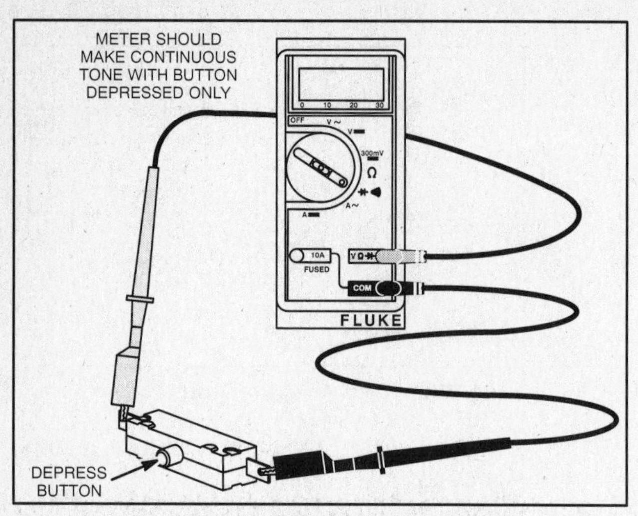

Fig. 128 - Testing Switch Assembly

1. To test the switch assembly using the VOA meter, leave meter in Ohms position.

2. Attach meter test leads to switch terminals, Fig. 129.

3. Meter should not display a reading, indicating no continuity.

4. When button is depressed the meter should display a reading, indicating continuity. Meter should indicate continuity only when button is depressed.

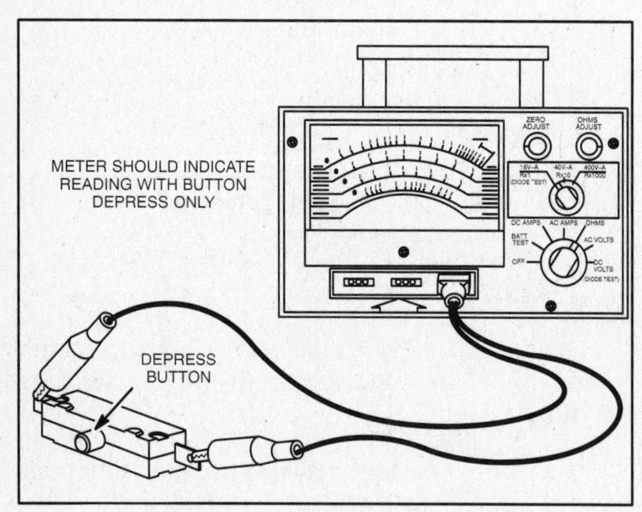

Fig. 129 - Testing Switch Assembly

When re-assembling switch, position starter button and return spring as noted in Fig. 123.

With the starter motor and controller disassembled, the cord assembly may be tested for continuity using the Digital Multimeter or with the VOA meter.

Assemble 120 Volt Control Assembly

1. Connect wires as shown in Fig. 130.

CAUTION: Incorrect assembly of black and white wires from cord to rectifier will cause motor to run backwards.

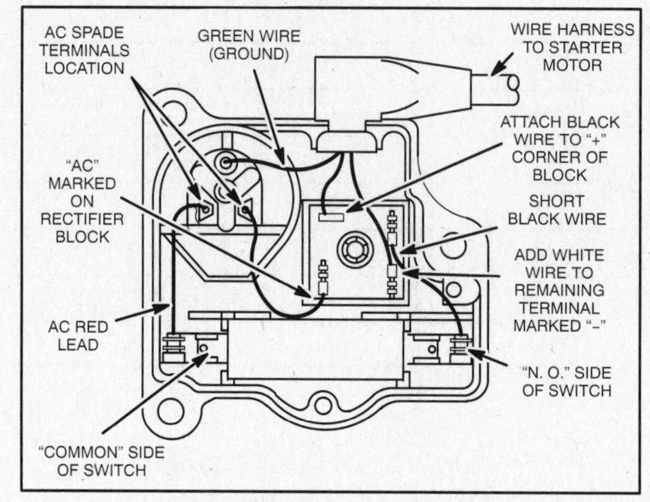

Fig. 130 - Wiring Diagram

2. Re-assemble backplate to housing using three (3) screws.

Assemble Starter Motor

1. When all parts have been thoroughly inspected, lightly lubricate the bearings with #20 oil and reassemble in the following manner.

2. Assemble wiring in commutator end cap for 120 volt AC motor as shown in Fig. 131.

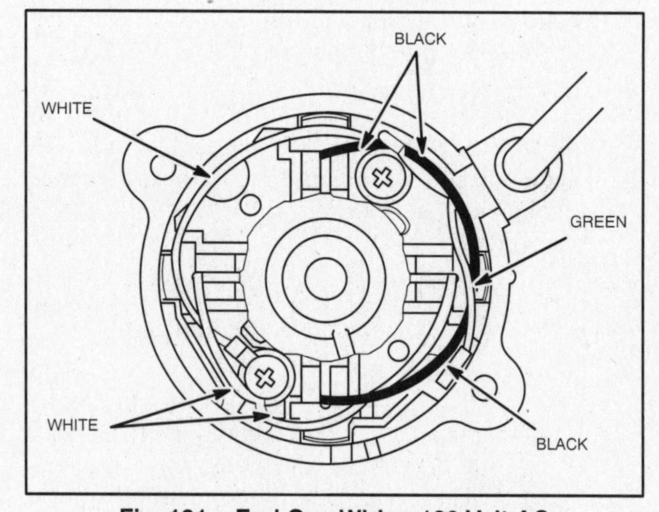

Fig. 131 - End Cap Wiring 120 Volt AC

3. Insert brushes and springs in their respective holders, except 4-3/8" and 4-9/16" housing starters.

NOTE: METRIC EQUIVALENTS ARE LISTED ON PAGE 63 OF THIS SECTION.

NOTE: A brush holding tool as shown in Fig's. 6 and 132 should be used to hold the brushes clear of the armature commutator during assembly.

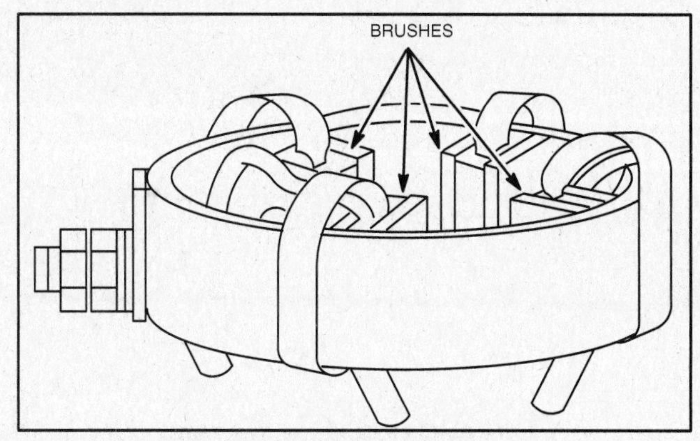

Fig. 132 - Positioning Brushes

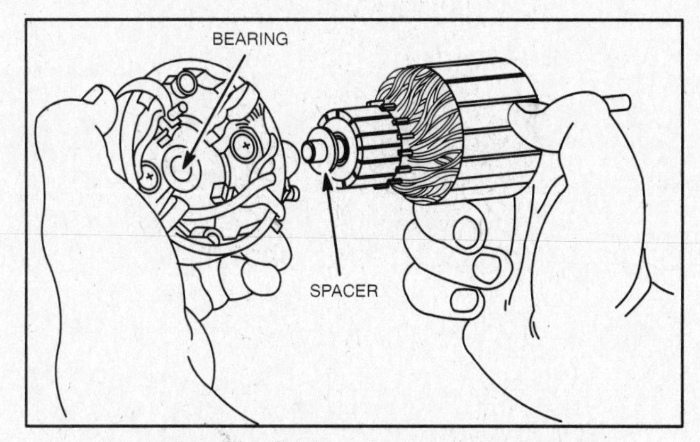

Fig. 133 - Assembling Armature to End Cap

Assemble Housing All Except 4-3/8", 4-9/16" Housings

1. Slide motor housing over armature with the notch toward commutator end cap.
2. Match alignment marks, Fig. 119.
3. Care should be used to prevent damage to magnets in motor housing during assembly.
4. Assemble spacers and drive head end bracket, again aligning match marks.
5. Assemble thru bolts and washers.
6. Torque thru bolts, 45 to 55 in. lbs. for 1/4-20 thru bolts and 40 to 45 in. lbs. for 10-24 thru bolts.
7. Armature end play is .007" to .048" after assembly.

Install Brushes, 4-3/8" and 4-9/16" Housings

With a small blade screwdriver, bend brush spring out and insert brush in brush holder, Fig. 134.

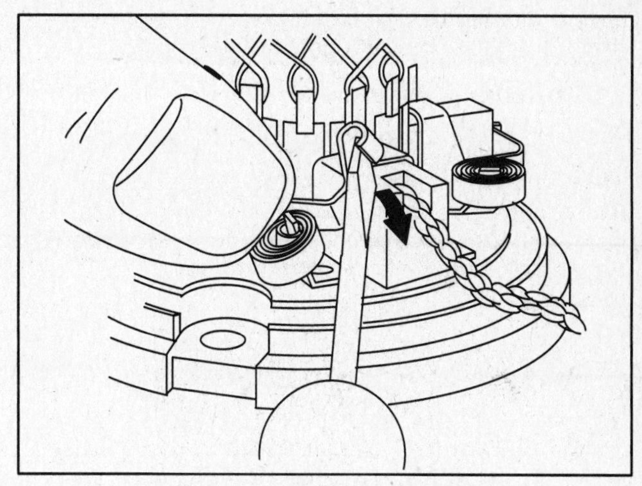
Fig. 134 - Installing Brushes

Assemble Housing to Brush End Cap 4-3/8", 4-9/16" Housings

This design of starter housing has a large notch which indexes over the insulated terminal, Fig. 135.

1. While pushing down on armature and brush end cap. Slide starter housing down until large notch indexes with insulated terminal boss, Fig. 135. DO NOT damage magnets in starter housing.

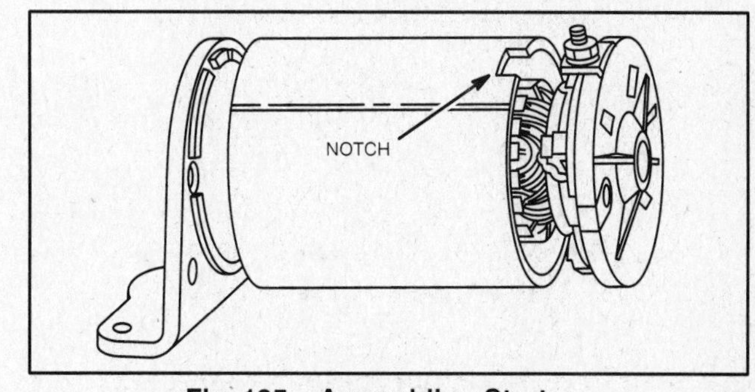

Fig. 135 - Assembling Starter

2. Assemble thru bolts and washers.
3. Torque thru bolts, 45 to 55 in. lbs. for 1/4-20 thru bolts and 40 to 45 in. lbs. for 10-24 thru bolts.

Before and after repairing the 120 volt AC starter motor, a Hi-Pot test must be made to prevent injury. If the proper test equipment is not available, take the starter motor to a qualified electric motor repair shop for testing.

NOTE: METRIC EQUIVALENTS ARE LISTED ON PAGE 63 OF THIS SECTION.

After assembly of the starter motor drive and Hi-Pot test is passed, the starter motor is now ready for installation to the engine.

AMERICAN BOSCH MITSUBISHI GEAR DRIVE STARTER MOTORS

120 Volt AC; 12 Volt DC Model Series 170000, 190000

These starter motors use a gear type engagement method, similar to an automobile starter. When the starter motor is activated, the pinion gear engages a ring gear attached to the engine flywheel and cranks the engine.

All 120 volt electric starters are equipped with a three prong plug for safety. The longer prong in this plug is connected to the starter motor housing. When the starter motor is plugged into the three wire cord supplied, and the cord is plugged into a properly grounded receptacle, it will protect the user from shock should the starter motor insulation fail for any reason. If a longer extension cord is used with this starter, it should also have three prongs and a three hole plug. DO NOT USE extension cords longer than 25 feet.

CAUTION: After servicing, the120 volt starter motor should be Hi-Pot tested before reinstalling on engine to determine if a shock hazard exists.

It is recommended a battery of 32 ampere hour capacity be used with the 12 volt starter. The battery cable size should be #4 or #6.

NOTE: A battery of higher amperage may be required for extremely cold weather starting conditions.

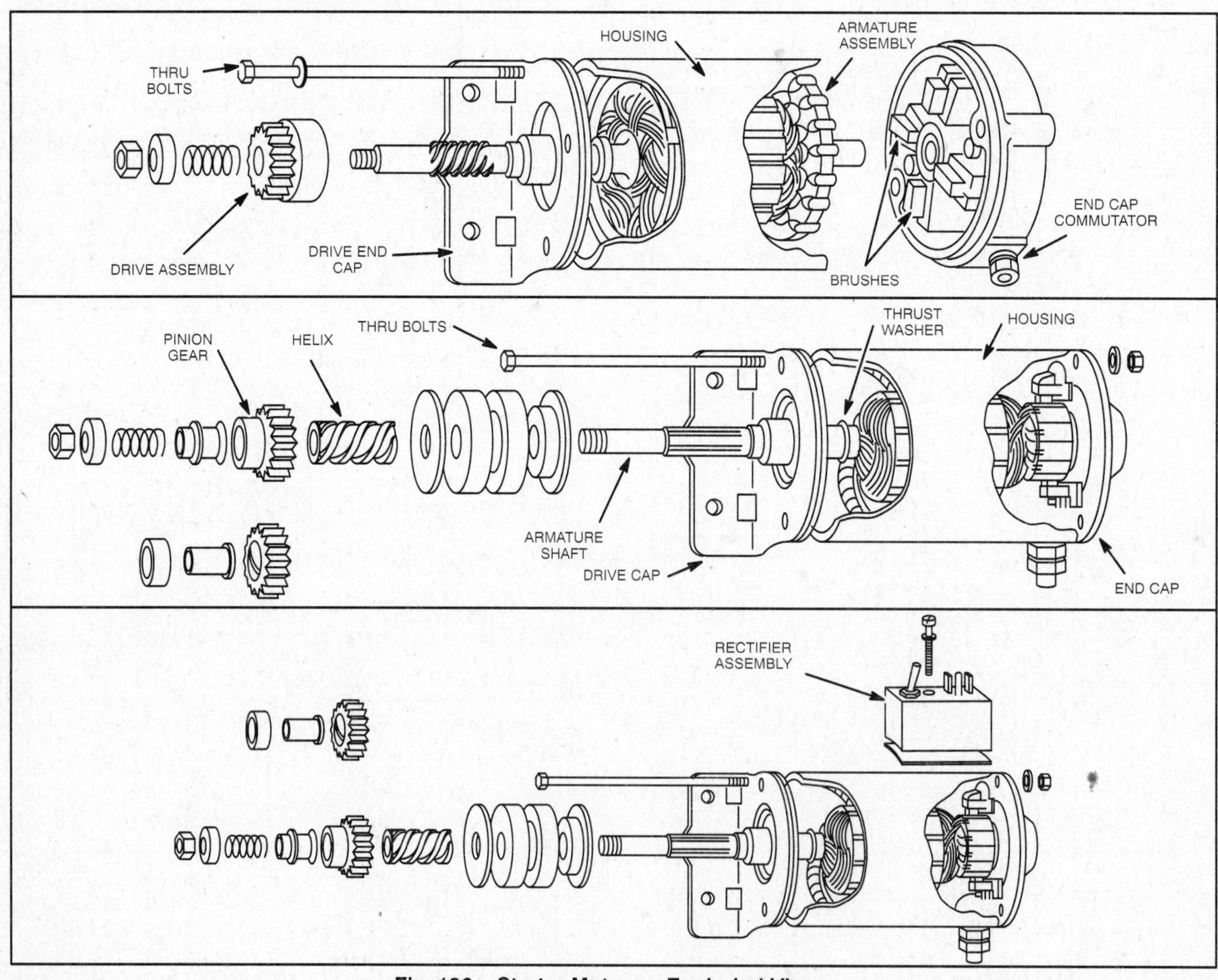

Fig. 136 – Starter Motors – Exploded Views

NOTE: METRIC EQUIVALENTS ARE LISTED ON PAGE 63 OF THIS SECTION.

Replace Ring Gear

To replace a worn or damaged flywheel ring gear, see page 35, Fig. 83.

NOTE: These starter motors use a steel pinion gear with a steel flywheel ring gear. Use only steel pinion gear with steel ring gear.

Check Engine

If a starting problem is encountered, check the engine thoroughly to be sure it is not the cause of starting difficulty. It is a good practice to remove the spark plug and rotate the crankshaft by hand, to be sure it rotates freely. Any belt, clutch or other parasitic load will affect cranking performance.

Service procedures for both the 12 volt and 120 volt starter motors are similar and will be covered together, except where noted otherwise.

A list is provided to aid in diagnosing problems for 12 volt DC and 120 volt AC systems. See page 3.

Check Starter Motor Drive

When the starter motor is activated, the pinion gear should engage the flywheel ring gear and crank the engine. This action can be observed by removing the starter shield. If the starter motor drive does not react properly, inspect the helix and pinion gear for freeness of operation. The pinion must move freely on the helix for proper starter motor operation. If any sticking occurs, this must be corrected. Fig. 137.

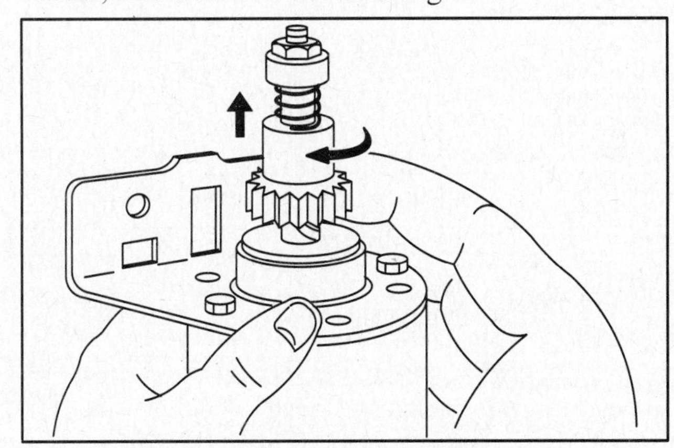

Fig. 137 - Checking Starter Motor Drive

Disassemble Starter Motor Drive

1. To remove the drive assembly for cleaning or replacement, clamp the pinion gear in a vise having brass jaws, to prevent damage to the gear teeth.
2. The lock nut may then be removed and the starter drive disassembled for cleaning or replacement.

The pinion gear should be inspected for damaged teeth. If a sticking condition exists between the pinion gear and the helix, the parts may be washed in a solvent such as Stanisol® or Varsol®. If the sticking condition is not corrected by cleaning, the complete drive assembly must be replaced. Individual parts of the drive assembly are not available.

Assemble Starter Motor Drive

1. Reverse disassembly procedure for assembling. When assembling helix to shaft, the spline must face threaded end of shaft, Fig. 136.
2. Torque lock nut to 170 in. lbs. This torque has an effect on pinion travel, so proper torque should be maintained.

NOTE: Do not lubricate drive assembly. If sticking occurs during freezing weather, use only a dry silicone spray on helix.

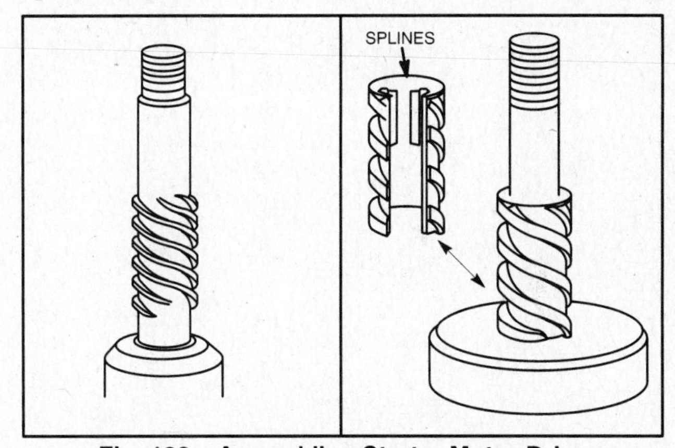

Fig. 138 - Assembling Starter Motor Drive

A performance test of the 120 volt starter motor may be made in the following manner:

Test 12 Volt Starter Motor

A performance test of the 12 volt DC and 120 volt AC starter motors may be made in the following manner

Equipment Needed

See page 3 for a starter mounting test bracket that can be made.

1. Digital Multimeter, Tool (#19357 or #19390) and DC Shunt, Tool #19359 or VOA Meter, Tool #19236 and DC Shunt.

NOTE: METRIC EQUIVALENTS ARE LISTED ON PAGE 63 OF THIS SECTION.

See Instruction Manual MS-6574 (Digital Multimeter) or Instruction Manual MS-7585 (VOA Meter) for installation procedure.

2. Tachometer capable of reading 10,000 RPM.
3. A 12 volt battery ± 0.3 volts.

NOTE: A 6 volt battery is required in some instances for test purposes only. This allows RPM readings to be made on a lower scale. See TABLE NO. 10.

To Test

1. Set the meter to read 300mV ⎓ (DC AMPS).
2. Connect the starter motor, battery and meter as shown in Fig's. 139 or 140.

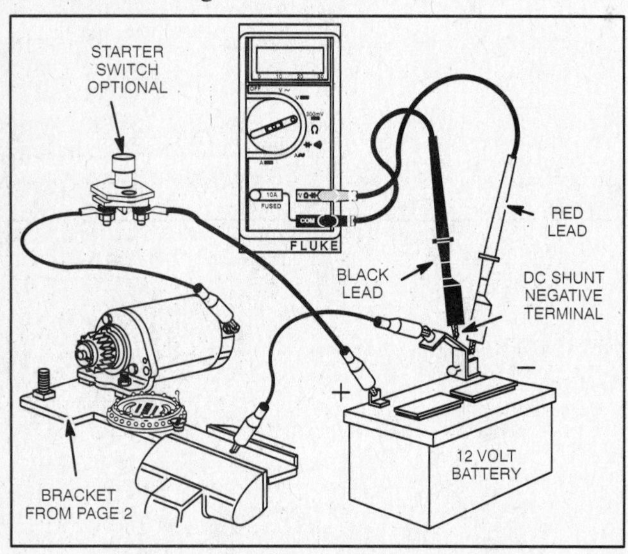

Fig. 139 – Testing 12 Volt Starter Motor Digital Multimeter

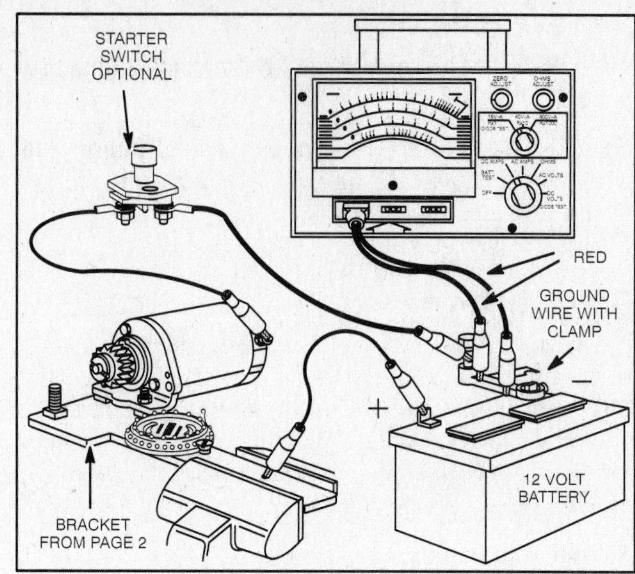

Fig. 140 – Testing 12 Volt Starter Motor – VOA Meter

3. Activate the starter motor and note readings of meter and tachometer (RPM). A starter motor in good condition will be within specifications listed in TABLE NO. 10. Disregard surge current.

If the 12 volt starter motor does not perform satisfactorily, see list on page 3 to aid in diagnosing problems.

TABLE NO. 10
12 VOLT STARTER MOTOR PERFORMANCE CHART

Starter Motor Identification	Voltage Required	Minimum Motor RPM	Maximum Amps	VOA Meter Scale
American Bosch SME-12A-8	6V ± 0.1	5000	25 (Disregard surge current)	40 V-A R x 10
American Bosch SMH-12A-11	12V ± 0.3	4800	16 (Disregard surge current)	16 V-A R x 1
American Bosch 01965-23-MO-30-SM	12V ± 0.3	5500	16 (Disregard surge current)	16 V-A R x 1
Mitsubishi MMO-4FL MMO-5ML MOO1TO2271	6V ± 0.1	6700	16 (Disregard surge current)	16 V-A R x 1

NOTE: METRIC EQUIVALENTS ARE LISTED ON PAGE 63 OF THIS SECTION.

Test the 120 Volt AC Starter Motor

A performance test of the 120 volt starter motor may be made in the following manner:

Equipment Needed

See page 3 for a starter mounting test bracket that can be made.

Digital Multimeter, Tool (#19357 or #19390) with Tool #19358, AC Shunt.

– or –

VOA Meter, Tool #19236 with 120 Volt Adapter, Tool #19242.

A tachometer capable of reading 10,000 RPM.

WARNING: Extreme care should be used in making this test to minimize the hazard of electrical shock.

CAUTION: Starter motor housing contains two powerful ceramic magnets that may crack if motor housing is clamped in a vise or struck with a hammer or hard object.

Fig. 141 – Testing 120 Volt Starter Motor Digital Multimeter

Fig. 142 – Testing 120 Volt Starter Motor – VOA Meter

To Test

1. Clamp the starter motor test bracket in a vise as shown in Fig's. 141 or 142.
2. Set meter to AC amps.
3. Insert leads into meter and plug starter motor cord into AC adapter.
4. Then connect AC adapter to a 120 volt outlet.
5. Refer to TABLE NO. 11 and note the maximum allowable amperage.
6. Depress starter switch button. When meter reading stabilizes (approximately 3 seconds), amperage should not exceed the specification shown.

CAUTION: If amperage is higher than specification shown, immediately stop the test! An amperage reading higher than number in chart indicates a shorted starter motor, which could be dangerous.

7. If amperage is within specification, check RPM of starter motor.

NOTE: METRIC EQUIVALENTS ARE LISTED ON PAGE 63 OF THIS SECTION.

TABLE NO. 11
120 VOLT STARTER MOTOR
PERFORMANCE CHART

Starter Motor Identification	Voltage Required	Minimum Motor RPM	Maximum Amperes
Amer. Bosch SME-110-C3 SME-110-C6 SME-110-C8	120	7400	3-1/2 (Disregard surge current)
Amer. Bosch 06026-28-M030SM	120	7400	3 (Disregard surge current)
Mitsubishi J282188	120	7800	3-1/2 (Disregard surge current)

If the 120 volt starter motor does not meet these specifications, it must be replaced.

Disassemble Starter Motor

1. Remove the lockwasher, nuts and thru bolts, Fig. 143.

2. The armature, drive cap and gear drive can now be removed as an assembly.

NOTE: THRU BOLTS AND NUTS MUST BE PLACED IN THE SAME POSITION AS WHEN REMOVED OR INTERFERENCE MAY RESULT.

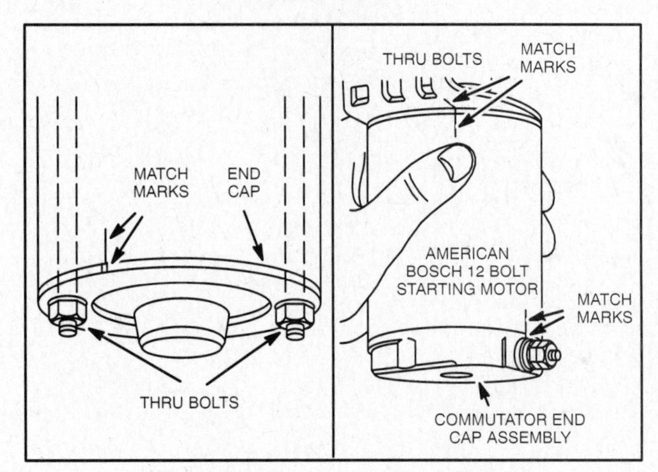

Fig. 143 - Removing Thru Bolts

CAUTION: Do not clamp the motor in a vise or strike the motor with a hammer. Some motors include two powerful ceramic magnets which can be broken or cracked if the motor housing is deformed or dented.

3. To remove the commutator end cap, lift the brush springs and slide brushes out of the brush holders.

4. Clean all dirt or corrosion from the armature, commutator end cap, drive end cap, etc.

5. The bearings, housing and armature should not be soaked in a cleaning solution.

6. The armature commutator may be cleaned with a fine sand paper.

   NOTE: DO NOT USE EMERY CLOTH AS EMERY WILL BECOME EMBEDDED IN THE COMMUTATOR CAUSING RAPID BRUSH WEAR.

7. If it is suspected that the armature, field coil or motor housing is defective, new parts should be tried in the motor.

8. If proper testing equipment is available, check the suspected armature or field coil to determine if it is defective.

9. The brushes should be checked for proper seating, weak brush springs, dirt, oil or corrosion.

10. Also check to be sure brushes are not sticking in their respective brush holders, Fig. 144.

NOTE: METRIC EQUIVALENTS ARE LISTED ON PAGE 63 OF THIS SECTION.

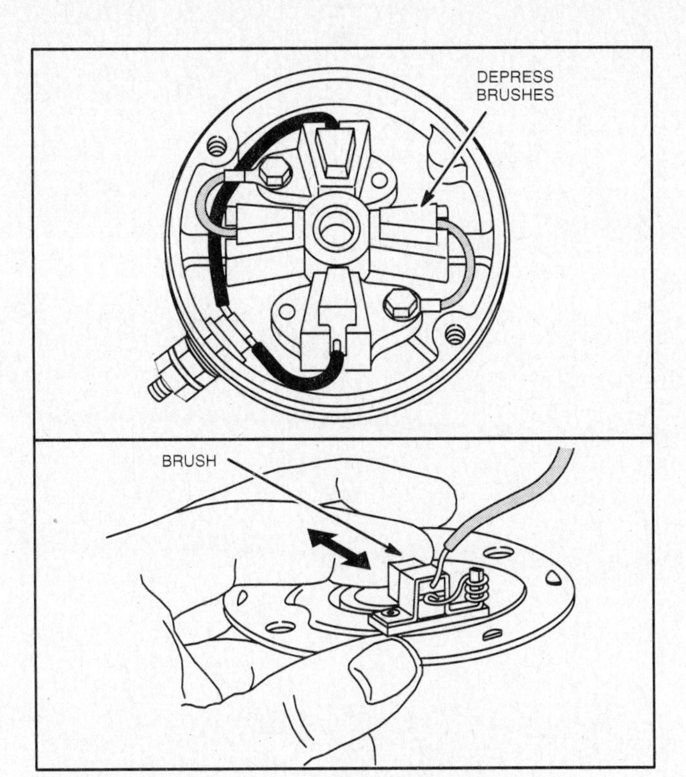

Fig. 144 - Checking Brushes

Assemble Starter Motor

1. When all parts have been thoroughly inspected, lightly lubricate the bearings with #20 oil and reassemble in the following manner.
2. Insert the brushes in their respective holders.

   NOTE: A tool such as shown in Fig. 6, page 5, should be used to hold the brushes clear of the armature commutator when assembling the commutator end cap to the motor housing.

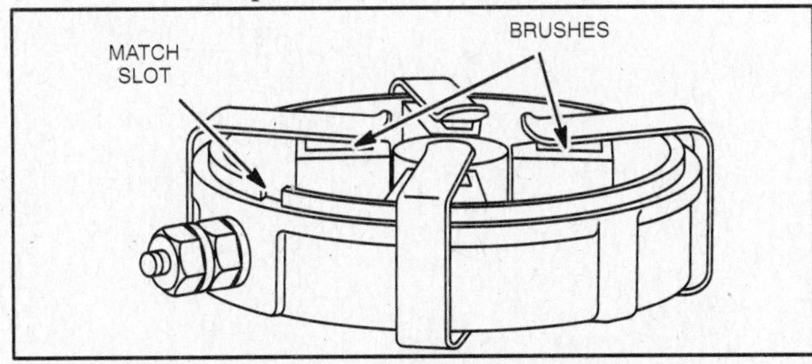

Fig. 145 - Inserting Brushes

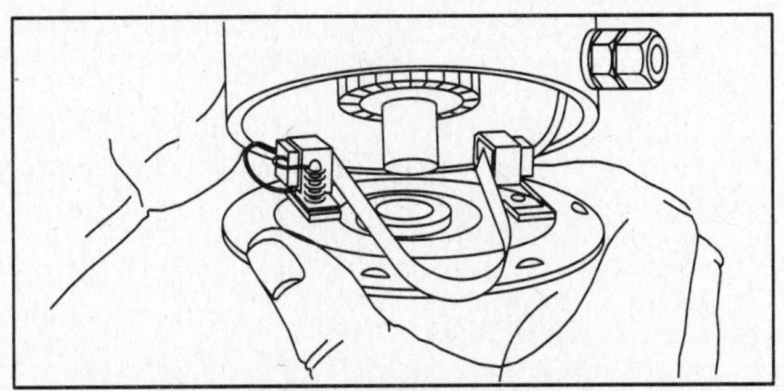

Fig. 146 - Installing End Cap

3. Slide the armature into the motor housing, being sure to match the drive end cap keyway to the stamped key in motor housing.
4. Assemble end cap, again matching the keyway to key in housing. Care should be used to prevent damage to ceramic magnets, where used.
5. Assemble thru bolts, lockwashers and nuts.
6. After assembly of the starter motor drive, the starter motor is now ready for installation to the engine.

12 Volt Electric Starter - Generator Unit

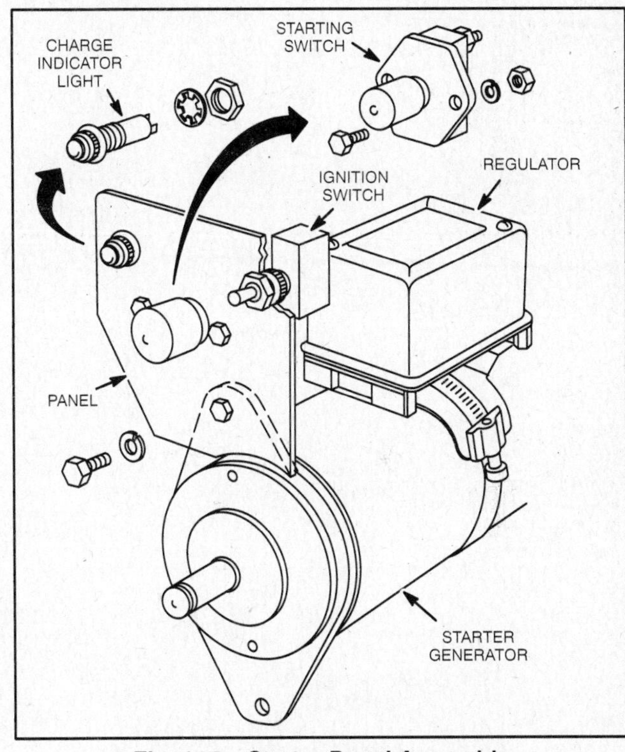

Fig. 147 - Starter Panel Assembly

Removing and Replacing Belts

1. Remove belt guard.
2. Loosen starter-generator unit mounting bolts and push the unit toward the engine as far as it will go.
3. After belt has been installed, apply a 30 lb. force to the upper pulley and flange.

NOTE: METRIC EQUIVALENTS ARE LISTED ON PAGE 63 OF THIS SECTION.

Electric Starters
12 Volt Starter-Generator

CAUTION: DO NOT run starter motor for more than one minute without cooling 15 minutes.

4. The belt(s) can then be removed.

NOTE: Starter-generator units on some models are equipped with two belts. On these units, both belts should be replaced even though only one belt appears to be worn. Use only matched sets of belts.

5. Do not force belts onto pulleys. There is sufficient adjustment to allow them to be slipped in place.

6. Tighten mounting bolts securely and replace belt guard, Fig's. 148 and 149.

NOTE: Belts are of special high strength design. Use only genuine factory replacements available at an Authorized Briggs & Stratton Service Center.

7B

12 Volt Starter-Generator Belt Adjustment Procedure

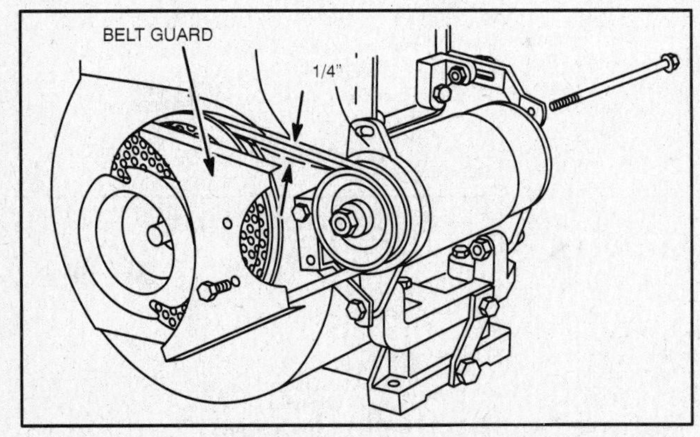

Fig. 148 – 12 Volt Starter – Generator (Low Position)

To adjust, tilt away from blower housing until belts move up and down 1/4" with thumb pressure at a point midway between pulleys. Tighten screws to hold in place and install guard and tighten in place, Fig's. 148 and 149.

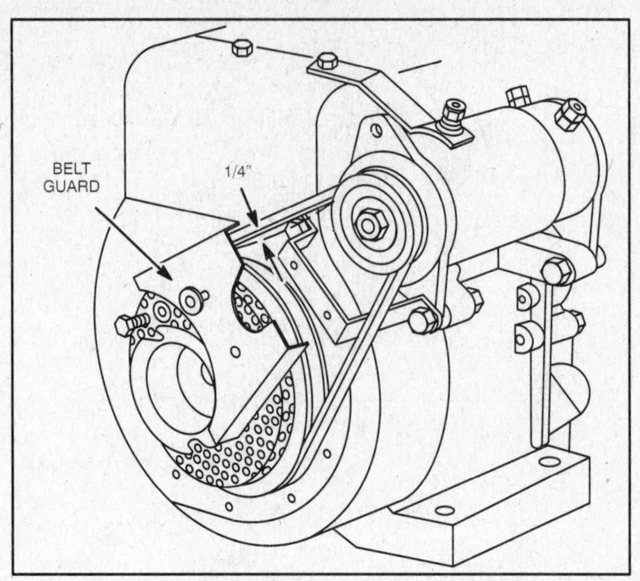

Fig. 149 – 12 Volt Starter – Generator (High Position)

Emergency Winter Operation

If run-down batteries are repeatedly experienced due too short or infrequent operation at low temperatures, it is advisable to temporarily increase the generator charge rate.

A simple method of increasing the charge rate is to disconnect the lead to the regulator BAT terminal and reconnect this lead to the regular (L) terminal. This bypasses the current-voltage feature of the regulator automatically increasing the amount of charge to the battery, Fig. 151.

CAUTION: Operate the regulator in this manner only during cold weather when operating periods are short or infrequent. Re-establish the original lead connections as soon as mild weather returns or operating time becomes normal: otherwise the battery will be damaged by overcharging.

Battery Size

A 12 volt battery of 50 ampere hour capacity is recommended. See Fig. 150 for battery cable sizes.

CAUTION: Battery must have negative (-) terminal grounded to engine or machine frame.

Warranty and Service

For warranty and service on all Delco-Remy parts, contact an AC Delco Service and Parts Dealer.

NOTE: METRIC EQUIVALENTS ARE LISTED ON PAGE 63 OF THIS SECTION.

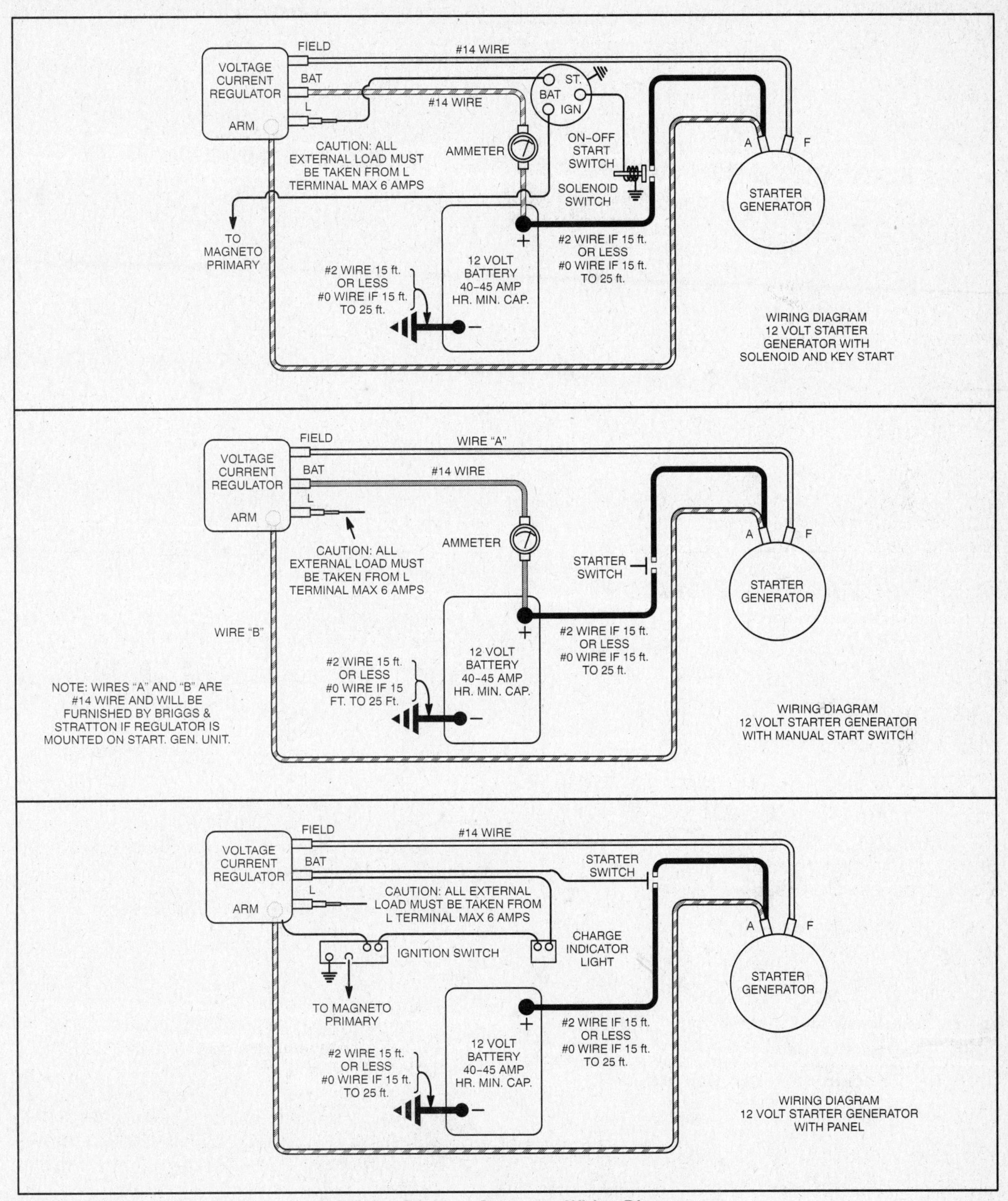

Fig. 150 – Starter – Generator Wiring Diagrams

Starter-Generator Wiring Diagrams

The three drawings shown in Fig. 150 illustrate the most common methods of wiring 12 volt starter-generator units.

NOTE: METRIC EQUIVALENTS ARE LISTED ON PAGE 63 OF THIS SECTION.

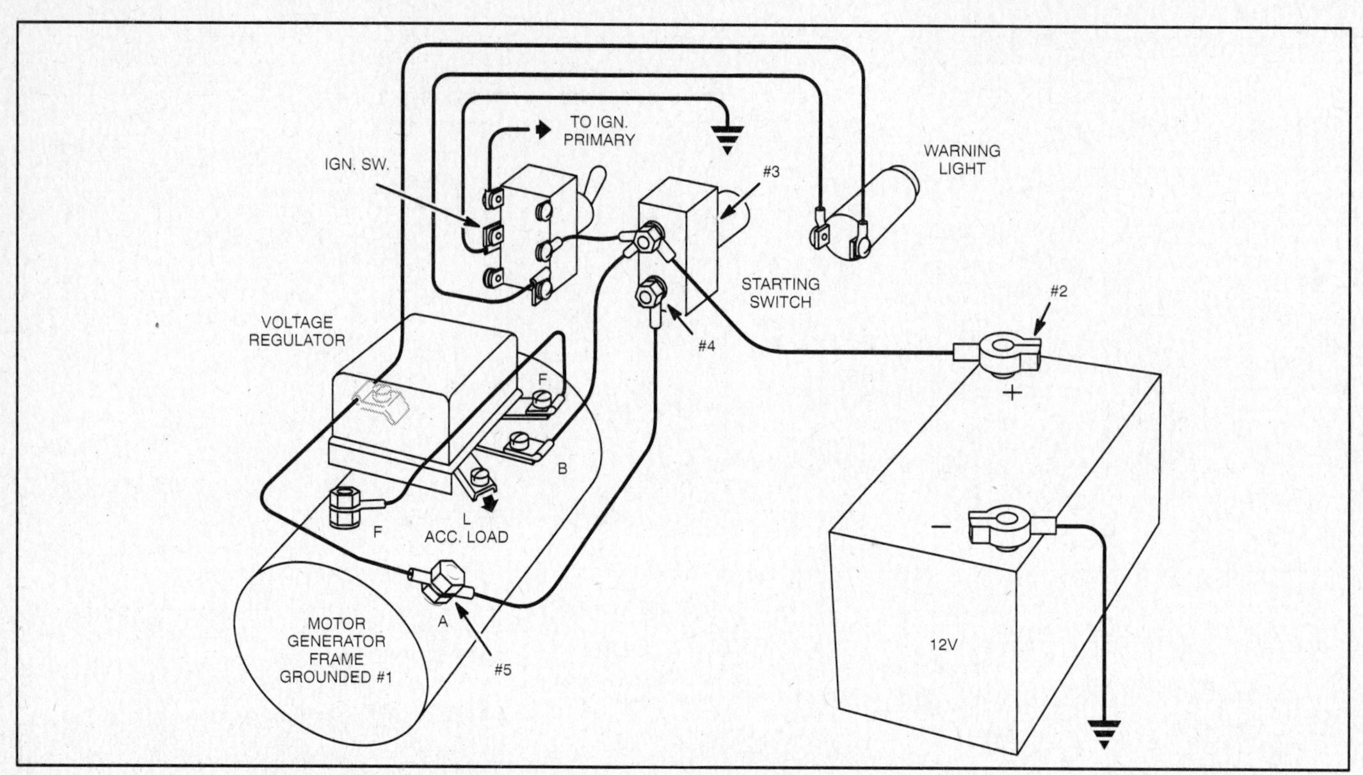

Fig. 151 – Wiring Diagram

CHECKING STARTER-GENERATOR AND REGULATOR (See Fig. 151)

1. Use Tool (#19357 or #19390), Digital Multimeter, or Tool #19236, VOA Meter.
2. Set meter to read DC volts for Steps 1 – 4.
3. Set meter to read DC amps for Step 5.

NOTE: All tests to be made with ignition off and starter switch pressed long enough for meter reading to stabilize.

Step 1. Checking Ground Resistance (Poor Connection)

1. Attach BLACK meter test lead to #1 (ground). Leave attached through Step 4.
2. Attach RED meter test lead to #2.
3. Press starter switch. Meter should read 10 volts or more.

Step 2. Checking Lead to Switch

1. Attach RED meter test lead to #3.
2. A low or no voltage reading while pressing starter switch indicates defective positive battery cable or connection.

Step 3. Checking Starter Switch

1. Attach RED meter test lead to #4.
2. The meter should read "close to battery voltage" when starter switch is pressed. Very low or no voltage indicates a defective starter switch.

Step 4. Checking Lead from Switch to Starter

1. Attach RED meter test lead to #5.
2. Press the starter switch. The meter should display "close to battery voltage." If the starter motor does not crank and battery voltage is displayed, the starter motor is defective. If voltage is not displayed, cable or connection between test-point #5 and #4 is defective.

Step 5. Generator-Regulator Test

1. Set meter to read DC amps.
2. Disconnect wire at voltage regulator terminal "B."
3. Attach RED meter test lead to terminal "B" and BLACK meter test lead to positive (+) battery terminal. The meter will register charge, if any, to the battery when the engine is running. Charging will start approximately 1800 to 2000 RPM, and will vary according to the battery state of charge.
4. If meter reads 10 amps or more, disconnect "F" terminal at regulator. If output remains high, the generator is defective. If output stops, the regulator is defective.

NOTE: METRIC EQUIVALENTS ARE LISTED ON PAGE 63 OF THIS SECTION.

5. If no charge is shown on meter, short the regulator "F" terminal to ground. Meter should then show a 10 amp or more charge. No charge would indicate a defective generator. A charge would indicate a defective regulator.

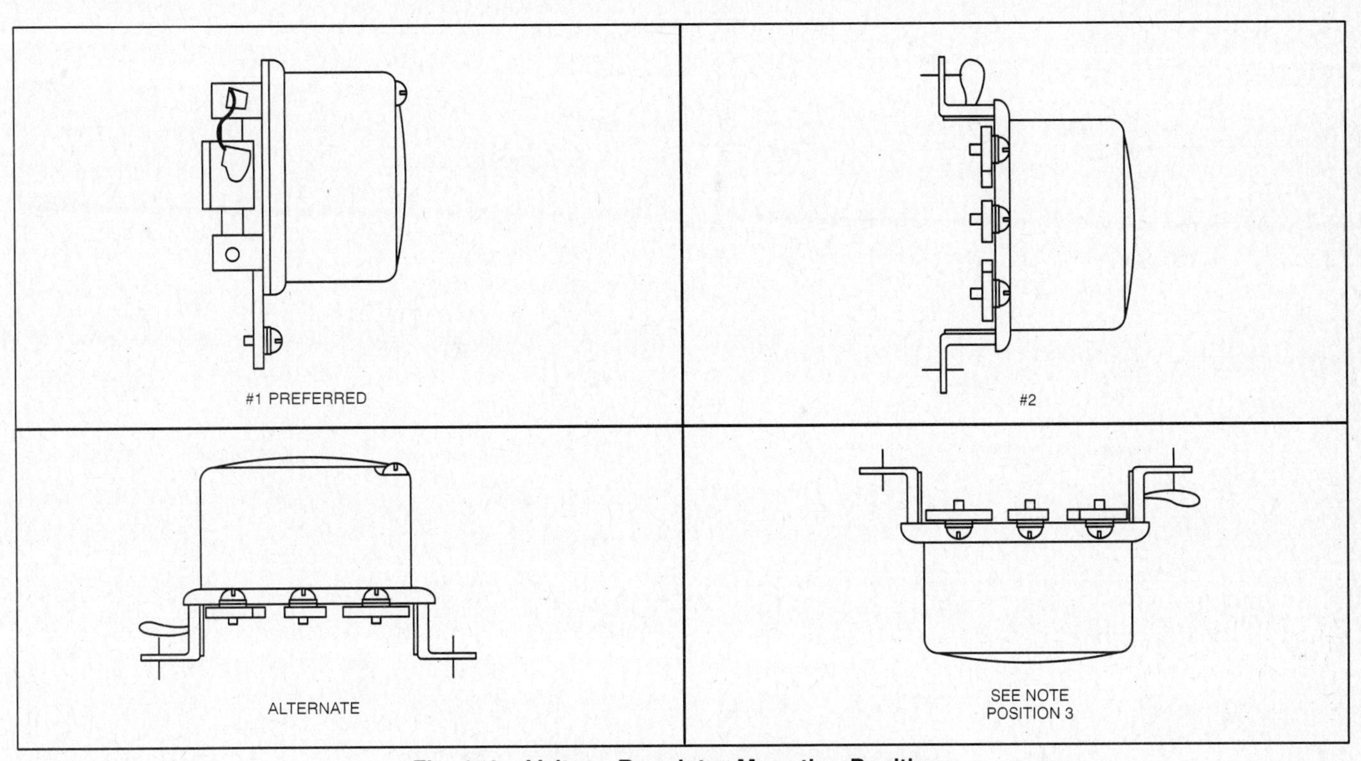

Fig. 152 - Voltage Regulator Mounting Positions

Installation of Voltage Regulators

NOTE Position: 3 Regulator will not function when installed in this position.

Regulator should be mounted at a point of minimum vibration.

There must be a good ground connection between regulator mounting feet and equipment frame and between the engine and equipment frame. If this is not possible, a #14 wire must be run from the grounded regulator mounting foot to the engine.

Battery Information

The battery used to operate starter motors on most Briggs & Stratton engines above 4 horsepower, is of the 12 volt, lead acid - wet cell type. This type is available as a maintenance free or dry charged battery.

The maintenance-free battery is filled with electrolyte at the time of manufacture. The level of electrolyte cannot be checked.

The dry charge battery is manufactured with fully charged plates. Electrolyte must be added at the time that the battery is placed in service. Before activating a dry charge battery, read and follow the manufacturer's recommended procedure, Fig. 153.

WARNING: BATTERIES PRODUCE HYDROGEN, AN EXPLOSIVE GAS. DO NOT store, charge or use a battery near an open flame or devices which utilize a pilot light or can create a spark.

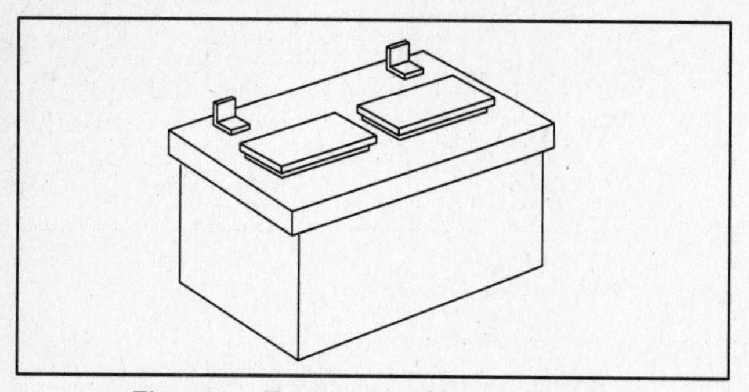

Fig. 153 - Typical Dry Charge Battery

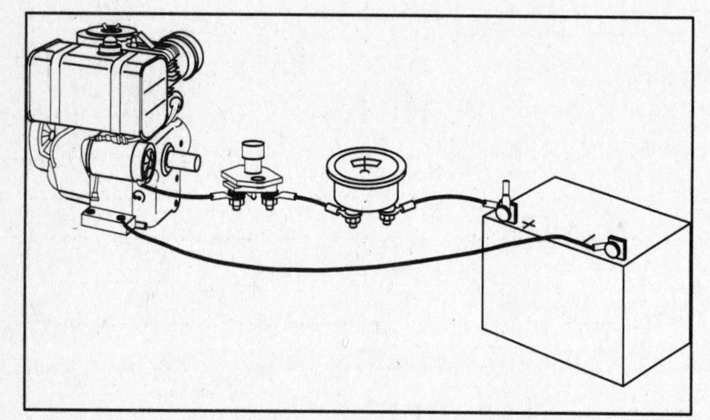

Fig. 154 - Typical 12V Wiring Diagram

Checking Battery

1. Physical check - clean if necessary,

   A. Corrosion

   B. Dirt

   C. Terminal and clamps (secure - good conditions)

2. Bring battery to full charge.

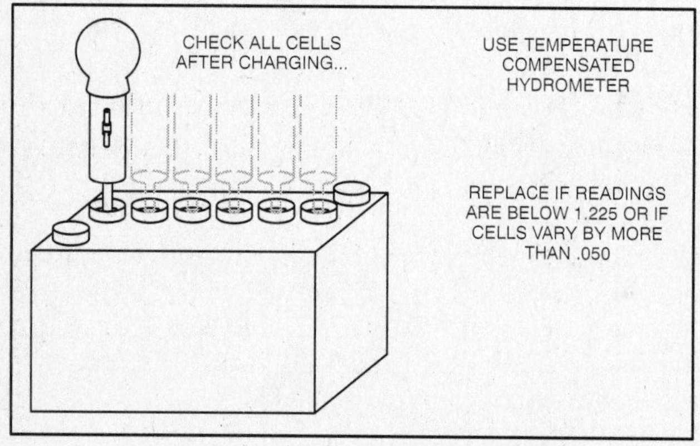

Fig. 155 - Checking 12V Battery Cells (Lead Acid - Wet Cell - Dry Charge)

DANGER: DO NOT EXCEED CHARGE RATE OF 1/10 AMPERE FOR EVERY AMPERE OF BATTERY RATING. Consult battery manufacturer for charging recommendations.

   A. Use a taper charger (automatically reduces charge rate).

   B. Fill battery cells with distilled water or tap water (unless maintenance free type) after charging (for batteries that have been in service).

   NOTE: If battery gets "Hot" to the touch or is spitting acid (gassing) excessively, unplug charger periodically.

3. With battery fully charged, check specific gravity readings of each cell with a Battery Hydrometer and record readings, Fig. 155. All readings should be above 1.250 (compensating for temperature). If specific gravity readings varied .050 or if ALL cells read less than 1.225, replace battery.

Installation:

1. Before installing battery, connect all equipment to be operated.

2. Place battery in holder with a flat base. Tighten hold downs evenly until snug. DO NOT over-tighten.

3. Connect positive terminal to positive post FIRST to prevent sparks from accidental grounding. Tighten connectors securely.

4. Connect negative terminal to negative battery terminal. Tighten connectors securely.

5. Use Digital Multimeter, Tool (#19357 or #19390) or VOA Meter, Tool #19326.

6. Attach RED meter test clip to positive (+) battery terminal.

7. Attach BLACK meter test lead to negative (-) battery terminal.

8. With ignition switch "OFF," press starter button.

   NOTE: If ignition switch and starter switch are the same switch, disconnect wire from spark plug and ground ignition using Ignition Tester, Tool #19051 or #19368.

9. Turn switch to "START." Meter should display 9 volts or more while cranking engine. If less than 9 volts, replace battery.

NOTE: METRIC EQUIVALENTS ARE LISTED ON PAGE 63 OF THIS SECTION.

METRIC EQUIVALENTS

DIMENSIONS, FRACTIONAL	
Inches	**Millimeters**
1/32	.8
5/64	2.0
3/32	2.4
1/8	3.0
3/16	5.0
1/4	6.0
3/8	9.5
1/2	13.0
5/8	16.0
3/4	19.0
7/8	22.0
1	25.4
1-1/8	28.0
1-1/4	31.9
2	51.0
2-1/4	57.0
3	76.0
3-1/16	78.0
3-1/2	89.0
3-21/32	93.0
3-3/4	95.0
3-13/16	97.0
4	100.0
4-3/8	111.0
4-9/16	115.9
5	127.0
10	254.0
Feet	**Meters**
4	1.2
5	1.5
6	1.8
15	4.57
25	7.60

DIMENSIONS, DECIMAL	
Inches	**Millimeters**
.005	.13
.007	.15
.010	.25
.025	.64
.030	.76
.038	??
.048	.96
.055	1.4
.176	4.47
.200	5.08
.225	5.72
1.23	31.24
1.32	33.53
WEIGHT	
Ounces	**Milliliter**
3/4	22
Pounds	**Kilograms**
30	13.6
TEMPERATURE	
Fahrenheit	**Centigrade**
-15	-26.1
-5	-20.5
20	-6.6
40	4.0
105	40.0

TORQUE		
In. Lbs.	**Kgcm**	**Nm**
20	23	2.3
25	28	2.8
35	40	3.9
40	45	4.5
45	52	5.1
55	65	6.3
90	104	10.0
140	161	15.8
170	195	19.2

NOTE: METRIC EQUIVALENTS ARE LISTED ON PAGE 63 OF THIS SECTION.

Use With Digital Multimeter Tool #19357

Section 7C
ALTERNATORS

The alternator systems used on Briggs & Stratton single cylinder engines can be identified by the color of the output wire and connector. Table No. 1 lists the various alternator systems and engine models where they are used. Figures can be used to identify type of alternator. Page number is for test procedures.

TABLE NO. 1

Basic Model Series	90000 110000	120700	130000	170000	190000	220000	240000	250000	280000	320000
System 3® System 4®	Fig. 1 p. 5									
1/2 Amp		Fig. 2 p. 6								
1.2 Amp (Current)			Fig. 3 p. 8							
1-1/2 Amp (Early)			Fig. 4 p. 8							
DC Only				Fig. 5 p. 10	Fig. 5 p. 10	Fig. 5 p. 10	Fig. 5 p. 10	Fig. 5 p. 10	Fig. 5 p. 10	Fig. 5 p. 10
AC Only					Fig. 6 p. 11	Fig. 6 p. 11	Fig. 6 p. 11	Fig. 6 p. 11	Fig. 6 p. 11	Fig. 6 p. 11
Dual Circuit				Fig. 7 p. 11	Fig. 7 p. 11	Fig. 7 p. 11	Fig. 7 p. 11	Fig. 7 p. 11	Fig. 7 p. 11	Fig. 7 p. 11
Tri- Circuit					Fig. 8 p. 13	Fig. 8 p. 13	Fig. 8 p. 13	Fig. 8 p. 13	Fig. 8 p. 13	Fig. 8 p. 13
Quad Circuit								Fig. 9 p. 15	Fig. 9 p. 15	
5 & 9 Amp Regulated					Fig. 10 p. 16			Fig. 10 p. 16	Fig. 10 p. 16	Fig. 10 p. 16
10 & 16 Amp Regulated					Fig. 11 p. 18	Fig. 11 p. 18	Fig. 11 p. 18	Fig. 11 p. 18	Fig. 11 p. 18	Fig. 11 p. 18

NOTE: All alternators are rated at 3600 RPM, except Model Series 90000, 110000, 120000 which are rated at 2800 RPM. Output is reduced as engine speed is lowered.

NOTE: METRIC EQUIVALENTS ARE LISTED ON PAGE 21 OF THIS SECTION.

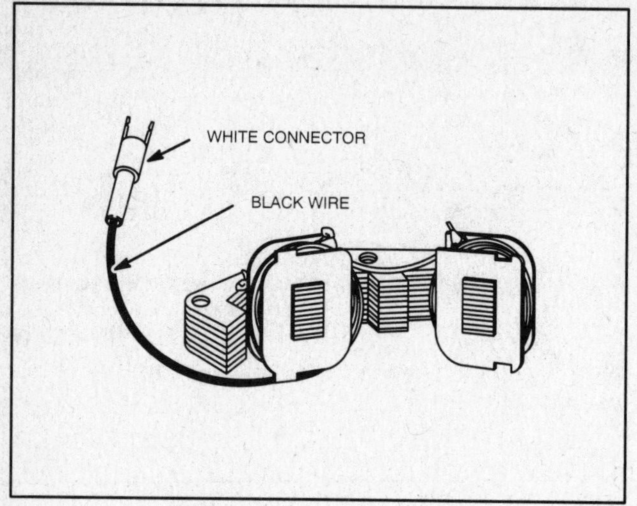

Fig. 1 - System 3® & 4®

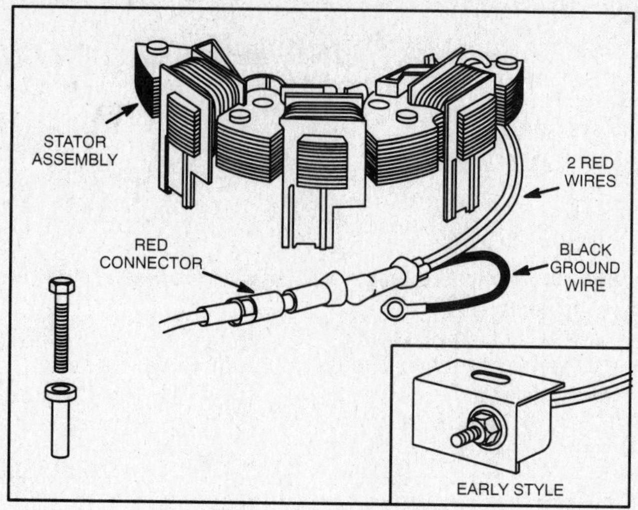

Fig. 4 - 1-1/2 Amp

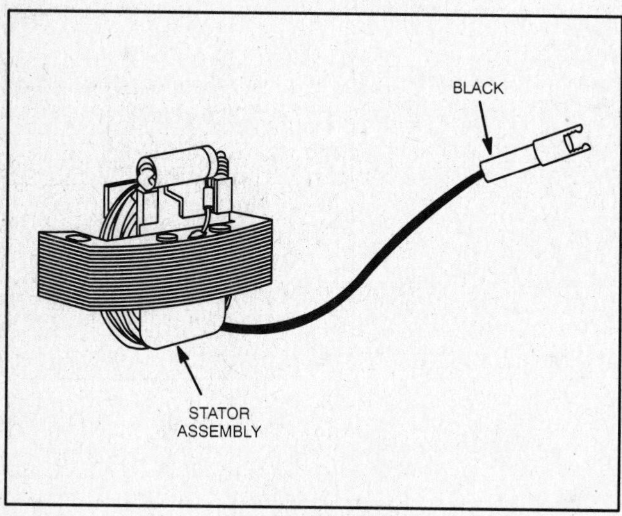

Fig. 2 - 1/2 Amp

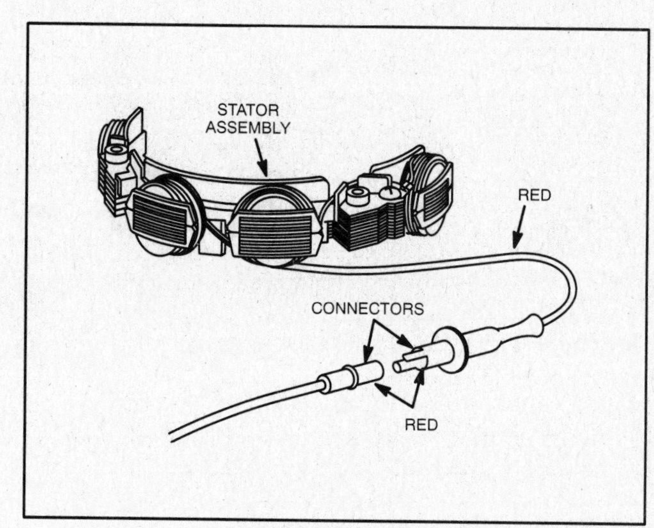

Fig. 5 - DC Only

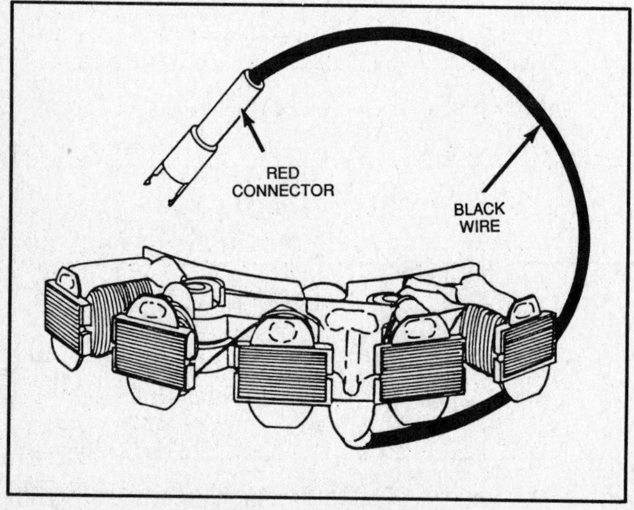

Fig. 3 - 1.2 Amp

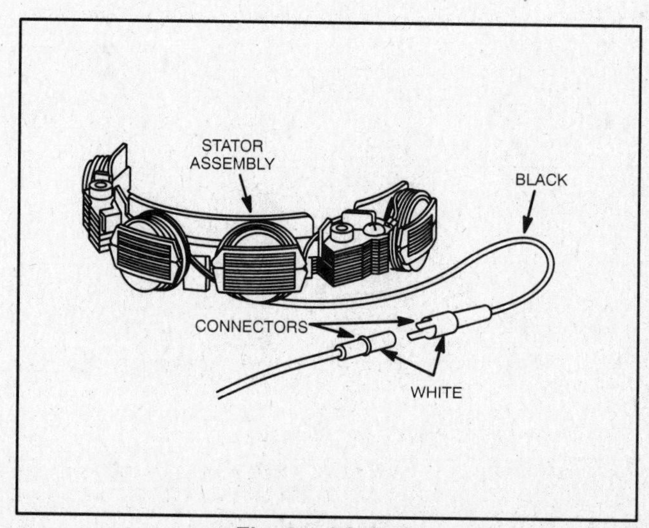

Fig. 6 - AC Only

NOTE: METRIC EQUIVALENTS ARE LISTED ON PAGE 21 OF THIS SECTION.

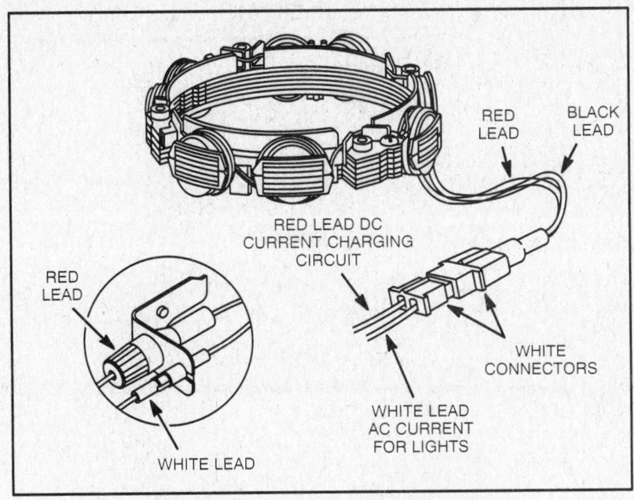

Fig. 7 - Dual Circuit (Current Style)

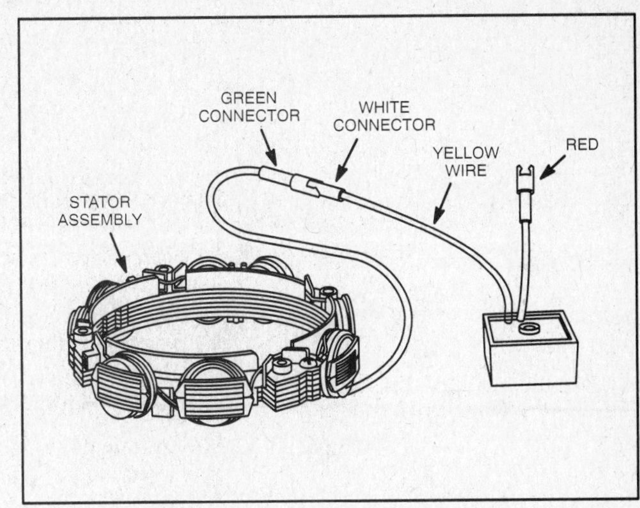

Fig. 10 - 5 or 9 Amp Regulated

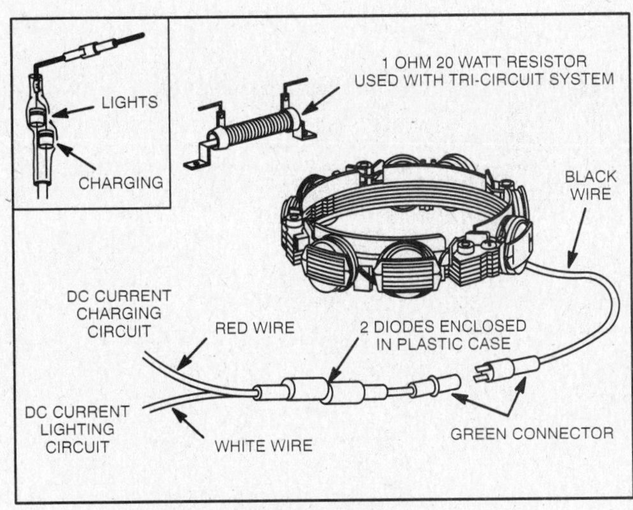

Fig. 8 - Tri-Circuit

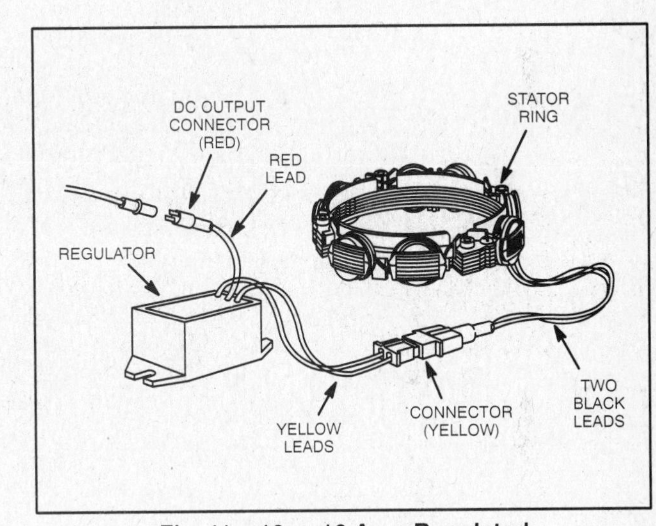

Fig. 11 - 10 or 16 Amp Regulated

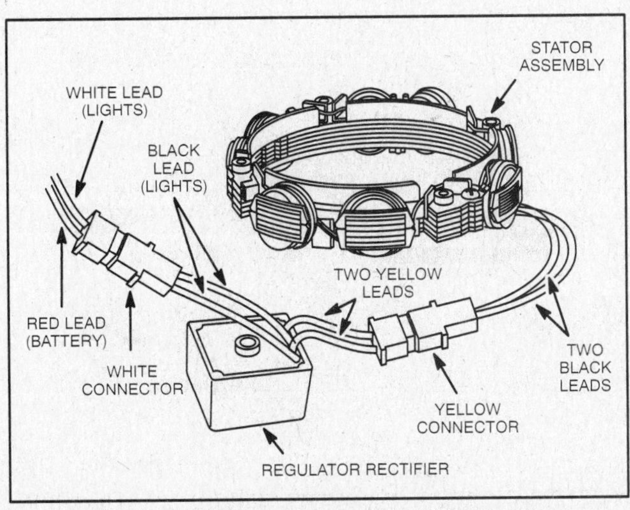

Fig. 9 - Quad Circuit

NOTE: METRIC EQUIVALENTS ARE LISTED ON PAGE 21 OF THIS SECTION.

COMPLAINT	POSSIBLE CAUSES
"Battery not charging"	Engine RPM too low Defective battery Loose or corroded battery ground leads Open, shorted, or grounded wires between output connector and battery Defective diode (open or shorted) Defective or improperly grounded regulator-rectifier Diode installed incorrectly (reversed) Damaged battery (shorted cells) Excessive current draw from accessories Low magnetic flux or damaged alternator magnets
"Battery in state of overcharge"	Severe battery vibration (missing or broken tie down straps) Battery rate of charge not matched to alternator output Damaged battery (shorted battery cells) Defective regulator One ohm resistor shorted or grounded (Tri-Circuit only) Battery too small (Amp/Hour Rating)
"Headlights not working"	Inline fuse "blown" (if so equipped) Defective headlights Loose or corroded wires Open, shorted, or grounded wires between output connector and headlights Defective diode (Tri-Circuit, open or shorted, white output lead side) Low magnetic flux or damaged alternator magnets
"Electric clutch not working" (Tri-Circuit)	Engine RPM too low Inline fuse "blown" (if so equipped) Loose or corroded wires Open, shorted or grounded wires between output connector and electric clutch Defective diode (open or shorted, red output lead side) NOTE: Battery will also not charge. Defective electric clutch switch Open, shorted, or grounded clutch circuit Low magnetic flux or damaged alternator magnets

EQUIPMENT TO TEST ALTERNATORS

The following list of equipment is recommended for testing alternators.

Digital Multimeter

The Digital Multimeter is available from your Briggs & Stratton source of supply. Order as Tool #19357. The meter may be used to read volts, ohms or amperes, and test diodes, when leads are inserted in the appropriate receptacle, Fig. 12.

NOTE: The Digital Multimeter is equipped with two fuses to prevent damage to the meter in the event that the input limits are exceeded. If the meter displays a reading of 0.00 when testing DC output (A⎓), check fuses in meter. Refer to FLUKE 23 Operators Manual for procedure for checking fuses. Replacement fuses are available from an electrical supply house.

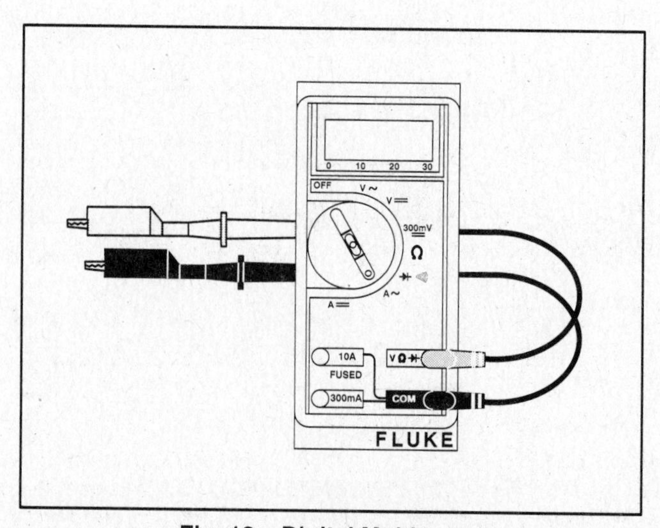

Fig. 12 - Digital Multimeter

NOTE: METRIC EQUIVALENTS ARE LISTED ON PAGE 21 OF THIS SECTION.

DC Shunt

The Digital Multimeter will withstand DC input of 10 to 20 Amps for up to **30** seconds. When checking DC output on 16 Amp regulated system, use the DC shunt, Tool #19359, to avoid blowing fuse in meter, Fig. 13.

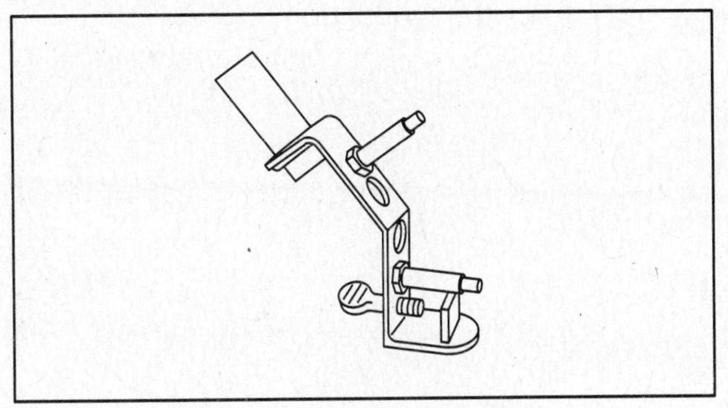

Fig. 13 - DC Shunt, Tool #19359

Tachometer

A tachometer is available from your Briggs & Stratton source of supply, Fig. 14. Order as Tool #19200. The tachometer measures from 800 to 50,000 RPM.

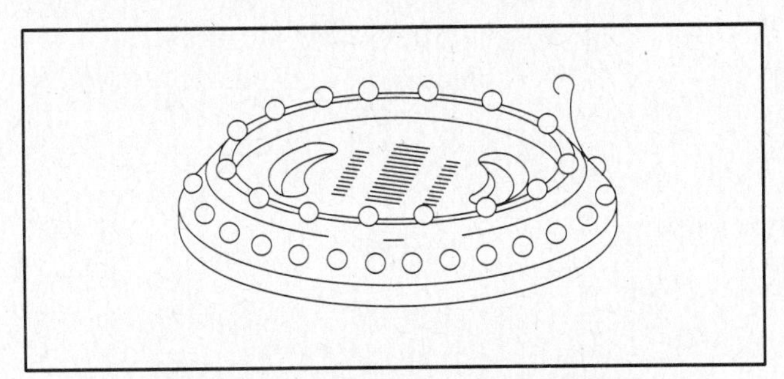

Fig. 14 - Tachometer - Tool #19200

TESTING ALTERNATOR OUTPUT

When checking alternators, make the tests in the following sequence.

1. Test alternator output.

2. Test diode(s) or regulator-rectifier (if equipped).

NOTE: All alternator output specifications are rated at a specific RPM. Before testing alternator output (volts, amps), first use an accurate tachometer and temporarily adjust engine speed to RPM specified in test instructions.

CAUTION: Upon completion of the alternator output test, always readjust the engine RPM to its correct Top No Load Governed Speed as found in the Service Engine Sales Manual Microfiche MS-6225 or the Service Sales Manual, MS-4052.

SYSTEM 3® AND 4® ALTERNATOR

The DC alternator is designed to operate as an integral part of the engine and is separate from the engine starting and ignition system. It is intended to provide DC charging current to a 6 or 12 volt battery. See Section 7B for 6 volt battery information. Contact battery or equipment manufacturer for 12 volt battery information.

Two basic styles of stators have been used. The early style was used before Date Code 84052300 on 6 volt systems, Fig. 15. The current style has been used since Date Code 84052200 on both 6 and 12 volt systems, Fig. 16.

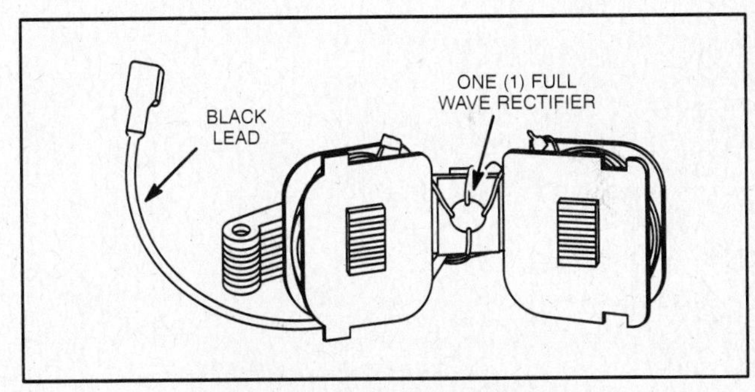

Fig. 15 - Early Style Stator

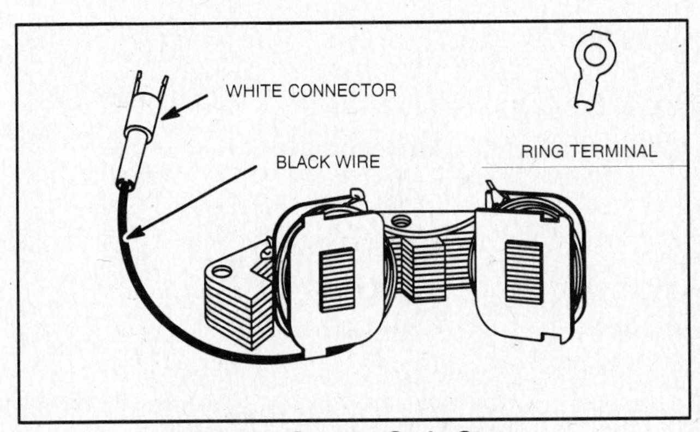

Fig. 16 - Current Style Stator

NOTE: METRIC EQUIVALENTS ARE LISTED ON PAGE 21 OF THIS SECTION.

Test Alternator Output

1. Insert RED test lead into 10 A receptacle in meter.
2. Insert BLACK test lead into COM receptacle in meter.
3. Rotate selector to A⎓ (DC amps) position.
4. Attach RED test clip to output terminal.
5. Attach BLACK test clip to a good engine ground.
6. With engine running at 2800 RPM,output should be no less than .5 amp DC, Fig. 17.
7. If low or no output, check stator air gap (current style only), Fig. 16.
8. If stator air gap is within specification and there is low or no output, replace stator.

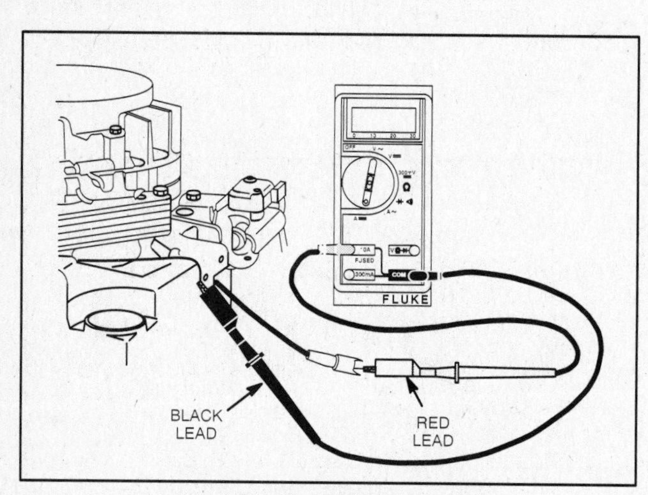

Fig. 17 – Testing DC Output

Adjust Stator Air Gap (Current Style Stator)

Stator air gap is .010 in. Rotate flywheel until magnets are away from stator. Loosen both stator mounting screws and move stator away from flywheel and tighten one screw. Place a .010 inch thick gauge between stator and flywheel. Turn flywheel until magnets are under stator. Loosen screw and let stator be pulled against flywheel magnet. Torque mounting screws to 25 in. lbs. Turn flywheel to remove gauge, Fig. 18.

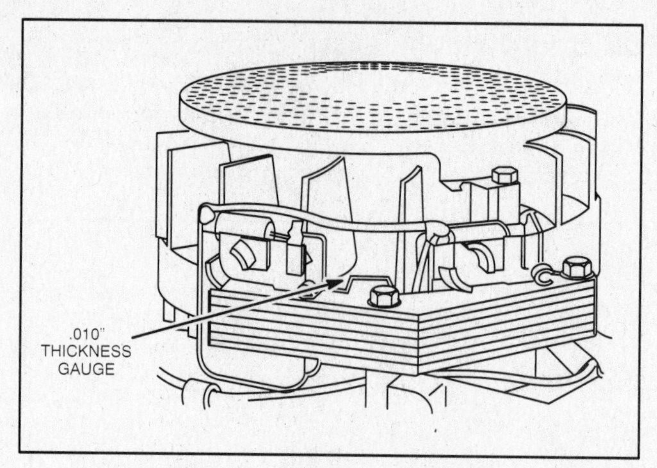

Fig. 18 – Adjusting Air Gap

1/2 AMP ALTERNATOR Used on MODEL SERIES 121700 – 124700

The 1/2 amp DC alternator is designed to operate as an integral part of the engine and is separate from the starting and ignition system. It is intended to provide DC charging current for a 12 volt battery. Contact battery or equipment manufacturer for battery information.

Test Alternator Output

Disconnect charging lead to battery at connector.

1. Insert RED test lead into 10 A receptacle in meter.
2. Insert BLACK test lead into COM receptacle in meter.
3. Rotate selector to A⎓ (DC amps) position.
4. Attach RED test clip to output terminal, Fig. 19.
5. Attach BLACK test clip to a good engine ground.
6. With engine running at 2800 RPM, output should be no less than .5 amp DC.
7. If low or no output, check stator air gap (current style only), Fig. 18.
8. If stator air gap is within specification and there is low or no output, replace stator.

NOTE: Air gap is not adjustable on early style stator.

NOTE: METRIC EQUIVALENTS ARE LISTED ON PAGE 21 OF THIS SECTION.

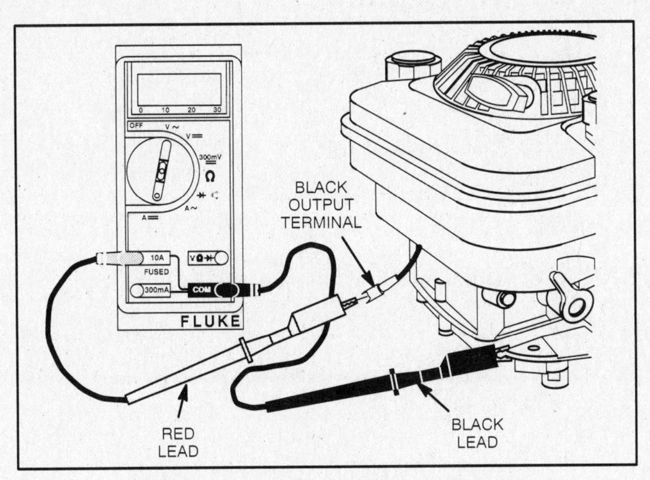

Fig. 19 - Testing Alternator Output

Adjust Stator Air Gap

Stator air gap is .006 to .008 in. Rotate flywheel until magnets are away from stator. Loosen both stator mounting nuts and move stator away from flywheel and tighten one nut. Place a .007 inch thick gauge between stator and flywheel. Turn flywheel until magnets are under stator. Loosen nut and let stator be pulled against flywheel magnet. Torque mounting nuts to 25 in. lbs. Turn flywheel to remove gauge, Fig. 20.

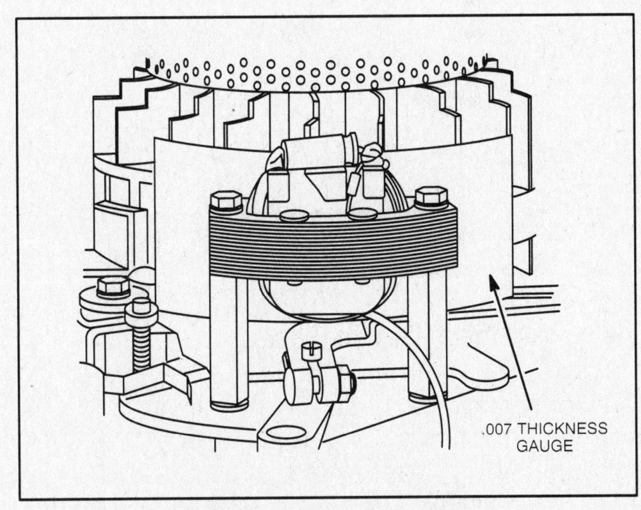

Fig. 20 - Adjusting Air Gap

1.2 AMP ALTERNATOR
Used on MODEL SERIES 130000
After Date Code 91032400

The 1.2 amp DC alternator provides current for charging a 12 volt battery.

Recommended battery size is 12 ampere hour for warm temperature operation and a 24 ampere hour battery should be used in cold service.

Testing Output

1. Insert RED test lead into 10 A receptacle in meter.
2. Insert BLACK test lead into COM receptacle in meter.
3. Rotate selector to A ⎓ (DC amps) position.
4. Attach RED test lead clip to DC output pin in connector, Fig. 21.
5. Attach BLACK test lead clip to positive (+) battery terminal.

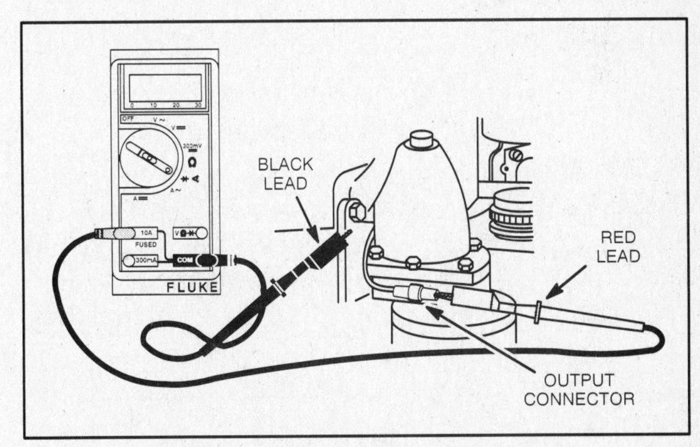

Fig. 21 - Testing Alternator Output

6. With engine running at 3600 RPM output should be no less than 1 amp DC.
   a. Output will vary with battery voltage. If battery voltage is at its maximum, output will be approximately 1 amp.
7. If low or no output is found, replace stator.

7C

NOTE: METRIC EQUIVALENTS ARE LISTED ON PAGE 21 OF THIS SECTION.

1-1/2 AMP ALTERNATOR Used on MODEL SERIES 130000
Before Date Code 91032500

The integral 1-1/2 amp alternator, with solid state rectifier, is designed for use with a compact battery. A 12 ampere hour battery is suggested for warm temperature operation and a 24 ampere hour battery should be used in cold service.

The alternator is rated at 3600 RPM. Output is reduced at lower engine RPM.

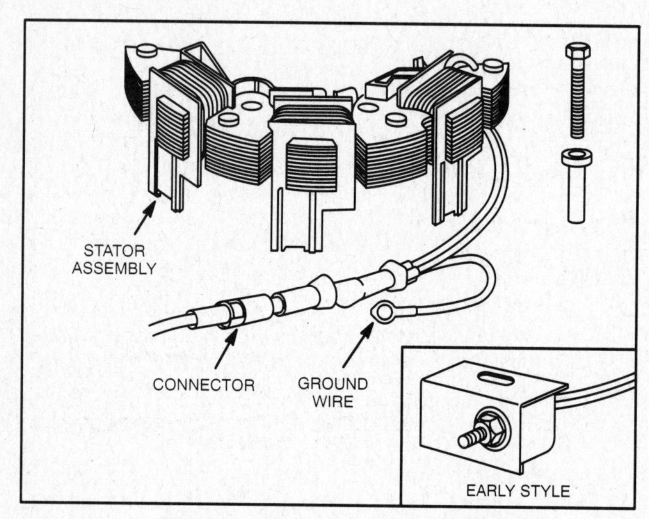

Fig. 22 – Alternator Assembly

WHEN CHECKING ALTERNATOR COMPONENTS, MAKE TESTS IN THE FOLLOWING SEQUENCE:

Check 1-1/2 Amp Non-Regulated Alternator

Check battery polarity. Negative (-) side of battery should be grounded to engine or frame; positive (+) side of battery to starter motor and alternator charge lead, Fig. 23. If reversed, rectifier and, or, battery will be damaged.

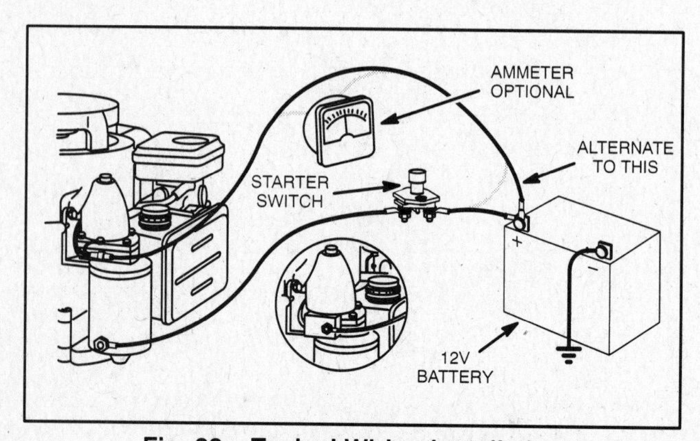

Fig. 23 – Typical Wiring Installation

Test Alternator Output

Disconnect charging lead at positive (+) battery terminal. Then disconnect charging lead at output terminal.

1. Insert RED test lead into 10A receptacle in meter.
2. Insert BLACK test lead into COM receptacle in meter.
3. Rotate selector to A ⎓ (DC amps) position.
4. Attach RED test lead clip to DC output terminal, Fig. 24.
5. Attach BLACK test lead clip to the engine ground.
6. With engine running at 3600 RPM, DC output should be no less than 1.2 amps DC.
7. If low output or no output is found, test rectifier.

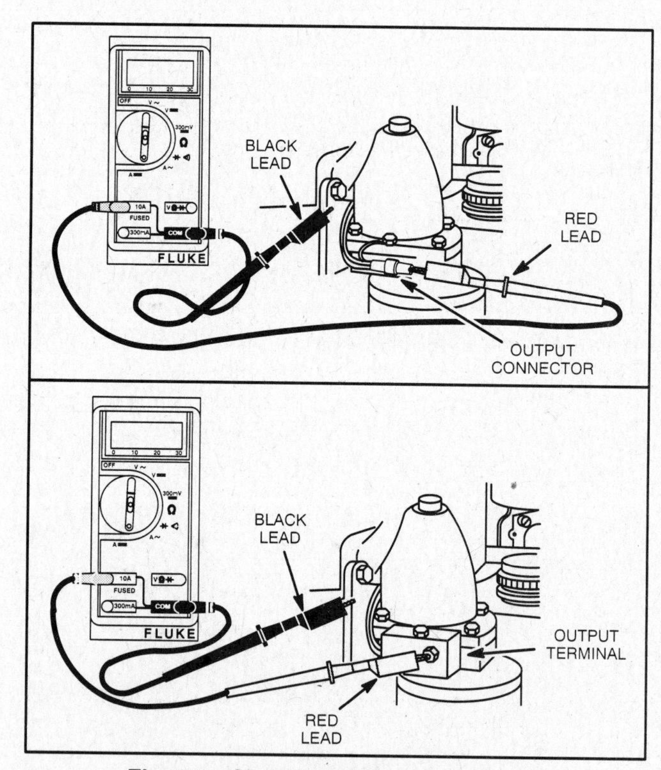

Fig. 24 – Checking Alternator Output

Test Rectifier (Diode Test)

In the Diode Test position, the meter will display the forward voltage drop across the diode(s) in the rectifier. If the voltage drop is less than 0.7 volts, the meter will "Beep" once as well as display the voltage drop. A continuous tone indicates continuity (shorted diode). An incomplete circuit (open diode) will be displayed as "OL."

NOTE: METRIC EQUIVALENTS ARE LISTED ON PAGE 21 OF THIS SECTION.

1. Insert RED test lead into VΩ⊣⊢ receptacle in meter.
2. Insert BLACK test lead into COM receptacle in meter.
3. Rotate selector to ⊣⊢ ·))) (Diode Test) position.
4. Attach BLACK test lead clip to output terminal. Leave BLACK test lead attached through Step 6, below.
5. Pierce one output wire with a pin and touch RED test lead probe to pin as shown in Fig. 25.
   a. Meter should "Beep."
   b. If meter makes a continuous tone or displays "OL" rectifier is defective. Replace.
6. Repeat test with other output wire.
   a. Meter should "Beep."
   b. If meter makes a continuous tone or displays "OL" rectifier is defective. Replace.

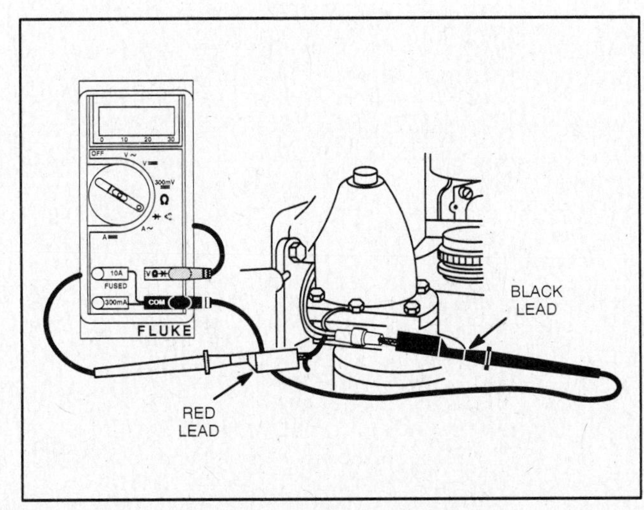

Fig. 25 - Testing Rectifier

7. Attach RED test lead clip to a clean unpainted area on engine (good ground). Leave RED test lead clip attached for remainder of test.
8. Pierce one stator output wire with a pin and touch BLACK test lead probe to pin as shown in Fig. 26.
   a. Meter should "Beep."
   b. If meter makes a continuous tone or displays "OL" rectifier is defective. Replace.
9. Repeat test with other stator output wire.
   a. Meter should "Beep."
   b. If meter makes a continuous tone or displays "OL" rectifier is defective. Replace.
10. If rectifier tests OK, replace stator. If rectifier is defective, replace rectifier. Then re-test DC output.

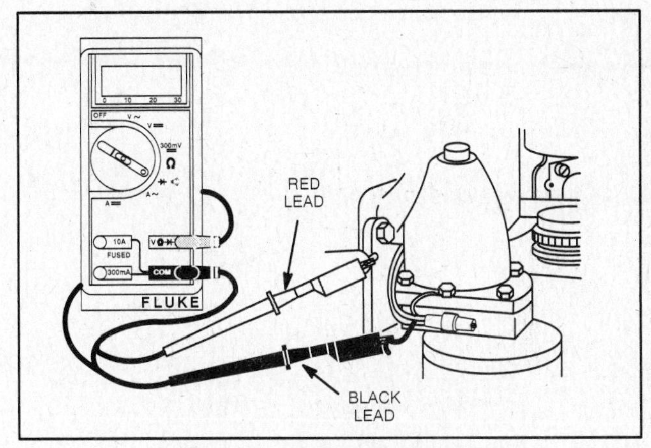

Fig. 26 - Testing Rectifier

Replace Defective Stator

Remove the blower housing, rotating screen, rewind clutch and flywheel. Note location of stator wires; under one coil spool, and between starter and starter drive housing as shown in Fig. 27. Remove ground wire or rectifier assembly (early style) from starter drive housing. Remove the two stator mounting screws and bushings.

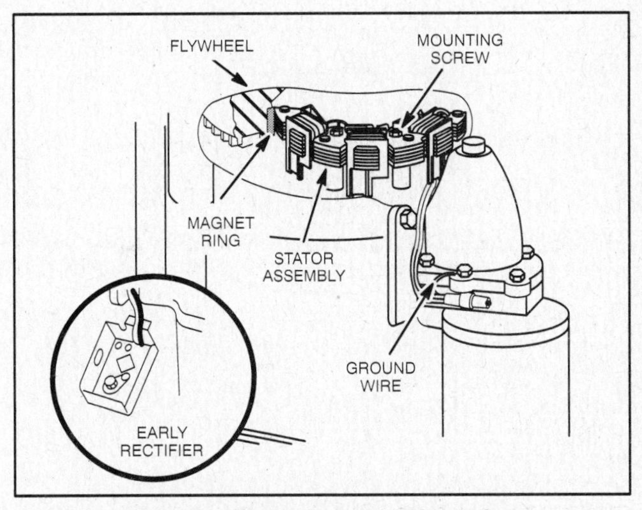

Fig. 27 - Stator Assembly Location

NOTE: METRIC EQUIVALENTS ARE LISTED ON PAGE 21 OF THIS SECTION.

Install new stator assembly with stator mounting screws and bushings. Be sure leads are properly positioned as shown in Fig. 28. While tightening mounting screws, push stator toward crankshaft to take up clearance in bushing. Torque mounting screws to 20 inch pounds.

Before re-assembly, locate stator wires against cylinder in order to clear ring gear and flywheel. Attach ground wire or rectifier assembly (early style) to drive housing. Replace flywheel and torque rewind clutch as noted on specification chart. Reassemble rotating screen and blower housing.

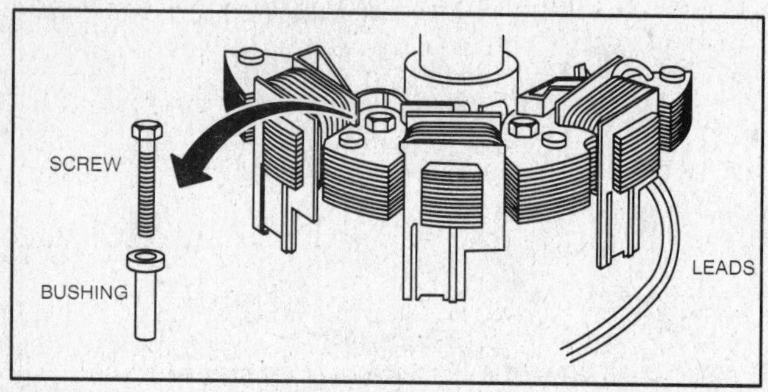

Fig. 28 – Assembling Stator

Replacing Rectifier

NOTE: Early style rectifier box is replaced by rectifier harness shown in Fig. 29.

Cut stator wires close to rectifier so that stator wires remain as long as possible. Discard old rectifier. Strip insulation back 3/8" from stator wires. Replacement rectifier has two exposed wires which are already stripped of insulation. Twist and solder each stator wire to a rectifier wire. Insulate each connection with electrical friction tape or shrink tubing. Keep connected areas as compact as possible. Attach ground wire to drive housing using original rectifier mounting screw, Fig. 27.

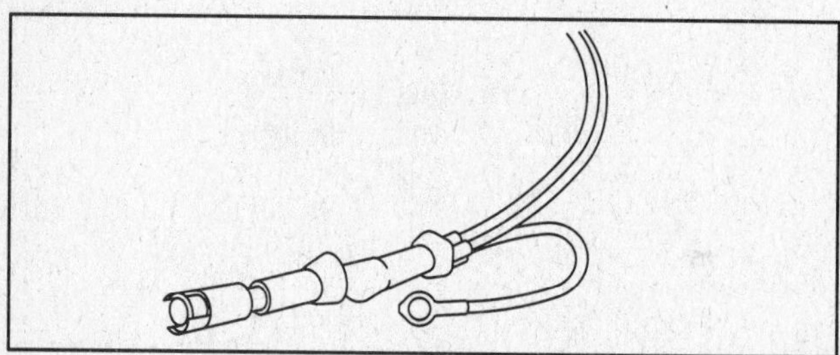

Fig. 29 – Replacement Rectifier

DC ONLY ALTERNATOR

The DC alternator provides DC current for charging a 12 volt battery. The current from the alternator is unregulated and is rated at 3 amps. The output rises from 2 amps at 2400 RPM to 3 amps at 3600 RPM.

Recommended battery sizes range from 30 ampere hour for warm temperature service to 50 ampere hour in coldest service.

WHEN CHECKING ALTERNATOR COMPONENTS, MAKE THE TEST IN THE FOLLOWING SEQUENCE:

Test Alternator Output

1. Insert RED test lead into 10 A receptacle in meter.
2. Insert BLACK test lead into COM receptacle in meter.
3. Rotate selector to A ⎓ (DC amps) position.
4. Attach RED test lead clip to DC output terminal, Fig. 30.
5. Attach BLACK test lead clip to positive (+) battery terminal.
6. With engine running at 3600 RPM, output should be between 2 to 4 amps DC.
   a. Output will vary with battery voltage. If battery voltage is at its maximum, output will be approximately 2 amps.
7. If no or low output is found, test diode.

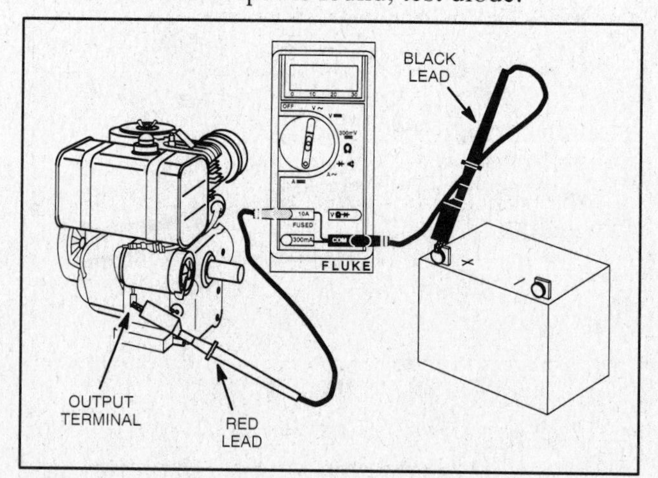

Fig. 30 – Testing Alternator Output

Test Diode

In the Diode Test position, the meter will display the forward voltage drop across the diode(s). If the voltage drop is less than 0.7 volts, the meter will "Beep" once as well as display the voltage drop. A continuous tone indicates continuity (shorted diode) An incomplete circuit (open diode) will be displayed as "OL."

NOTE: METRIC EQUIVALENTS ARE LISTED ON PAGE 21 OF THIS SECTION.

1. Insert RED test lead into V Ω ⊣ receptacle in meter.
2. Insert BLACK test lead into COM receptacle in meter.
3. Rotate selector to ⊣ ·))) (Diode Test) position.
4. Attach RED test lead clip to point "A" and Black test lead clip to point "B," Fig. 31. (It may be necessary to pierce wire with a pin as shown.)
   a. If meter "Beeps" once, diode is OK.
   b. If meter makes a continuous tone, diode is defective (shorted).
   c. If meter displays "OL," proceed to step 5.
5. Reverse test leads.
   a. If meter "Beeps" once, diode is installed backwards.
   b. If meter still displays "OL," diode is defective (open).
6. If diode tests OK, replace the stator.

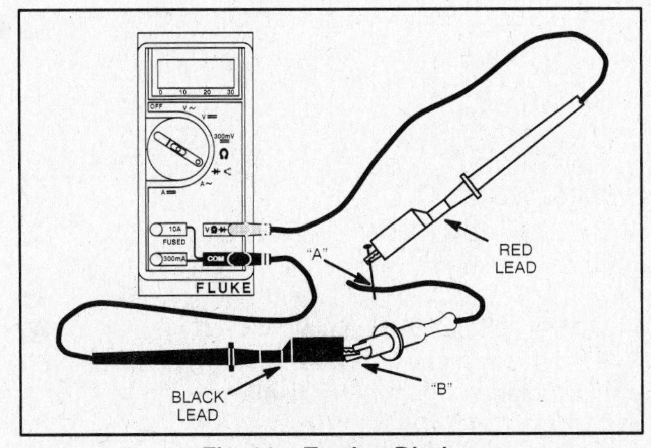

Fig. 31 – Testing Diode

NOTE: Service replacement diode harnesses are available. Use Rosin Core solder when installing new harness. Use shrink tubing or tape for all connections. DO NOT USE CRIMP CONNECTORS.

AC ONLY ALTERNATOR

The AC alternator provides current for headlights only. Current for the lights is available as long as the engine is running. The output depends upon engine speed. 12 volt lights with a total rating of 60 to 100 watts may be used. With lights rated at 70 watts, the voltage rises from 8 volts at 2400 RPM to 12 volts at 3600 RPM, so the brightness of the light changes with the engine speed.

Test AC Output

1. Insert RED test lead into V Ω ⊣ receptacle in meter.
2. Insert BLACK test lead into COM receptacle in meter.
3. Rotate selector to V∼ (AC volts) position.
4. Attach RED test lead clip to AC output terminal, Fig. 32.
5. Attach BLACK test lead clip to engine ground.
6. With engine running at 3600 RPM, AC output should be no less than 14 volts.

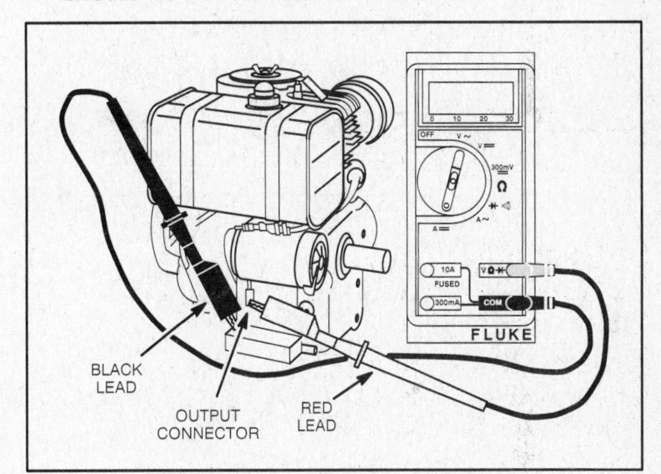

Fig. 32 – Testing AC Output

DUAL CIRCUIT ALTERNATOR

The dual circuit alternator uses a single polarized plug with two pins. One pin is for charging the battery and the second is for the lights. Earlier dual circuit alternators used a separate connector for each of the circuits, Fig. 33.

The dual circuit alternator provides DC current for battery charging and an independent AC circuit for headlights. The battery is not used for lights, so lights are available even if battery is disconnected or removed.

Current for lights is available as long as the engine is running. The output depends upon engine speed, so brightness of the lights changes with engine speed. 12 volt lights with a total rating of 60 to 100 watts may be used. With lights rated at 70 watts, the voltage rises from 8 volts at 2400 RPM to 12 volts at 3600 RPM.

NOTE: METRIC EQUIVALENTS ARE LISTED ON PAGE 21 OF THIS SECTION.

ALTERNATORS
Dual Circuit

The current from the DC side of the alternator is unregulated and is rated at 3 amps. The output rises from 2 amps at 2400 RPM to 3 amps at 3600 RPM.

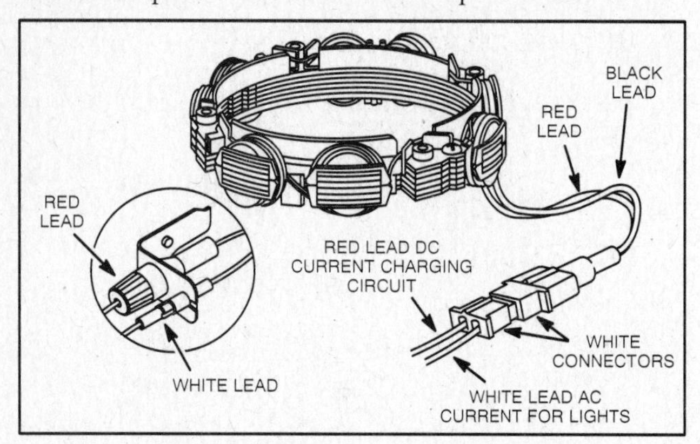

Fig. 33 - Dual Circuit Alternator

Checking Battery Installation

Check if battery polarity is correct. Negative (-) side of battery should be grounded to engine or frame; positive (+) side of battery to alternator output lead, Fig. 34.

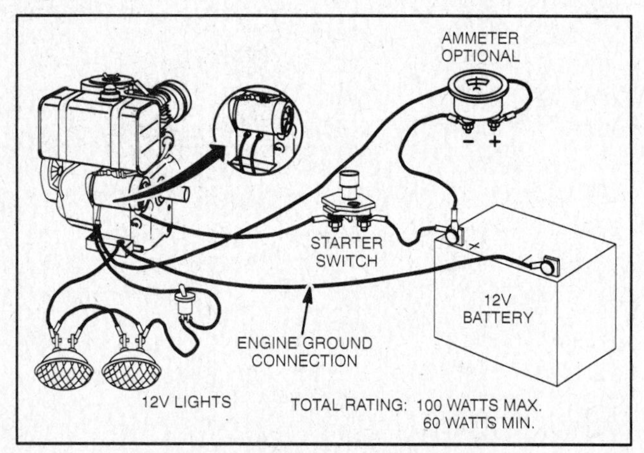

Fig. 34 - Typical Wiring Diagram

WHEN CHECKING ALTERNATOR COMPONENTS, MAKE TESTS IN THE FOLLOWING SEQUENCE:

Test Alternator Output

1. Insert RED test lead into 10 A receptacle in meter.
2. Insert BLACK test lead into COM receptacle in meter.
3. Rotate selector to A ⎓ (DC amps) position.
4. Attach RED test lead clip to DC output pin in connector, Fig. 35.
5. Attach BLACK test lead clip to positive (+) battery terminal.

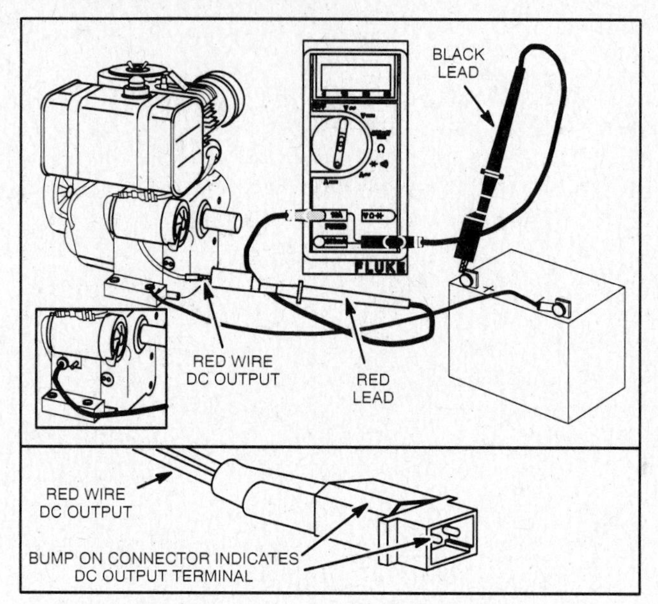

Fig. 35 - Testing Alternator Output

6. With engine running at 3600 RPM output should be between 2 to 4 AMPS DC.
   a. Output will vary with battery voltage. If battery voltage is at its maximum, output will be approximately 2 amps.
7. If no output or low output is found, test diode.

Diode Test

In the Diode Test position, the meter will display the forward voltage drop across the diode(s). If the voltage drop is less than 0.7 volts, the meter will "Beep" once as well as display the voltage drop. A continuous tone indicates continuity (shorted diode) An incomplete circuit (open diode) will be displayed as "OL."

1. Insert RED test lead into VΩ▶| receptacle in meter.
2. Insert BLACK test lead into COM receptacle in meter.
3. Rotate selector to ▶| ·))) (Diode Test) position.
4. Attach RED test lead clip to point "A" and Black test lead clip to point "B," Fig. 36. (It may be necessary to pierce wire with a pin as shown.)
   a. If meter "Beeps" once, diode is OK.
   b. If meter makes a continuous tone, diode is defective (shorted). Replace.
   c. If meter displays "OL," proceed to step 5.

NOTE: METRIC EQUIVALENTS ARE LISTED ON PAGE 21 OF THIS SECTION.

5. Reverse test leads.
   a. If meter "Beeps" once, diode is installed backwards.
   b. If meter still displays "OL," diode is defective (open). Replace.
6. If diode tests OK, Check stator for bare wires or other obvious defects. If grounded leads are not visible, replace the stator.

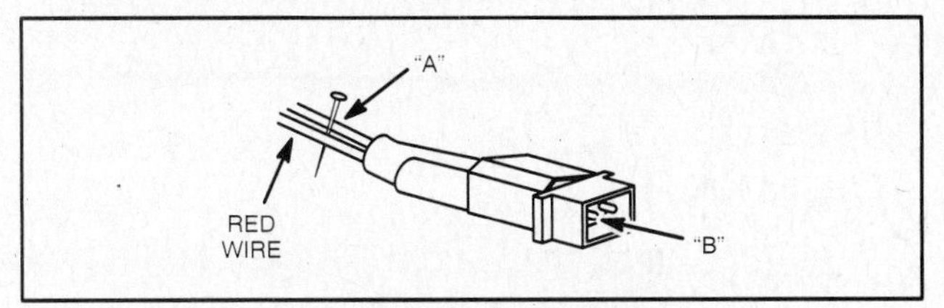

Fig. 36 Testing Diode

NOTE: Service replacement diode harnesses are available. Use Rosin Core solder when installing new harness. Use shrink tubing or tape all connections. DO NOT USE CRIMP CONNECTORS.

AC Output Test

1. Insert RED test lead into V Ω ⊣⊢ receptacle in meter.
2. Insert BLACK test lead into COM receptacle in meter.
3. Rotate selector to V∼ (AC volts) position.
4. Attach RED test lead clip to AC output terminal, Fig. 37.
5. Attach BLACK test lead clip to engine ground.

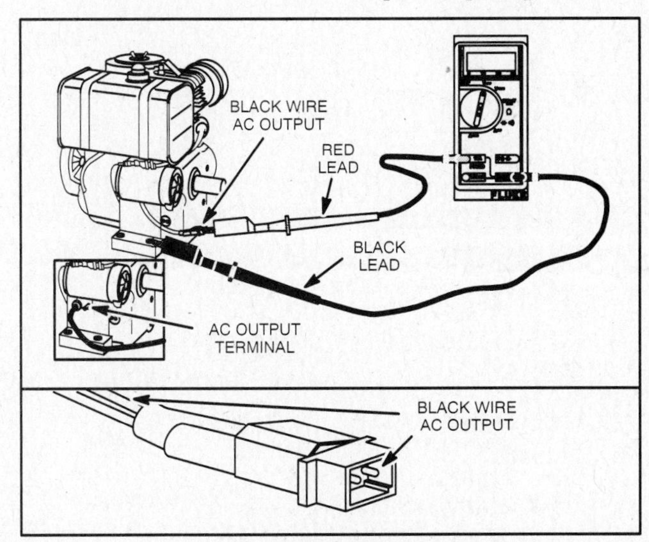

Fig. 37 - Testing AC Output

6. With engine running at 3600 RPM output should be no less than 14 volts AC.
7. If no output or low output is found, replace stator.

TRI-CIRCUIT ALTERNATOR

The tri-circuit alternator provides alternating current through a single output lead and connector to a wiring harness containing two diodes.

One diode rectifies the AC current to 5 Amps – (negative) DC for lights. The second diode rectifies the AC current to 5 Amps + (positive) DC for battery charging and external loads, such as an electric clutch, Fig. 38.

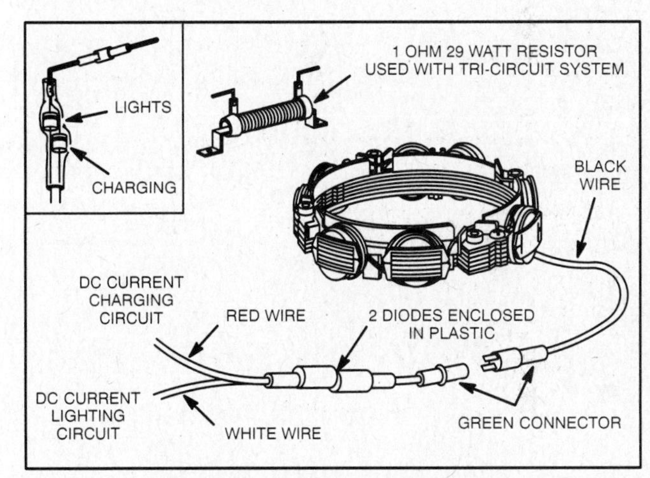

Fig. 38 - Tri-Circuit Alternator

NOTE: Some equipment manufacturers supply the diodes as an integral part of the equipment wiring harness.

A 1 Ohm 20 Watt resistor is placed in series with the (+) DC charging lead, limiting the charging current to approximately 3 amps when the clutch is not engaged. When the clutch is engaged the resistor is bypassed allowing full output to the battery and clutch.

NOTE: The 1 Ohm 20 Watt resistor is supplied by the equipment manufacturer, when required.

The battery is not used for the lights, so lights are available even if the battery is disconnected or removed. Current for the lights is available as long as the engine is running. The output depends upon engine RPM, so the brightness of the lights changes with engine speed.

NOTE: METRIC EQUIVALENTS ARE LISTED ON PAGE 21 OF THIS SECTION.

Test Alternator Output

1. Insert RED test lead into VΩ⏆ receptacle in meter.
2. Insert BLACK test lead into COM receptacle in meter.
3. Rotate selector to V~ (AC volts) position.
4. Attach RED test lead clip to output terminal, Fig. 39.
5. Attach BLACK test lead clip to engine ground.

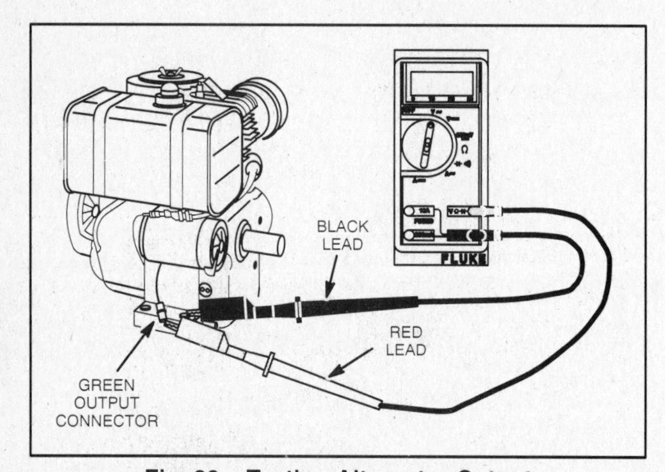

Fig. 39 - Testing Alternator Output

6. With engine running at 3600 RPM, output should be no less than 28 Volts AC.
7. If no output or low output is found, replace stator.
8. If alternator output is good, test diodes located in wiring harness.

Diode Test

NOTE: One diode is for the charging circuit and the other diode is for the lighting circuit.

In the Diode Test position, the meter will display the forward voltage drop across the diode(s). If the voltage drop is less than 0.7 volts, the meter will "Beep" once as well as display the voltage drop. A continuous tone indicates continuity (shorted diode) An incomplete circuit (open diode) will be displayed as "OL."

Charging Circuit (Red Wire)

1. Insert RED test lead into VΩ⏆ receptacle in meter.
2. Insert BLACK test lead into COM receptacle in meter.
3. Rotate selector to ⏆ ·))) (Diode Test) position.
4. Attach BLACK test lead clip to point "A," Fig. 40. (It may be necessary to pierce wire with a pin as shown.)
5. Insert RED test lead probe into harness connector.
   a. If meter "Beeps" once, diode is OK.
   b. If meter makes a continuous tone, diode is defective (shorted). Replace.
   c. If meter displays "OL," proceed to step 6.
6. Reverse test leads.
   a. If meter "Beeps" once, diode is installed backwards.
   b. If meter still displays "OL," diode is defective (open). Replace.

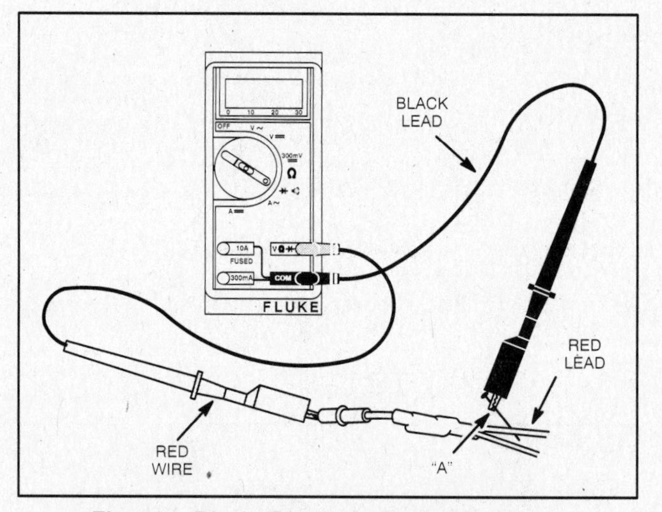

Fig. 40 - Diode Testing - Charging Circuit

Lighting Circuit (White Wire)

1. Insert RED test lead into VΩ⏆ receptacle in meter.
2. Insert BLACK test lead into COM receptacle in meter.
3. Rotate selector to ⏆ ·))) (Diode Test) position.
4. Attach RED test lead clip to point "A," Fig. 41. (It may be necessary to pierce wire with a pin as shown.)

NOTE: METRIC EQUIVALENTS ARE LISTED ON PAGE 21 OF THIS SECTION.

5. Insert BLACK test lead probe into harness connector.

   a. If meter "Beeps" once, diode is OK.

   b. If meter makes a continuous tone, diode is defective (shorted). Replace.

   c. If meter displays "OL," proceed to step 6.

6. Reverse test leads.

   a. If meter "Beeps" once, diode is installed backwards.

   b. If meter still displays "OL," diode is defective (open).

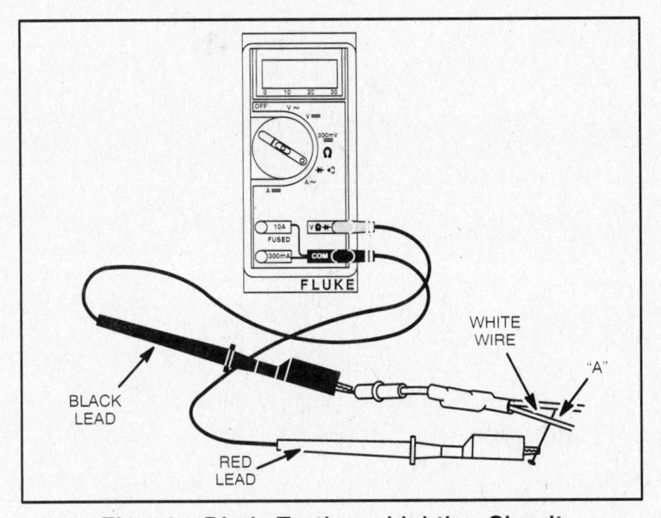

Fig. 41 - Diode Testing - Lighting Circuit

NOTE: Service replacement diode harnesses are available.

QUAD CIRCUIT ALTERNATOR

The quad circuit alternator system provides AC current through two output leads to the regulator-rectifier. The regulator-rectifier converts AC current to DC and provides unregulated current (5 amps – DC) for lighting and regulated current (5 amps + DC) for charging the battery. The charging rate will vary with engine RPM and temperature.

NOTE: The quad circuit and 10–16 amp regulated system use the same stator.

WHEN CHECKING ALTERNATOR COMPONENTS, MAKE TESTS IN THE FOLLOWING SEQUENCE:

Test Alternator Output

1. Insert RED test lead into VΩ⊣⊢ receptacle in meter.

2. Insert BLACK test lead into COM receptacle in meter.

3. Rotate selector to V~ (AC volts) position.

4. Attach RED test lead clip to one of the output pins in the yellow connector, Fig. 42.

5. Attach BLACK test lead clip to the other output pin. (Test lead clips may be attached to either output pin.)

6. With engine running at 3600 RPM, AC output should be no less than 20 volts AC.

7. If no or low output is found, replace stator.

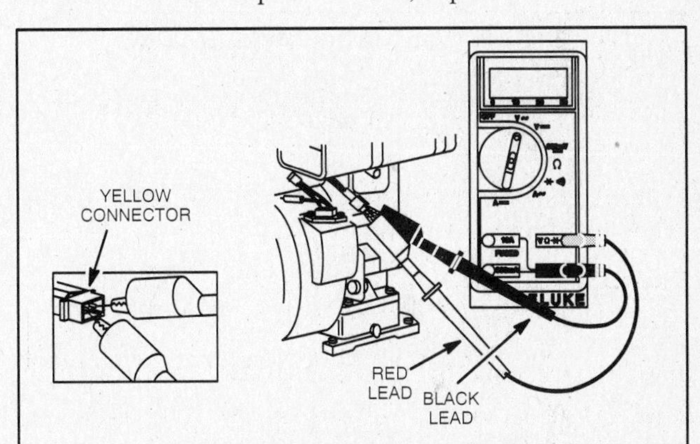

Fig. 42 - Testing Alternator Output

Test Charging Circuit (+ DC)

NOTE: Regulator-rectifier will not function unless it is grounded to engine. Make sure the regulator-rectifier is securely mounted to engine.

When testing regulator-rectifier for amperage output a 12 volt battery with a minimum charge of 5 volts is required. There will be no charging output if battery voltage is below 5 volts.

NOTE: Connect test leads before starting engine. Be sure connections are secure. If a test lead vibrates loose while engine is running, regulator-rectifier may be damaged.

1. Insert RED test lead into 10 A receptacle in meter.

2. Inset BLACK test lead into COM receptacle in meter.

3. Rotate selector to A⎓ (DC amps) position.

NOTE: METRIC EQUIVALENTS ARE LISTED ON PAGE 21 OF THIS SECTION.

4. Attach RED test lead clip to charging output pin (red wire), Fig. 43.

5. Attach BLACK test lead clip to positive (+) battery terminal.

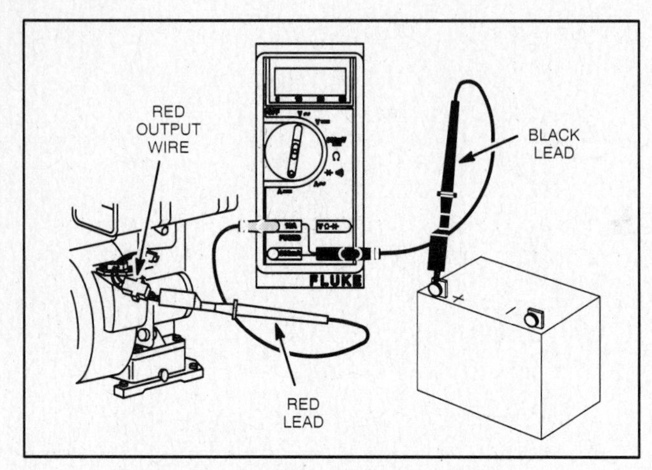

Fig. 43 - Testing Regulator Output

6. With engine running at 3600 RPM output should be 3 to 5 amps.

Amperage will vary with battery voltage, for example, if battery voltage was below 11 volts output reading would be approximately 5 amps. If battery voltage is at its maximum, the amperage will be less.

7. If no output or low output is found, replace regulator-rectifier.

Test Lighting Circuit (- DC)

The black wire from the regulator-rectifier provides 5 amps (-) DC and is used only for lighting. If the headlights do not operate, make sure that the problem is not with the bulbs, wiring and/or light switch.

To test the lighting circuit the following tools are required.

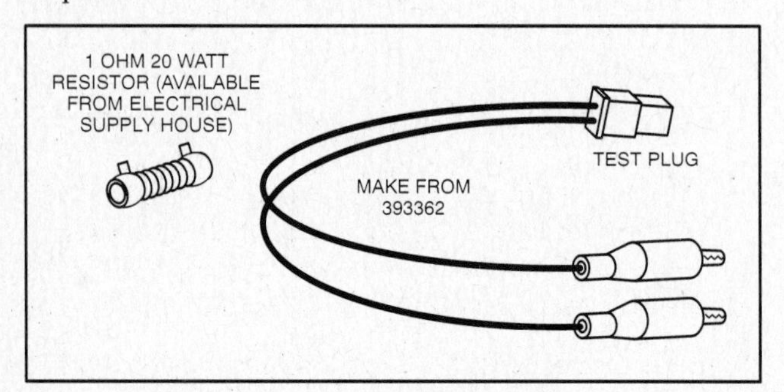

Fig. 44 - Test Equipment

1. Insert RED test lead into 10 A receptacle in meter.

2. Inset BLACK test lead into COM receptacle in meter.

3. Rotate selector to A ⎓ (DC amps) position.

4. Connect test harness to output connector and attach alligator clips to 1 ohm 20 watt resistor as shown in Fig. 45.

5. Attach RED test lead clip to resistor, and BLACK test lead clip to positive (+) battery terminal.

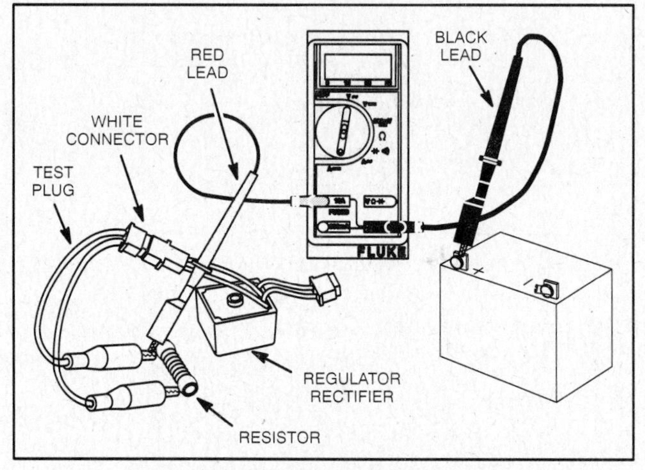

Fig. 45 - Testing Lighting Circuit

6. With engine running at 3600 RPM output on the meter should be approximately 8 amps.

7. If no output or low output is found, replace the regulator-rectifier.

CAUTION: RESISTOR GETS HOT! CONDUCT TEST AS QUICKLY AS POSSIBLE.

5 & 9 AMP REGULATED ALTERNATOR

The 5 & 9 amp regulated alternator systems provide AC current through a single lead to the regulator-rectifier. The regulator-rectifier converts the AC current to DC, and regulates current to the battery. The charging rate will vary with engine RPM and temperature.

Alternator output (5 or 9 amp) is determined by the flywheel alternator magnet size. The stator and regulator-rectifier are the same for the 5 and 9 amp system.

The 5 & 9 amp regulated system and the Tri-Circuit system use the same stator.

WHEN CHECKING ALTERNATOR COMPONENTS, MAKE TESTS IN THE FOLLOWING SEQUENCE:

NOTE: METRIC EQUIVALENTS ARE LISTED ON PAGE 21 OF THIS SECTION.

Testing Alternator Output

Temporarily, disconnect stator wire harness from regulator-rectifier.

1. Insert RED test lead into VΩ⊣⊢ receptacle in meter.
2. Insert BLACK test lead into COM receptacle in meter.
3. Rotate selector to V~ (AC volts) position.
4. Attach RED test lead clip to output terminal, Fig. 46.
5. Attach BLACK test lead clip to engine ground.

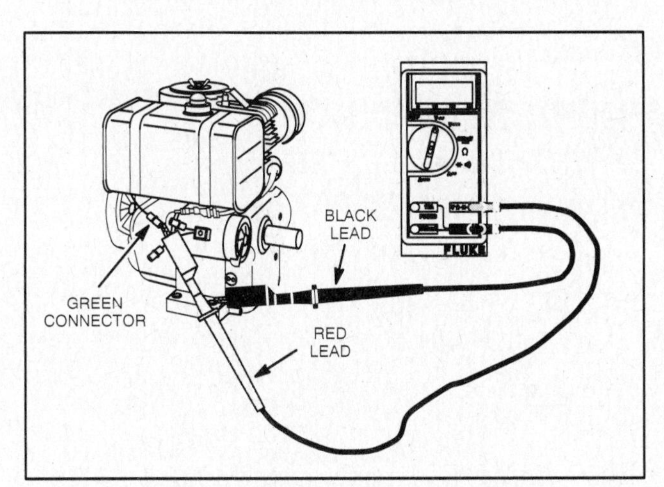

Fig. 46 - Testing Alternator Output

6. With the engine running at 3600 RPM, AC output should be no less than:

28 Volts AC - 5 Amp System
40 Volts AC - 9 Amp System

7. If no or low output is found, replace the stator.

Testing Regulator-Rectifier

NOTE: Regulator-rectifier will not function unless it is grounded to engine. Make sure the regulator-rectifier is securely mounted to engine.

When testing regulator-rectifier for amperage output, a 12 volt battery with a minimum charge of 5 volts is required. There will be no charging output if battery voltage is below 5 volts.

NOTE: Connect test leads before starting engine. Be sure connections are secure. If a test lead vibrates loose while engine is running, the regulator-rectifier may be damaged.

1. Insert RED test lead into 10 A receptacle in meter.
2. Insert BLACK test lead into COM receptacle in meter.
3. Rotate selector to A⎓ (DC amps) position.
4. Attach RED test lead clip to DC output terminal on regulator-rectifier, Fig. 47.
5. Attach BLACK test lead clip to positive (+) battery terminal.

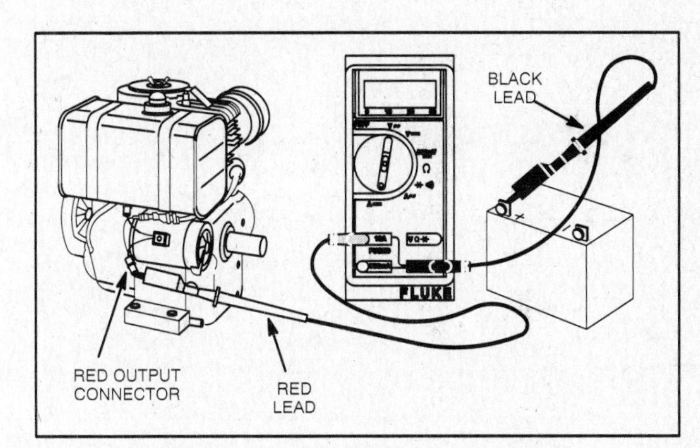

Fig. 47 - Testing Regulator-Rectifier

6. With the engine running at 3600 RPM. The output should be:

*** 3-5 Amps - 5 Amp System**
*** 3-9 Amps - 9 Amp System**

* Depending upon battery voltage. For example, if the battery voltage was below 11 volts, the output reading would be 5 or 9 amps, depending upon the alternator system being tested. If battery voltage is at its maximum, the amperage will be less.

7. If no or low output is found, be sure that regulator-rectifier is grounded properly and all connections are clean and secure. If there is still no or low output, replace the regulator-rectifier.

NOTE: METRIC EQUIVALENTS ARE LISTED ON PAGE 21 OF THIS SECTION.

10 & 16 AMP REGULATED ALTERNATOR

The 10 & 16 amp regulated alternator system provides AC current through two output leads to the regulator-rectifier. The regulator-rectifier converts the AC current to DC, and regulates the current to the battery. The charging rate will vary with engine RPM and temperature.

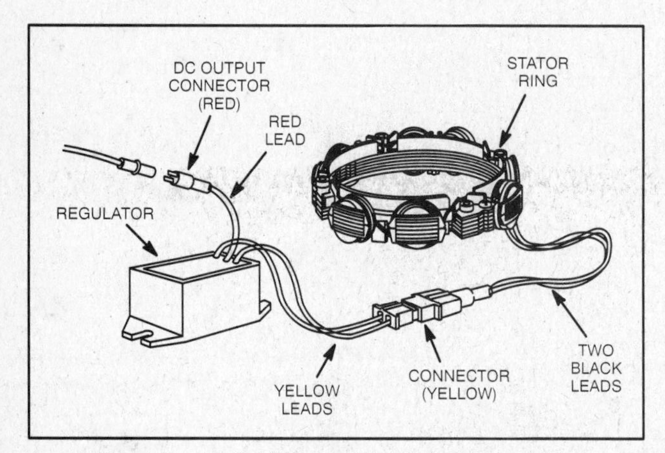

Fig. 48 - 10 & 16 Amp Alternator Assembly

Alternator output (10 or 16 Amp) is determined by flywheel alternator magnet size. Therefore, stator and regulator-rectifier are the same for the 10 and 16 amp system.

WHEN CHECKING THE ALTERNATOR COMPONENTS, MAKE THE TESTS IN THE FOLLOWING SEQUENCE:

Test Alternator Output

1. Insert RED test lead into VΩ⊣⊢ receptacle in meter.
2. Insert BLACK test lead into COM receptacle in meter.
3. Rotate selector to V∼ (AC volts) position.
4. Insert RED and BLACK test lead probes into output terminals in yellow connector, as shown in Fig. 49. (Meter test clip leads may be attached to either terminal.)

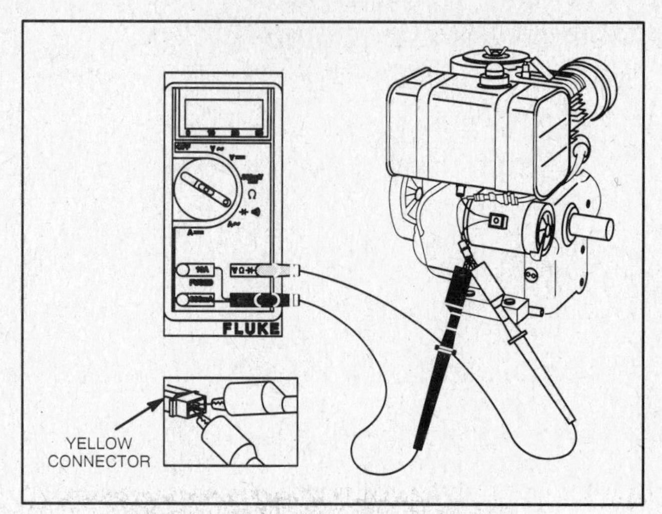

Fig. 49 - Testing Alternator Output

5. With the engine running at 3600 RPM output should be no less than:

20 Volts - 10 Amp System
30 Volts - 16 Amp System

* If alternator output test indicates a 16 Amp system, see special instructions for testing regulator-rectifier.

6. If no or low output is found. check for bare wires or any other obvious defects. If "shorted" leads are not visible, replace the stator.

Test Regulator-Rectifier

NOTE: The Digital Multimeter will withstand DC input of 10 to 20 Amps for up to **30** seconds. When checking DC output of 16 Amp regulated system, use DC Shunt, Tool #19359, to avoid blowing fuse in meter. See special instructions for installation procedure on 16 Amp system.

NOTE: Regulator-rectifier will not function unless it is grounded to engine. Make sure the regulator-rectifier is securely mounted to engine.

When testing regulator-rectifier for amperage output, a 12 volt battery with a minimum charge of 5 volts is required. There will be no charging output if battery voltage is below 5 volts.

NOTE: Connect test leads before starting engine. Be sure connections are secure. If a test lead vibrates loose while engine is running, the regulator-rectifier may be damaged.

NOTE: METRIC EQUIVALENTS ARE LISTED ON PAGE 21 OF THIS SECTION.

Testing Regulator-Rectifier 10 Amp System

1. Insert RED test lead into 10 A receptacle in meter.
2. Insert BLACK test lead into COM receptacle in meter.
3. Rotate selector to A ⎓ (DC amps) position.
4. Attach RED test lead clip to DC output terminal on regulator-rectifier, Fig. 50.

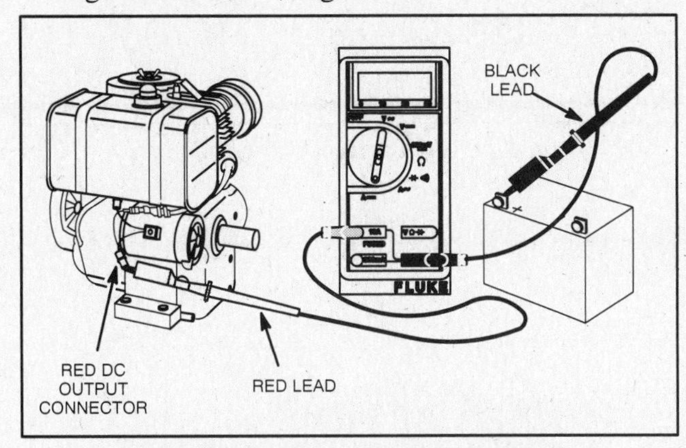

Fig. 50 – Testing Regulator-Rectifier

5. Attach BLACK test lead clip to positive (+) battery terminal.
6. With the engine running at 3600 RPM. The output should be:

*** 3–10 Amps – 10 Amp System**

* Depending upon battery voltage. For example, if the battery voltage was 10 volts, the output reading would be 10 amps. If battery voltage is at its maximum, the amperage will be less.

7. If no or low output is found, be sure that regulator-rectifier is grounded properly and all connections are clean and secure. If there is still no or low output, replace the regulator-rectifier.

Testing Regulator-Rectifier 16 Amp System

To avoid blowing fuse in meter when testing DC output of 16 Amp system the DC Shunt, Tool # 19359 is required.

The DC Shunt **must** be installed on the – (**negative**) terminal of the battery, Fig. 51. All connections must be clean and tight for correct amperage readings.

1. Install shunt on negative battery terminal.
2. Insert RED test lead into VΩ⊣⊢ receptacle in meter and connect to RED post terminal on shunt, Fig. 51.
3. Insert BLACK test lead into COM receptacle in meter and connect to BLACK post terminal on shunt.
4. Rotate selector to 300mV ⎓ position.
5. Attach RED test lead clip to DC output terminal on regulator-rectifier, Fig. 51.

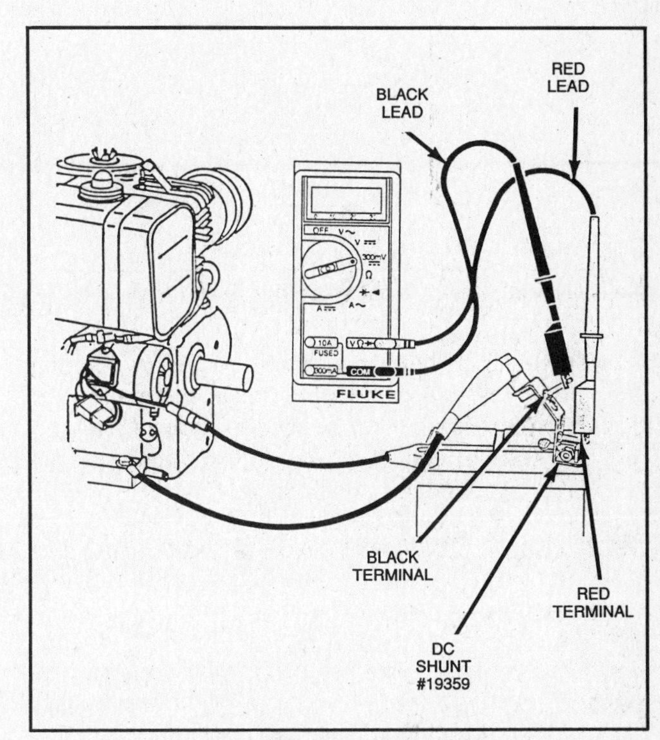

Fig. 51 – Testing Regulator-Rectifier 16 Amp System With DC Shunt

6. With the engine running at 3600 RPM. The output should be:

*** 3–16 Amps – 16 Amp System**

* Depending upon battery voltage. For example, if the battery voltage was below 11 volts, the output reading would be 16 amps. If battery voltage is at its maximum, the amperage will be less.

7. If no or low output is found, be sure the regulator-rectifier is grounded properly and all connections are clean and secure. If there is still no or low output, replace the regulator-rectifier.

BATTERIES

The battery used on Briggs & Stratton single cylinder engines is of the 12 volt, lead acid-wet cell type. This type is available as a maintenance free or dry charged battery.

NOTE: METRIC EQUIVALENTS ARE LISTED ON PAGE 21 OF THIS SECTION.

Batteries

The maintenance-free battery is filled with electrolyte at the time of manufacture. The level of electrolyte cannot be checked, Fig. 52.

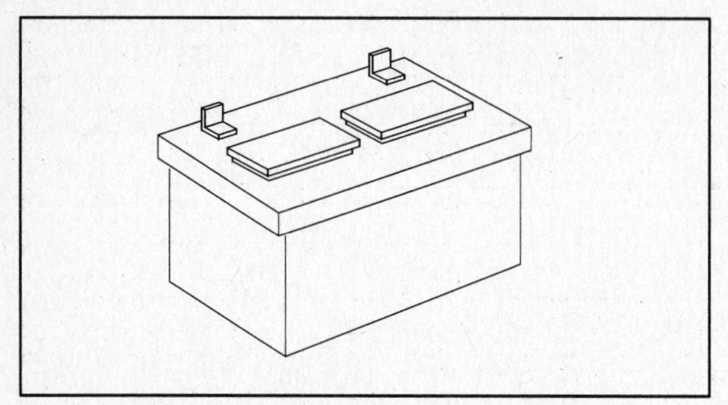

Fig. 52 – Typical Wet Charge Battery

The dry charged battery is manufactured with fully charged plates. Electrolyte must be added at the time that the battery is placed in service. Before activating a dry charged battery, read and follow the manufacturer's recommended procedure.

Recommended battery sizes range from a minimum 30 ampere hour for warm temperature service to 50 ampere hour in coldest service.

WARNING: BATTERIES PRODUCE HYDROGEN, AN EXPLOSIVE GAS. DO NOT store, charge or use a battery near an open flame or devices which utilize a pilot light or can create a spark.

Installation:

1. Before installing battery, connect all equipment to be operated, Fig. 53.
2. Place battery in holder with a flat base. Tighten hold down evenly until snug. DO NOT overtighten.
3. Connect positive terminal to positive post FIRST to prevent sparks from accidental grounding. Tighten connectors securely.
4. Connect negative terminal to negative battery terminal. Tighten connectors securely.

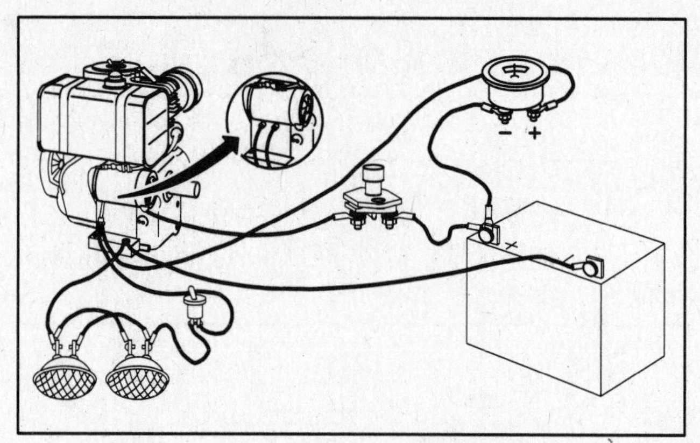

Fig. 53 – Typical 12V Wiring Diagram

Checking Battery

1. Physical check – clean if necessary.
   a. Corrosion
   b. Dirt
   c. Terminal and clamps (secure – good condition)
2. Bring battery to full charge.

WARNING: BATTERIES CONTAIN SULFURIC ACID. To prevent serious burns, avoid any contact with battery acid.

WARNING: DO NOT EXCEED CHARGE RATE OF 1/10 AMPERE FOR EVERY AMPERE OF BATTERY RATING. Consult battery manufacturer for charging recommendations.

   a. Use a taper charger (automatically reduces charge rate).
   b. Fill battery cells with distilled water or tap water (unless maintenance free type) after charging (for batteries that have been in service).

WARNING: If battery gets "Hot" to the touch or spitting acid (gassing) excessively, unplug charger periodically.

NOTE: METRIC EQUIVALENTS ARE LISTED ON PAGE 21 OF THIS SECTION.

3. With battery fully charged, check specific gravity readings of each cell with a Battery Hydrometer and record readings, Fig. 54.

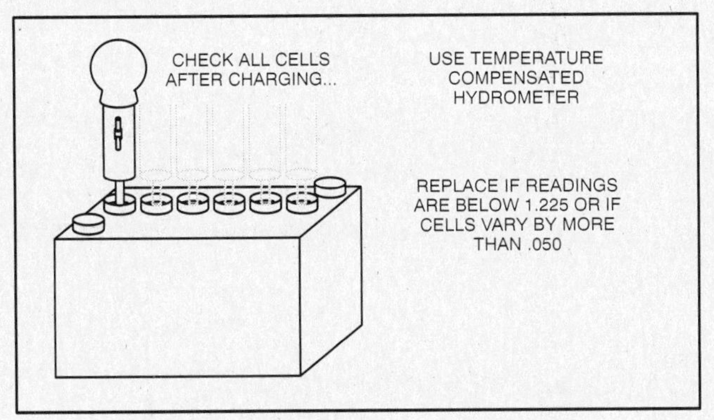

Fig. 54 - Checking 12V Battery Cells (Lead Acid - Wet Cell - With Fill Caps)

All readings should be above 1.250 (compensating for temperature). If specific gravity readings varies .050 or if ALL cells read less than 1.225, replace battery.

METRIC EQUIVALENTS

DIMENSIONS, FRACTIONAL	
Inches	**Millimeters**
3/8	9.53
1/2	12.7
18	460.0
DIMENSIONS, DECIMAL	
.006	.15
.007	.17
.008	.20
.010	.25

TORQUE		
In. Lbs.	**Kgcm Kpcm**	**Nm**
20	23	2.2
25	29	2.8

7C

NOTE: METRIC EQUIVALENTS ARE LISTED ON PAGE 21 OF THIS SECTION.

Section 8
LUBRICATION

SECTION INDEX

8

NOTE: METRIC EQUIVALENTS ARE LISTED ON PAGE 10 OF THIS SECTION.

OIL

Oil has four purposes. It cools, cleans, seals and lubricates. Most Briggs & Stratton engines are lubricated with a gear driven splash oil slinger or a connecting rod dipper.

Oil Capacity

OIL CAPACITY CHART

Basic Model Series	Capacity Pints
Vertical Crankshaft Aluminum Cylinders	
60000, 80000, 90000, 100700, 110000, 120000	1-1/4
100900, 130000	1-3/4
170000, 190000	2-1/4
220000, 250000, 280000	3
Horizontal Crankshaft Aluminum Cylinders	
60000, 80000, 90000, 100200, 130000	1-1/4
170000, 190000	2-3/4
220000, 250000	2-1/2
Horizontal Crankshaft Cast Iron Cylinders	
230000, 240000, 300000, 320000	4

Oil Recommendations

We recommend the use of a high quality detergent oil classified "For Service SE, SF, SG," such as Briggs & Stratton 30 weight oil, part #100005 or 1000028. Detergent oils keep the engine cleaner and retard the formation of gum and varnish deposits. No special additives should be used with recommended oils.

NOTE: Do Not Mix Oil With Gasoline.

SAE VISCOSITY GRADES

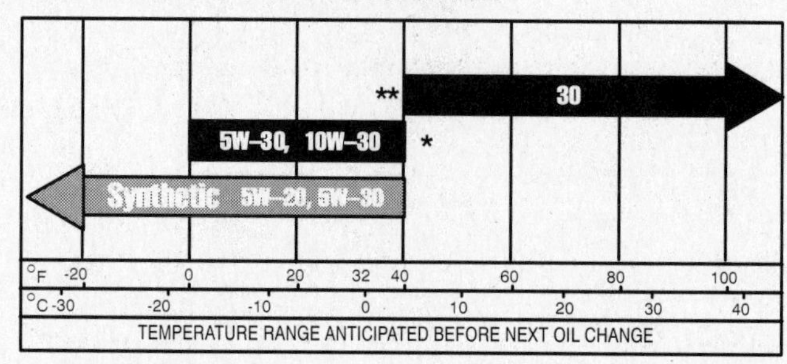

* Air cooled engines run hotter than automotive engines. Use of multi-viscosity oils (10W-30, etc.) above 40° F will result in high oil consumption and possible engine damage. Check oil level more frequently if using these types of oils.

** SAE 30 oil, if used below 40° F, will result in hard starting and possible engine bore damage due to inadequate lubrication.

Change Oil (Crankcase)

Change oil after first five hours of operation. Thereafter change engine oil each season or every fifty hours of operation, under normal operating conditions. Change engine oil weekly or every twenty five hours of operation if the engine is operated under heavy load, or in high ambient temperatures.

Remove oil drain plug and drain oil while engine is warm. Replace drain plug, Fig. 2, Illus. 1 or Illus. 2. Remove dipstick, Fig. 1 or oil fill plug, Fig. 2. Refill with new oil of proper weight and classification. Replace dipstick, Fig. 1 or oil fill plug, Fig. 2, Illus. 1.

BE SURE OIL LEVEL IS MAINTAINED. Fill to full mark, Fig. 1.

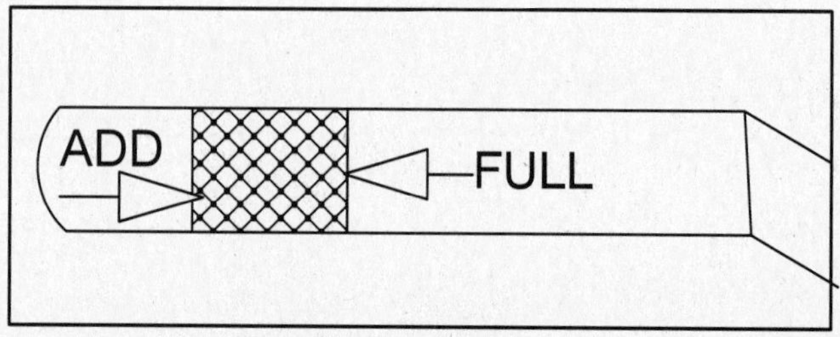

Fig. 1 - Dipstick

NOTE: METRIC EQUIVALENTS ARE LISTED ON PAGE 10 OF THIS SECTION.

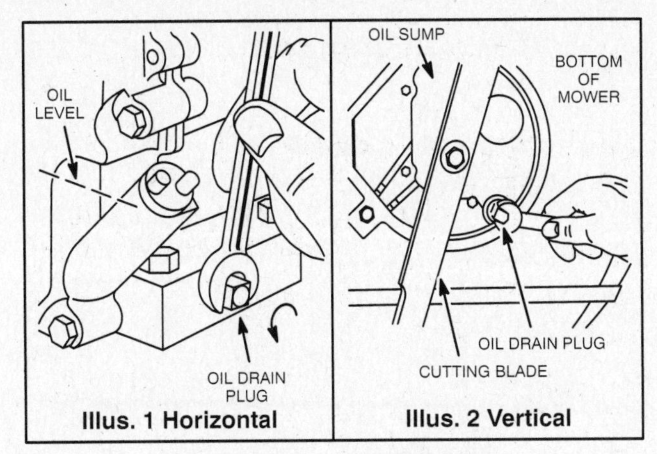

Fig. 2 - Change Oil Crankcase

Check Oil Aluminum Engines (6 to 1 Gear Reduction Models)

Model Series 60000, 80000, 100200, 130000

1. Remove oil level plug and oil fill plug, Fig. 3.
2. Loosen four screws holding gear case cover to drain oil every one hundred (100) hours of operation.
3. Retighten cover screws to 85 in. lbs. torque.
4. Refill gear case with same oil as used in engine crankcase.
5. Pour oil into filler hole until oil runs out of oil level check hole.
6. Replace both plugs making sure oil fill plug with vent hole is installed in top hole, Fig. 3.

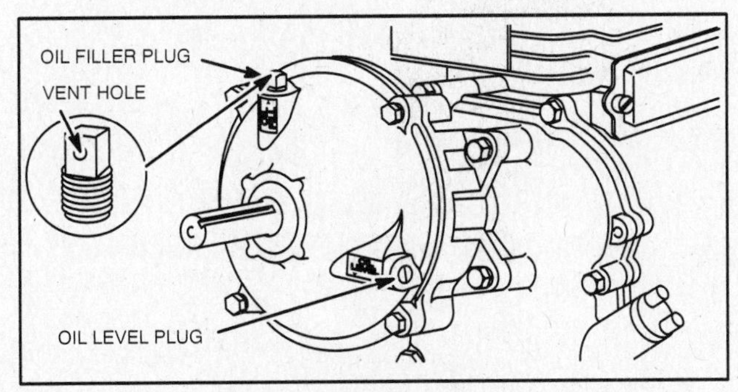

Fig. 3 - Check Oil Level

Models 170000, 190000, 221400

1. Remove drain plug in bottom of gear case cover and drain oil every 100 hours of operation, Fig. 4.
2. Replace plug.
3. To refill, remove oil check plug and oil fill plug and pour oil (same grade as used in crankcase) into filler hole until it runs out level check hole.
4. Replace both plugs. Oil fill plug has a vent hole and must be installed on top of gear case cover.

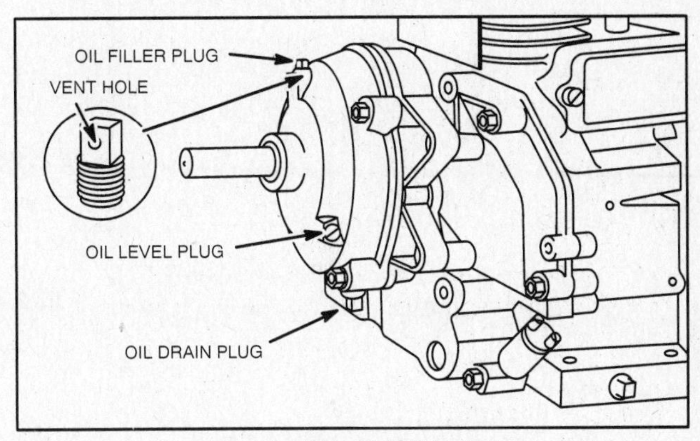

Fig. 4 - Check Oil Level

Models 230000, 240000

The reduction gears are lubricated by engine crankcase oil. Remove drain plug from gear case cover to drain oil remaining in gear case when changing oil in engine crankcase, Fig. 5.

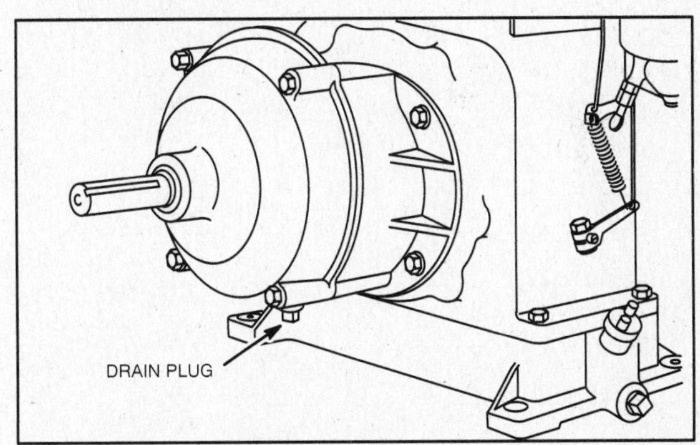

Fig. 5 - Change Oil

EXTENDED OIL FILL AND DIPSTICKS

1. When installing the extended oil fill and dipstick assembly, the tube must be installed so the "O" ring seal is firmly compressed.
2. To do so, push the tube downward toward the sump, then tighten blower housing screw, which is used to secure the tube and bracket.
3. When the cap and dipstick assembly is fully depressed or screwed down, it seals the upper end of the tube, Fig. 6.

NOTE: METRIC EQUIVALENTS ARE LISTED ON PAGE 10 OF THIS SECTION.

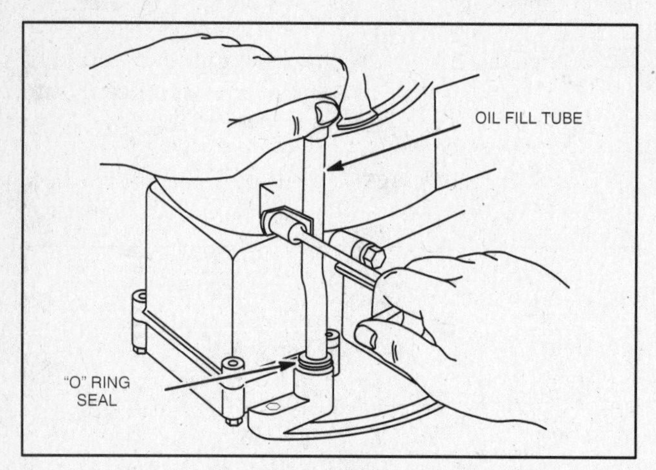

Fig. 6 – Extended Oil Fill and Dipstick

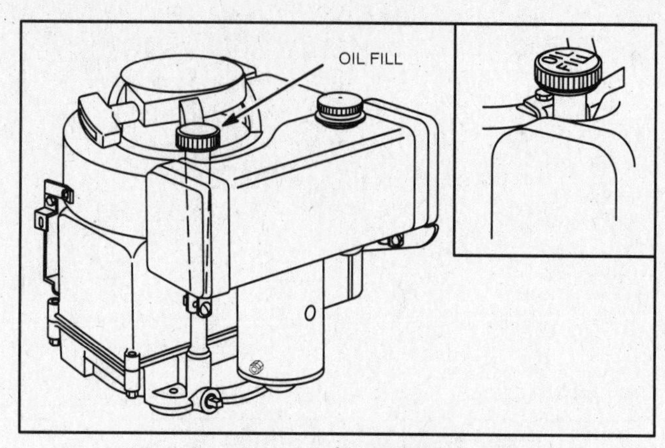

Fig. 8 – Model Series 170700,190700, 250000, 280000

A LEAK AT THE SEAL BETWEEN THE TUBE AND SUMP, OR AT THE SEAL AT THE UPPER END OF THE DIPSTICK CAN RESULT IN A LOSS OF CRANKCASE VACUUM, AND A DISCHARGE OF SMOKE THROUGH THE MUFFLER.

Caution owners not to overfill the sump or crankcase with oil when using the extended filler and dipstick. The dipstick is marked "DO NOT OVERFILL." Excessive oil will cause a smoking condition, as the engine attempts to discharge the surplus oil.

Various styles of extended Oil Fill and Dipsticks are shown in Figs. 7, 8, 9, and 10.

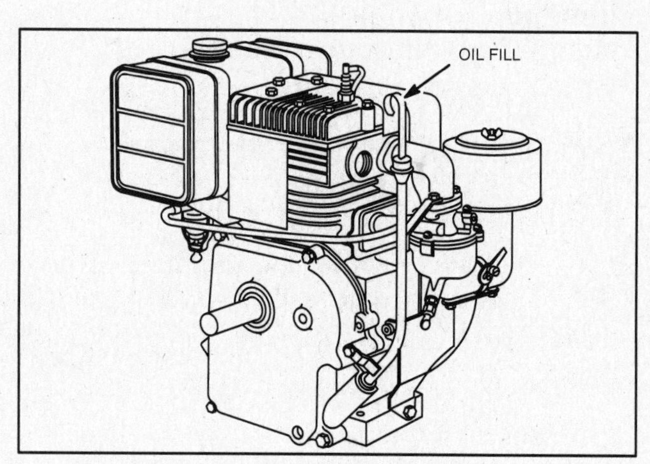

Fig. 9 – Model Series 170400, 190400, 195400

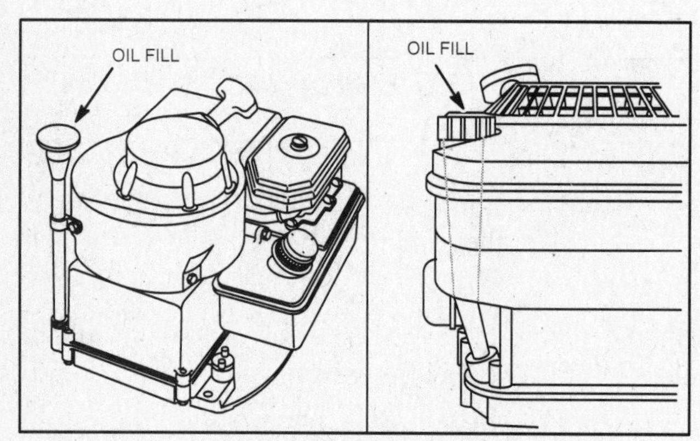

Fig. 7 – Model Series 92000, 100000, 110000, 120000, 130000

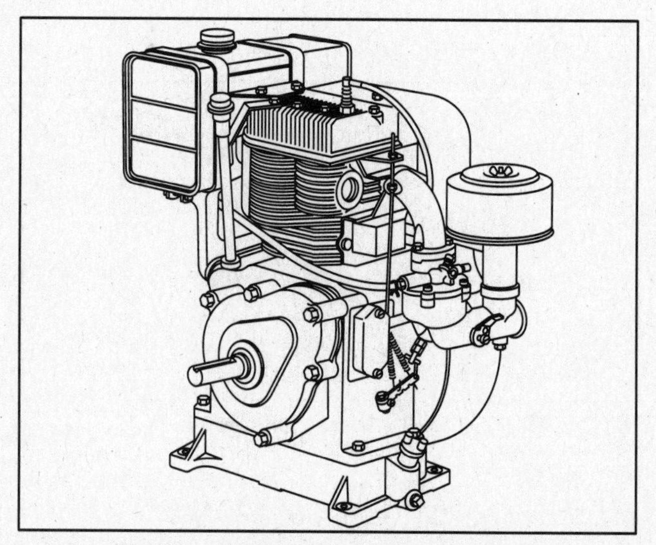

Fig. 10 – Model Series 300000, 320000

NOTE: METRIC EQUIVALENTS ARE LISTED ON PAGE 10 OF THIS SECTION.

BREATHER

It is the breather's function to maintain a vacuum in the crankcase. The breather has a fiber disc valve, which limits the direction of air flow caused by the piston moving back and forth. Air can flow out of the crankcase, but the one way valve blocks the return flow, thus maintaining a vacuum in the crankcase.

A partial vacuum must be maintained in the crankcase to prevent oil from being forced out of engine, at the piston rings, oil seals, breaker plunger (if so equipped) and gaskets.

Checking Breathers

If the fiber disc valve is stuck or binding, the breather cannot function properly and must be replaced. A .045" wire gauge should not enter the space between the fiber disc valve and body. (A spark plug wire gauge may be used.) Check as shown in Fig. 11.

NOTE: The fiber disc valve is held in place by an internal bracket which will be distorted if pressure is applied to the fiber disc valve. Therefore, do not apply force when checking with wire gauge.

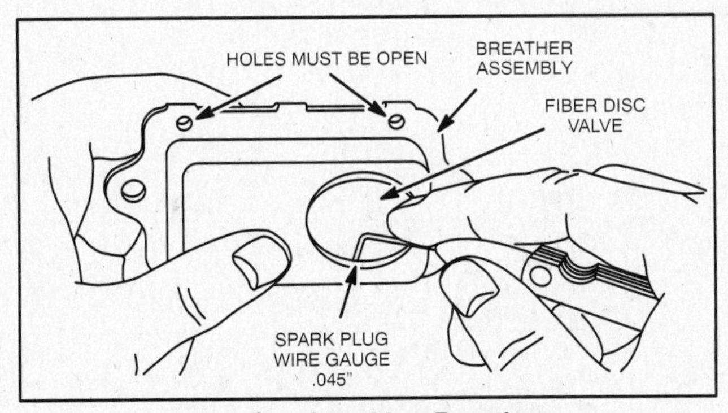

Fig. 11 - Checking Breather

If breather is removed for inspection, or valve repair, a new gasket should be used when replacing breather. Tighten screws securely to prevent oil leakage.

Most breathers are now vented through the air cleaner, to prevent dirt from entering the crankcase. Check to be sure venting elbows or tube are not damaged and seal properly.

Various breather assemblies are illustrated in Fig. 12.

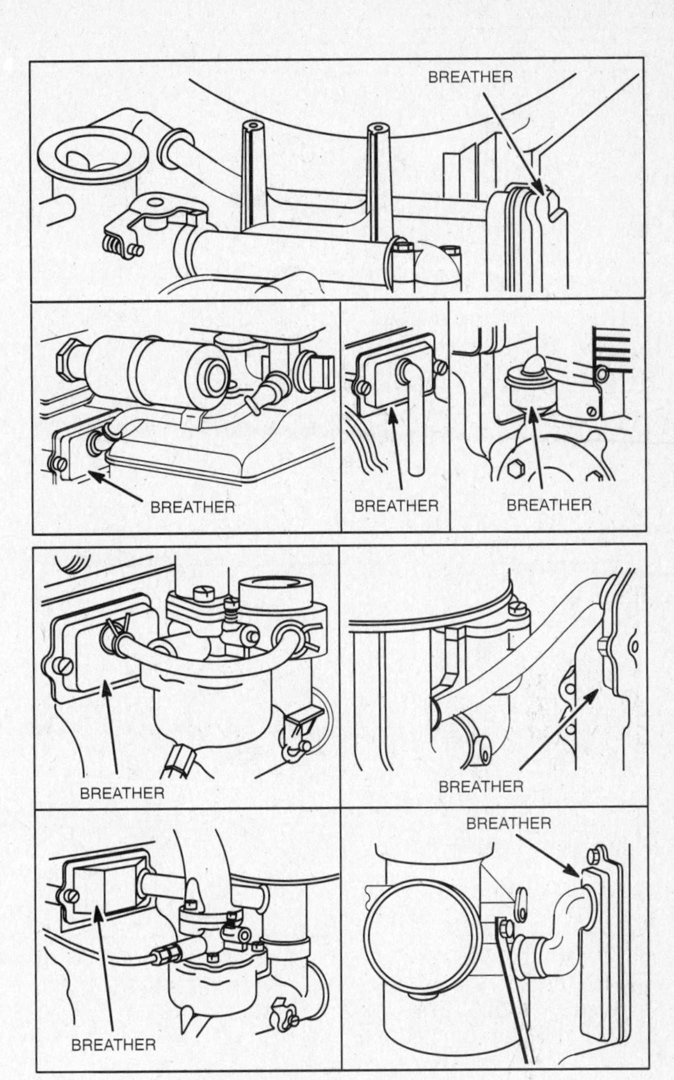

Fig. 12 - Breather Assemblies

OIL DIPPER

ALUMINUM ALLOY AND CAST IRON ENGINES

In the splash system, the dipper dips into the oil reservoir in base of engine. There is no pump nor moving parts. Install connecting rod and dipper by engine model series as shown in Fig. 13.

NOTE: METRIC EQUIVALENTS ARE LISTED ON PAGE 10 OF THIS SECTION.

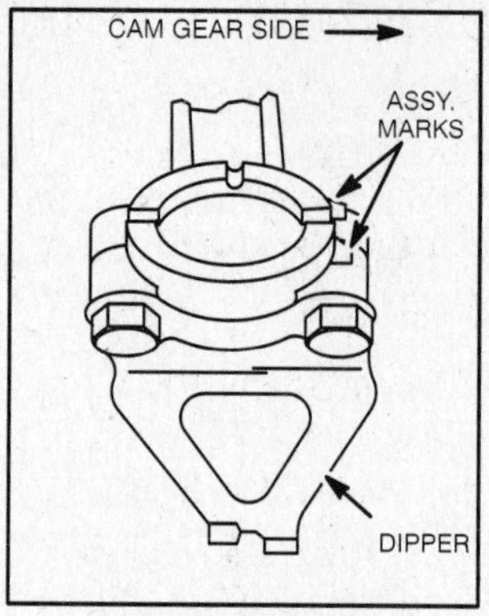

Aluminum Model Series 60000

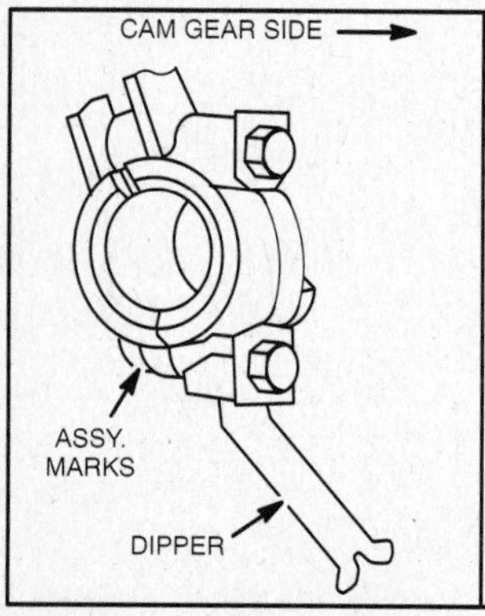

Aluminum Model Series 80000, 90000, 111000, 112000, 170000, 190000, 220000, 250000, 280000

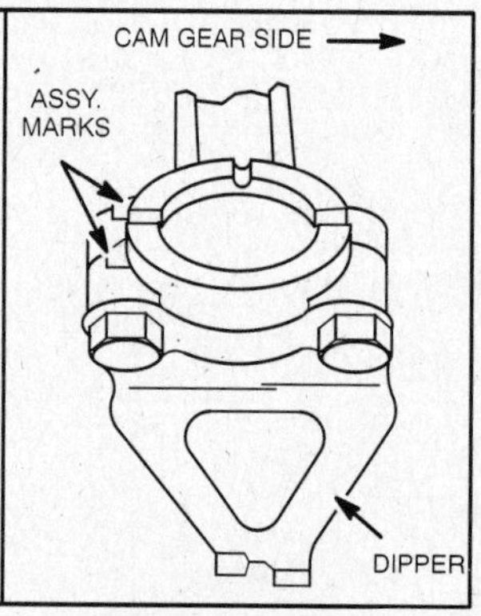

Aluminum Model Series 100200, 130000, 170000

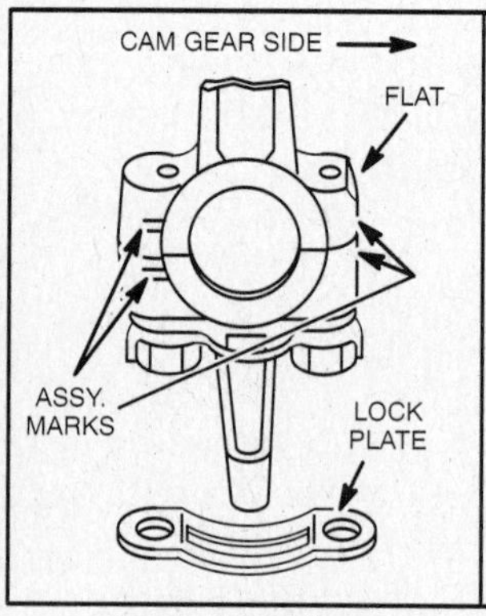

Early Cast Iron Model Series 230000

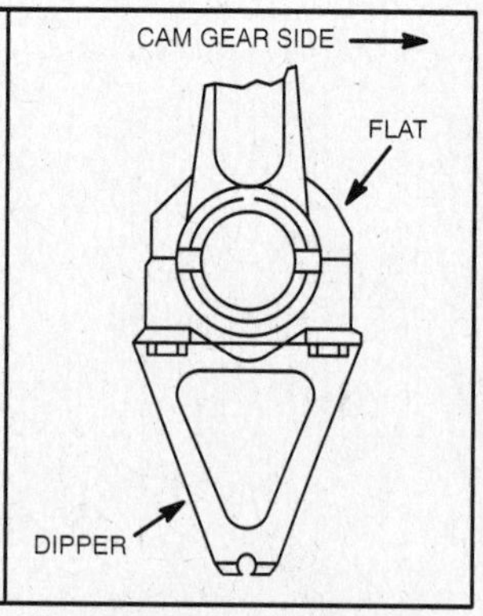

Cast Iron Model Series 230000, 240000, 300000, 320000

Fig. 13 - Connecting Rod Installation, Horizontal Crankshaft Engines

OIL SLINGER

Aluminum Alloy Engines

The oil slinger is driven by the cam gear. Old style slingers using a die cast bracket assembly have a steel bushing between the slinger and the bracket. Replace bracket on which the oil slinger rides if worn to a diameter of .490" or less. Replace steel bushing if worn, Fig. 14. Illus. 1. Newer style oil slingers have a stamped steel bracket. Unit is a one piece assembly, Fig. 14. Illus. 2 and Fig. 15. Spring washer is used only on Models 100900, 130900. Inspect gear teeth, old and new style; replace if worn.

NOTE: On Model Series 130700, 130900, 131700, 132900 equipped with right angle drive P.T.O. DO NOT USE SPRING WASHER on oil slinger bracket.

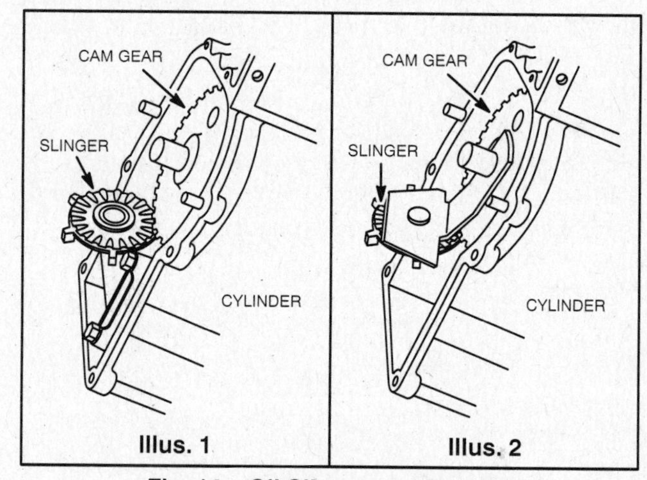

Fig. 14 - Oil Slinger and Bracket

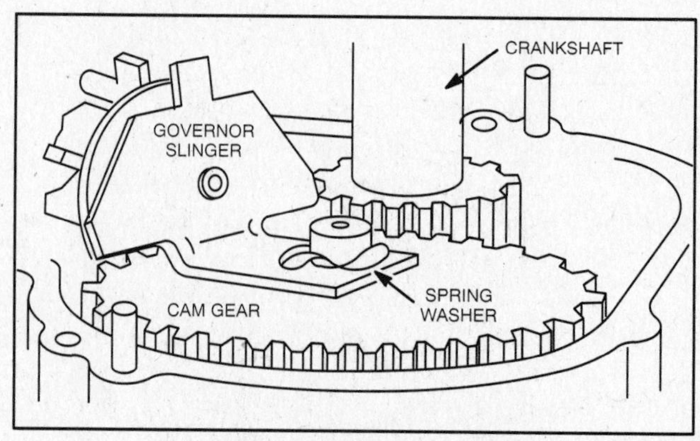

Fig. 15 - Oil Slinger and Bracket Vertical Crankshaft Engines

NOTE: METRIC EQUIVALENTS ARE LISTED ON PAGE 10 OF THIS SECTION.

OIL GARD®

Some models of Briggs & Stratton engines are equipped with Oil Gard®, a low oil shut off system designed to prevent engine damage before the engine becomes damaged by running with insufficient oil.

Two types of Oil Gard® have been used, one is a float operated prevent ignition system and the other is a spark gap prevent ignition system, Figs. 16 and 17.

Principles of Operation, Float Type

This Oil Gard® system uses a float to operate a magnetic switch, depending on oil level in engine crankcase. When oil level is at correct level, the float raises up opening the magnetic switch. When oil level drops to a level where oil level is too low, the float drops and causes the magnetic switch to close.

When this happens, two things occur.

1. The ignition primary current will cause the warning light to flash.
2. The engine will stop.

The engine cannot be restarted until the oil level is restored to correct level opening switch contacts, Fig. 16.

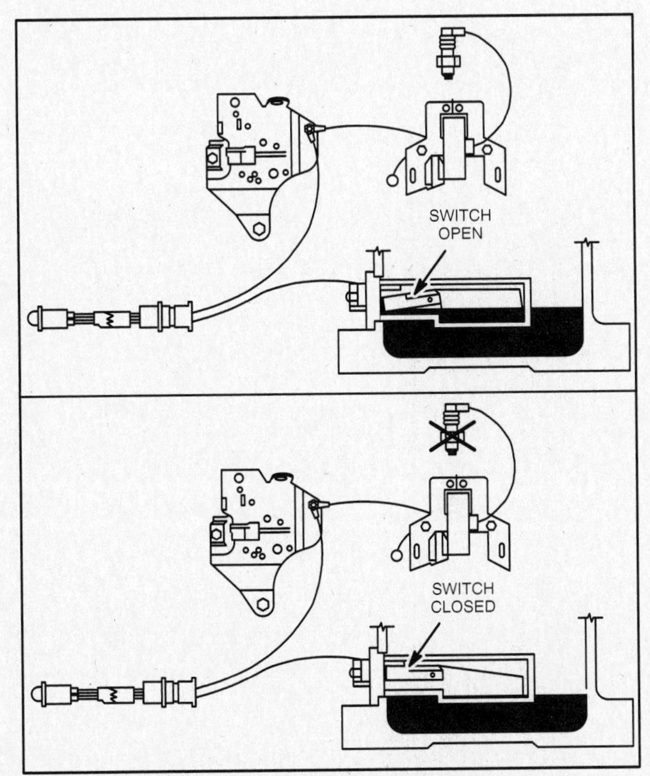

Fig. 16 - Float Type Oil Gard®

Principles of Operation, Spark Gap Type

This Oil Gard® system uses an oil level sensor with a spark gap connected to a high tension lead from the ignition armature. When oil is the correct level, the spark gap is filled with oil and a spark will not jump the gap.

When oil level drops to the point where the spark gap is exposed to air in the crankcase, the resistance of the gap is lower than the spark plug gap. The armature will fire across the Oil Gard® sensor instead of the spark plug stopping the engine. The engine cannot be restarted until the oil level is returned to normal, Fig. 17.

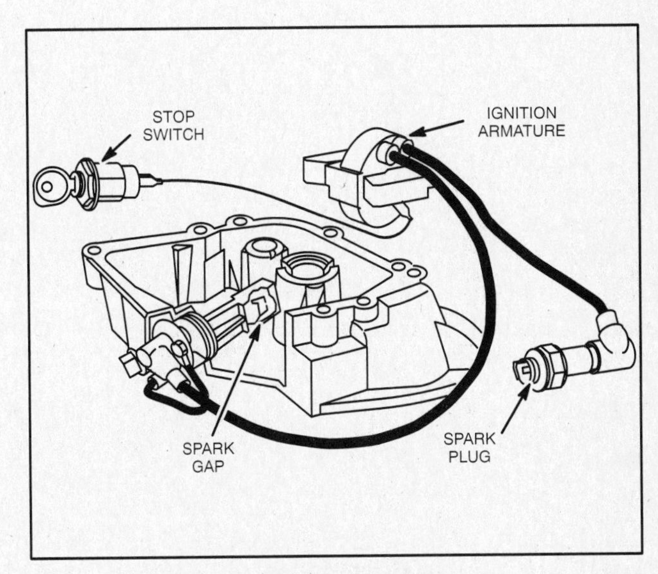

Fig. 17 - Spark Gap Oil Gard®

8

NOTE: METRIC EQUIVALENTS ARE LISTED ON PAGE 10 OF THIS SECTION.

TROUBLESHOOTING OIL GARD® SYSTEMS

Troubleshooting an Oil Gard® system need not be a complicated or time-consuming process. When a problem occurs, a basic understanding of how the Oil Gard® switch and its component parts function is all that is needed in order to locate the problem or cause of failure with this low-oil warning system. If a problem does occur, review the principle of operation, Figs. 18 and 19.

USE THE CHARTS AND ILLUSTRATIONS TO ASSIST IN TROUBLESHOOTING PROBLEMS WHICH COULD OCCUR WITH THE LOW-OIL WARNING SYSTEM . . . OIL GARD®. The chart lists the failures that are most likely to occur first with given references by letter designation on the illustration.

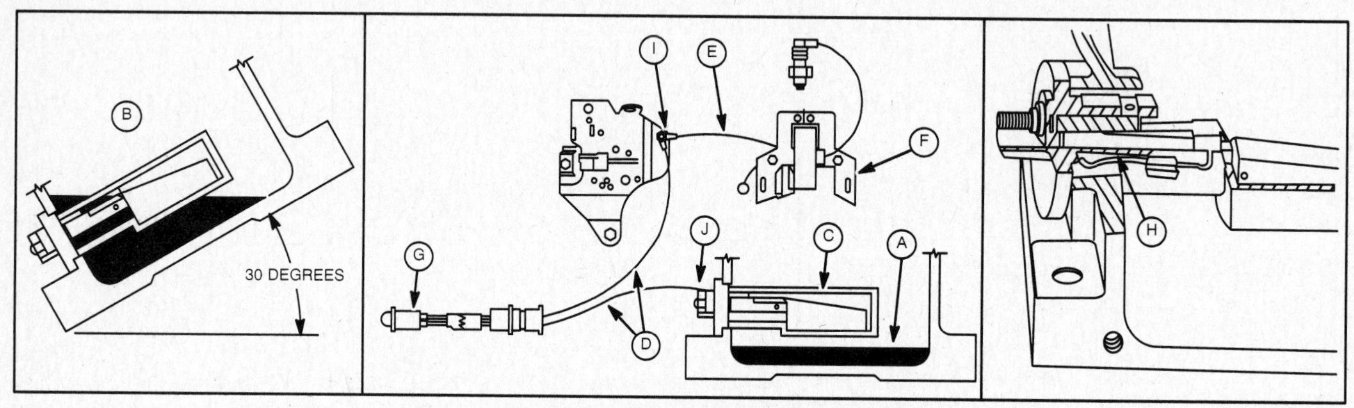

Fig. 18 – Typical Oil Gard® Problems, Float Type

The table below lists possible problems with the probable cause and cure. Refer to Fig. 18.

PROBLEM	LETTER	CAUSE	CURE
No Spark – Light Flashes	A	Low Oil in Crankcase	Refill With Oil
	B	Excessive Angle of Operation	Reduce Angle of Operation
	C	Defective Oil Gard® Switch	Replace Switch
No Spark – Light Does Not Flash – Correct Amount of Oil in Crankcase	D	Wiring Harness Grounded	Repair or Replace Wiring Harness
	E	Stop Wire Grounded	Repair or Replace Wire
	F	Defective Magnetron® Armature	Replace Armature
Spark Present – Light Does Not Flash – Low on Oil	G	Defective Light or Harness	Replace Light
	H	Oil Gard® Switch Wire Not Making Ground	Adjust Wire
	C	Defective Oil Gard® Switch	Replace
Intermittent Spark	D or E	Grounded Stop Wire or Harness	Repair or Replace Wire or Harness
	C	Defective Oil Gard® Switch	Replace Switch
	H	Oil Gard® Switch Wire Not Making Ground	Adjust Switch Wire
No Spark – Light Does Not Flash – Low on Oil	I or J	Wiring Harness Connections Reversed	Reverse Connections

NOTE: METRIC EQUIVALENTS ARE LISTED ON PAGE 10 OF THIS SECTION.

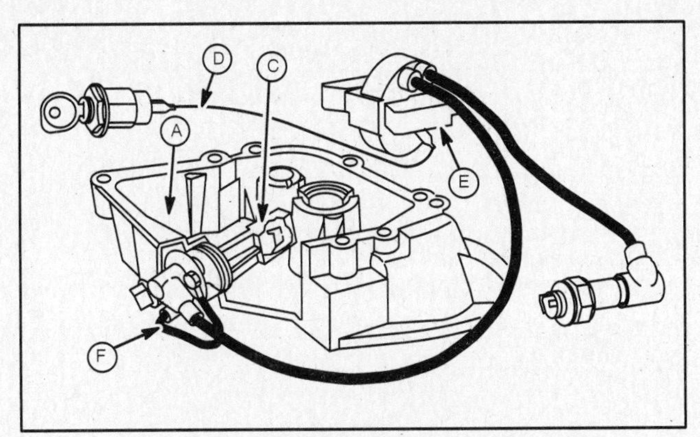

Fig. 19 – Typical Oil Gard® Problems, Spark Gap Type

The table below lists possible problems with the probable cause and cure. Refer to Fig. 19.

PROBLEM	LETTER	CAUSE	CURE
No Spark	A	Low Oil in Crankcase	Refill With Oil
	B	Excessive Angle of Operation	Reduce Angle of Operation
	C	Defective Oil Gard® Sensor	Replace Sensor
No Spark – Correct Amount of Oil in Crankcase	D	Stop Wire Grounded	Repair or Replace Wire
	E	Defective Magnetron® Armature	Replace Armature
Spark Present – Low on Oil	F	Defective Ground Wire	Repair or Replace Wire
	C	Defective Oil Gard® Sensor	Replace Sensor
Intermittent Spark	D	Stop Wire Grounded	Repair or Replace Wire
	C	Defective Oil Gard® Sensor	Replace Sensor

8

NOTE: METRIC EQUIVALENTS ARE LISTED ON PAGE 10 OF THIS SECTION.

<table>
<tr><th colspan="3">METRIC EQUIVALENTS</th></tr>
<tr><th colspan="3">CAPACITY, FRACTIONAL</th></tr>
<tr><th>Pints</th><th colspan="2">Liters</th></tr>
<tr><td>1-1/4</td><td colspan="2">.6</td></tr>
<tr><td>1-3/4</td><td colspan="2">.8</td></tr>
<tr><td>2-1/4</td><td colspan="2">1.1</td></tr>
<tr><td>2-1/2</td><td colspan="2"></td></tr>
<tr><td>2-3/4</td><td colspan="2">1.3</td></tr>
<tr><td>3</td><td colspan="2">1.4</td></tr>
<tr><td>4</td><td colspan="2">1.9</td></tr>
<tr><th colspan="3">DIMENSIONS, DECIMAL</th></tr>
<tr><th>Inches</th><th colspan="2">Millimeters</th></tr>
<tr><td>.045</td><td colspan="2">1.14</td></tr>
<tr><td>.490</td><td colspan="2">1.24</td></tr>
<tr><th colspan="3">TEMPERATURE</th></tr>
<tr><th>Fahrenheit</th><th colspan="2">Centigrade</th></tr>
<tr><td>40</td><td colspan="2">4</td></tr>
<tr><th colspan="3">TORQUE</th></tr>
<tr><th>In.
Lbs.</th><th>Kgcm
Kpcm</th><th>Nm</th></tr>
<tr><td>85</td><td>98</td><td>960</td></tr>
</table>

NOTE: METRIC EQUIVALENTS ARE LISTED ON PAGE 10 OF THIS SECTION.

Section 9
PISTONS – RINGS – RODS

INDEX, SECTION 9

PISTON PINS

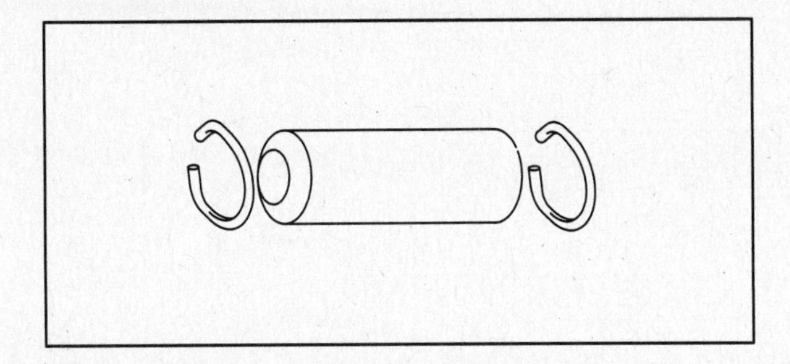

PISTONS

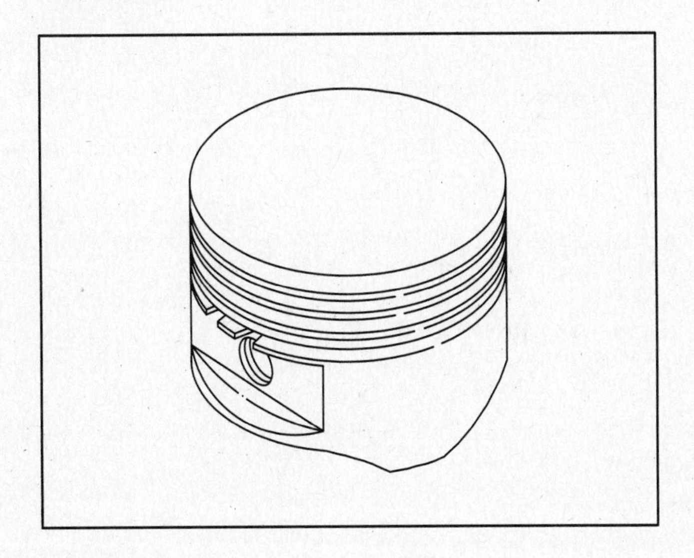

RINGS

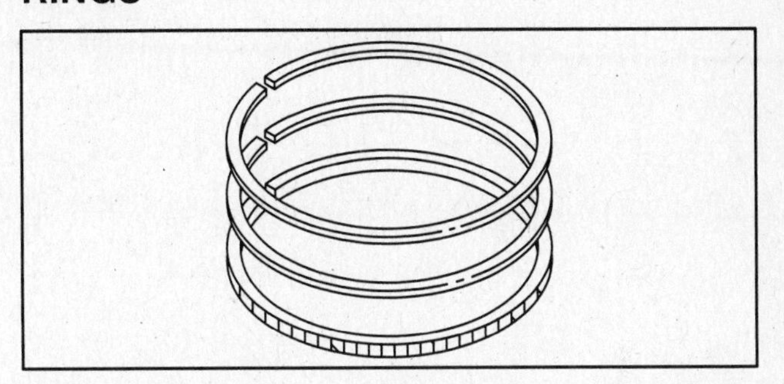

CONNECTING RODS

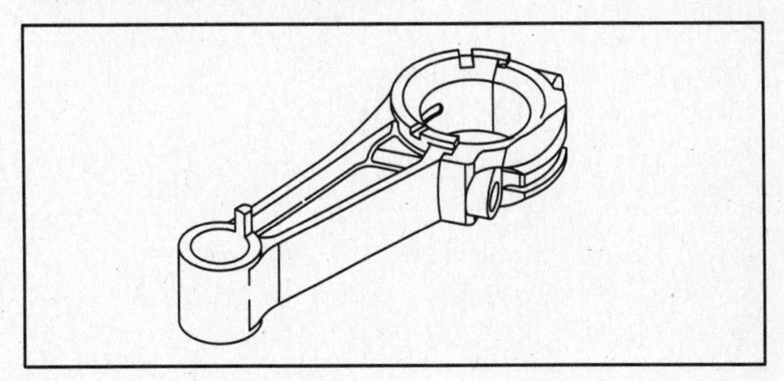

9

NOTE: METRIC EQUIVALENTS ARE LISTED ON PAGE 8 OF THIS SECTION.

REMOVE PISTON AND CONNECTING ROD

To remove piston and connecting rod from engine, bend down rod lock, when used, Fig. 1. Connecting rods without locks use one, two thin washers or washer head screws instead of locks. On connecting rods with dippers held by both connecting rod bolts, no washers or rod locks are used.

Remove connecting rod cap. Remove any carbon or ridge at top of cylinder bore to prevent ring breakage on cast iron sleeves or cast iron cylinders. The ridge does not have to be removed on aluminum cylinder bores. Push piston and rod out through top of cylinder.

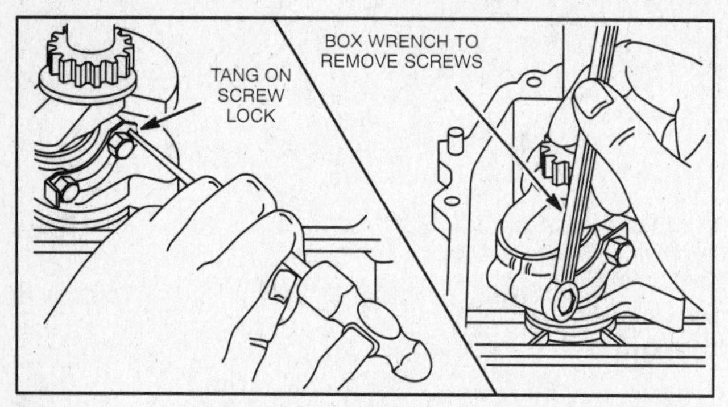

Fig. 1 – Bending Rod Lock

NOTE: All pistons are suppose to have oil drain slots or drilled holes in the oil control ring groove except for Model Series 120000 which do not have drain slots or holes but use drain slots in the ring lands.

Pistons used in SLEEVE BORE aluminum alloy engines are stamped with the letter "L," Fig. 2, Illus. 1. These pistons **CANNOT BE USED** in Kool-Bore® (aluminum bore) engines.

Pistons used in Kool-Bore® (aluminum bore) engines are chrome plated. These chrome plated pistons **CANNOT BE USED** in SLEEVE BORE engines, Fig. 2, Illus. 2.

Fig. 2 – Piston Variations

REMOVE CONNECTING ROD
(Except Model Series 120000)

To remove connecting rod from piston, remove piston pin lock with thin nose pliers. One end of the pin is drilled to facilitate removal of the lock, Fig. 3.

REMOVE CONNECTING ROD
Model Series 120000

Remove the piston lock from piston with thin nose pliers. Push piston pin out of piston from opposite side of piston.

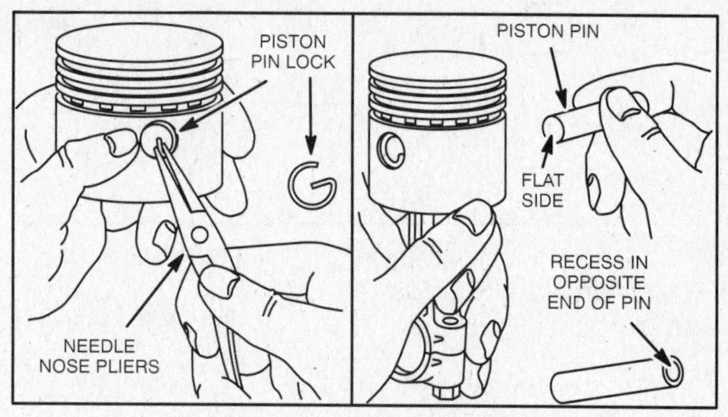

Fig. 3 – Removing Rod

REMOVE PISTON RINGS

Remove piston rings using Piston Ring Expander Tool, #19340, Fig. 4.

NOTE: Some oil control rings consist of two thin steel rails and a spring expander. These steel rails cannot be removed with Piston Ring Expander, Tool #19340. Grasp one end of the steel rail and wind the rail from the oil ring groove into the next ring groove. Repeat into the top ring groove and then off the piston.

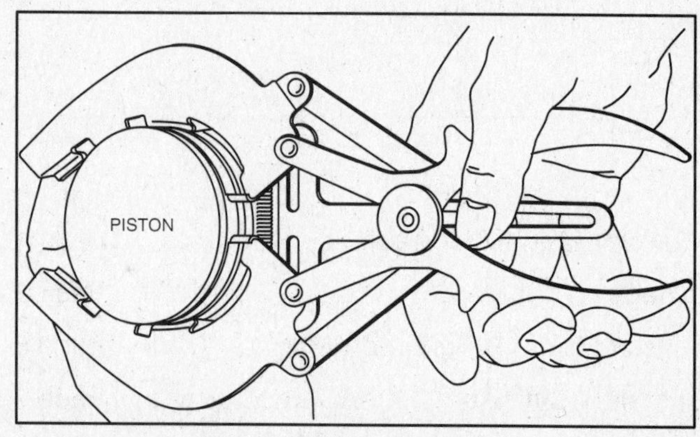

Fig. 4 – Removing Rings

NOTE: METRIC EQUIVALENTS ARE LISTED ON PAGE 8 OF THIS SECTION.

CHECK PISTON

If cylinder is to be resized, there is no reason to check the piston, since a new oversized piston assembly will be used.

If, however, the cylinder is not to be resized, and the piston shows no signs of wear or scoring, the piston should be checked.

Check Piston Ring Land Wear

To do so, clean carbon from top ring groove. Place a NEW ring in the groove and measure the space between the ring and the ring land. If a .007 inch thick feeler gauge, Model Series 60000 through 130000, or .009 inch thick feeler gauge, Model Series 170000 through 320000, can be inserted, the piston is worn and should be replaced, Fig. 5.

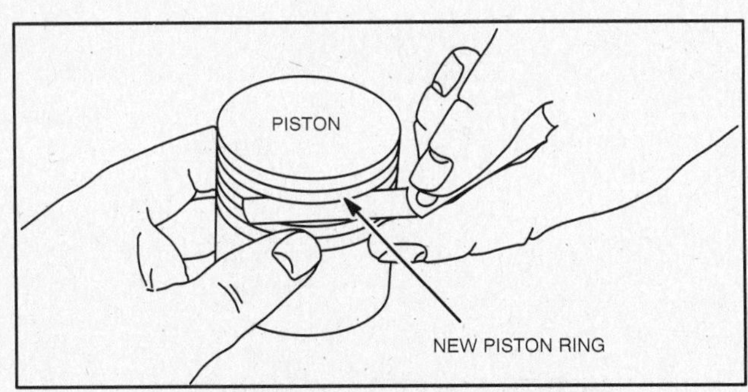

Fig. 5 - Checking Ring Grooves

Check Piston Ring End Gaps

To check rings, first clean all carbon from the ends of the rings and from the cylinder bore. Insert old rings one at a time 1 inch down into the cylinder. Check gap with feeler gauge, Fig. 6. If ring gap is greater than shown in Table No. 1, the ring should be rejected.

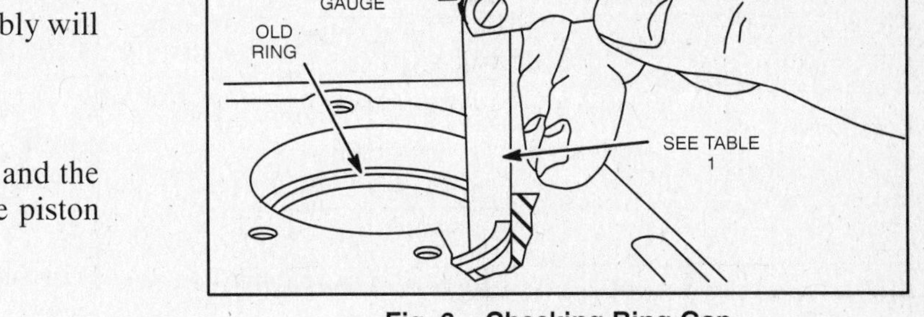

Fig. 6 - Checking Ring Gap

NOTE: Do not deglaze cylinder walls when installing piston rings in aluminum cylinder engines.

Chrome Rings

NOTE: Chrome ring sets are available for all current aluminum and cast iron cylinder models (except Model Series 100700), no honing or deglazing is required. The cylinder bore can be "worn to" a maximum of .005" oversize when using chrome rings. See Service Bulletin 479 or Engine Parts List.

TABLE NO. 1
Ring End Gap Reject Size

	Compression Rings	Oil Ring
Aluminum Cylinder Bores	.035"	.045"
Cast Iron Cylinder Bores	.030"	.035"

CONNECTING ROD

If the crankpin bearing in the rod is scored, the rod must be replaced. Rejection sizes of crankpin bearing hole and piston pin bearing hole are shown in Table No. 2. Piston pins .005" oversize are available in case the connecting rod and piston are worn at the piston pin bearing. If, however, the crankpin bearing in the connecting rod is worn, the rod should be replaced. Do not attempt to "file" or "fit" the rod.

NOTE: METRIC EQUIVALENTS ARE LISTED ON PAGE 8 OF THIS SECTION.

TABLE NO. 2
Connecting Rod Reject Size

Basic Model Series	Crank Pin Bearing	Piston Pin Bearing
Aluminum Cylinder		
60000	.876"	.492"
80000	1.001"	.492"
90000, 100700, 110000, 120000	1.001"	.492"
100200, 100900	1.001"	.555"
130000	1.001"	.492"
170000	1.095"	.674"
190000	1.127"	.674"
220000, 250000, 280000	1.252"	.802"
Cast Iron Cylinder		
230000	1.189"	.736"
240000	1.314"	.674"
300000, 320000	1.314"	.802"

If the piston pin is worn .0005" out of round or below the rejection sizes listed in Table No. 3, it should be replaced.

TABLE NO. 3
Piston Pin Reject Sizes

Basic Model Series	Piston Pin O.D.	Pin Bore I.D.
Aluminum Cylinder		
60000, 80000, 90000, 100700, 110000, 120000	.489"	.491"
100200, 100900	.552"	.554"
130000	.489"	.491"
170000, 190000	.671"	.673"
220000, 250000, 280000	.799"	.801"
Cast Iron Cylinder		
230000	.734"	.736"
240000	.671"	.673"
300000, 320000	.799"	.801"

ASSEMBLE PISTON AND CONNECTING ROD

Piston pins are a push-fit in piston and connecting rod. Some pistons use a piston pin with one end flat and the other end drilled. All other pistons use a hollow piston pin. Some pistons use two piston pin locks while other pistons use one piston pin lock and a piston pin stop in the piston.

Piston Without Notch on Head

Install one piston pin lock in piston pin bore groove. (Do not install lock if only one piston pin bore has lock groove until after installing piston pin.) Place rod inside piston and slide piston pin into piston from side opposite lock or piston pin stop then through piston and rod until pin seats on lock or stop. Install second piston pin lock.

Piston With Notch on Head

The notch on the piston faces toward the magneto side of the engine. Install one pin lock in pin bore groove on side opposite notch.

NOTE: METRIC EQUIVALENTS ARE LISTED ON PAGE 8 OF THIS SECTION.

On all pistons (with notch on head) except Model Series 300000, 320000 place rod in piston with offset rod cap to left side of piston, Fig. 7. Push piston pin from notch side of piston through piston and rod until pin seats on lock. Install second piston pin lock, (when used) Fig. 7.

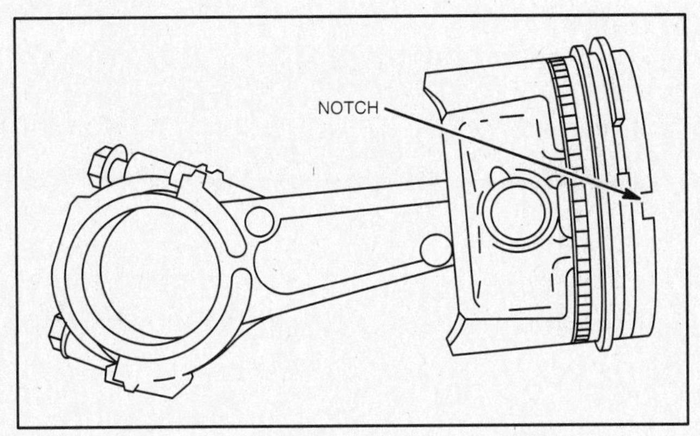

Fig. 7 - Assembling Piston and Rod

Model Series 300000, 320000 have a notch and a letter "F" on piston. Install pin lock in pin bore groove opposite the notch and letter "F." Place rod in piston with assembly marks on same side as notch and letter "F" on piston. Install pin through piston and rod until pin seats on lock. Install second lock, Fig. 8.

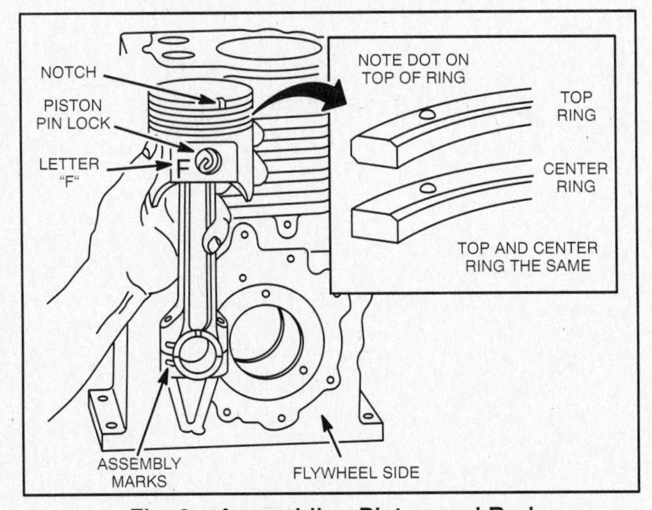

Fig. 8 - Assembling Piston and Rod

INSTALL PISTON RINGS ON PISTON

Install oil control ring first, then center compression ring and top compression ring last, as shown in Fig. 9 and Fig. 10. Use Piston Ring Expander, Tool #19340. Install expander under oil control ring, when so equipped, Figs. 9 and 10.

NOTE: When installing new piston rings in a cylinder bore that is within specification shown, Section 11, page 1, Table No. 1, the cylinder bore should be reconditioned. The proper cylinder cross hatch ensures proper lubrication and piston ring rotation. See "Cylinder Finish," Section 11, page 3.

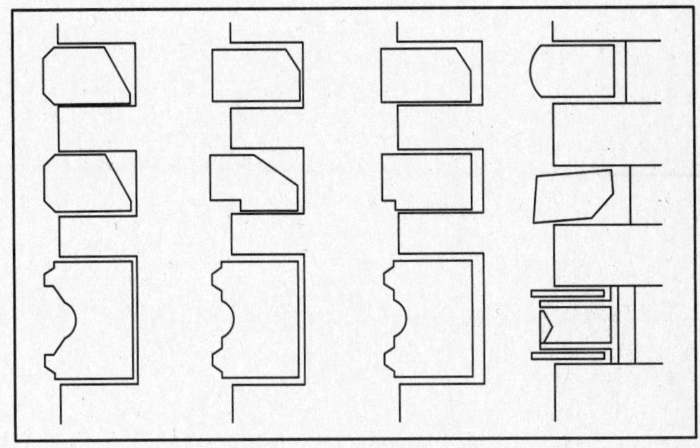

Fig. 9 - Aluminum Bore Rings

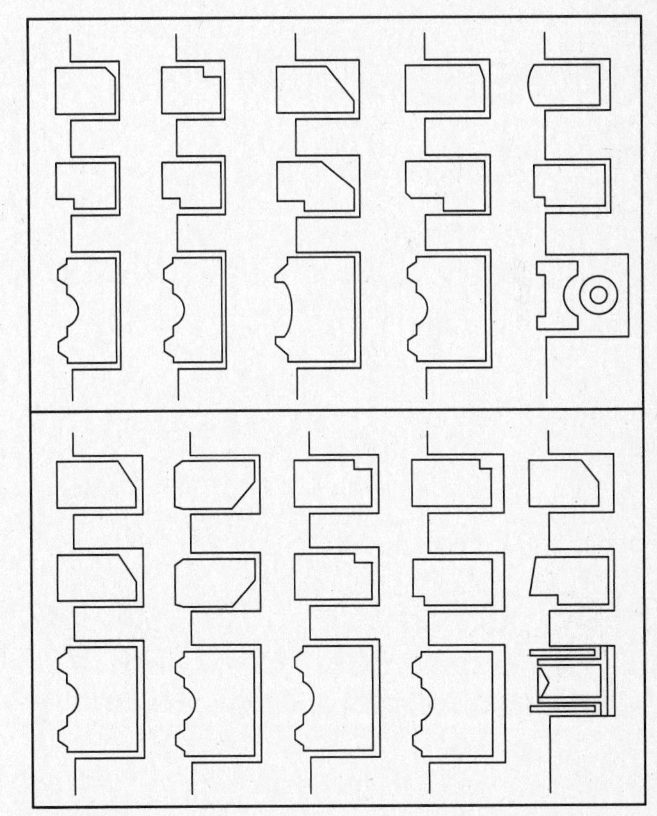

Fig. 10 - Cast Iron Sleeve and Cast Iron Cylinder

NOTE: Some compression rings have an identifying dot on the top of the ring. Always install ring(s) with dot facing top of piston.

NOTE: METRIC EQUIVALENTS ARE LISTED ON PAGE 8 OF THIS SECTION.

NOTE: On oil rings that use two thin steel rails and spring expander, install expander first. Twist one steel rail at a time down from one ring groove to the next and onto the expander.

INSTALL PISTON AND ROD ASSEMBLY IN CYLINDER

1. Oil piston rings and piston skirt. Compress rings with, Ring Compressor (Model Series 60000 through 130000), Tool #19070 or with Ring Compressor (Model Series 170000 and up), Tool #19230.

   NOTE: On aluminum bore engines, use ring compressor as shown, Fig. 11, Illus. 2. On cast iron sleeve and cast iron cylinder engines, use compressor as shown, Fig. 11, Illus. 1.

2. Place piston and compressor upside down on bench and push piston down until head of piston is even with edge of compressor.

3. Tighten compressor until piston cannot be turned in compressor.

4. Then loosen compressor until piston can be turned with slight resistance.

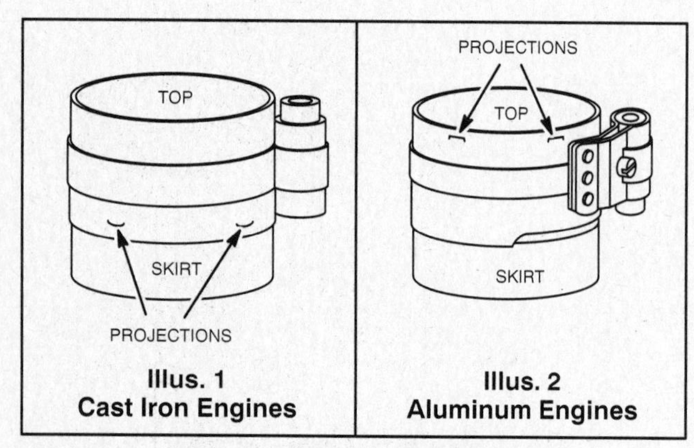

Fig. 11 – Compression Rings

Do not attempt to install piston and ring assembly without ring compressor.

Install in Cylinder (Piston Without Notch On Head)

1. Place connecting rod and piston assembly with compressed rings into cylinder bore.

2. Position rod so correct side is facing cam gear and turn crankshaft until crankpin is at top dead center, Figs. 12 and 13.

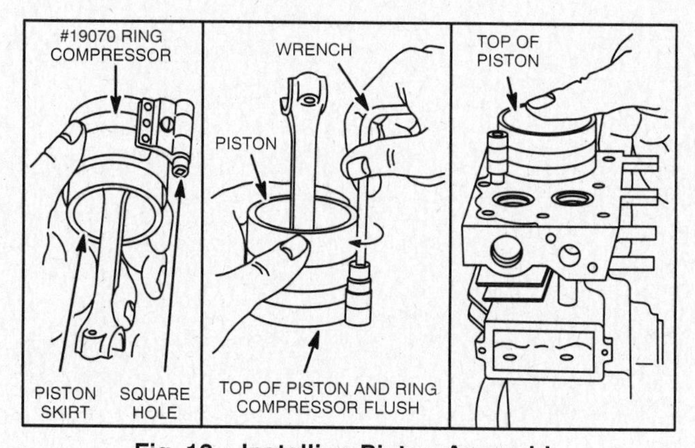

Fig. 12 – Installing Piston Assembly

Install in Cylinder (Piston With Notch On Head)

1. Place rod and piston assembly with compressed rings into cylinder bore with notch on piston facing magneto side of engine.

2. Turn crankshaft until crankpin is at top dead center, Fig. 12.

3. Place shop rag over piston and ring compressor to protect hands.

4. Push piston down by hand until rod rests on crankpin.

5. Oil crankpin and install rod cap with match marks aligned, Fig. 13.

NOTE: METRIC EQUIVALENTS ARE LISTED ON PAGE 8 OF THIS SECTION.

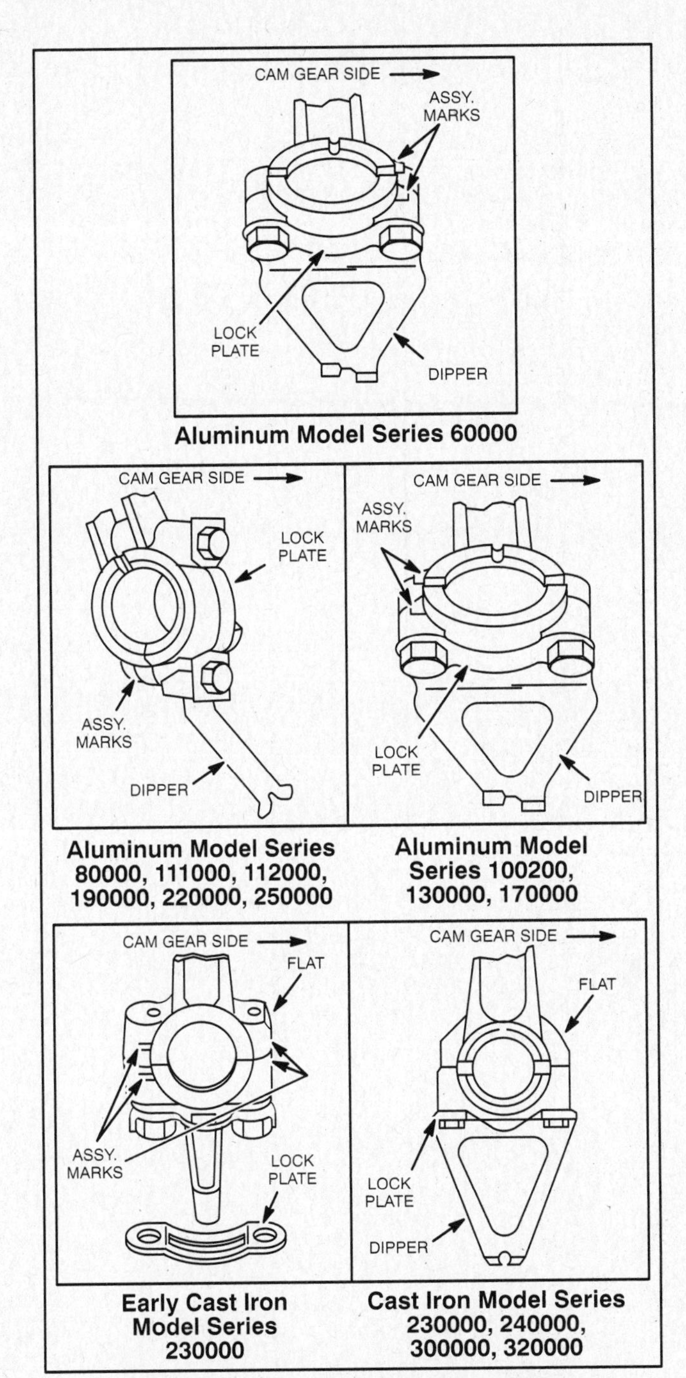

Fig. 13 - Connecting Rod Installation, Horizontal and Vertical Crankshaft Engines. Vertical Crankshaft Engines Do Not Use Dippers

6. Assemble connecting rod screw, rod lock (when supplied), and dipper (when required). Torque screws with Tool #19197 or 19393, Torque Wrench, to specifications listed in Table No. 4.

7. Rotate crankshaft at least two complete revolutions to be sure connecting rod and crankshaft turn freely and rod does not hit cylinder or cam gear.

   NOTE: If rod hits, rod is installed wrong or cam gear is out of time. Correct.

8. If rod and crankshaft are free, bend rod lock (when used) against flats on screw heads, Fig. 14.

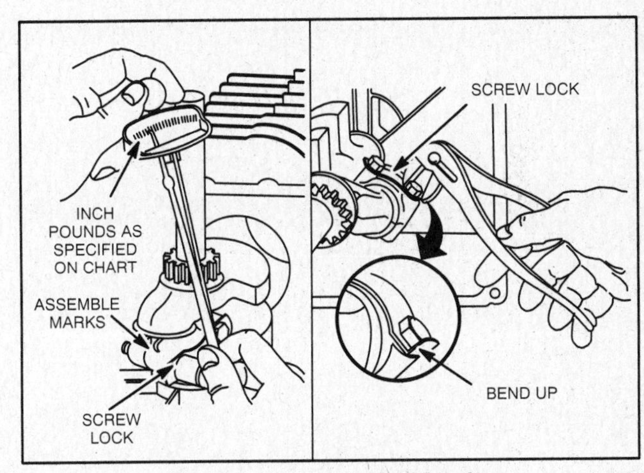

Fig. 14 - Bending Rod Locks

NOTE: Some service rods are shipped with two thick washers under screw heads. Remove and discard these washers. Use two thin washers when no dipper is used. Use one thin washer under screw not holding dipper. No washers are required when dipper is held by both screws or equipped with washer head screw.

TABLE NO. 4
Connecting Rod Screw Torque

Basic Model Series	Torque
Aluminum Cylinder	
60000, 80000, 90000, 100000, 110000, 120000, 130000	100 In. Lbs.
170000	165 In. Lbs.
190000, 220000, 250000, 280000	185 In. Lbs.
Cast Iron Cylinder	
230000, 240000, 300000, 320000	190 In. Lbs.

NOTE: METRIC EQUIVALENTS ARE LISTED ON PAGE 8 OF THIS SECTION.

METRIC EQUIVALENTS

DIMENSIONS, DECIMAL	
Inches	Millimeters
.0005	.01
.005	.13
.007	.18
.009	.23
.030	.76
.035	.89
.045	1.14
.489	12.42
.491	12.47
.492	12.50
.552	14.02
.554	14.07
.555	14.10
.671	17.04
.673	17.09
.674	17.12
.734	18.64
.736	18.69

DIMENSIONS, DECIMAL	
Inches	Millimeters
.799	20.29
.801	20.35
.802	20.37
.876	22.25
1.001	25.43
1.095	27.81
1.127	28.63
1.189	30.20
1.252	31.80
1.314	33.38

TORQUE		
In. Lbs.	Kgcm Kpcm	Ncm
100	115	1130
165	190	1865
185	215	2090
190	220	2150

9

NOTE: METRIC EQUIVALENTS ARE LISTED ON PAGE 8 OF THIS SECTION.

Section 10
CRANKSHAFTS, CAM GEARS, GEAR REDUCTIONS & AUXILIARY DRIVES

INDEX, SECTION 10

AUXILIARY DRIVES

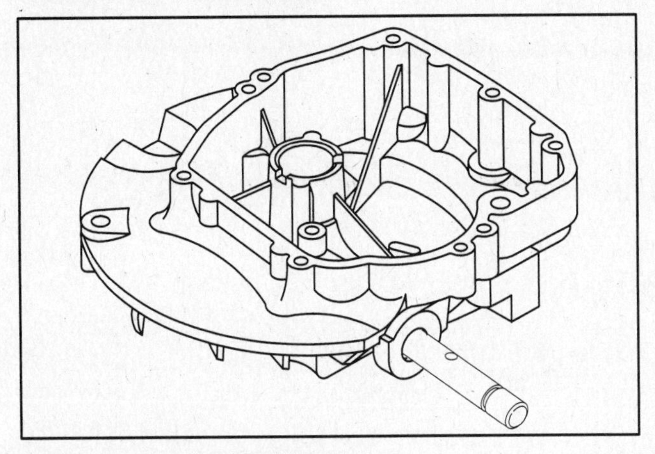

BALL BEARINGS

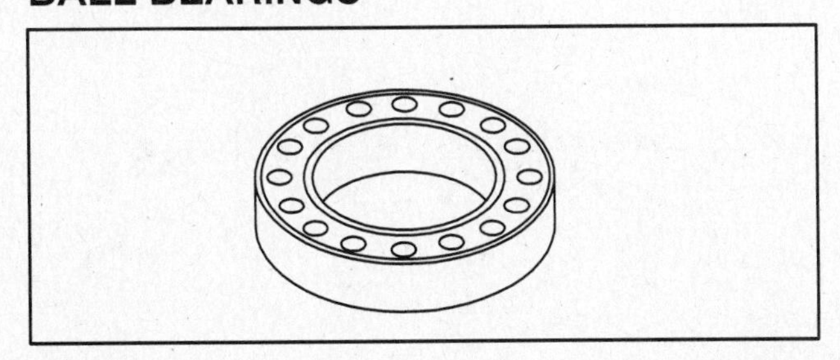

BEARING SUPPORTS

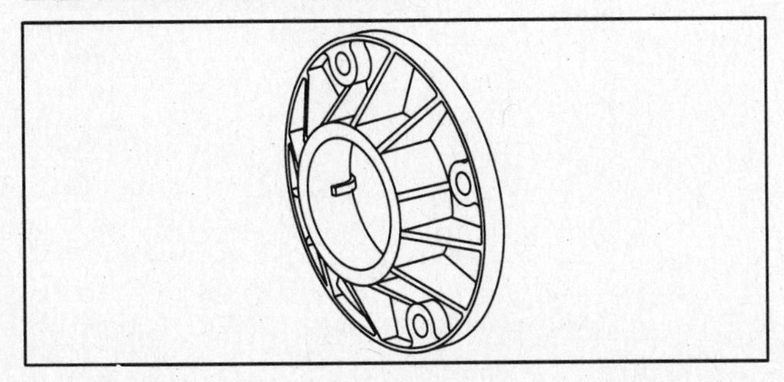

CAM GEARS

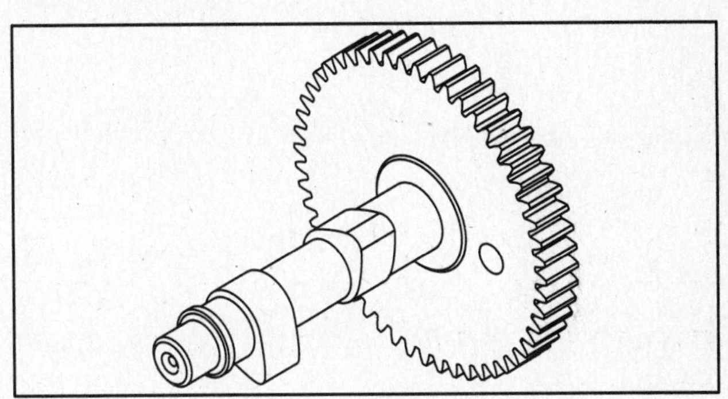

NOTE: METRIC EQUIVALENTS ARE LISTED ON PAGE 26 OF THIS SECTION.

INDEX, CONT'D
SECTION 10

CAM GEARS, CONT'D

CRANKSHAFTS

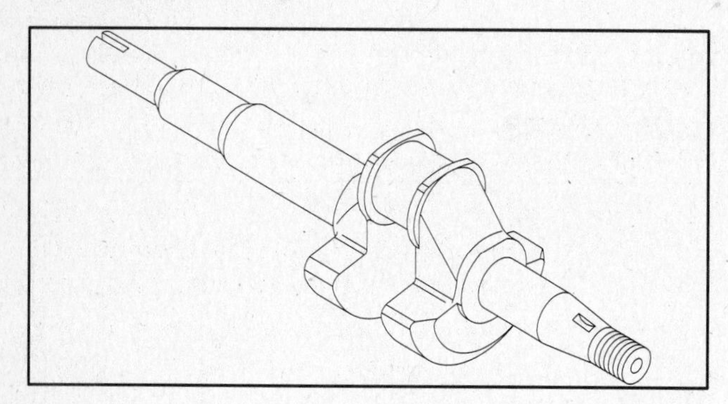

CRANKSHAFTS, CONT'D

GEAR REDUCTIONS

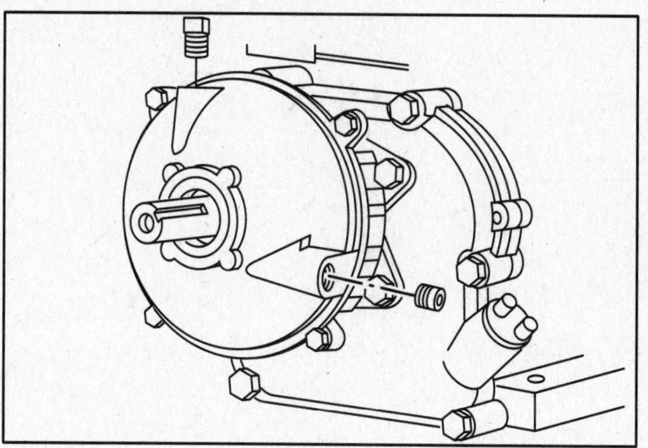

REMOVAL

Crankshaft and Cam Gear, Aluminum Cylinder Engines

1. To remove the crankshaft from aluminum alloy engines, remove rust or burrs from the power take-off end of the crankshaft.

2. Remove crankcase cover or sump. If sump or cover sticks, tap lightly with soft hammer on alternate sides near dowels.

3. Turn crankshaft to align the crankshaft and cam gear timing marks.

4. Lift out the cam gear.

5. Remove connecting rod and piston and then remove crankshaft.

NOTE: On ball bearing models, crankshaft and cam gear must be removed together, Fig. 1.

NOTE: METRIC EQUIVALENTS ARE LISTED ON PAGE 26 OF THIS SECTION.

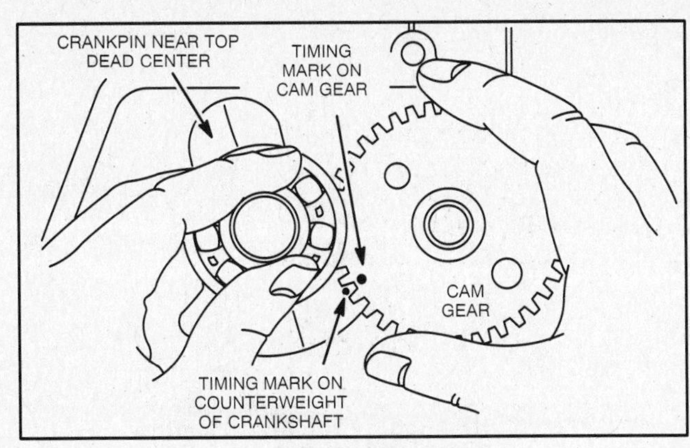

Fig. 1 - Ball Bearing Engines

Cast Iron Cylinder Engines

Model Series 230000 - Plain Bearings

1. Remove rust or burrs from the power take-off end of the crankshaft.
2. Remove crankshaft cover.
3. Rotate crankshaft to approximate position shown in Fig. 2.
4. Pull out crankshaft from PTO side, twisting slightly, if necessary, to clear cam gear.

Model Series 230000, 240000, 300000, 320000 - Ball Bearings

NOTE: On 240000, 300000, 320000, piston and connecting rod must be removed from engine to allow crankshaft removal.

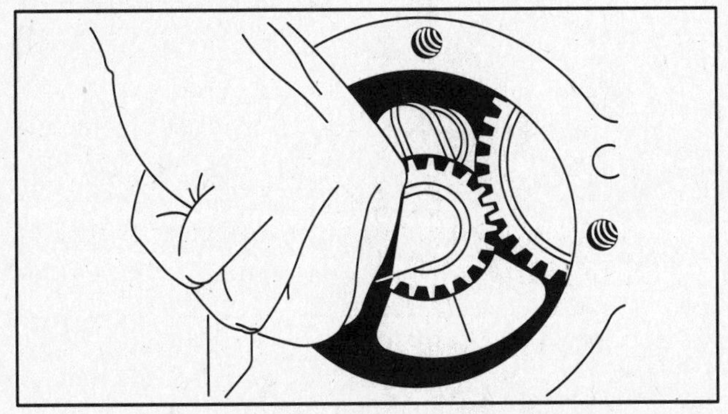

Fig. 2 - Remove or Install Crankshaft

1. Remove rust or burrs from the power take-off end of the crankshaft.
2. Remove crankcase cover and bearing support.
3. Rotate crankshaft to position shown, Fig. 2.

   NOTE: On some models, it may be necessary to position crankshaft approximately 180° from position shown in Fig. 2.

4. Pull crankshaft out, turning as needed to remove crankshaft.

Remove Cam Gear, Cast Iron Engines, Except Model Series 300400, 301400, 302400, 320400, 325400

1. To remove cam gear from all cast iron models, except the 300000 and 320000, use a long punch to drive the cam gear shaft out toward the magneto side. (Save plug.) Fig. 3. Do not burr or peen end of shaft while driving out.
2. Hold cam gear while removing punch so gear does not drop and nick.

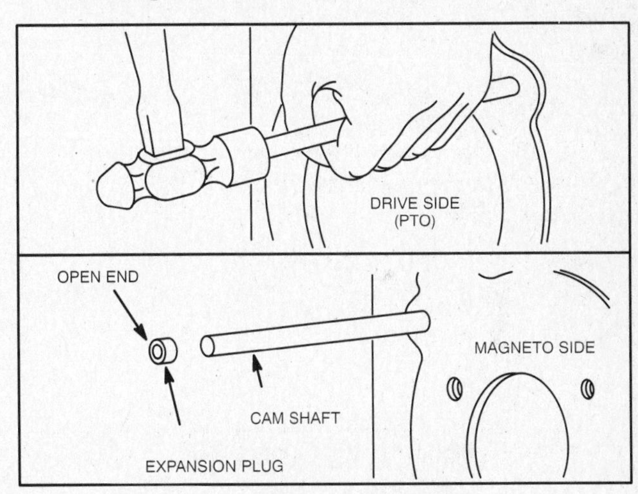

Fig. 3 - Remove Camshaft

Model Series 300400, 320400

1. Remove short bolt and Belleville washer from PTO drive gear, Fig. 4.
2. Loosen long bolt and Belleville washer two (2) turns on magneto side and tap head of bolt with hammer to loosen cam gear shaft.
3. Turn bolt out while pushing out cam gear shaft, Fig. 5.
4. Remove bolts from cam gear bearing, Fig. 6 and while holding cam gear, remove cam gear bearing and remove cam gear.

NOTE: METRIC EQUIVALENTS ARE LISTED ON PAGE 26 OF THIS SECTION.

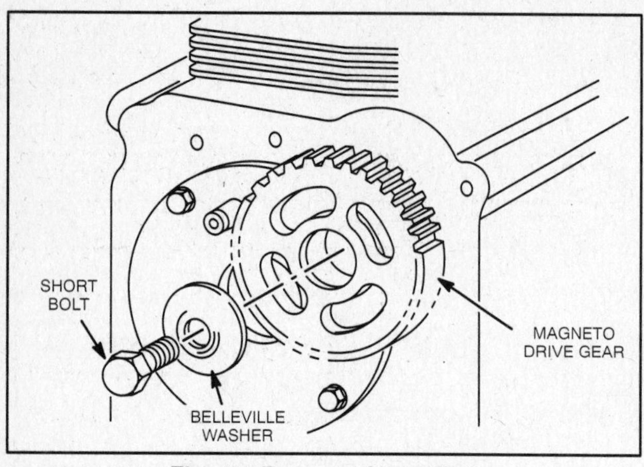

Fig. 4 - Remove Short Bolt

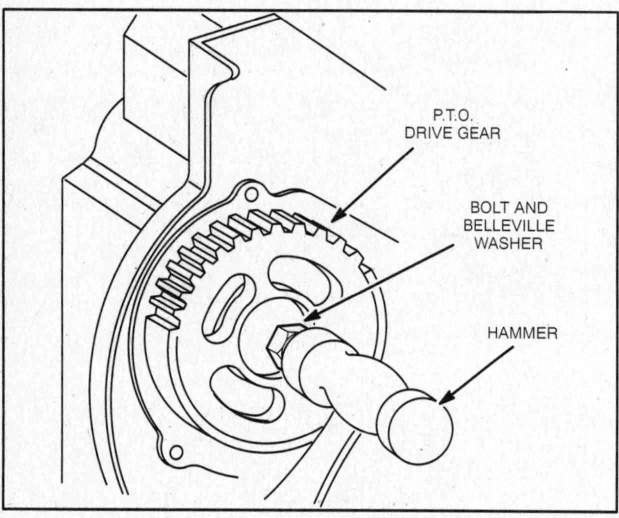

Fig. 5 - Remove Long Bolt

Model Series 301400, 302400, 325400, 326400

1. Loosen long bolt two (2) turns.
2. Use hammer to drive out cam gear shaft and cam gear plug.
3. Loosen bolt while pushing out cam gear shaft and plug.
4. Remove bolts and cam gear bearing, Fig. 5.
5. Remove cam gear, Fig. 6.

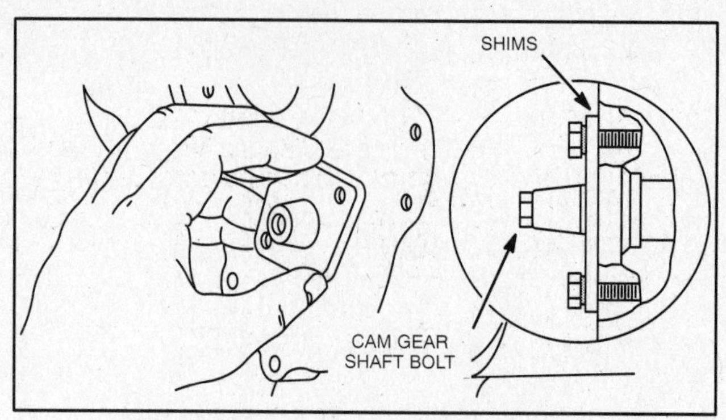

Fig. 6 - Removing Cam Gear Bearing

CHECKING CRANKSHAFT

All Engines

TABLE NO. 1 shows rejection sizes of various wear points of crankshaft. Discard crankshaft if worn smaller than size shown in table. Keyways should be checked to be sure they are not worn or spread. Remove burrs from keyway edges to prevent scratching bearing and oil seals. Fig. 7 shows various points to be checked on crankshaft.

NOTE: DO NOT STRAIGHTEN BENT CRANKSHAFTS.

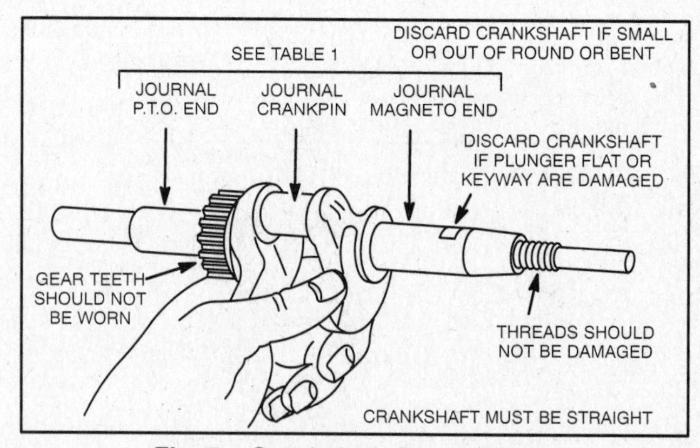

Fig. 7 - Crankshaft Check Points

NOTE: .020" undersize connecting rods may be obtained for use on reground crankpin journals. See TABLE NO. 2 for grinding dimensions. Complete instructions are included with undersize rod. (See Illustrated Parts List to find appropriate undersize connecting rod.)

NOTE: METRIC EQUIVALENTS ARE LISTED ON PAGE 26 OF THIS SECTION.

TABLE NO. 1 – CRANKSHAFT REJECT SIZES

MODEL SERIES	PTO JOURNAL	CRANKPIN JOURNAL	MAGNETO JOURNAL
ALUMINUM CYLINDER	**Inches**	**Inches**	**Inches**
60000	.873	.870	.873
80000*, 90200, 92000*, 93000*, 94000, 95000, 96000	.873	.996	.873
110700*, 110900*, 111900*	.873	.996	.873
100200, 100900, 130000	.998	.996	.873
100700, 120000	1.060	.996	.873
170000	1.179	1.090	.997
190000	1.179	1.122	.997
220000, 250000, 280000	1.376	1.247	1.376
CAST IRON CYLINDER	**Inches**	**Inches**	**Inches**
230000♦	1.3769♦	1.1844	1.3769
240000♦	Ball♦	1.3094	Ball
300000, 320000	Ball	1.3094	Ball

* Auxiliary Drive Models PTO Journal Reject Size 1.003 in.
# Synchro-Balance™ Magneto Journal Reject Size 1.179 in.
♦ Gear Reduction PTO 1.179 in.

TABLE NO. 2, .020" UNDERSIZE CONNECTING ROD CRANKPIN GRINDING DIMENSIONS

MODEL SERIES	CRANKSHAFT		
	Crankpin Dia.	Fillet Radius	Crankshaft Throw
80000, 90000	.9788/.9783"	.130/.110"	1.0100/.990"
100200, 100900	.9788/.9783"	.088/.070"	1.0645/1.0605"
100700, 110000	.9788/.9780"	.130/.110"	.9750/.9650"
130000	.9788/.9783"	.130/.110"	1.2210/1.2170"
170000	1.0724/1.0720"	.130/.110"	1.1895/1.1855"
190000	1.1043/1.1039"	.130/.120"	1.3770/1.3730"
220000	1.2293/1.2289"	.130/.120"	1.1895/1.1855"
233400	1.1668/1.1664"	.130/.110"	1.6350/1.6150"
240000	1.2918/1.2914"	.130/.110"	1.6350/1.6150"
250000, 280000	1.2293/1.2289"	.130/.120"	1.3145/1.3105"
300000, 320000	1.2918/1.2914"	.130/.120"	1.6350/1.6150"

NOTE: METRIC EQUIVALENTS ARE LISTED ON PAGE 26 OF THIS SECTION.

Check Cam Gear – All Engines

Inspect gear teeth for wear and nicks. Cam gear journals and lobe rejection sizes are shown in TABLE NO. 3.

TABLE NO. 3 – CAM GEAR REJECT SIZES

MODEL SERIES	CAM GEAR JOURNAL	CAM LOBE
ALUMINUM CYLINDER	**Inches**	**Inches**
60000, 80000*	.498	.883 or See Note Below
82500, 82900, 92000, 93000, 94000, 95000, 96000	.498	.883
90200, 100700, 120000	.498	See Note Below
110000	.436 Mag. .498 P.T.O.	.870
100200, 100900, 130000	.498	.950
170000, 190000	.498	.977
220000, 250000, 280000	.498	1.184
CAST IRON CYLINDER	**Inches**	**Inches**
230000	.497	1.184
240000	.497	1.184
300000, 320000	.8105 Mag. .6145 P.T.O.	1.184

* Auxiliary Drive Models PTO .751 in.
NOTE: On Model Series 60000, 80000 with plastic cam gear and all 90200, 100700, 120000 replace cam gear if cam lobes are pitted or galled.

Checking Compression Release (Yoke Type)

Yoke type compression releases use a spring loaded yoke at the exhaust cam lobe to open the exhaust valve during starting. When engine starts, centrifugal force causes the yoke to overcome spring tension and yoke swings away from exhaust tappet returning engine to normal compression, Fig. 8.

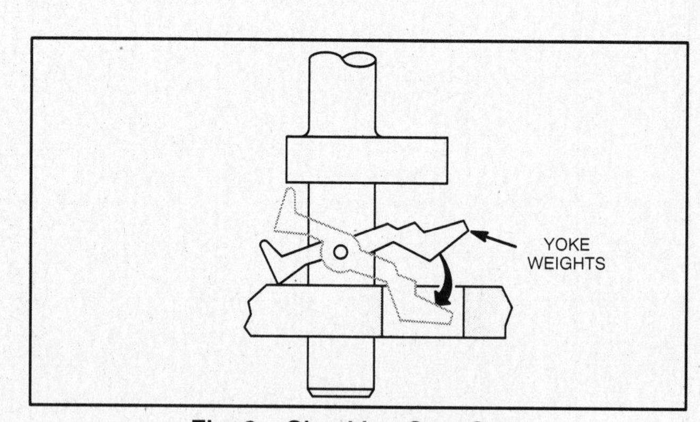

Fig. 8 – Checking Cam Gear

1. To check, move yoke weights away from face of cam gear and release.

2. Yoke should return to compression release position without binding or sticking.

3. Replace cam gear if yoke binds, yoke pivot pin is worn, or return spring is broken, Fig. 8.

Model Series 111200, 111900

This cam gear has Easy-Spin® plus a compression release on the exhaust cam. In the starting position, the cam moves the rocker cam so it will open the exhaust valve at the same time as the Easy-Spin® lobe. When the engine starts, the cam moves out and lets the rocker cam move down and the exhaust valve operates normally.

NOTE: METRIC EQUIVALENTS ARE LISTED ON PAGE 26 OF THIS SECTION.

1. To check, move cam to the running position, Fig. 9.
2. Push rocker cam against the actuator cam.
3. Release the actuator cam. Actuator cam spring should pull actuator cam against the shoulder pin causing rocker cam to raise up to starting position, Fig. 10.
4. There should be no binding. Replace if binding exists.

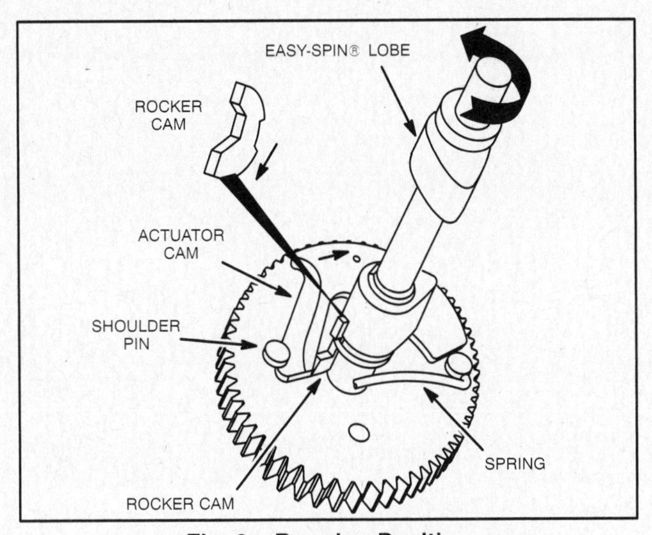

Fig. 9 – Running Position

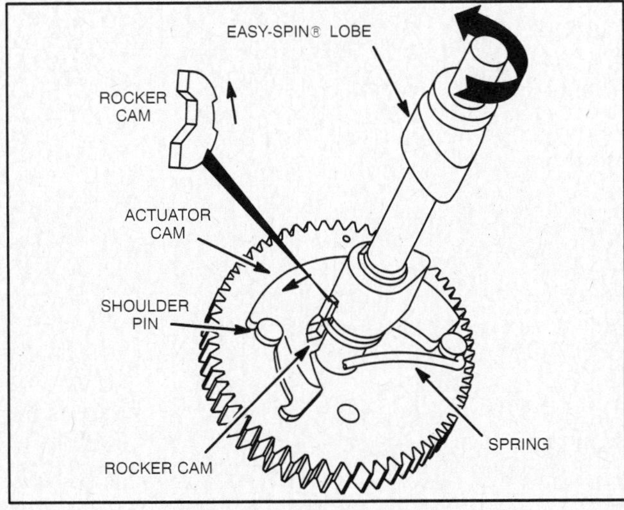

Fig. 10 – Start Position

BALL BEARINGS

Remove

The ball bearing is a press fit on the crankshaft. If bearing is to be removed, use an arbor press, as shown in Fig. 11.

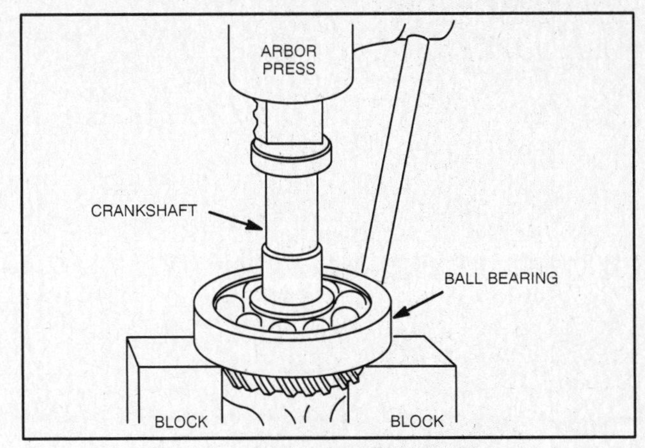

Fig. 11 – Removing Ball Bearing

Install Ball Bearings

1. Heat bearing in hot oil (250° F max.).

   NOTE: Bearing must not rest on the bottom of the pan in which it is heated.

2. Place crankshaft in vise with bearing side up. When bearing is quite hot it will become a slip fit on the crankshaft journal.
3. Grasp bearing with the shield down and thrust it down on the crankshaft, Fig. 12.
4. The bearing will tighten on the shaft until cooled. DO NOT QUENCH.

NOTE: Bearing shield faces crankshaft crankpin.

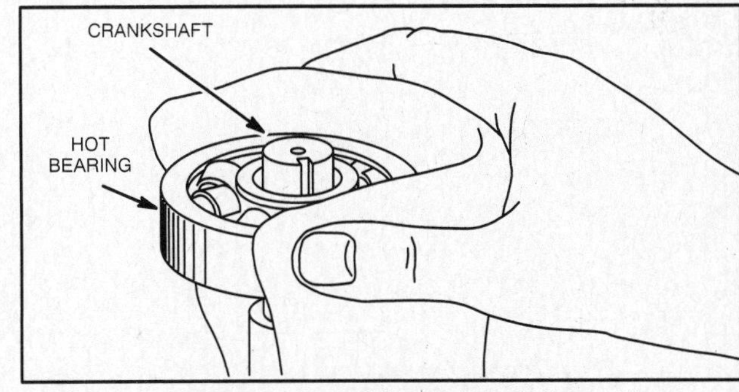

Fig. 12 – Installing Ball Bearing

INSTALL CRANKSHAFT AND CAM GEAR

Aluminum Cylinders – Plain Bearing

1. Install tappets first.
2. Use Seal Protector Kit, Tool #19356, TABLE NO. 4, when installing crankshaft.

NOTE: METRIC EQUIVALENTS ARE LISTED ON PAGE 26 OF THIS SECTION.

TABLE NO. 4
SEAL PROTECTORS

Tool #1	Color	Crankshaft Journal Size
19334/1	White	.787
19334/2	Red	.875
19334/3	Blue	.984
19334/4	Orange	1.000
19334/5	Brown	1.062
19334/6	Green	1.181
19334/7	Yellow	1.378
19356/8	Purple	1.317
19356/9	Black	1.503

3. Turn crankshaft until timing mark is facing carburetor side of cylinder. Install cam gear with timing marks aligned, Fig. 13.

NOTE: Many Model Series have a removable timing gear. Install timing gear with inner chamfer toward crank pin. This assures the timing mark will be visible, Fig. 13.

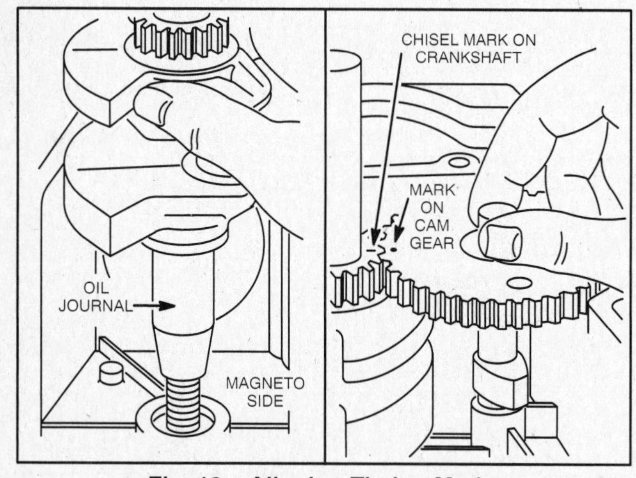

Fig. 13 – Aligning Timing Marks

INSTALL CRANKSHAFT AND CAM GEAR

Aluminum Cylinders – Ball Bearing

On crankshaft with ball bearings, the gear teeth are not visible. The timing mark is on the crankshaft counterweight.

1. Install tappets.
2. Use Seal Protector Kit, Tool #19356, TABLE NO. 4, when installing crankshaft.
3. Install both crankshaft and cam gear together, with timing marks aligned, Fig. 14.

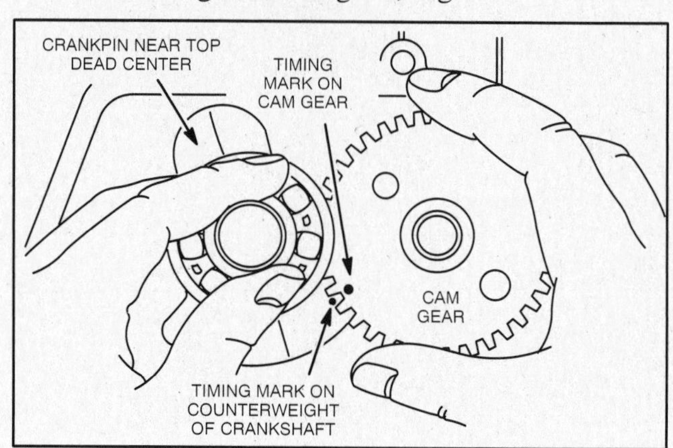

Fig. 14 – Ball Bearing Engines

Install Crankcase Cover or Sump All Aluminum Model Series

Use Seal Protector Kit, Tool #19356, TABLE NO. 4, to protect oil seal when installing crankcase cover or sump. DO NOT FORCE COVER OR SUMP. Make sure mechanical governor gear is engaged with cam gear.

Torque Crankcase Cover or Sump All Aluminum Model Series

Torque crankcase cover or sump to specifications listed in TABLE NO. 5.

TABLE NO. 5
CRANKCASE COVER OR SUMP TORQUE

Model Series	Torque In. Lbs.
60000, 80000, 90000, 120000	85
100200, 100900	120
100700, 110000	85
130000	120
140000, 170000, 190000, 220000, 250000, 280000	140

NOTE: On Model Series 100900, 130700, 131700, and 130900 a spring washer is used on cam gear as shown in Fig. 15. Model Series 130780, 130980, 131780, and 132980 do not use a spring washer.

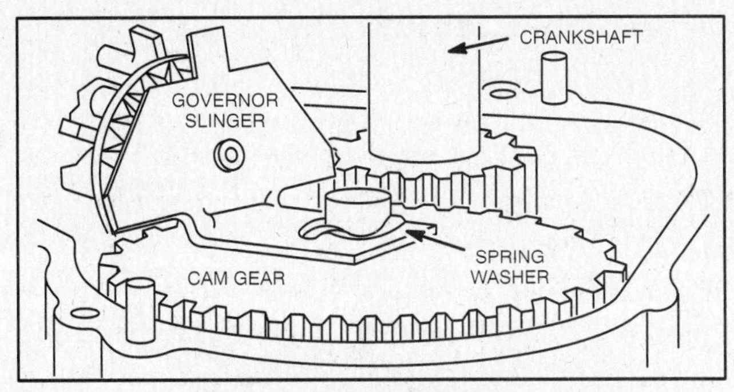

Fig. 15 - Sump Installation - Model Series 100900 and 130900

INSTALL CRANKSHAFT AND CAM GEAR - CAST IRON CYLINDERS

Install Crankshaft and Cam Gear Plain Bearing

1. Assemble tappets in cylinder and insert cam gear.
2. Push camshaft into cam hole in cylinder from flywheel (magneto) side thru cam gear.
3. With a blunt punch and arbor press or hammer, press or drive camshaft until end is flush with outside of cylinder on power take-off side of cylinder.
4. Place a small amount of sealer such as Permatex 2® on camshaft plug, when used, and press in plug on flywheel side of cylinder.
5. Install crankshaft aligning timing marks, Fig. 16.

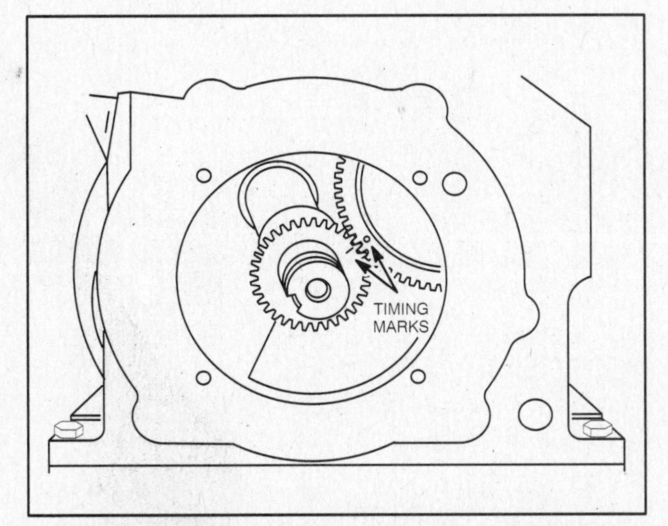

Fig. 16 - Timing Marks, All Other Model Series

Install Crankshaft and Cam Gear Ball Bearing Except Model Series 300000, 320000

1. Install breaker plunger (when used) and tappets.
2. Insert cam gear into cylinder.

   NOTE: On some models, push cam gear forward into recess in front of cylinder.
3. Install crankshaft into cylinder.
4. Rotate crankshaft and cam gear until timing marks align and push cam gear into engagement with gear on crankshaft with timing marks together.
5. Install camshaft into cylinder and cam gear from magneto side of cylinder. Camshaft should be flush with power take-off side of cylinder.
6. Place a small amount of sealant on plug and press into camshaft hole on flywheel side of cylinder, Fig. 17.

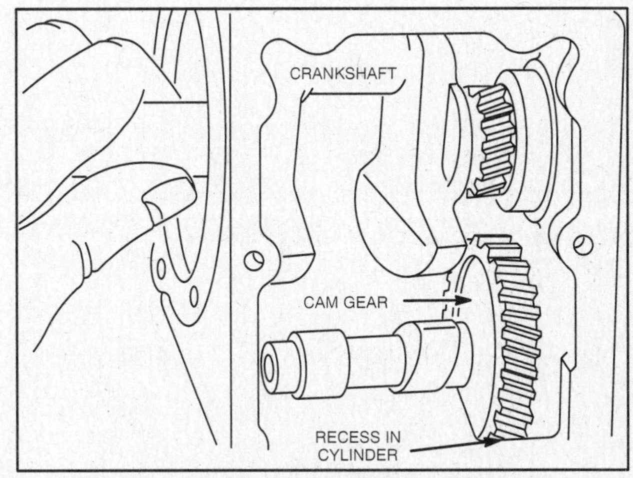

Fig. 17 - Installing Crankshaft and Cam Gear

NOTE: METRIC EQUIVALENTS ARE LISTED ON PAGE 26 OF THIS SECTION.

Install Crankshaft and Cam Gear Model Series 300000, 320000

1. Install breaker plunger (when used) and tappets.
2. Insert cam gear from power take-off side of cylinder, Fig. 18.

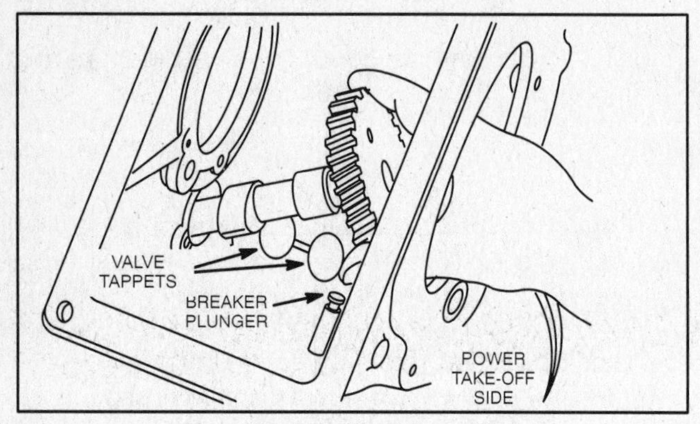

Fig. 18 – Inserting Cam Gear

3. Slide cam gear shaft thru power take-off bearing side and into cam gear, Fig. 19.

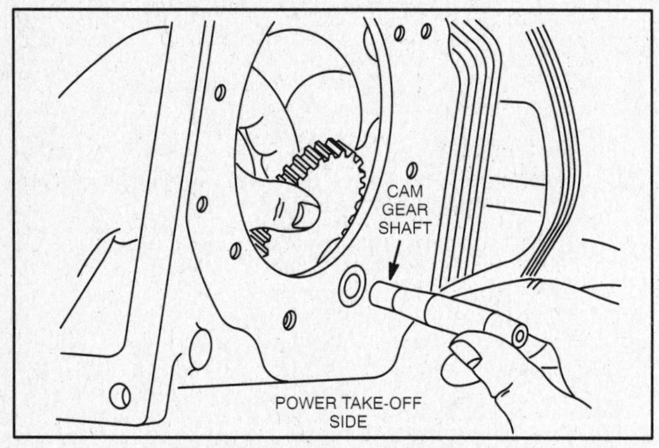

Fig. 19 – Installing Camshaft

4. Install magneto side cam gear bearing on cylinder.
5. Torque bearing screws to 90 in. lbs.
6. Install long cam gear bolt (5-1/2") finger tight to prevent loss of camshaft, Fig. 20.

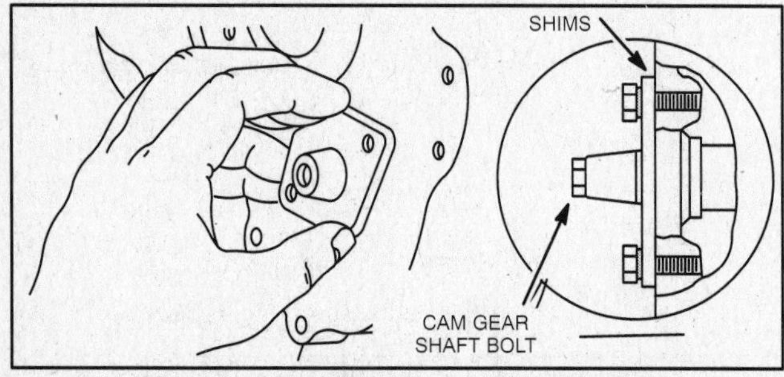

Fig. 20 – Installing Cam Gear Bearing

Check Cam Gear End Play

Cam gear end play is machined at the factory and requires no adjustment unless magneto side cam bearing or cam gear is replaced. End play is .002"-.008".

1. Push cam gear against magneto side of cylinder and insert feeler gauge between cam gear and power take-off side of cylinder to check end play.
2. If end play is more than .008", use service bearing assembly Kit #299706. Kit contains a new bearing and shims, .005", .007", and .009" thick to adjust end play. Install new bearing without shims and measure end play. If .002" or less, add shims to obtain proper end play.
3. Torque bearing screws to 90 in. lbs.

Install Crankshaft Model Series 300000, 320000

Timing mark is a notch on crankshaft throw directly in line with gear tooth that will engage cam gear at timing mark on cam gear.

1. Mark top of tooth with chalk or crayon.
2. With timing marks aligned, install crankshaft. Use care when installing crankshaft not to damage crankpin, Fig. 21.

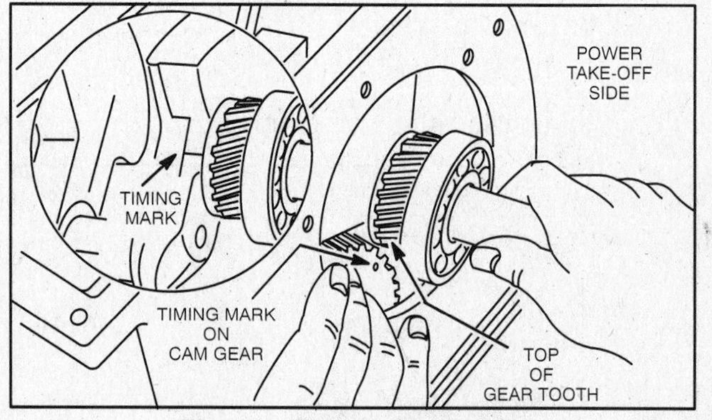

Fig. 21 – Timing Crankshaft

Install Bearing Supports – Model Series 230000, 240000, 300000, 320000

Install bearing supports with new gaskets. Torque power take-off cover to 190 in. lbs. and magneto support to 90 in. lbs., Fig. 22.

NOTE: METRIC EQUIVALENTS ARE LISTED ON PAGE 26 OF THIS SECTION.

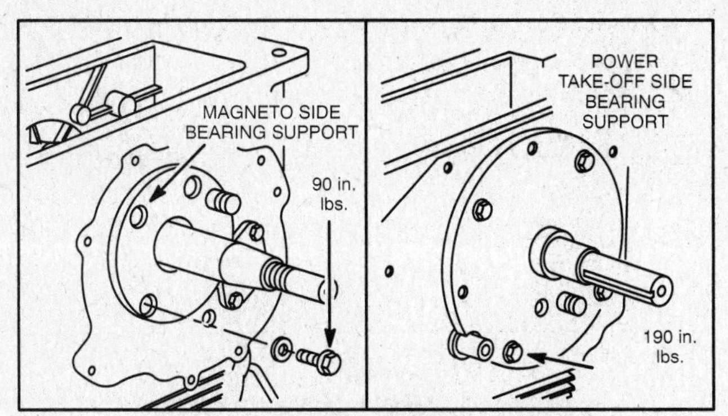

Fig. 22 - Installing Bearing Supports

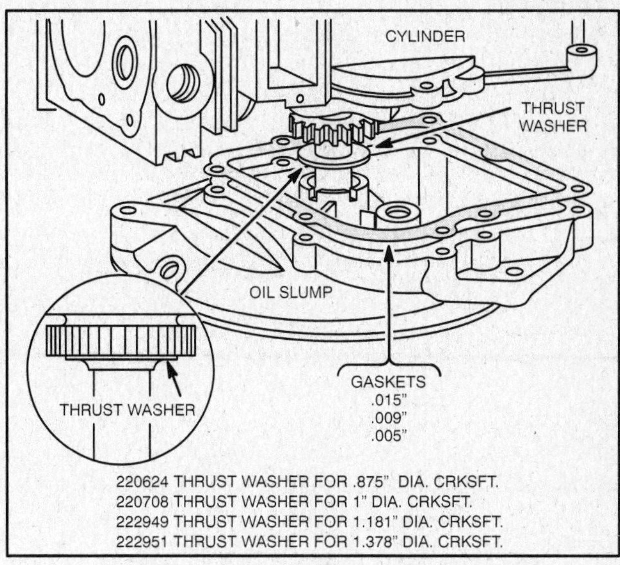

Fig. 23 - Adjusting Crankshaft End Play

Crankshaft End Play
All Model Series

Crankshaft end play is .002"-.008" on all models except Model Series 92500, 92900 with code numbers having "5" as the next to last digit (example, 88042151) and Model Series 100700, 120000 which have .002"-.030" end play. Procedures for adjusting end play vary between cast iron cylinders, aluminum cylinders, plain and ball bearing models.

Check Crankshaft End Play
Aluminum Cylinders - Plain Bearings

When crankcase cover or sump is installed with a .015" thick gasket, end play should be .002"-.008" except Model Series 92500, 92900 with "5" as second to last digit of code number and Model Series 100700, 120000 which should be .002"-.030".

If end play is less than stated above, use additional gaskets, .005", .009", or .015" in various combinations to get proper end play, Fig. 23.

If end play is more than .008" with one .015" thick gasket or more than .030" with one .015" thick gasket on Model Series 92500, 92900 with "5" as next to last digit of code number and Model Series 100700, 120000, a thrust washer is available that can be used on the power take-off end of the crankshaft, with additional .005", .009" or .015" gasket to reduce end play to proper end play, Fig. 23.

Check Crankshaft End Play
Aluminum Cylinders - Ball Bearings

End play is adjusted the same way as on plain bearing engines. If thrust washer is required, it is used on the magneto end of the crankshaft.

NOTE: Thrust washers cannot be used on engine with two ball bearings. Replace worn parts.

Check Crankshaft End Play
Plain and Ball Bearing
Model Series 230000, 240000

With one .020" thick gasket and magneto bearing support in place, crankshaft end play should be .002"-.008". If end play is less than .002", additional gaskets, .005", .009" or .020" in various combinations can be used to get the correct end play.

If end play is more than .008", use one .005" or one .009" thick gasket to obtain .002"-.008", Fig. 24.

NOTE: METRIC EQUIVALENTS ARE LISTED ON PAGE 26 OF THIS SECTION.

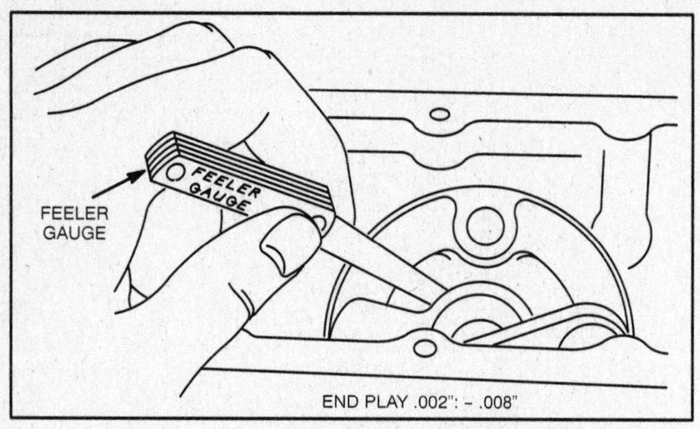

Fig. 24 - Checking Crankshaft End Play

If end play is more than .008" with a .005" thick gasket, a thrust washer can be used on the power take-off end of the crankshaft, Fig. 25.

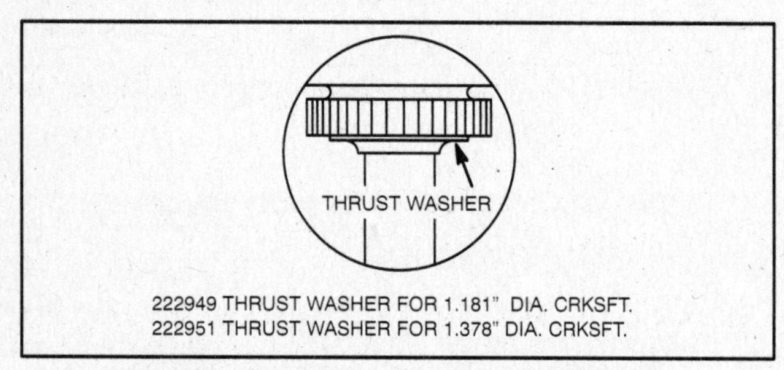

Fig. 25 - Correcting Crankshaft End Play

NOTE: Thrust washers cannot be used on crankshaft with two ball bearings. Replace worn parts.

Check Crankshaft End Play Model Series 300000, 320000

Crankshaft end play is machined at the factory and does not have to be checked unless the bearing supports or crankshaft has been replaced.

If end play is less than .002", add service shims .005", .010" or .015" to get proper end play. If end play is more than .008", use service bearing support kit Part #299705, which includes the above shims to get proper end play.

GEAR REDUCTION, MODEL SERIES 60000, 80000, 100200, 110000, 130000

Drain and Disassemble Gear Reduction

1. Note position of gear reduction assembly on engine, Fig. 29.
2. Remove oil vent plug.
3. Loosen four cap screws holding gear case cover assembly.
4. Pull cover away from gear case assembly to drain gear case.
5. After gear case is drained, remove screws and cover, Fig. 26.

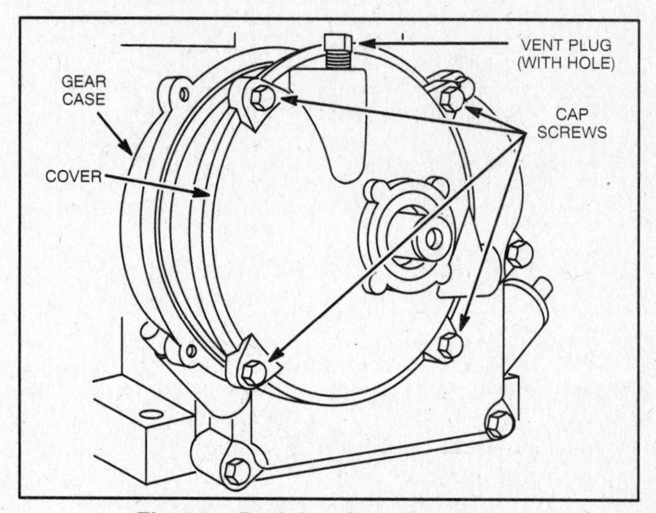

Fig. 26 - Draining Gear Reduction and Removing Cover

Remove Drive Shaft Assembly and Gear Case Assembly

1. Remove drive shaft assembly from gear case.
2. Bend down two screw locks if so equipped, and remove four cap screws.
3. Slide gear case off engine, Fig. 27.

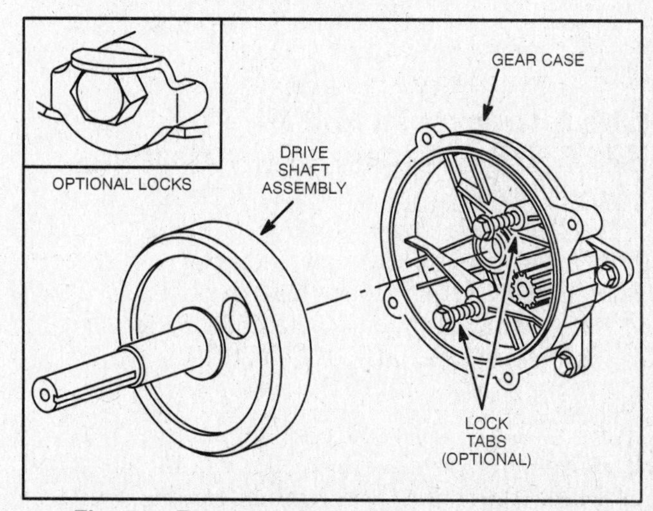

Fig. 27 - Removing Drive Gear and Gear case

NOTE: METRIC EQUIVALENTS ARE LISTED ON PAGE 26 OF THIS SECTION.

Inspect Drive Shaft, Gear Case, and Cover Assemblies

Inspect seals for cracks, tears, or hardening. Replace seals if damaged or hard. Inspect crankshaft pinion gear and drive gear for worn, cracked, or chipped teeth. Replace if damaged or worn. Inspect gear case and cover for cracks, damaged mounting or gasket surfaces. Replace if damaged.

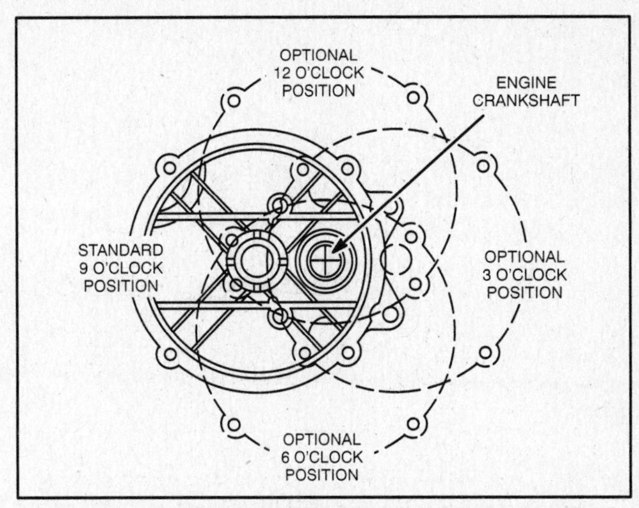

Fig. 29 – Positioning Bearing Housing Assembly

ASSEMBLE GEAR REDUCTION

Install Seals

1. Install seals with sealing lip towards inside of gear case or cover assemblies until seal is flush with case or cover, Fig. 28.

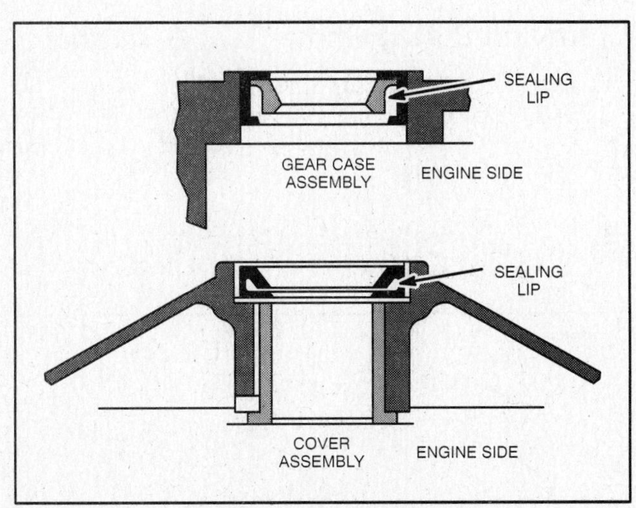

Fig. 28 – Installing Seals

Install Gear Case Assembly

NOTE: The housing must be installed in the same position as when removed, Fig. 29.

2. Install cork gasket on crankcase cover (when used).
3. Slide gear case assembly onto crankshaft and bearing housing assembly.
4. Install two short screws and lockwashers.
5. Install two long screws and screw locks if so equipped with tabs down and next to gear case ribs of gear case.
6. Torque four screws to 140 in. lbs.
7. Bend locks up against flats on head of cap screws, Fig. 30, when used.

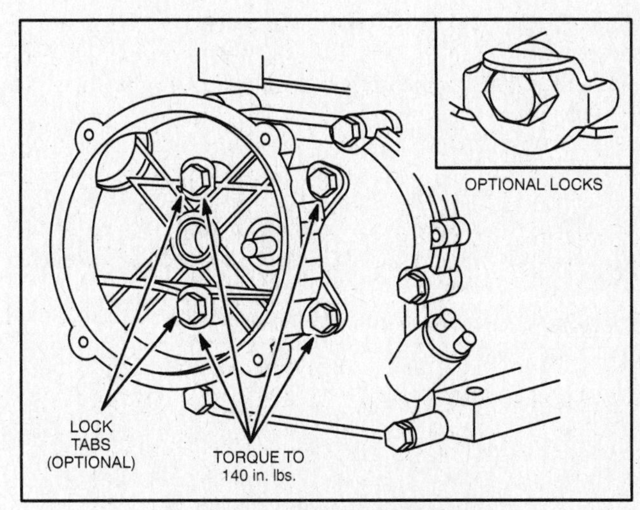

Fig. 30 – Installing Gear Case

8. Slide drive shaft assembly into gear case bearing and engage crankshaft pinion gear.

NOTE: METRIC EQUIVALENTS ARE LISTED ON PAGE 26 OF THIS SECTION.

9. Insert WHITE Seal Protector, Tool #19334 or #19356, into seal of gear case cover.

10. Place new gasket on gear case assembly.

11. Slide cover and seal protector on to gear case and drive shaft until cover is seated on new gasket. Remove seal protector.

12. Torque four screws to 90 in. lbs., Fig. 31.

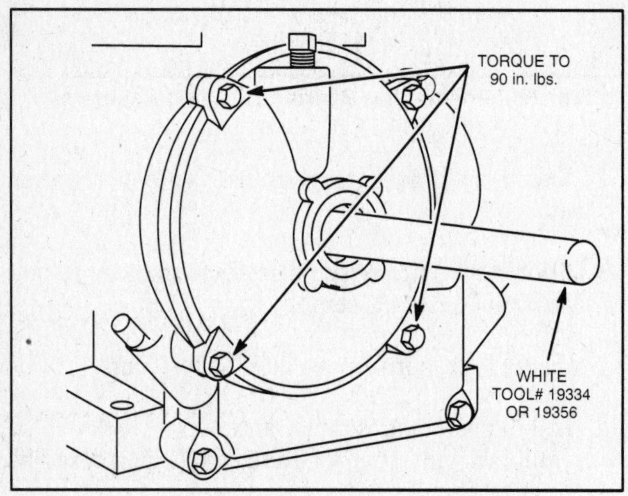

Fig. 31 – Installing Gear Case Cover

Fill Gear Case with Lubricant

1. To fill gear case, remove oil level plug with allen wrench and vent plug.

2. Fill gear case with SAE 30 weight oil for temperatures above 50° F. Use 10W30 weight oil between 50° and 0° F. Use 5W20 or 5W30 weight oil below 0° F.

3. Fill gear case just to the point of overflowing at the lower hole.

4. Install allen socket plug in lower hole and torque to 90 in. lbs.

5. Install vent plug with hole in top hole and torque to 40 in. lbs., Fig. 32.

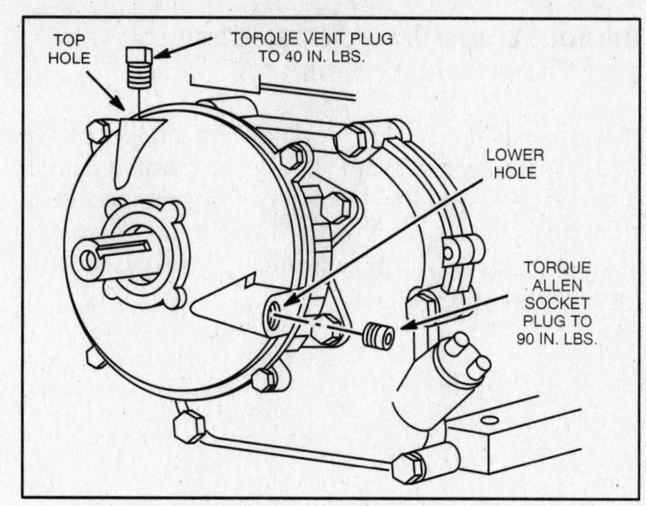

Fig. 32 – Filling Gear Case

GEAR REDUCTION, MODEL SERIES 170000, 190000, 220000, 230000, 240000, COUNTERCLOCKWISE ROTATION

Drain and Disassemble Gear Reduction

1. Remove oil vent plug if so equipped.

2. Then remove drain plug from bottom of gear case cover assembly.

3. After gear case is drained, loosen and remove four cap screws and cover, Fig. 33.

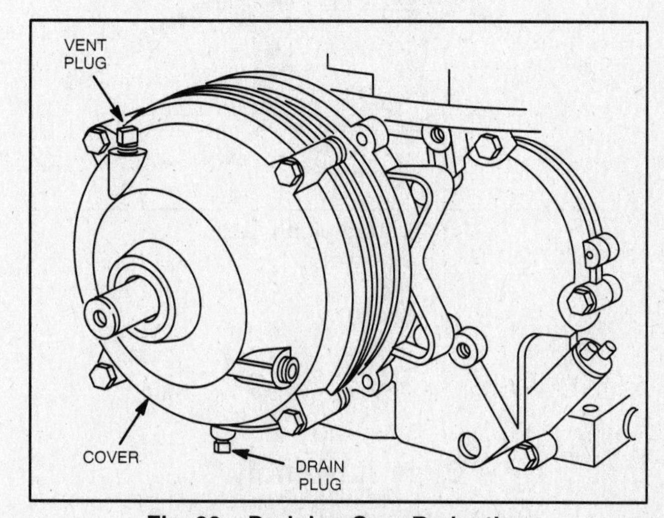

Fig. 33 – Draining Gear Reduction and Removing Cover

NOTE: METRIC EQUIVALENTS ARE LISTED ON PAGE 26 OF THIS SECTION.

Remove Drive Shaft Assembly and Gear Case Assembly

1. Note position of gear case assembly, Fig. 36.
2. Remove drive shaft assembly off gear case.
3. Bend down two screw locks if so equipped, and remove four cap screws.
4. Slide gear case assembly from engine, Fig. 34.

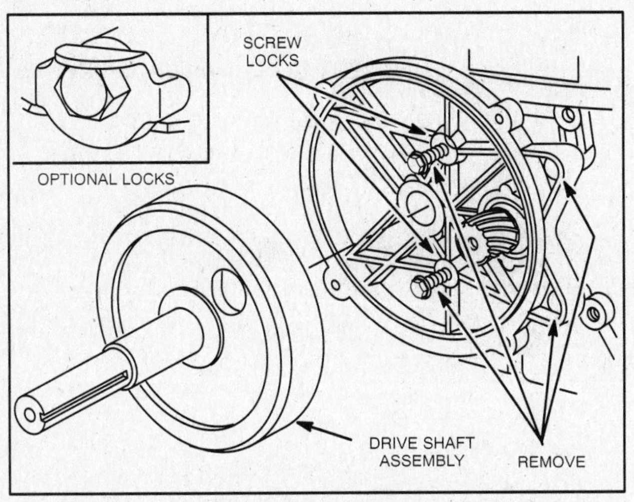

Fig. 34 - Removing Drive Gear and Gear Case

Inspect Drive Shaft, Gear Case, and Cover Assemblies

Inspect seals for cracks, tears, or hardening. Replace seals if damaged or hard. Inspect crankshaft pinion gear and drive gear for worn, cracked, or chipped teeth. Replace if damaged or worn. Inspect gear case and cover assemblies for cracks, damaged mounting or gasket surfaces. Replace if damaged.

ASSEMBLE GEAR REDUCTION

Install Seals

Install seal(s) with sealing lip towards inside of gear case or cover until seal is flush with surface of case (when used) or cover, Fig. 35.

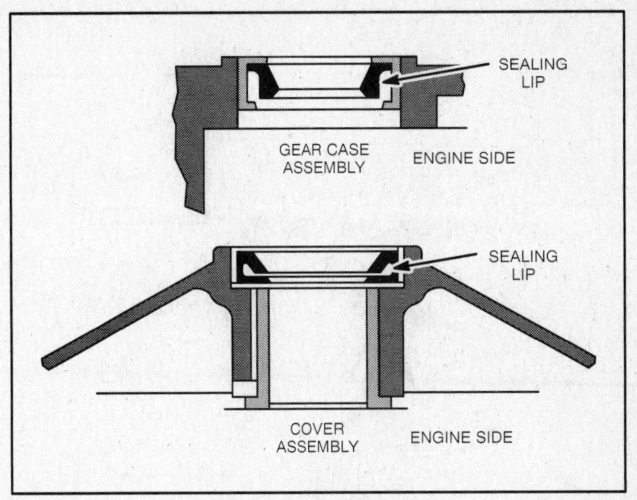

Fig. 35 - Installing Seals

Install Gear Case Assembly

1. Install gear case assembly in original position, Fig. 36.

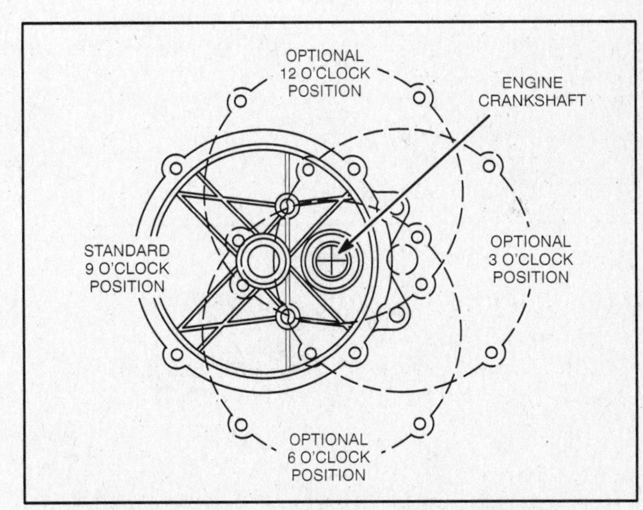

Fig. 36 - Positioning Gear Case Assembly

2. Slide gear case assembly and new gasket onto crankshaft and crankcase cover assembly.
3. Install two short screws and lockwashers.
4. Install two long screws and screw locks with tabs down, if so equipped, and next to gear case ribs of gear case.
5. Torque four screws to 140 in. lbs.

NOTE: METRIC EQUIVALENTS ARE LISTED ON PAGE 26 OF THIS SECTION.

6. Bend locks up against flats on head of cap screws, Fig. 37.

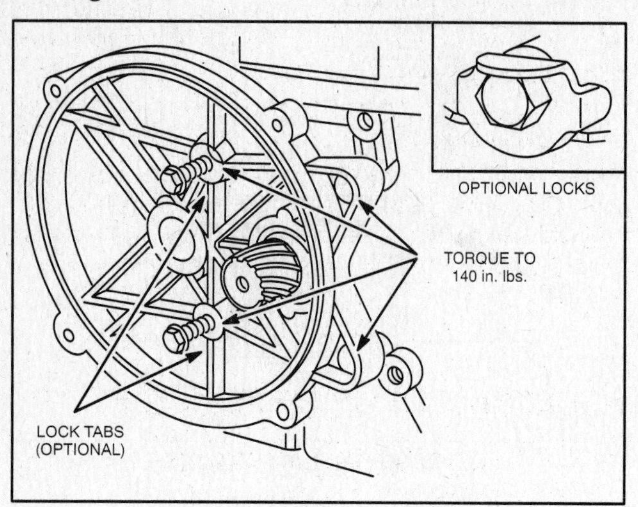

Fig. 37 – Installing Gear Case

7. Slide drive shaft assembly into gear case bearing and engage crankshaft pinion gear.

8. Insert GREEN Seal Protector, Tool #19334 or #19356, into seal of gear case cover.

9. Place new gasket on gear case assembly.

10. Slide cover and seal protector unto gear case until cover is seated on new gasket.

11. Remove seal protector.

12. Torque four screws to 190 in. lbs., Fig. 38.

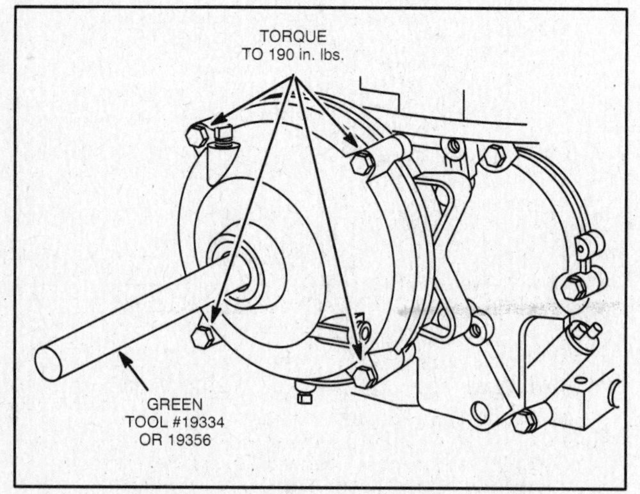

Fig. 38 – Installing Gear Case Cover

Fill Gear Case with Lubricant

1. Install drain plug in bottom of gear case if so equipped, and torque to 65 in. lbs.

2. To fill gear case, remove oil level plug with allen wrench. Fill gear case with SAE 30 weight oil for temperatures above 50° F. Use 10W30 weight oil between 50 ° and 0° F. Use 5W20 or 5W30 weight oil below 0° F.

3. Fill gear case just to the point of overflowing at the lower hole.

4. Install allen socket plug in lower hole if so equipped, and torque to 90 in. lbs.

5. Install vent plug in top hole if so equipped, and torque to 40 in. lbs., Fig. 39.

NOTE: On Model Series 230000, 240000, the gear reduction and the engine use the same oil supply.

1. Fill the crankcase with the proper weight and service classification oil for the temperature that the engine will be run at.

2. Start and run engine and then stop engine.

3. Recheck oil level and add oil as required to bring engine oil level up to full. See Section 8, Lubrication.

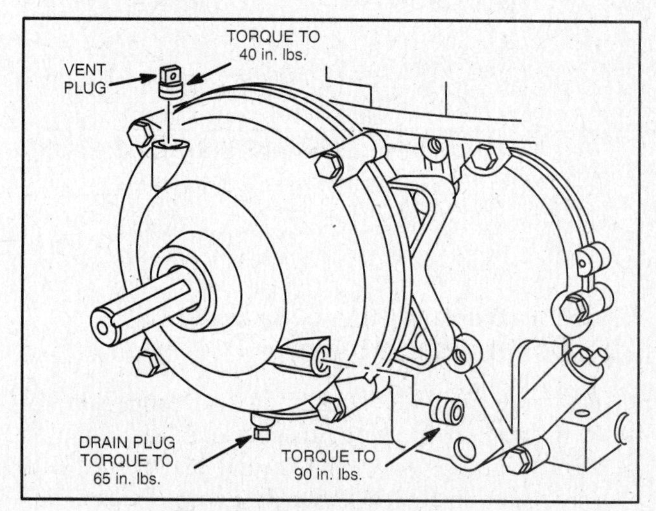

Fig. 39 – Filling Gear Case

GEAR REDUCTION, MODEL SERIES 230000 CLOCKWISE PTO ROTATION

Drain and Disassemble Gear Reduction

1. Note position of gear reduction case on engine, Fig. 44. Drain gear reduction by loosening all the cover cap screws one to two turns and pulling cover away from gear case.

NOTE: METRIC EQUIVALENTS ARE LISTED ON PAGE 26 OF THIS SECTION.

2. After gear case is drained, remove cap screws and cover, Fig. 40.

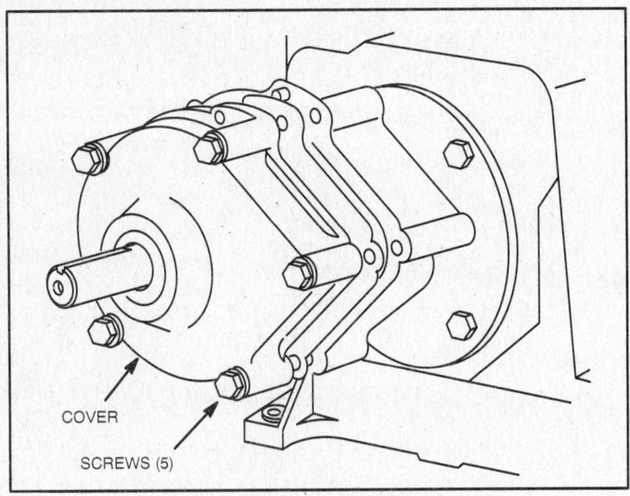

Fig. 40 - Draining Gear Reduction and Removing Cover

Remove Drive Shaft Assembly and Gear Case

Remove four cap screws and lockwashers. Slide gear case and drive shaft off engine, Fig. 41.

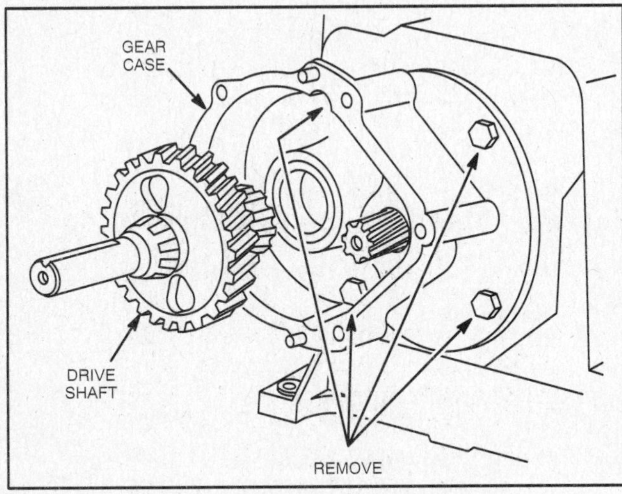

Fig. 41 - Removing Gear Case

Remove Bearings

Bearing cup in gear case cover is a slip fit while bearing cup may be either a slip or press fit in gear case. When removing bearing cups take note of which cup has shims. Press roller bearing by supporting the bearing and pressing out the shaft and gear assembly. Do not reuse bearings that have been pressed off.

Inspect Gear Case and Cover Assemblies

Inspect seals for cracks, tears, or hardening. Replace seals if damaged or hard. Inspect crankshaft pinion gear and drive gear for worn, cracked, or chipped teeth. Replace if damaged or worn. Inspect gear case and cover assemblies for cracks, damaged mounting or gasket surfaces. Replace if damaged. Inspect bearing cup and tapered rollers bearings for roughness, pitting and cracks. Replace if damaged.

ASSEMBLE GEAR REDUCTION

Install Tapered Roller Bearings

1. Heat bearing in hot oil (350° F max.).

   NOTE: Bearing must not rest on the bottom of the pan in which it is heated.

2. Place drive shaft and gear assembly in vise with bearing side up. When bearing is quite hot it will become a slip fit on the drive shaft journal.

3. Grasp bearing and thrust it down on the drive shaft against flange of gear, Fig. 42.

4. The bearing will tighten on the shaft while cooling. DO NOT QUENCH.

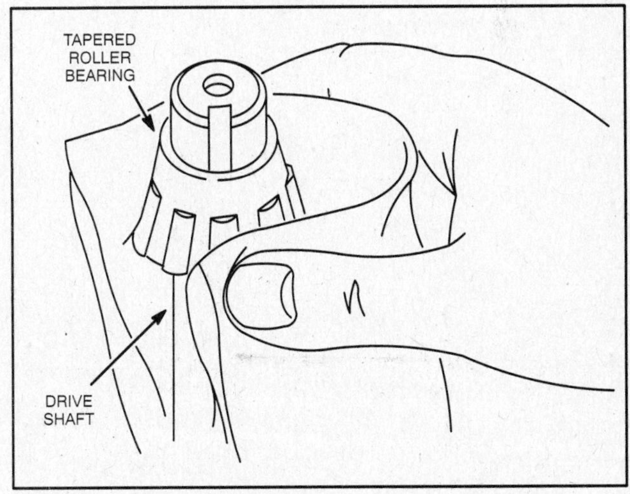

Fig. 42 - Installing Tapered Roller Bearings

Install Seals

Install seal with sealing lip towards inside of gear case cover until metal case of seal is flush with gear case cover, Fig. 43.

NOTE: METRIC EQUIVALENTS ARE LISTED ON PAGE 26 OF THIS SECTION.

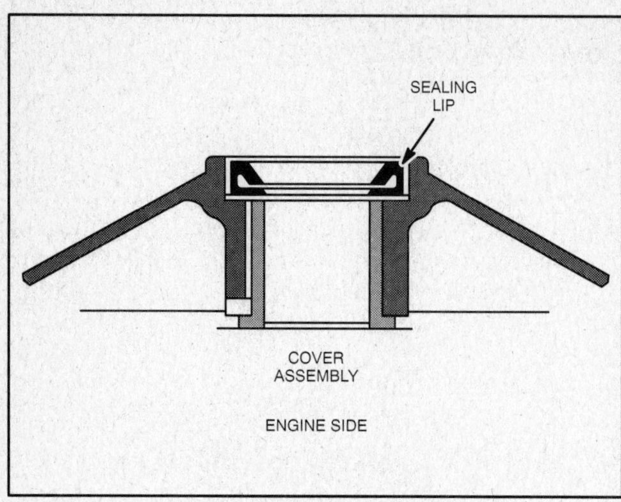

Fig. 43 - Installing Seal

Install Gear Case Assembly

Install gear case in same position as when removed from engine, Fig. 44. Torque screws and lockwashers to 140 in. lbs.

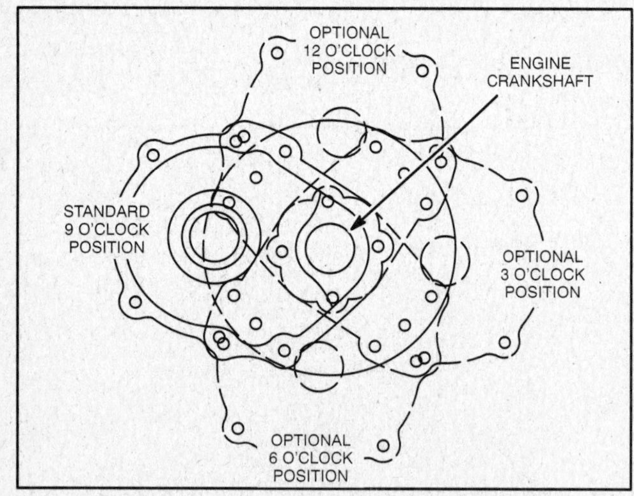

Fig. 44 - Positioning Gear Case Assembly

Install Gear Case Cover Assembly

1. Place bearing cup in bearing cup counterbore of gear case assembly without shims.
2. Slide drive shaft assembly into gear case bearing and engage crankshaft pinion gear.
3. Place bearing cup in bearing cup counterbore of gear case cover assembly without shims.
4. Place a new cover gasket on gear case assembly dowel pins.
5. Insert Green Seal Protector, Tool #19334 or #19356 into seal of gear case cover.
6. Slide gear case assembly and seal protector onto gear case assembly.
7. Install screws and lockwashers and torque screws to 190 in. lbs., Fig. 45.

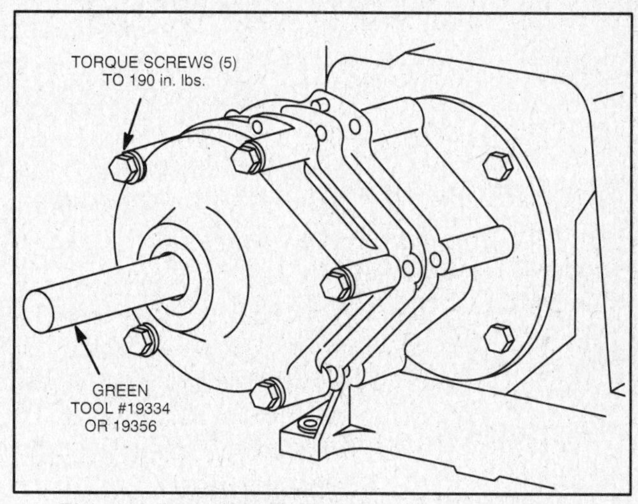

Fig. 45 - Installing Gear Case Cover Assembly

Adjust Roller Bearing Pre-load

1. Place a dial indicator against end of drive shaft.
2. Push in on drive shaft and turn shaft slowly to seat roller bearing in bearing cup as indicated by no further needle movement on dial indicator.
3. Set dial indicator to zero.
4. Pull out on drive shaft and rotate drive shaft slowly to seat roller bearing.
5. Note dial indicator reading.
6. Repeat both steps to verify dial indicator reading, Fig. 46.

NOTE: If a dial indicator is not available, use a sprocket or pulley and check end play as shown in Fig. 47.

NOTE: METRIC EQUIVALENTS ARE LISTED ON PAGE 26 OF THIS SECTION.

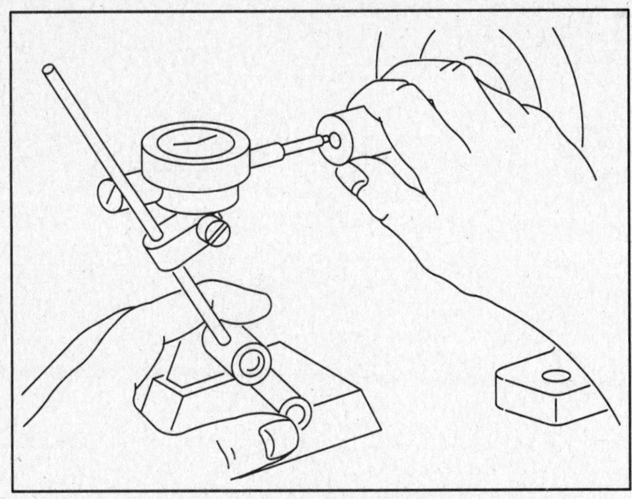
Fig. 46 - Checking End Play with Dial Indicator

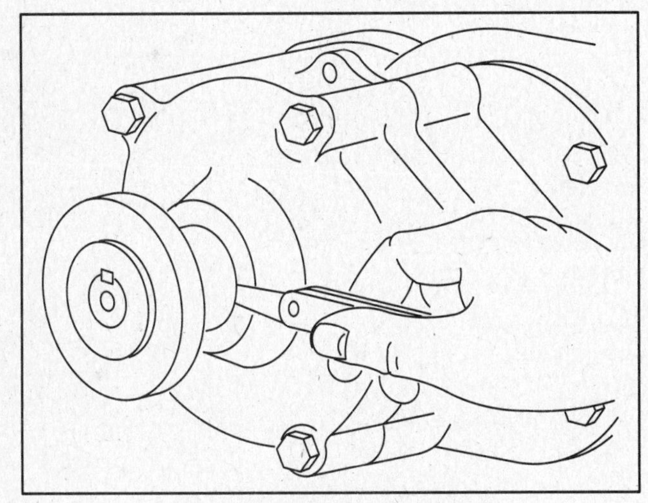
Fig. 47 - Checking End Play Using Pulley Pocket

Shim Bearing Cup

1. Remove gear case cover assembly and drive shaft (if shims were behind bearing cup in gear case assembly). Shims are .003" and .010" thick.

2. Use as many shims as needed to equal total end play plus .002 to .005" more than total end play without shims.

3. Install shims behind bearing cup and reinstall cup, drive shaft assembly and gear case cover assembly as outlined above in INSTALL GEAR CASE COVER ASSEMBLY.

Fill Gear Case with Lubricant

On Model Series 230000 the gear reduction and the engine use the same oil supply.

1. Fill the crankcase with the proper weight and service classification oil for the temperature that the engine will be run at.

2. Start and run engine and then stop.

3. Recheck oil level and add oil as required to bring engine oil level up to full, Fig. 48. See Section 8, Lubrication, for oil recommendations.

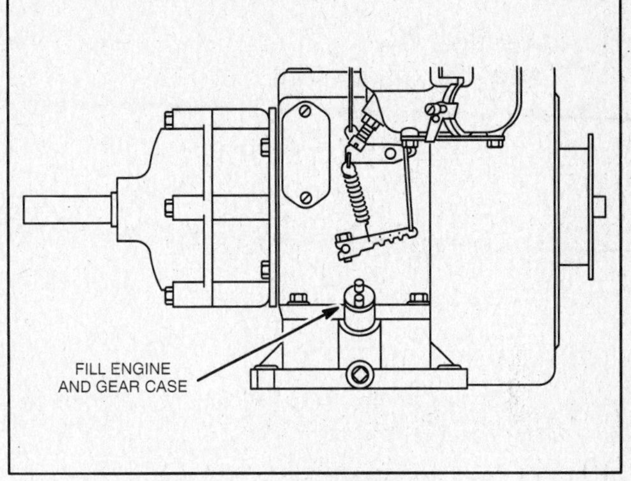

Fig. 48 - Filling Gear Case

Auxiliary PTO – Model Series 92580, 92980, 94580, 94980, 110980, 111980, 121780, 122780, 124780

This auxiliary power take-off shaft is perpendicular to the crankshaft. It rotates at the rate of one revolution for every 8-1/2 revolutions of the crankshaft. On these models, the cam gear, worm gear and oil slinger are a factory assembly and are not available as separate pieces, Fig. 49.

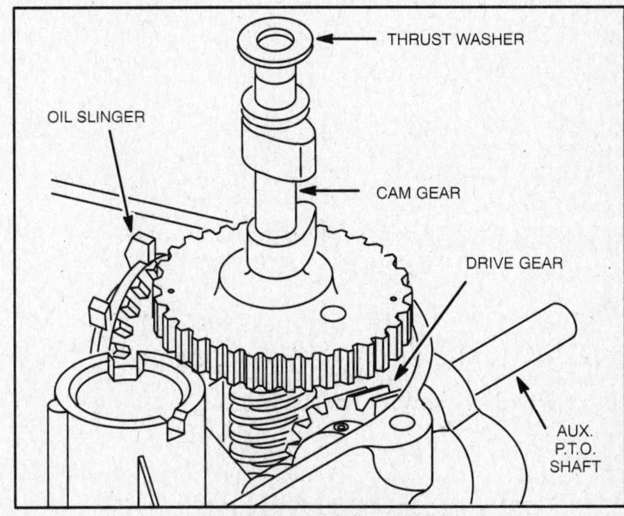

Fig. 49 - Auxiliary PTO

NOTE: METRIC EQUIVALENTS ARE LISTED ON PAGE 26 OF THIS SECTION.

NOTE: If rotation is counterclockwise, the thrust washer is placed next to the worm gear on camshaft.

Remove Sump All Model Series except 120000

1. Remove rust or burrs from the power take-off end of the crankshaft.

   NOTE: One of the six (6) sump mounting screws is located under the auxiliary drive cover.

2. Remove the cover.
3. Lift out shaft stop, Fig. 50.
4. Slide gear and shaft sideways to expose head of sump mounting screw.
5. Use 7/16" socket to remove screw.
6. Remove remaining screws and remove sump.

10

NOTE: Use care when driving out roll pin to prevent damage to threads.

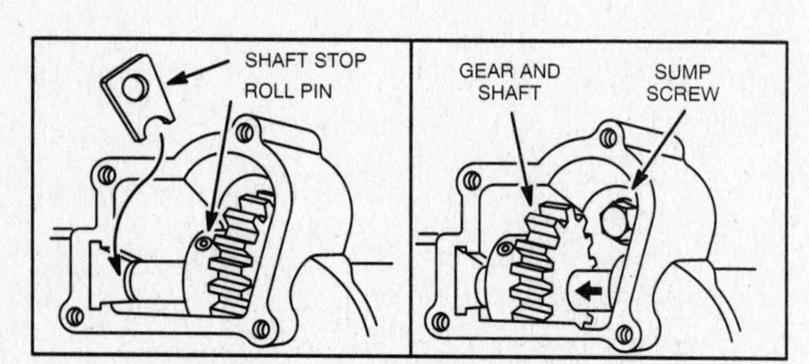

Fig. 50 - Remove and Install Sump Screw

When installing cover, Fig. 51, put non-hardening sealant on cover screws.

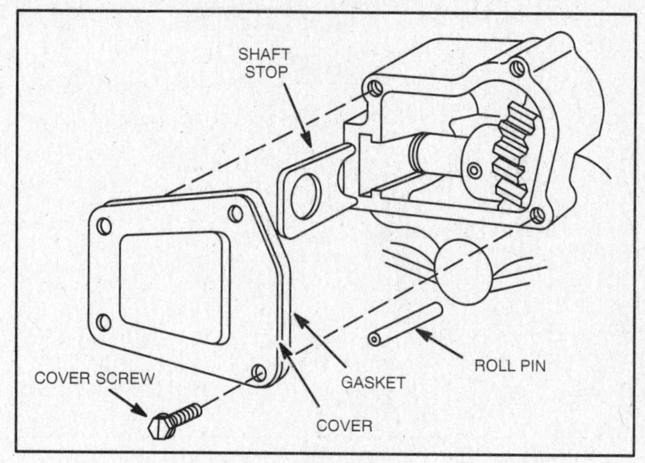

Fig. 51 - Installing Cover

Remove Sump and Drive Shaft, Model Series 120000

1. Remove all rust and burrs from crankshaft before removing sump.
2. Remove seven (7) sump bolts and lift off sump.
3. To remove auxiliary PTO shaft, remove Allen screw from sump, Fig. 52.
4. With a 3/16" pin punch drive out roll pin in bevel gear thru Allen screw hole.
5. Remove PTO shaft stop and slide out PTO shaft.

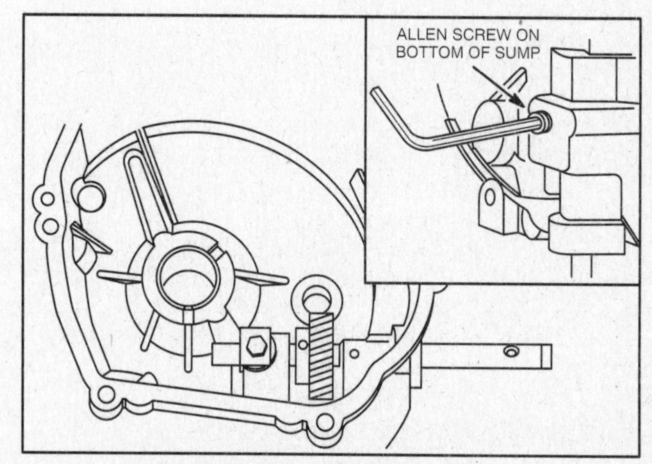

Fig. 52 - Removing Drive Shaft

NOTE: METRIC EQUIVALENTS ARE LISTED ON PAGE 26 OF THIS SECTION.

Remove Sump and Drive Shaft, Auxiliary Drive Shaft with Clutch, Model Series 110980

This auxiliary power take-off shaft is perpendicular to the crankshaft. It rotates at the rate of one revolution for every 8-1/2 revolutions of the crankshaft. Rotation of the shaft is controlled by a clutch on the cam gear. The clutch is engaged or disengaged by a control lever mounted on the oil sump.

Early production cam gears, Fig. 53, are serviced as an assembly consisting of cam gear oil slinger, clutch hub, clutch spring and clutch sleeve assembly. Later production cam gears are serviced as individual parts except for the cam gear which consists of cam gear, oil slinger and clutch hub.

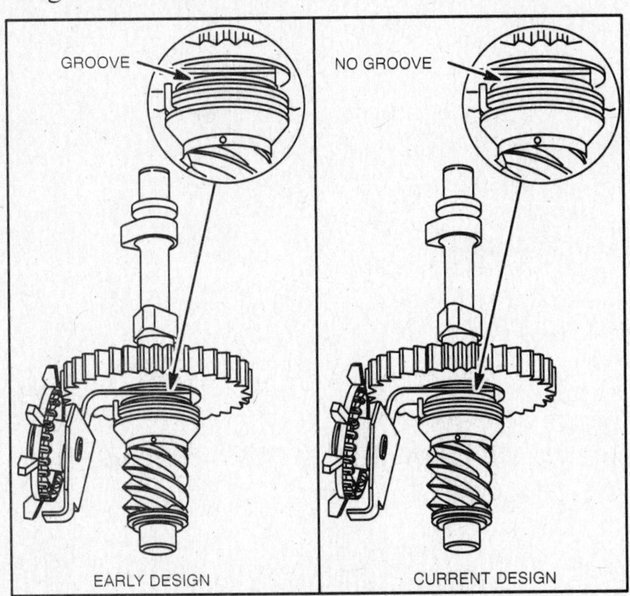

Fig. 53 - Cam Gear and Clutch

1. Remove rust or burrs from the power take-off end of the crankshaft.

   NOTE; Sump is held on by six screws. Five screws are exposed. The sixth screw is under the auxiliary drive cover, Fig. 50.

2. Remove cover and lift out shaft stop, Fig. 50.
3. Slide drive shaft and gear over to expose head of cap screw. Cap screw can be removed with 7/16" socket.
4. Remove remaining screws and remove sump.

Inspect Clutch Operation

1. Push on spring tang, "A," Fig. 54, turning spring and clutch sleeve in a counterclockwise direction.
2. Spring and sleeve should rotate approximately 1/8 turn. Worm gear should not rotate in the same direction.
3. With clutch released, worm gear should rotate freely in both directions.

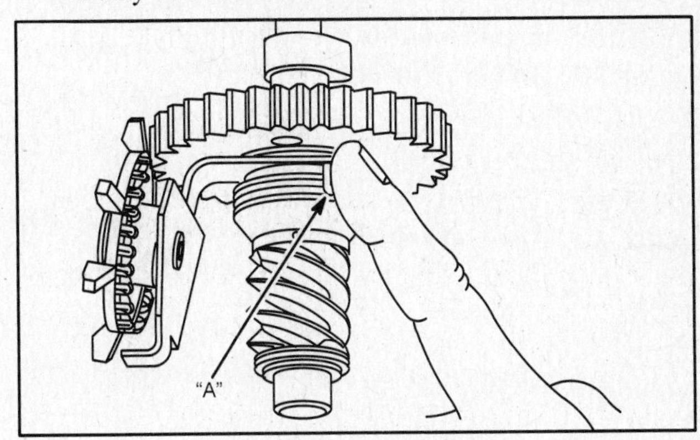

Fig. 54 - Inspect Clutch

Check Cam Gear

Check worm gear end play using feeler gauges at point "A," Fig. 55. End play should not be less than .004", or more than .017".

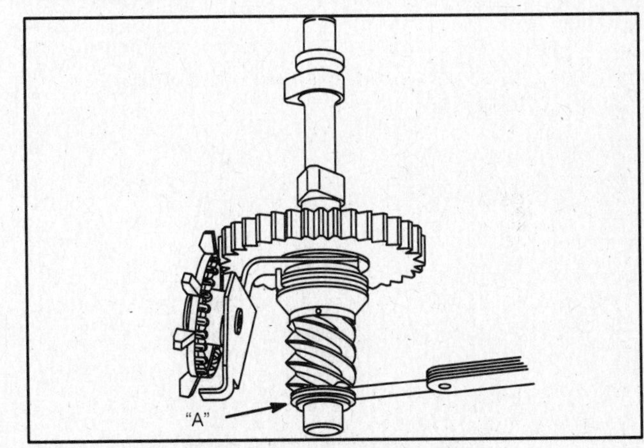

Fig. 55 - Check Cam Gear

Cam Gear Disassembly - Early Design

1. Remove "E" ring retainer.
2. Slide off copper washer, thick thrust washer, worm and thin thrust washer.
3. Cam gear, oil slinger, clutch sleeve and springs are serviced with a current production assembly.

Inspect Parts

Inspect for worn, burred or broken parts and replace as required.

NOTE: METRIC EQUIVALENTS ARE LISTED ON PAGE 26 OF THIS SECTION.

Assemble Cam Gear - Early Design

1. Slide worm gear with thin thrust washer on cam gear.

2. Slide on thick thrust washer. Slide on copper colored washer with gray coated side toward thick thrust washer.

3. Install "E" ring retainer and check worm end play as described in "Check Cam Gear" section. Inspect cam gear assembly as outlined in "Inspect Clutch Operation" section.

Disassemble Cam Gear - Current Design

1. Remove "E" ring.

2. Slide off thrust washers and worm gear.

3. Use thin blade screwdriver or similar tool to pry lower clutch spring tab out of hole in clutch sleeve, Fig. 56.

4. Remove clutch sleeve.

5. Slide clutch spring down, Fig. 57 and lift out upper spring tab to remove spring. Cam gear, oil slinger and clutch drive hub are serviced as an assembly.

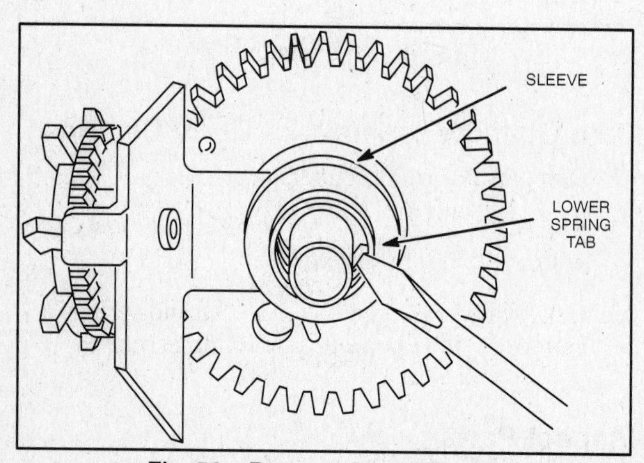

Fig. 56 - Remove Clutch Sleeve

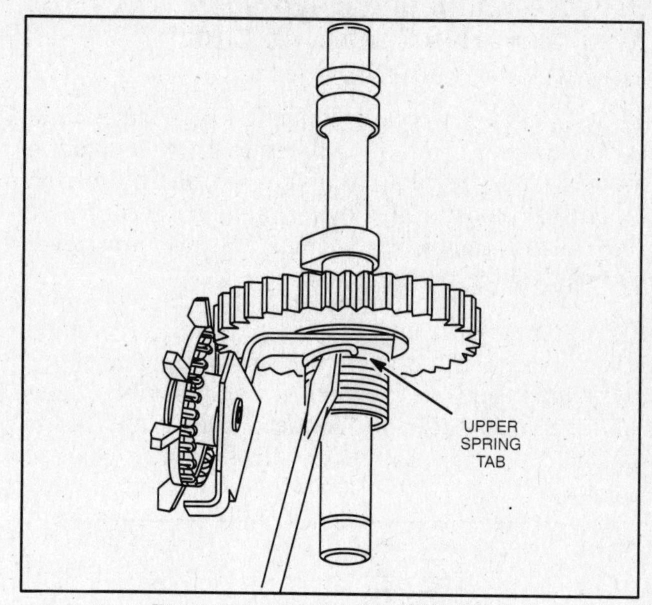

Fig. 57 - Remove Clutch Spring

Inspect Parts

Inspect for worn, broken or burred parts. Replace as required.

Assemble Cam Gear - Current Design

1. Assemble clutch spring as shown in Fig. 58.

2. Align hole in clutch sleeve with tab or spring and slide on.

3. Depress spring tab, if required. When clutch sleeve is in place, spring tab should be in sleeve hole, Fig. 59.

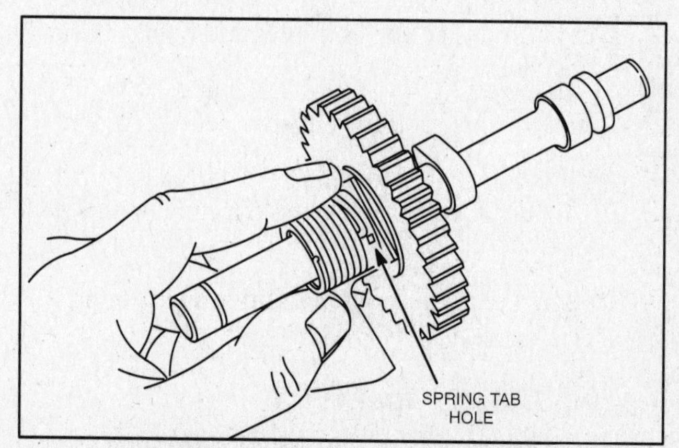

Fig. 58 - Assemble Clutch Spring

NOTE: METRIC EQUIVALENTS ARE LISTED ON PAGE 26 OF THIS SECTION.

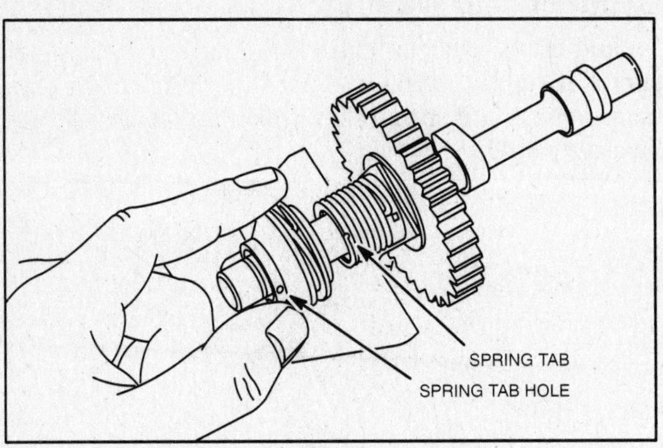

Fig. 59 - Install Clutch Sleeve

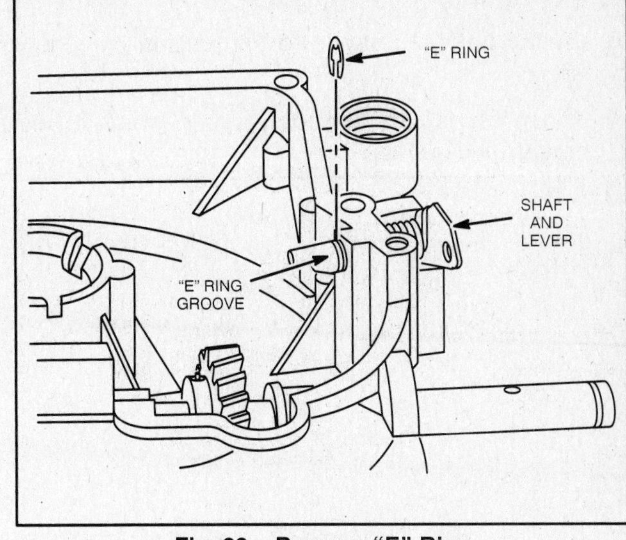

Fig. 60 - Remove "E" Ring

4. Slide thin thrust washer and worm on cam gear. Slide in thick thrust washer.

5. Slide on copper washer with gray coated side toward thrust washer.

6. Install "E" ring and check worm gear end play as described in "Check Cam Gear," this section, page 21. Inspect cam gear assembly as outlined in "Inspect Clutch Operation" section, page 21.

Remove Control Lever Shaft

1. Remove "E" ring, Fig. 60.

2. Slide control lever and shaft out slowly until lever clears boss on sump.

3. Slowly release spring tension and then remove shaft, spring and "O" ring seal.

4. Inspect shaft assembly for loose lever, worn or broken parts. Replace as needed.

Assemble Control Lever and Shaft Assembly

1. Install return spring on shaft and lever assembly as shown in Fig. 61.

2. Then install "O" ring seal on shaft.

3. Lubricate "O" ring and shaft lightly with engine oil.

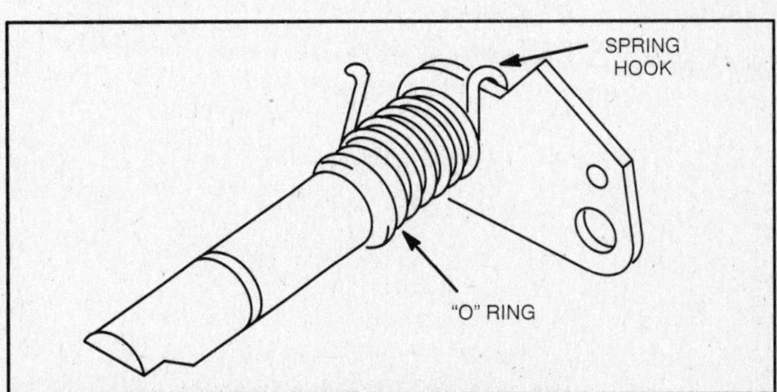

Fig. 61 - Assemble Spring

NOTE: METRIC EQUIVALENTS ARE LISTED ON PAGE 26 OF THIS SECTION.

4. Slide control lever assembly into shaft bore, Fig. 62, as far as it will go.
5. Rotate lever clockwise to put tension on return spring.
6. When lever clears stop boss, push lever and spring in until lever stops.

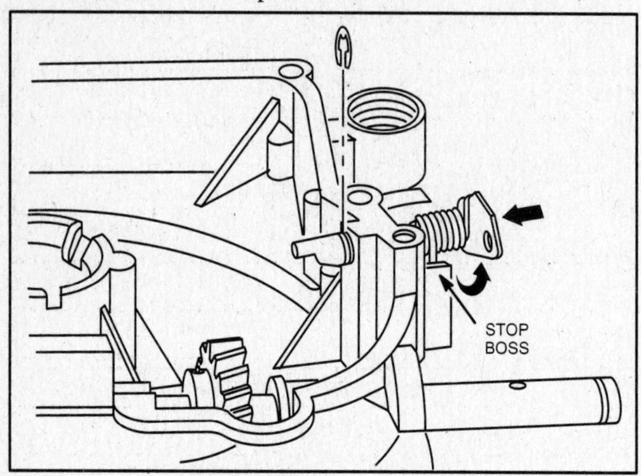

Fig. 62 – Lever Installation

7. Install “E” ring. Leg of spring may need to be pushed against sump, Fig. 63.

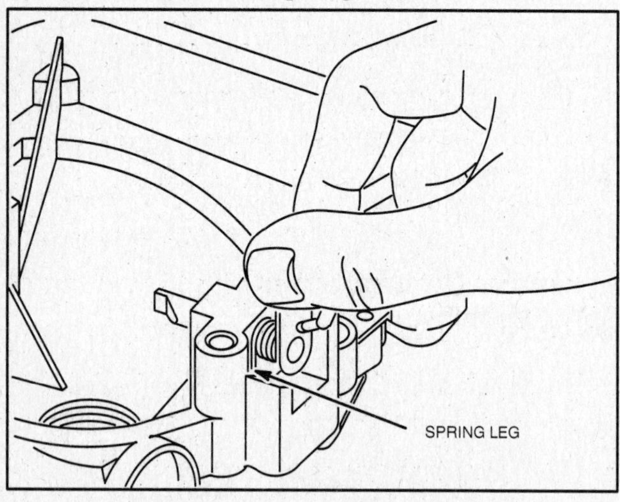

Fig. 63 – Spring Installation

Cylinder Clip Washer

Should clip washer in cylinder require replacing, be sure flat on clip washer is in line with flat on cam bearing boss and spring tabs are on both sides of cam bearing web, Fig. 64.

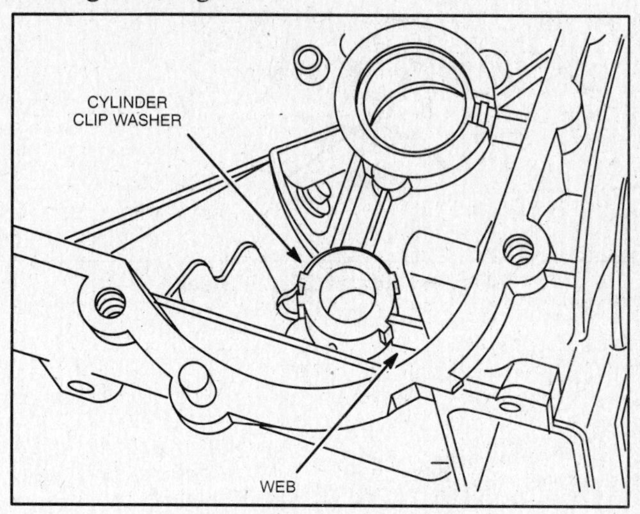

Fig. 64 – Cylinder Clip Washer

NOTE: METRIC EQUIVALENTS ARE LISTED ON PAGE 26 OF THIS SECTION.

METRIC EQUIVALENTS

DIMENSIONS, DECIMAL	
Inches	Millimeters
.002	.05
.003	.08
.004	.10
.005	.13
.007	.18
.008	.20
.009	.23
.010	.25
.015	.38
.017	.43
.020	.51
.030	.76
.070	1.78
.088	2.24
.110	2.79
.120	3.05
.130	3.30
.436	11.07
.497	12.62
.498	12.65
.6145	15.61
.751	19.08
.787	19.99
.8105	20.59
.870	22.10
.873	22.17
.875	22.23
.883	22.43
.950	24.13
.9650	24.511
.9750	24.765
.977	24.82
.9780	24.841
.9783	24.849

DIMENSIONS, DECIMAL	
Inches	Millimeters
.9788	24.862
.984	24.99
.990	25.146
.996	25.30
.997	25.32
.998	25.35
1.000	25.40
1.003	25.48
1.0100	25.654
1.060	26.92
1.062	26.97
1.0605	26.937
1.0645	27.038
1.0720	27.229
1.0724	27.239
1.090	27.69
1.1039	28.039
1.1043	28.049
1.122	28.50
1.1664	29.627
1.1668	29.637
1.179	29.95
1.181	30.00
1.1844	30.07
1.1855	30.111
1.1895	30.213
1.2170	30.912
1.2210	31.013
1.2289	31.214
1.2293	31.224
1.247	31.67
1.2914	32.802
1.2918	32.812
1.3094	33.25

NOTE: METRIC EQUIVALENTS ARE LISTED ON PAGE 26 OF THIS SECTION.

METRIC EQUIVALENTS (Cont'd.)

DIMENSIONS, DECIMAL	
Inches	**Millimeters**
1.3105	33.287
1.3145	33.388
1.317	33.45
1.3730	34.874
1.376	34.95
1.3769	34.97
1.3770	34.976
1.378	35.00
1.503	38.18
1.6150	41.021
1.6350	41.529
DIMENSIONS, FRACTIONAL	
Inches	**Millimeters**
3/16	4.75
5-1/2	140.00

TEMPERATURE	
Fahrenheit	**Centigrade**
0	-17
50	10
250	120
350	177

TORQUE		
In. Lbs.	**Kgcm Kpcm**	**Nm**
40	46	4.5
65	75	7.3
85	98	9.6
90	104	10.2
120	138	13.6
140	161	15.8
190	219	21.4

NOTE: METRIC EQUIVALENTS ARE LISTED ON PAGE 26 OF THIS SECTION.

Section 11
CYLINDERS & BEARINGS

INDEX, SECTION 11

BEARINGS

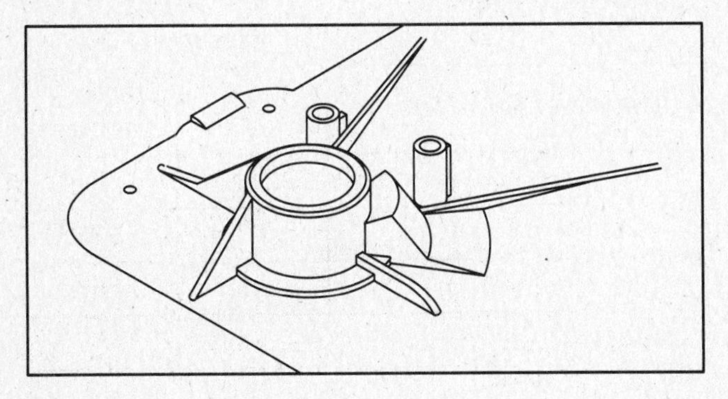

CYLINDERS

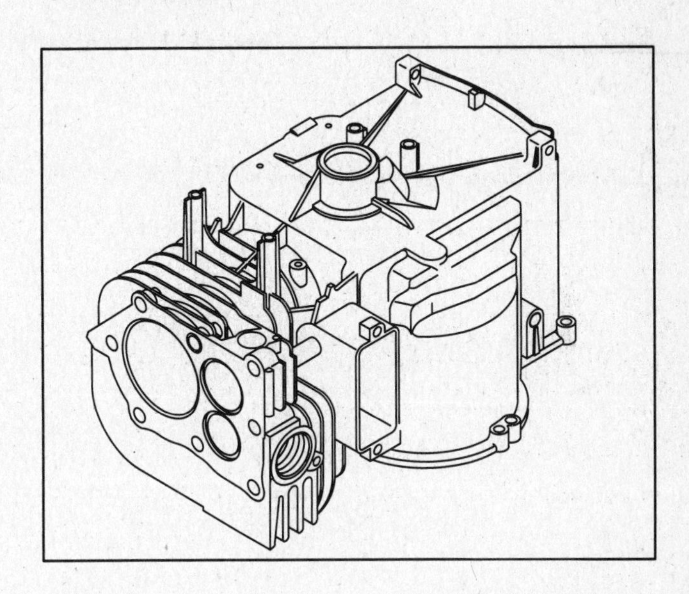

11

INSPECTION

All Models

Always inspect the cylinder after the engine has been disassembled. Visual inspection will show if there are any cracks, stripped bolt holes, broken fins or if the cylinder wall is damaged. Use a telescoping gauge and dial caliper or inside micrometer to determine the size of the cylinder bore. Measure at right angles, Fig. 1. TABLE NO. 1 lists the standard cylinder bore sizes.

If the cylinder bore is more than .003" oversize, or .0015" out of round on cast iron cylinders, or .0025" out of round on aluminum cylinders, it must be resized.

NOTE: METRIC EQUIVALENTS ARE LISTED ON PAGE 13 OF THIS SECTION.

CYLINDERS

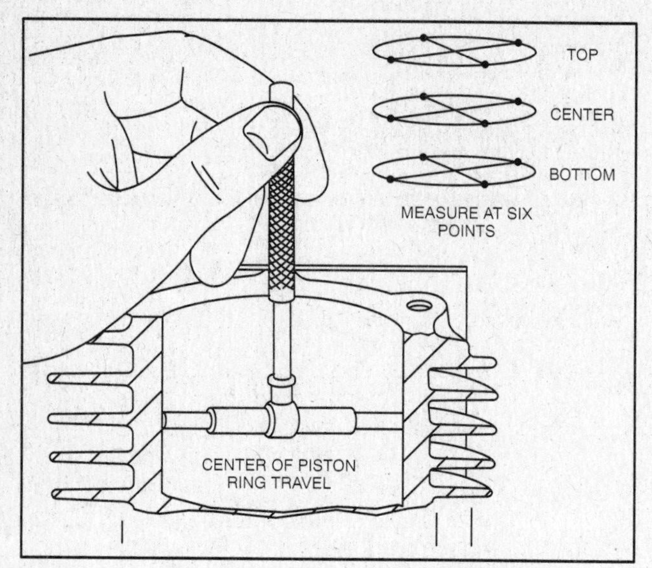

Fig. 1 – Checking Cylinder Bore

NOTE: When installing new piston rings in a cylinder bore that is within specification shown, the cylinder bore should be reconditioned. The proper cylinder cross hatch ensures proper lubrication and piston ring rotation. See "Cylinder Finish," page 4. Some engine models produced at the factory have diamond bored cylinders which do not have cross hatch finish.

NOTE: Chrome ring sets are available for most models. See Bulletin #479 or Illustrated Parts List. They are used to control oil consumption in bores worn up to .005" over standard and do not require re-honing the bore to seat.

RESIZING

Resize Cylinder Bore to Next Oversize All Models

ALWAYS RESIZE TO EXACTLY .010", .020", OR .030" OVER STANDARD BORE SIZE AS SHOWN IN TABLE NO. 1. IF THIS IS DONE ACCURATELY, THE STOCK OVERSIZE PISTON AND RINGS WILL FIT CORRECTLY AND PROPER CLEARANCES WILL BE MAINTAINED. Cylinders, either cast iron or aluminum, can be accurately resized with hone sets listed in TABLE NO. 2.

Use stones and lubrication recommended by hone manufacturers for various cylinder bores to obtain proper cylinder wall finish.

TABLE NO. 1

Model Series	Standard Bore Size Diameter	
Aluminum Cylinder	**Max. Inches**	**Min. Inches**
60000 after Ser. #5810030	2.3750	2.3740
80000	2.3750	2.3740
90000, 100700	2.5625	2.5615
100200, 100900	2.5000	2.4990
110000	2.7812	2.7802
120000	2.6885	2.6875
130000	2.5625	2.5615
170000, 190000	3.0000	2.9990
220000, 250000, 280000	3.4375	3.4365
Cast Iron Cylinder	**Max. Inches**	**Min. Inches**
230000	3.0000	2.9990
240000	3.0625	3.0615
300000	3.4375	3.4365
320000	3.5625	3.5615

NOTE: METRIC EQUIVALENTS ARE LISTED ON PAGE 13 OF THIS SECTION.

If a boring bar is used, a hone must be used after the boring operation to produce the proper cylinder wall finish.

Honing can be done with a portable electric drill, but it is easier to use a drill press.

To Set Up For Honing

1. Clean cylinder at top and bottom to remove burrs, pieces of base and head gaskets.

2. Fasten cylinder to a heavy iron bracket or use honing plate, Fig. 2. Some cylinders require shims.

3. Use a level to align drill press spindle with bore.

4. Oil surface of drill press table liberally. Set plate and cylinder on drill press table. (Do not anchor to drill press table.) If using portable drill, set plate and cylinder on floor.

5. Place hone drive shaft in chuck of drill or portable drill.

6. Slip hone into cylinder, Fig. 2, Illus. 2.

7. Connect drive shaft to hone and set stop on drill press so hone can only extend 3/4" to 1" from top and bottom of cylinder. If using a portable drill, cut a wood block to place inside of cylinder as a stop, Fig. 2, Illus. 2.

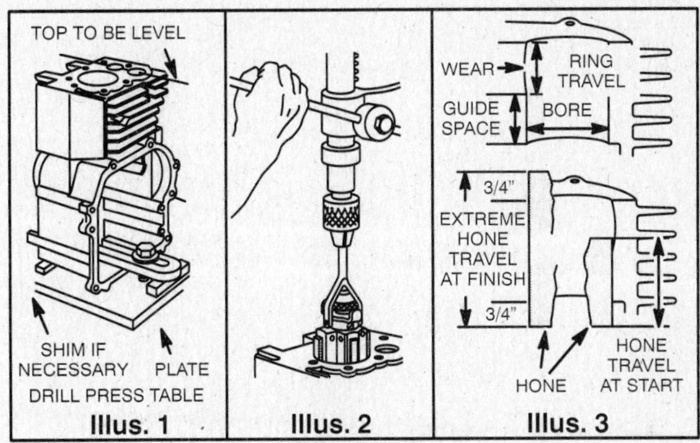

Fig. 2 – Honing Cylinder
(See page 4 for enlarged drawing.)

To Hone Cylinder

1. Place hone in middle of cylinder bore.

2. Tighten adjusting knob with finger or small screwdriver until stones fit snugly against cylinder wall. DO NOT FORCE.

   NOTE: Hone should operate at 300 to 700 RPM. Lubricate hone as recommended by manufacturer.

3. Connect drive shaft to hone. Be sure that cylinder and hone are centered and aligned with drive shaft and drill spindle.

4. Start drill and, as hone spins, move it up and down at lower end of cylinder. Fig. 2, Illus. 3.

NOTE: The cylinder is not worn at the bottom but is round so it will guide the hone to straighten cylinder bore. As the bottom of the cylinder increases diameter, gradually increase strokes until hone travels full length of bore. Do not extend hone more than 3/4" to 1" at either end of cylinder bore.

TABLE NO. 2
Cylinder Hones

Hone Set #	Bore Material	Bore Size	Stone Set #	Carrier Set #
19205	Aluminum	1-7/8 to 2-3/4"	19206	19205
19205	Aluminum	2-5/8 to 3-1/2"	19207	19205
	Cast Iron	1-7/8 to 2-3/4"	19303 (60 grit)	19205
	Cast Iron	1-7/8 to 2-3/4"	19304 (220 grit)	19205
19211	Cast Iron	2-1/2 to 3-5/16" 2-1/2 to 3-5/16"	19212 (60 grit) 19213 (220 grit)	19214 19214
19211	Cast Iron	3-5/16 to 4-1/8" 3-5/16 to 4-1/8"	19212 (60 grit) 19213 (220 grit)	19215 19215

NOTE: METRIC EQUIVALENTS ARE LISTED ON PAGE 13 OF THIS SECTION.

Fig. 2 (Cont'd.)

5. As cutting tension decreases, stop hone and tighten adjusting knob.

6. Check cylinder bore frequently with an accurate micrometer. Hone about .0005" larger to allow for shrinkage when cylinder cools.

NOTE: On cast iron cylinders, change from rough stones to finishing stones when within .0015" of desired size. Then use finishing stones.

ALWAYS HONE .010", .020", OR .030" ABOVE THE STANDARD DIMENSIONS GIVEN IN TABLE NO. 1.

Cylinder Finish

The finish on a resized or reconditioned cylinder should have a crosshatch appearance, Fig. 3. Proper stones, lubrication and drill speed along with rapid movement of hone within the cylinder during the last few strokes, will produce this finish. Crosshatching will allow proper lubrication and ring rotation.

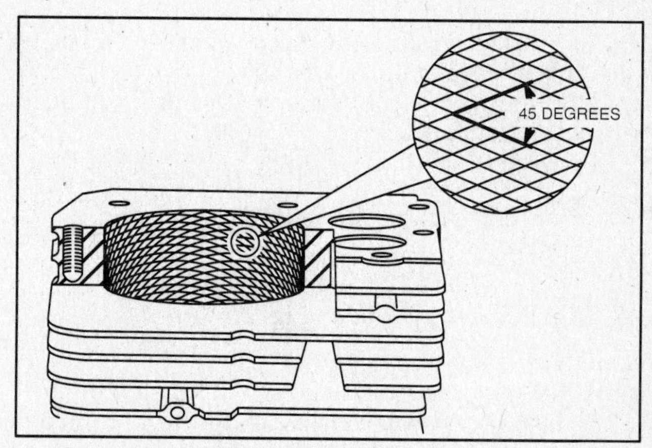

Fig. 3 – Cross Hatch

Cylinder Cleaning

IT IS MOST IMPORTANT THAT THE ENTIRE CYLINDER AND CRANKCASE BE THOROUGHLY CLEANED AFTER HONING. FIRST WASH THE CYLINDER AND CRANKCASE CAREFULLY IN A SOLVENT SUCH AS KEROSENE OR COMMERCIAL SOLVENT. THEN THOROUGHLY WASH CYLINDER AND CRANKCASE USING A STIFF BRUSH WITH SOAP AND HOT WATER. CLEAN UNTIL ALL TRACES OF HONING GRIT ARE GONE.

HONING GRIT IS HIGHLY ABRASIVE AND WILL CAUSE RAPID WEAR TO ALL OF THE INTERNAL COMPONENTS OF THE ENGINE UNLESS IT IS COMPLETELY REMOVED.

NOTE: METRIC EQUIVALENTS ARE LISTED ON PAGE 13 OF THIS SECTION.

BEARINGS

BALL BEARING

To check a ball bearing, rotate the bearing slowly by hand; if any roughness is noted, bearing should be replaced.

Wash bearing in a clean solvent. Re-oil with engine oil during assembly.

Ball bearings are a press fit on the crankshaft. If bearing is to be replaced, it should be removed in an arbor press, Fig. 4. (Bearing should not be reused if removed from crankshaft.)

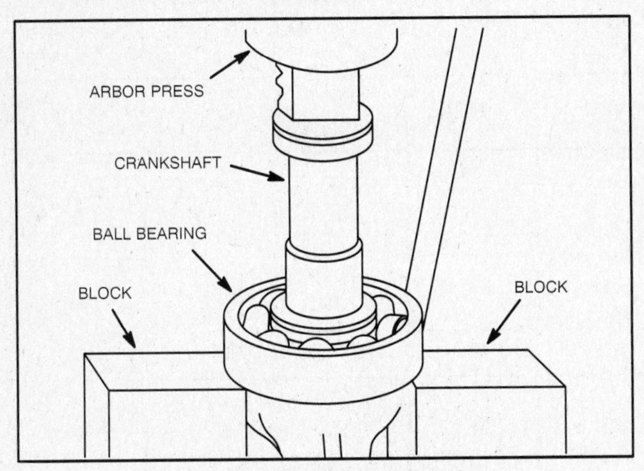

Fig. 4 - Removing Ball Bearings

1. To install, heat bearing in hot (250° F max.) oil.
2. Place crankshaft in a vise with bearing side up. When bearing is hot, it will be a slip fit on crankshaft journal.
3. Grasp bearing with the shield down and slide it on the crankshaft, Fig. 5. The bearing will tighten while cooling. Do not quench.

NOTE: Bearing shield faces crankshaft crankpin.

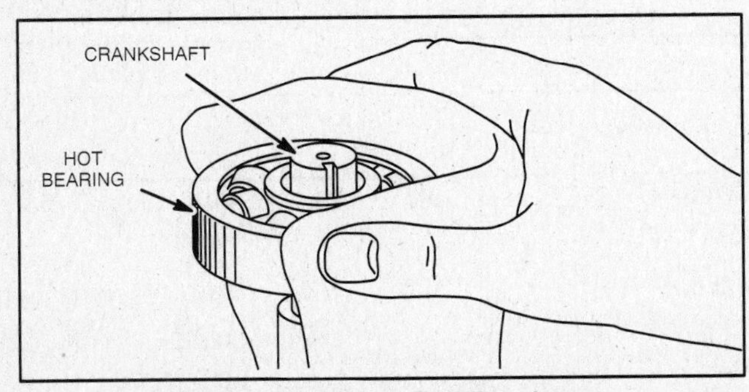

Fig. 5 - Installing Ball Bearings

PLAIN BEARINGS

Checking

Bearings should be replaced if scored or if plug gauge will enter. Try gauge at several locations in bearing, Fig. 6. See gauge listing in TABLE NO. 4 or TABLE NO. 5. If gauge is not available, refer to TABLE NO. 3 for reject dimensions.

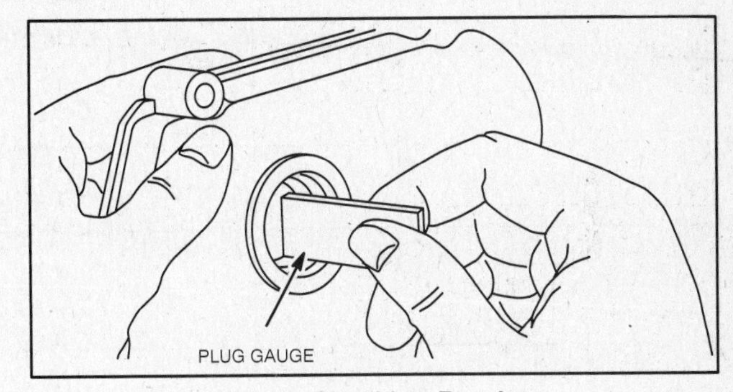

Fig. 6 - Checking Bearing

TABLE NO. 3
Cylinder Bearing Reject Size Chart

Model Series	Magneto Bearing	PTO Bearing
Aluminum Cylinder	**Inches**	**Inches**
60000, 80000*	.878	.878
90000*	.878	.878
100700, 120000	.878	1.065
100200, 100900, 130000	.878	1.003
110000*	.878	.878
170000#, 190000#	1.004	1.185
220000, 250000, 280000	1.383	1.383
Cast Iron Cylinder		
230000♦	1.382	1.382
240000, 300000, 320000	BALL	BALL

♦ Gear Reduction PTO - 1.185"

* Auxiliary drive models PTO Bearing Reject Size 1.003"

Synchro-Balanced Magneto Bearing Reject Size 1.185"

NOTE: METRIC EQUIVALENTS ARE LISTED ON PAGE 13 OF THIS SECTION.

REPAIR MAGNETO AND SUMP OR CRANKCASE COVER BEARINGS

Aluminum Cylinder Engines

Most aluminum cylinder engines use the aluminum cylinder material as a bearing. When the bearing is worn beyond reject, as measured by plug gauge listed in TABLE NO. 4 Magneto or TABLE NO. 5 PTO, bearings can be reamed out and rebushed with either a steel backed aluminum or a DU bearing. If gauge is not available, refer to TABLE NO. 3 for reject dimensions. Refer to Illustrated Parts List by Model Series and Type Number for part numbers.

Some Model Series engines are built with replaceable DU or needle bearing. Use plug gauge listed in TABLE NO. 4 Magneto or TABLE NO. 5 PTO to check DU for reject. If gauge is not available, refer to TABLE NO. 3 for reject dimensions.

TABLE NO. 4
Magneto Bearing Repair Tool Chart

Aluminum Model Series	Cylinder Support	Pilot	Counter-bore Reamer	Reamer Guide Bushing Mag.	Bushing Driver	Pilot Guide Bushing PTO	Finish Reamer	Plug Gauge
60000, 80000, 90000	19123	19096	19099	19101	19124	19094* 19097■	19095*♦	19166
92590*, 92990*, 110900*, 111900*, 112900	19123	19096	19099	19101	19124	⊄	19095*♦	19166
100200, 100900, 130000	19123	19096	19099	19101	19124	19168	19095♦	19166
100700, 120000	19123	19096	19099	19101	19124	19373	19095♦	19166
170000, Steel Backed 190000, Aluminum 192700, Bearing	19227	19096	19172	19170	19179	19169	19173*♦	19178
170000, DU 190000, Bearing 192700	19227	–	–	–	19179	–	–	19178
171700, Steel Backed 191700, Aluminum 193700, Bearing	19227	19096	19174	19201	19179	19169	19175*♦	19178
171700, DU 191700, Bearing 193700	19227	19096	19281	19301	19179	19169	–	19178
220000, 250000, 280000	19227	19220●	19224●	19222●	19226●	19220●	–	19219
Cast Iron Model Series								
230000, 240000, 300000, 320000	**Replace Support and Cover**							19117

♦ Tools for steel backed aluminum bushing, only in positions shown.
⊄ Use sump or crankcase cover with 7/8" diameter bearing and 19094 guide.
• Tools for DU Bushing only, in positions shown.
* Plain bearing crankcase cover.
■ Ball bearing crankcase cover.
NOTE: Tools listed may be used to install either steel backed aluminum bushing or DU bushing except as noted above.

NOTE: METRIC EQUIVALENTS ARE LISTED ON PAGE 13 OF THIS SECTION.

TABLE NO. 5
PTO Bearing Repair Tool Chart

Aluminum Model Series	Cylinder Support	Pilot	Counter-bore Reamer	Reamer Guide Bushing Mag.	Bushing Driver	Pilot Guide Bushing PTO	Finish Reamer	Plug Gauge
60000, 80000, 90000	19123	19096	19099	19100	19124	19094	19095*♦	19166
92590*, 92990*, 110900*, 111900*, 112900	19123	19096	19099	19101	19124	19094	19095*♦	-
100200, 100900, 130000	19123	19096	19172	19186V 19170H	19124	19094	19173¢ ♦	19178
100700 120000	Replace Sump If Bearing is Worn or Damaged							
170000, 190000, 192700	19227	19096	19174♦	19171♦	19179	19168	19175♦	19178
171700, 191700, 193700	19227	19096	19174♦	19171♦	19179	19169	19175♦	19178
220000, 250000, 280000	19227	19223●	19224●	19222●	19226●	19220●	-	19219
Cast Iron Model Series								
230000, 240000, 300000, 320000	**Replace Support and Cover**							19117

♦ Tools for steel backed aluminum bushing, only in positions shown.
• Tools for DU Bushing only, in positions shown.
* Plain bearing crankcase cover.
■ Ball bearing crankcase cover.
NOTE: Tools listed may be used to install either steel backed aluminum bushing or DU bushing except as noted above.

Repair Worn Aluminum Bearings

Select tools needed to repair bearing from Table No. 4. Remove and discard oil seal from bearing to be repaired. Place pilot guide bushing in bearing opposite of bearing to be repaired. Have flange of bushing on inside of crankcase.

NOTE: When Pilot, Tool #19066, has been modified by adding a 4-1/2" long, 3/8" dia. threaded extension, place pilot guide bushing flange on outside of crank-case, Fig. 7.

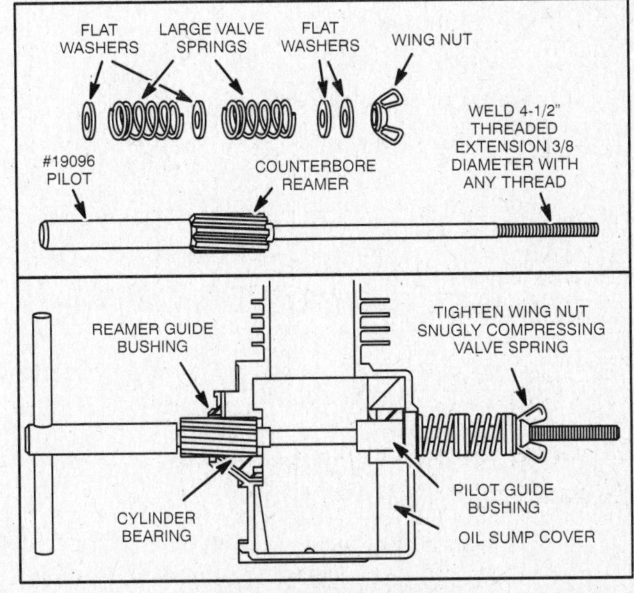

Fig. 7 - Modified Pilot

NOTE: METRIC EQUIVALENTS ARE LISTED ON PAGE 13 OF THIS SECTION.

1. Place reamer guide bushing in oil seal bore of bearing to be repaired. The reamer guide bushing and pilot guide bushing will center the counter-bore reamer, even though both bearings are worn.
2. Place counterbore reamer on pilot and insert into cylinder until tip of pilot enters pilot guide bushing and counterbore reamer enters reamer guide bushing, Fig's. 8 and 9.

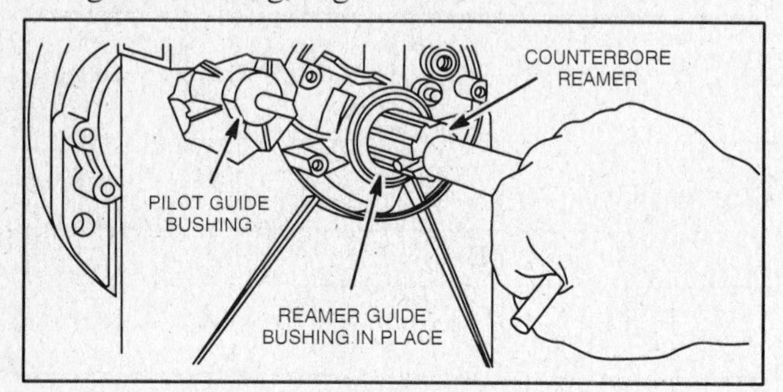

Fig. 8 – Counterbore Reaming

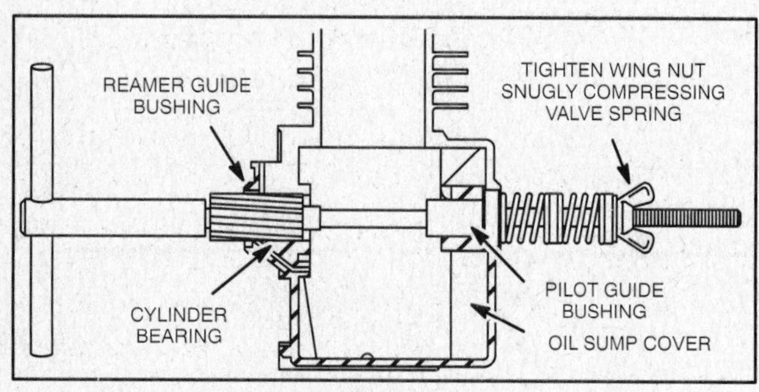

Fig. 9 – Counterbore Reaming with Threaded Extension

3. Turn counterbore reamer clockwise with steady pressure until it is completely through the worn bearing. Lubricate reamer with kerosene or similar solvent lubricant while reaming.

   NOTE: Do not counterbore ream without lubricant. Aluminum will build up on reamer flutes causing damage to reamer and result in oversize counterbores.

4. Remove sump or crankcase cover and remove reamer and pilot from crankcase. DO NOT REMOVE REAMER THROUGH COUNTER-BORED BEARING.
5. Remove guide bushings and clean out all chips.

Install Bushing, Cylinder (Steel Backed Aluminum)

1. Hold new bushing against cylinder or crankcase cover with notch next to reamed out bearing and in line with notch in cylinder or cover.
2. Note position of split in bushing.
3. With a chisel or screwdriver and hammer, make a notch in reamed out bearing opposite split in bearing, Fig. 10.

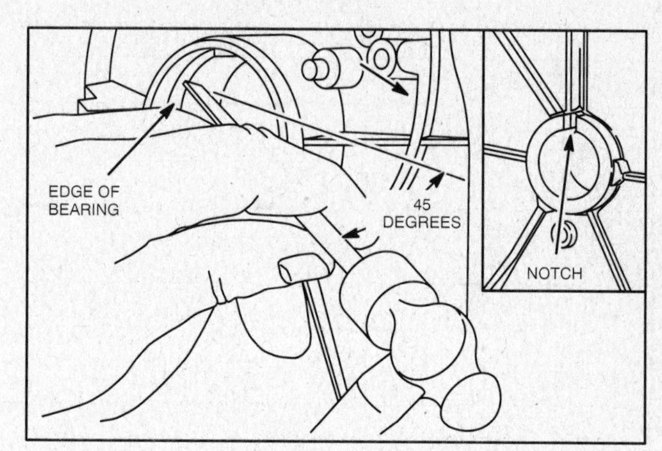

Fig. 10 – Notching Cylinder or Crankcase Cover

NOTE: On Model Series 171700, 191700, magneto bearing replacement, place bushing against inside of cylinder with notch in line with oil hole in cylinder and against reamed out bearing. Note position of split in bearing. With a chisel or a screwdriver and a hammer, make a notch on inside edge of reamed out bearing opposite split, Fig. 11.

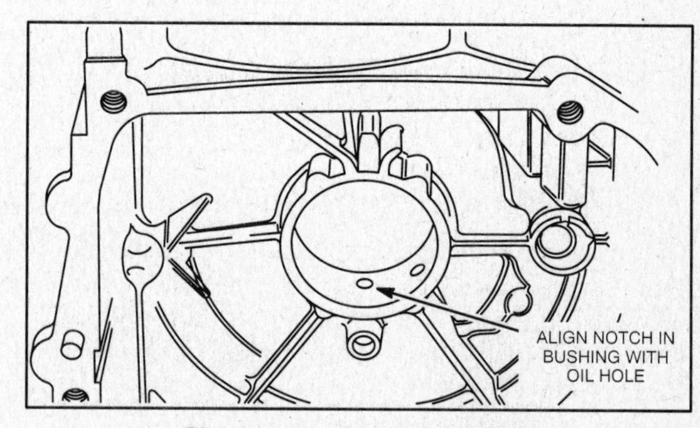

Fig. 11 – Location of Oil Hole

4. Select tools needed from Table No. 4 to press in new bushing.
5. Press in new bushing keeping notch in line with notch in cylinder or crankcase cover until outer edge of new bushing is flush with outer end of reamed out bushing.
6. If notch does not line up, bushing can be pressed into recess of cylinder support and reinstalled.

NOTE: METRIC EQUIVALENTS ARE LISTED ON PAGE 13 OF THIS SECTION.

On Model Series 171700, 191700, 193700 magneto bushing notch should be in line with oil hole and oil hole should be open after installation, Fig. 12.

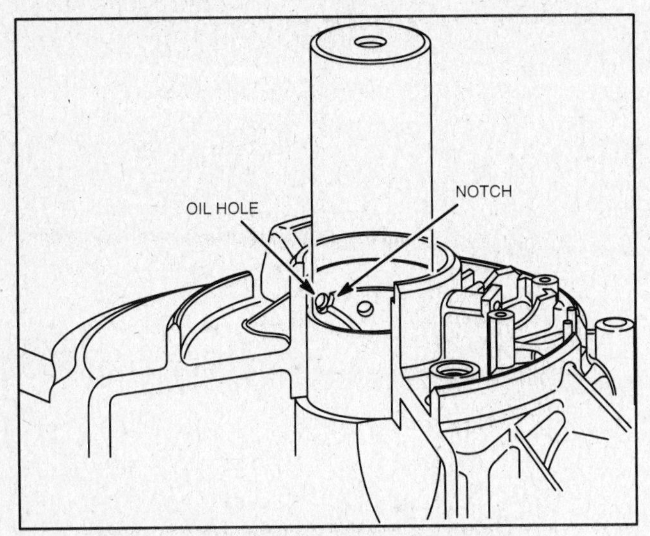

Fig. 12 - Installing Bushing Model Series 171700, 191700, 193700

7. Stake bushing into notch that was made in cylinder before bushing was pressed in. Reassemble cylinder and cover.

8. Then use tools from TABLE NO. 4 to finish ream bushing using kerosene or other solvent lubricant until finish reamer is completely through bushing.

9. Remove cover and reamer together.

10. Clean out all chips.

11. Install new oil seal, as required.

On rebushed cylinders that were breaker point equipped, a burr may occur in breaker point plunger hole. Use Finish Reamer, Tool #19058, to remove burr.

Install Bushing, Sump (Steel Backed Aluminum)

1. Place bushing on outside of sump with two notches in line with two oil grooves on inside and against reamed out bearing.

2. Note position of split in bushing.

3. With a chisel or screwdriver and hammer, make a notch in reamed out bearing opposite split in bushing, Fig. 13.

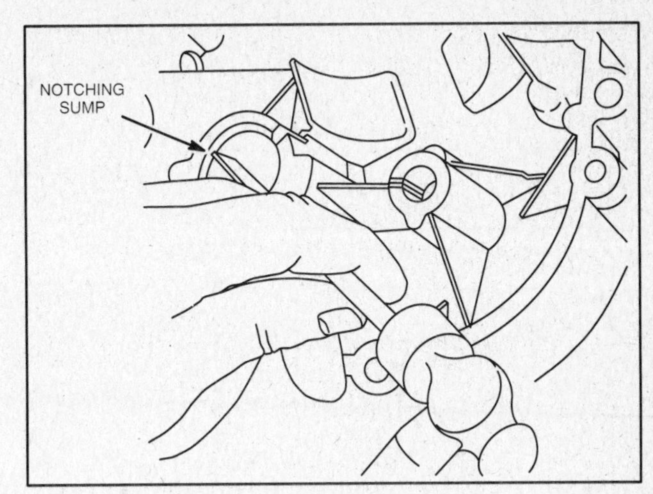

Fig. 13 - Notching Sump

4. Select tools from TABLE NO. 4 to press in new bushing.

5. Press in new bushing until bushing is flush with outer edge of reamed out bearing. If notches do not line up, bushing can be pressed through into recess of cylinder support and reinstalled.

6. Stake bushing into notch that was made before bushing was pressed in.

7. Reassemble cylinder and sump and finish ream new bushing with tools from TABLE NO. 4. Lubricate reamer with kerosene or other solvent lubricant until reamer is completely through bushing.

8. Remove sump and reamer together and clean out all chips. Install new oil seal.

Install DU Bushing, Cylinder or Crankcase Cover

1. Place DU bearing on cylinder or cover bearing with oil hole in line with oil hole in cylinder or cover bearing. If cover bearing does not have oil hole, place split of bearing as shown in Fig. 14.

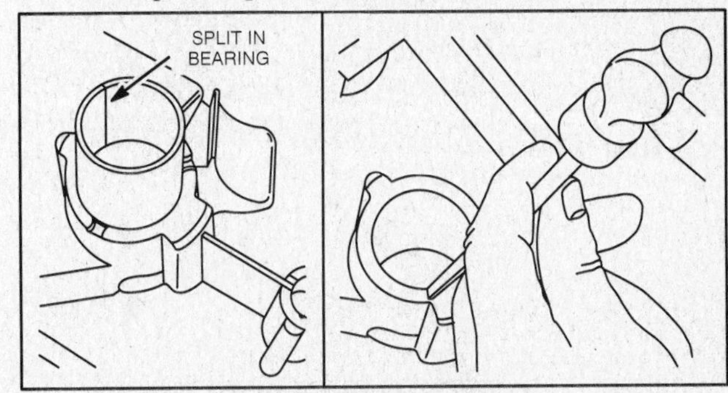

Fig. 14 - Locating Bearing

2. Press bearing to dimension shown in TABLE NO. 6 and Fig. 15.

11

NOTE: METRIC EQUIVALENTS ARE LISTED ON PAGE 13 OF THIS SECTION.

Measure from seal surface on magento side and from sump or crankcase cover thrust surface.

TABLE NO. 6

Model Series	Depth Mag.	Depth P.T.O.
60000, 80000, 90000, 1002000, 100900, 110000, 130000	1/32"	1/32"
170000, 190000	3/32"	1/32"
171700, 191700, 193700	1/64"	*
220000, 250000, 280000	7/64"	1/8"

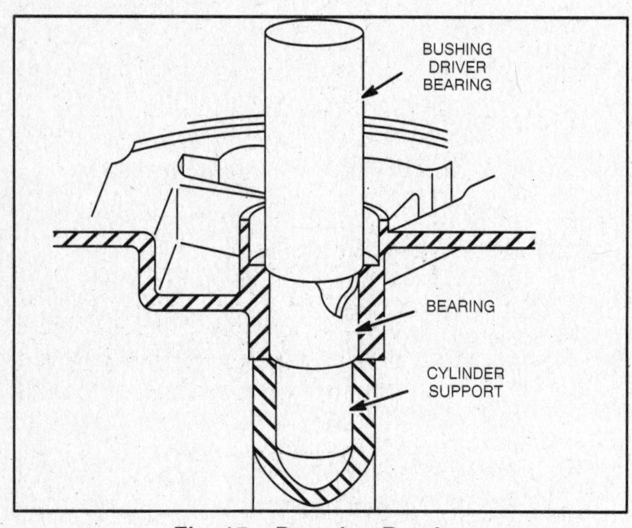

Fig. 15 - Pressing Bearing

3. Stake bearing as shown, Fig's. 16, 17, 18, and 19.

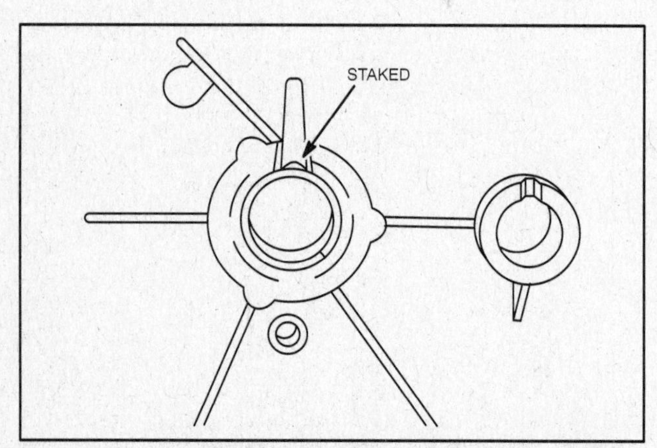

Fig. 16 - Staking Bearing Model Series 60000, 80000, 90000, 100200, 100900, 110000, 120000, 130000 Cylinder or Crankcase Cover

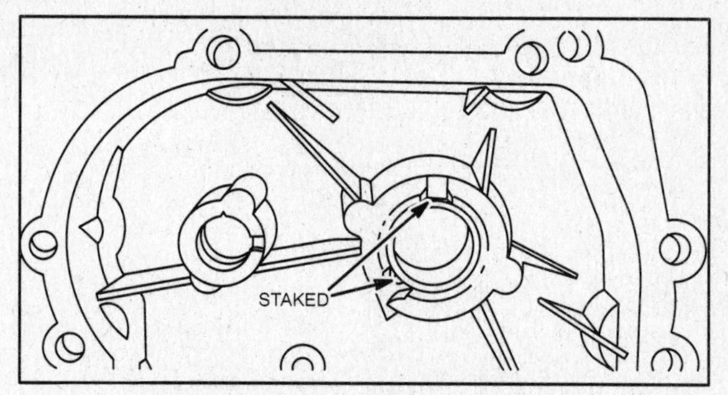

Fig. 17 - Staking Bearing Model Series 60000, 80000, 90000, 100200, 100900, 110000, 120000, 130000, Sump

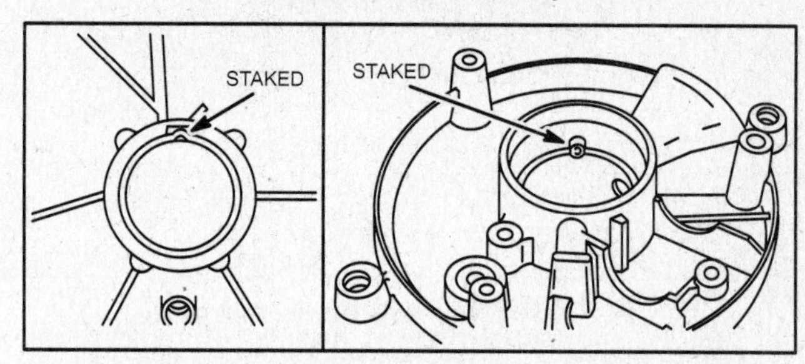

Fig. 18 - Staking Bearing Model Series 190000, 220000, 250000, 280000 Cylinder or Crankcase Cover

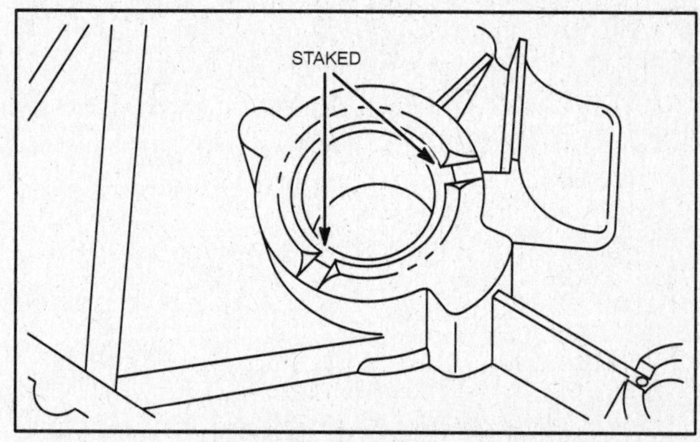

Fig. 19 - Staking Bearing Model Series 220000, 250000, 280000 Sump

NOTE: Model 92590, 92990, 110990, 111990. The magneto bearing can be replaced as above; if the sump bearing is worn, the sump must be replaced. No tools are available for replacing the sump bearing.

Install Crankcase Cover or Sump All Aluminum Model Series

Use Seal Protector Kit, Tool #19356, TABLE NO. 7, to protect oil seal when installing crankcase cover or sump. DO NOT FORCE COVER OR SUMP. Make sure mechanical governor gear is engaged with cam gear.

NOTE: METRIC EQUIVALENTS ARE LISTED ON PAGE 13 OF THIS SECTION.

TABLE NO. 7
Seal Protectors

Tool #1	Color	Crankshaft Journal Size
19334/1	White	.787"
19334/2	Red	.875"
19334/3	Blue	.984"
19334/4	Orange	1.000"
19334/5	Brown	1.062"
19334/6	Green	1.181"
19334/7	Yellow	1.378"
19356/8	Purple	1.317"
19356/9	Black	1.503"

Torque Crankcase Cover or Sump All Aluminum Model Series

Torque crankcase cover or sump to specifications listed in TABLE NO. 8.

TABLE NO. 8
Crankcase Cover or Sump Torque

Model Series	Torque In. Lbs.
60000, 80000, 90000, 120000	85
100200, 100900	120
100700, 110000	85
130000	120
170000, 190000, 220000, 250000, 280000	140

NOTE: On Model Series 100900, 130700, 131700, and 130900 a spring washer is used on cam gear as shown in Section 10, page 9, Fig. 15. Model Series 130780, 130980, 131780, and 132980 do not use a spring washer.

REPLACE OIL SEAL

The oil seal is assembled with the sharp edge of the leather or rubber toward the inside of the engine. Lubricate inside diameter of oil seals with "Lubriplate" or engine oil, before assembling engines.

Most oil seals are pressed in, flush with the hub. However, Models 60000, 80000, 100000 and 130000 using a ball bearing with mounting flange have the seal pressed 3/16" below crankcase mounting flange, Fig. 20.

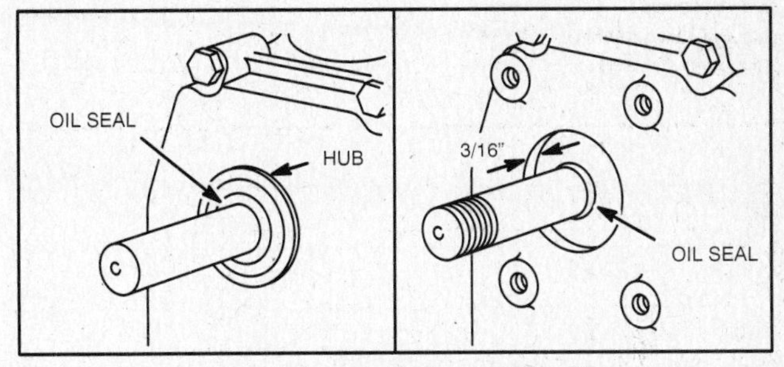

Fig. 20 - Replacing Oil Seal

Check Cam Gear Bearing

Check cam gear bearing using #19164 plug gauge as shown, Fig. 21. If 1/4" or more of gauge enters bearing bore, bearing is worn beyond reject, and the cylinder, sump or crankcase cover must be replaced.

NOTE: On Model Series 111200, 112200, 111900, 112900, Plug Gauge, Tool #19164, is used on the sump or crankcase cover cam gear bearing. Reject size for cylinder cam gear bearing is .443" or larger. On auxiliary drive Model Series 110980, PTO reject size is .493". No gauge is available for these bearings.

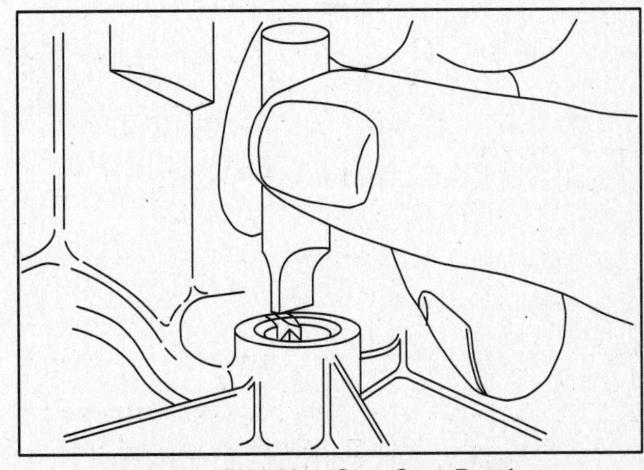
Fig. 21 - Checking Cam Gear Bearing

NOTE: METRIC EQUIVALENTS ARE LISTED ON PAGE 13 OF THIS SECTION.

METRIC EQUIVALENTS

DIMENSIONS, DECIMAL	
Inches	Millimeters
.0005	.01
.0015	.04
.0025	.06
.003	.08
.005	.13
.010	.38
.020	.51
.030	.76
.443	11.00
.493	12.52
.787	19.98
.875	22.23
.878	22.30
.984	24.99
1.000	25.4
1.003	25.50
1.004	25.50
1.062	26.97
1.065	27.50
1.181	30.00
1.185	30.10
1.317	33.45
1.378	35.00
1.382	35.10
1.383	35.13
1.503	38.18
2.3740	60.30
2.3750	60.33
2.5615	65.06
2.5625	65.09
2.4990	63.47
2.5000	63.50

DIMENSIONS, DECIMAL, cont'd	
Inches	Millimeters
2.6875	68.263
2.6885	68.288
2.7490	69.82
2.7500	69.85
2.7802	70.62
2.7812	70.64
2.9990	76.17
3.0000	76.20
3.0615	77.762
3.0625	77.786
3.4365	87.29
3.4375	87.31
3.5615	90.462
3.5625	90.488

DIMENSIONS, FRACTIONAL	
Inches	Millimeters
1/64	.38
1/32	.79
3/32	2.36
7/64	2.77
1/8	3.18
3/16	4.75
1/4	6
5/16	8
3/8	9
1/2	13
11/16	17
3/4	19
7/8	22
1	25
1-7/16	36
1-11/16	43

NOTE: METRIC EQUIVALENTS ARE LISTED ON PAGE 13 OF THIS SECTION.

METRIC EQUIVALENTS, Cont'd

DIMENSIONS, FRACTIONAL, cont'd	
Inches	Millimeters
1-7/8	48
2-1/2	63
2-5/8	67
2-3/4	70
3	76
3-5/16	84
3-1/2	89
3-7/8	98
4-1/8	105
4-1/2	114
4-3/4	121
5-3/4	146
5-13/16	148
6	152
6-3/4	171
7	178
9-1/2	241
9-3/4	248
11	279
12	305
20	508

TEMPERATURE	
Fahrenheit	Centigrade
250°	120°

TORQUE		
In. Lbs.	Kgcm Kpcm	Nm
85	98	9.6
120	138	13.5
140	160	15.8

NOTE: METRIC EQUIVALENTS ARE LISTED ON PAGE 13 OF THIS SECTION.

Section 12
SYNCHRO-BALANCE™

NOTE: This section covers the following specific Model Series Engines that are equipped with Synchro-Balance™. They are 171700, 191700, 193700, 195700, 196700, 251400, 251700, 252400, 252700, 253400, 253700, 254400, 255400, 255700, 256700, 257700, 258700, 259700, 28A700, 28B700, 28C700, 28D700, 28E700, 28M700, 280700, 281700, 282700, 283700, 284700, 285700, 286700, 289700, 300400, 301400, 302400, 320400, 325400, 326400. These Models will be referred to, in this section, as Model Series 170000, 190000, 250000, 280000, 300000, and 320000, except when a procedure applies to a specific Model or Models.

INDEX, SECTION 12

Synchro-Balance™, Model Series 170000, 190000, 250000 280000, Vertical Crankshaft

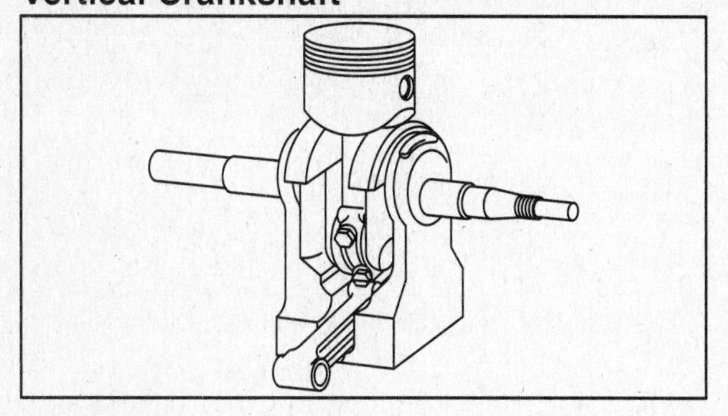

Synchro-Balance™, Model Series 250000, Horizontal Crankshaft

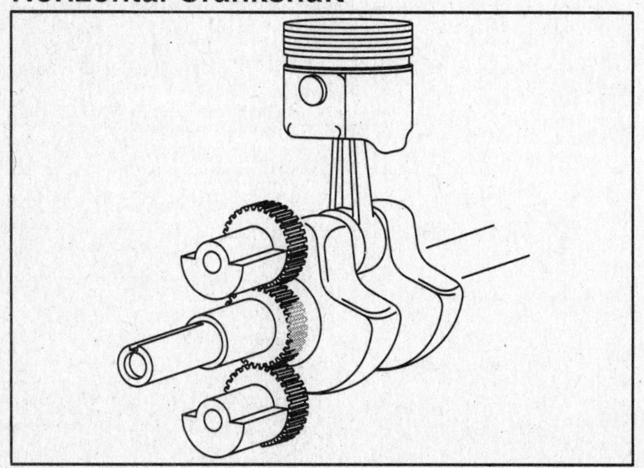

Synchro-Balance™, Model Series 300000, 320000

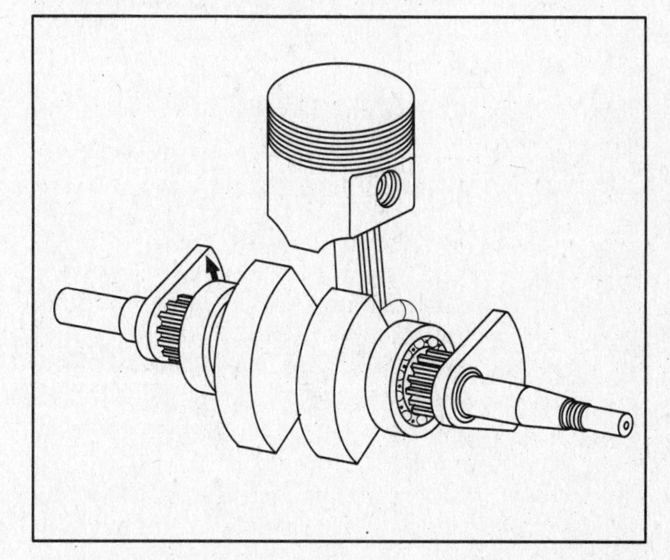

NOTE: METRIC EQUIVALENTS ARE LISTED ON PAGE 7 OF THIS SECTION.

Operation

Briggs & Stratton uses two methods of Synchro-Balancing engines.

One system uses counterweights that are geared to rotate in a direction opposite from the crankshaft counterweights, Fig. 1 The other system uses a counterweight that oscillates opposite to the direction of the piston. Each system performs the same function of substantially reducing engine vibration, thereby giving exceptionally smooth engine performance.

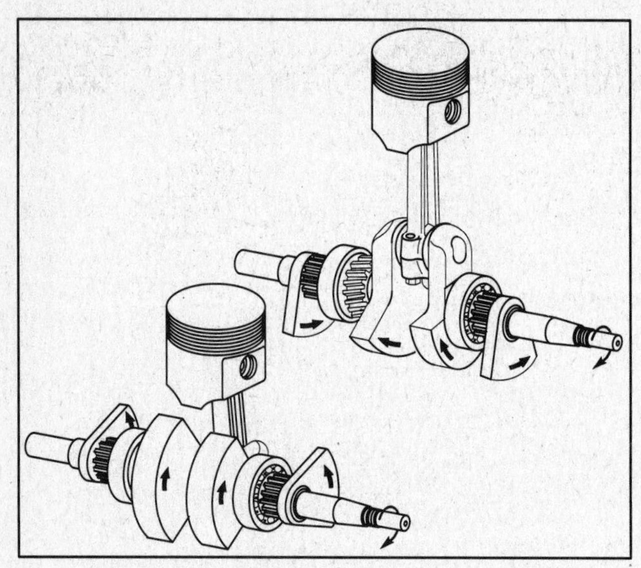

Fig. 1 – Cast Iron Engines, Counterbalance

ASSEMBLING AND TIMING ROTATING SYNCHRO-BALANCE™, CAST IRON ENGINES

CAUTION: On some Model Series 326400 engines, the Synchro-Balance™ cover did not have the balance gear and bearing. DO NOT ATTEMPT TO START THESE ENGINES UNTIL reinstalled in the equipment to prevent kickback when starting.

1. Remove all traces of oil or dirt from tapered surfaces of drive gears and camshaft before assembling gears to camshaft.
2. Turn crankshaft until piston is at top dead center.
3. Remove long 5-1/2" cam gear shaft bolt.
4. Place magneto drive gear on cam gear taper.
5. Install bolt with Belleville washer, finger tight, Fig. 2.

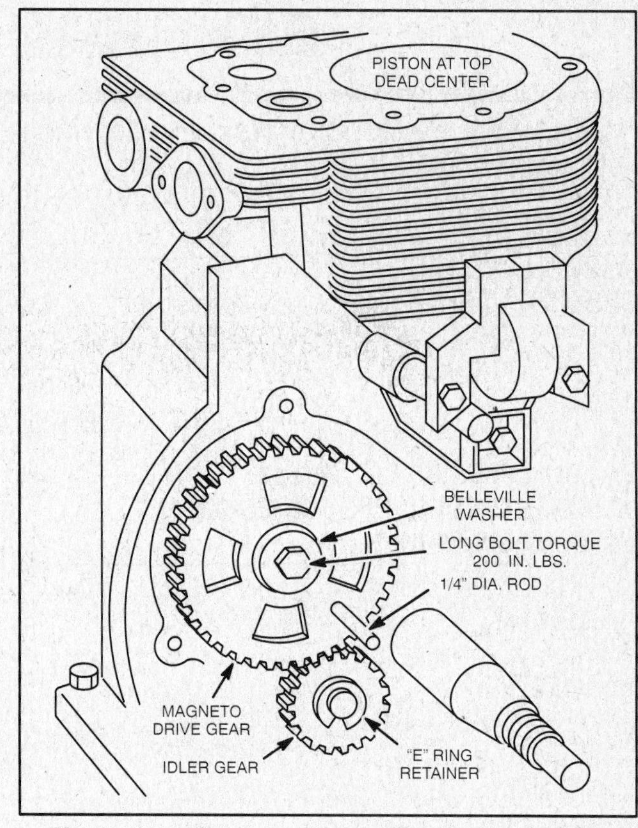

Fig. 2 – Installing and Timing Magneto Drive Gear

NOTE: On Model Series 300400 and 320400 only, place PTO drive gear on the other end of camshaft. Install short cam gear bolt with Belleville washer, finger tight, Fig. 3.

6. To time drive gears, insert short pieces of 1/4" rod through 1/4" holes in drive gears, and into locating holes in crankshaft bearing support plates, Fig. 2.

   NOTE: For Model Series 300400 and 320400 also see Fig. 3.

7. With piston at exactly TOP DEAD CENTER, torque cam gear bolt(s) (with 1/4" rods in place) to 200 inch pounds. Be certain piston does not move.
8. Remove the 1/4" rods.
9. Install idler gear(s).
10. Install snap in "E" rings to retain gears. No further timing is necessary, Figs. 2 and 3.

NOTE: METRIC EQUIVALENTS ARE LISTED ON PAGE 7 OF THIS SECTION.

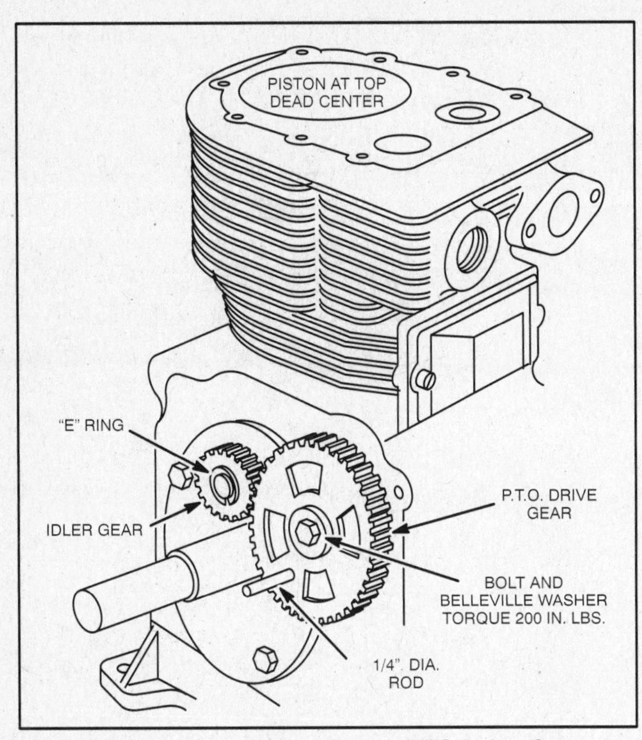

Fig. 3 - Installing and Timing PTO Drive Gear

The counterweights and ball bearings are an integral part of the covers and cannot be removed. Lubricate ball bearings and gears with a few drops of engine oil.

NOTE: PISTON MUST BE AT TOP DEAD CENTER.

Timing Counterweight

1. Remove the timing hole screw from cover assembly, Fig. 4.

2. Insert a short piece of 1/8" rod through timing hole in cover and into machining hole in counterweight, Fig. 4. The rod holds the counterweight in the proper position while cover is installed on engine.

   NOTE: One of the screws holding the breather can also be used, instead of 1/8" rods.

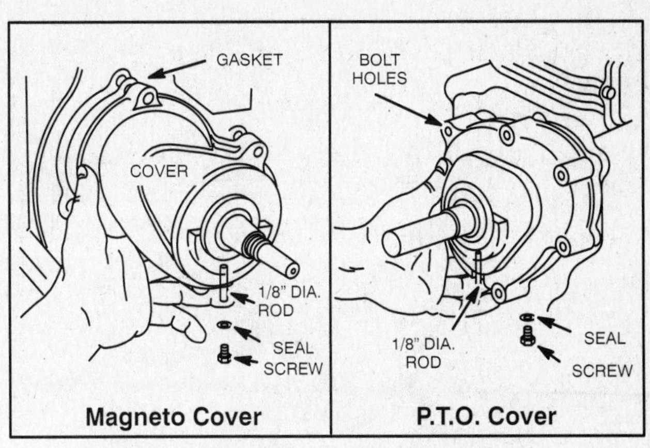

Fig. 4 - Removing Timing Hole Screw

3. Install cover assembly and gasket, using seal protector to avoid damage to oil seal and making sure that bolt holes line up with tapped holes in cylinder.

4. To minimize gear backlash, push magneto side cover toward idler gear and torque bolts to 120 inch pounds.

   NOTE: For Model Series 300400 and 320400 repeat above for PTO cover, torquing bolts to 200 inch pounds.

5. Remove timing rods or screws.

6. Coat threads of timing hole screws with a non-hardening sealant such as Permatex® II, then install screw and fiber sealing washer.

ROTATING COUNTERBALANCE MODEL SERIES 250000

These Model Series utilize two gear driven counterweights in constant mesh with the crankshaft gear.

The cut-away view illustrates these gears, mounted in the crankcase cover, and how the Synchro-Balance™ counterweights rotate in opposite direction to crankshaft rotation, Fig. 5.

NOTE: METRIC EQUIVALENTS ARE LISTED ON PAGE 7 OF THIS SECTION.

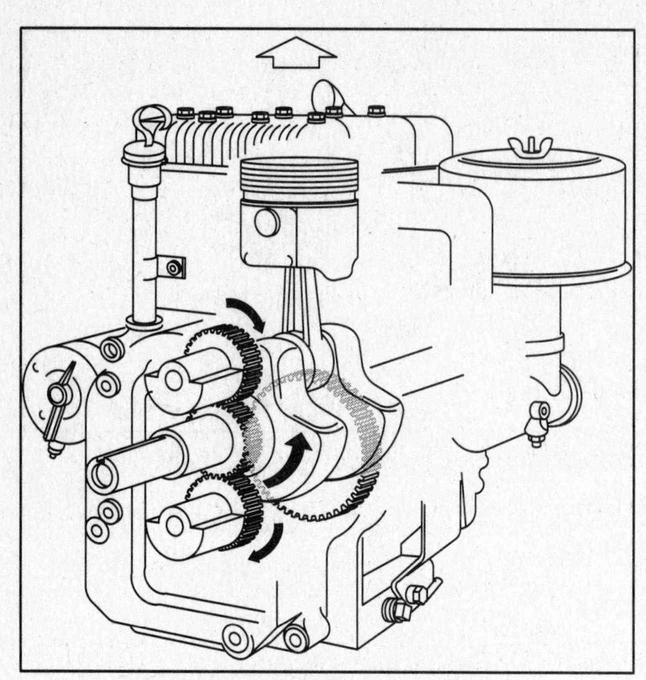

Fig. 5 – Aluminum Engines, Rotating Counterbalance System

Service Procedures for Model Series 250000

The gear driven counterweights must be properly aligned when cover is installed.

If counterweights are removed from crankcase cover, exercise care in handling or cleaning to prevent losing needle bearings.

Assembly of Counterweights

1. Install counterweights on shafts in crankcase cover.

2. Install counterweight retainers and torque screws to 50 inch pounds.

Timing Counterweights Gears

1. To do so, remove two small screws from cover and insert 1/8" diameter locating pins or breather screws and extended dipstick tube screw through screw hole and into timing hole provided in counterweights, Fig. 6.

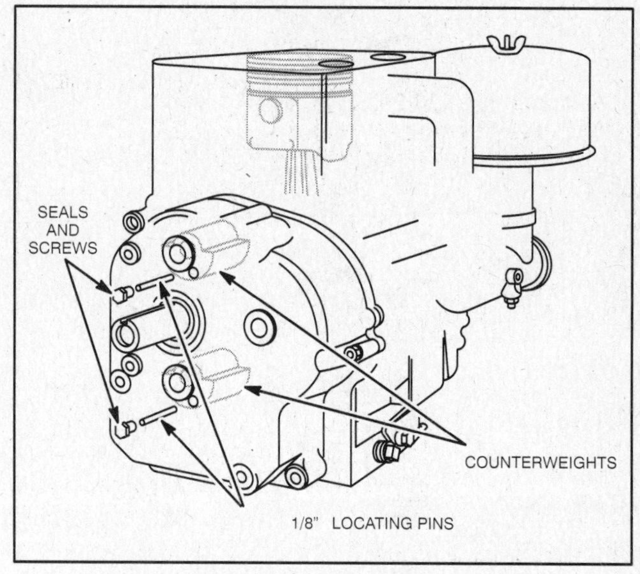

Fig. 6 – Timing Counterbalance Gears

2. With piston at TOP DEAD CENTER, install the crankcase cover assembly and cover gasket.

3. Remove the locating pins or screws.

4. Coat threads of timing hole screws with a non-hardening sealant such as Permatex® II, then install screws and fiber sealing washers.

OSCILLATING COUNTERBALANCE SYSTEM MODEL SERIES 170000, 190000, 250000, 280000

Disassemble Oscillating Counterbalance System

1. After removing sump, open connecting rod lock and remove connecting rod screws.

2. Remove connecting rod and piston from engine. Remove crankshaft and counterweight assembly.

NOTE: METRIC EQUIVALENTS ARE LISTED ON PAGE 7 OF THIS SECTION.

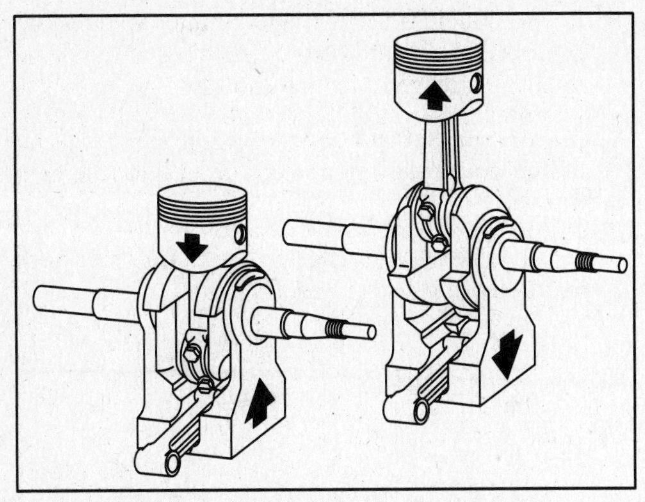

Fig. 7 - Oscillating Counterbalance

3. Remove crankshaft gear. If gear is tight, pry gear off with two screwdrivers being careful not to damage gear.

   NOTE: Save the key on Model Series 171700. On current production Model Series 252700, 253700, 255700, 256700, and all 280000 engines the woodruff key can be removed, if required, Fig. 8.

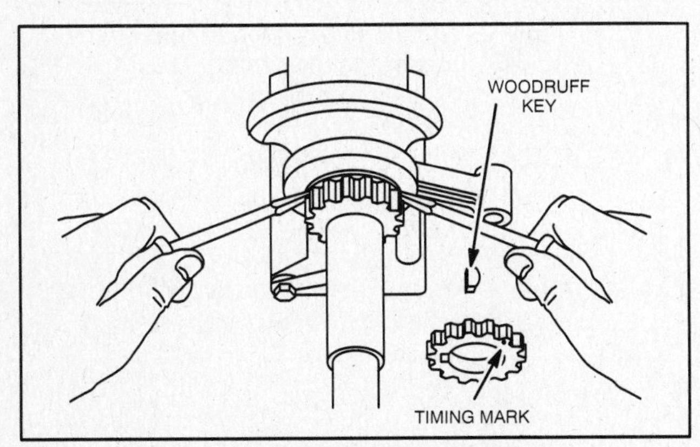

Fig. 8 - Removing Crankshaft Gear

4. Open lock (when used) and remove screw(s) from counterweight.

5. Remove PTO side weight, dowel pin(s), link and spacer(s) (when used).

6. Remove crankshaft from magneto side counterweight, Fig. 9.

   NOTE: Newer assemblies contain only one screw, one dowel pin and are not equipped with spacers and lock.

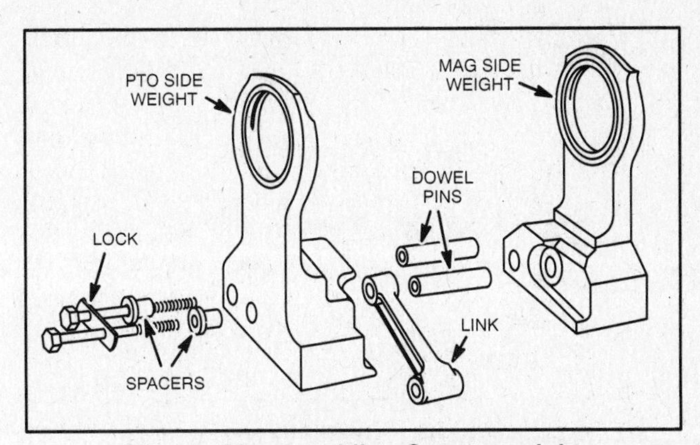

Fig. 9 - Disassembling Counterweight

Inspect Counterbalance System

Check counterweight bearings and crankshaft eccentrics for wear as listed in Table No. 1.

TABLE NO. 1
REJECT SIZES

Model Series	Eccentric	Bearing
170000, 190000	1.870"	1.881"
250000	2.120"	2.131"
280000	2.202"	2.212"

If counterweight bearings are discolored, scored or worn to reject or over, counterweights must be replaced as a set. If crankshaft eccentrics are discolored, scored or worn to reject or less, the crankshaft and eccentrics must be replaced as a set except on current production Model Series 252700, 253700, 255700, 256700 and all 280700, 281700, 283700, and 286700 with woodruff keys. Only the eccentrics need to be replaced on models with woodruff keys.

Assemble Counterweight Assembly and Crankshaft

1. Assemble magneto side eccentric on crankshaft with chamfer toward crankpin. Make sure eccentric is seated against counterweight on crankshaft.

2. Slide magneto side counterweight onto crankshaft, Fig. 10.

3. Place crankshaft and counterweight in a vise with soft vise jaws or shop rags to protect magneto journal.

4. Install dowel pin(s). Slip link over dowel pin with rounded edge of free end up, Fig. 10.

5. Slide PTO side counterweight onto dowel pin(s) and crankshaft eccentric.

NOTE: METRIC EQUIVALENTS ARE LISTED ON PAGE 7 OF THIS SECTION.

6. Install screw(s), spacer(s) (when used) and lock (when used). On counterweights with one screw, torque screw to 115 in. lbs. On counterweights with two screws, torque screws to 80 in. lbs. and bend lock up against flat of screw.

   NOTE: On counterweight assemblies using one screw, rotate crankshaft to check for binding. If binding exists, loosen screw and retorque screw. Check again for freedom of rotation.

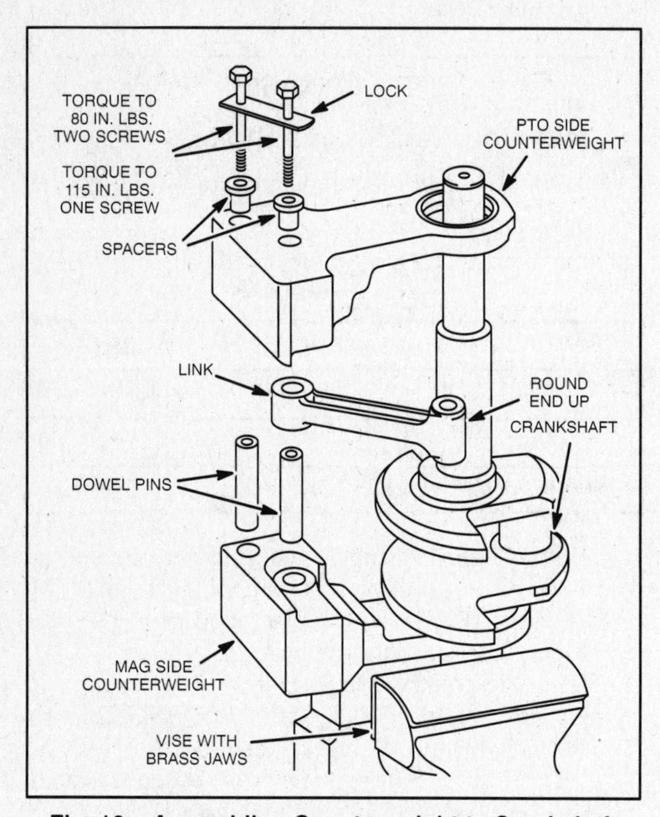

Fig. 10 – Assembling Counterweight to Crankshaft

7. If woodruff key was removed, install in crankshaft. Slide crankshaft gear onto crankshaft with chamfer toward eccentric. If gear is tight, lay gear on a light bulb to expand it before installing.

8. Lay cylinder on its side with cylinder head to the left. Use Seal Protector Kit, Tool #19334 or #19356 in magneto crankshaft seal.

9. Place crankshaft and counterweight assembly into cylinder and start magneto journal into magneto bearing.

10. Align link with crankcase link pin and push assembly into place, Fig. 11.

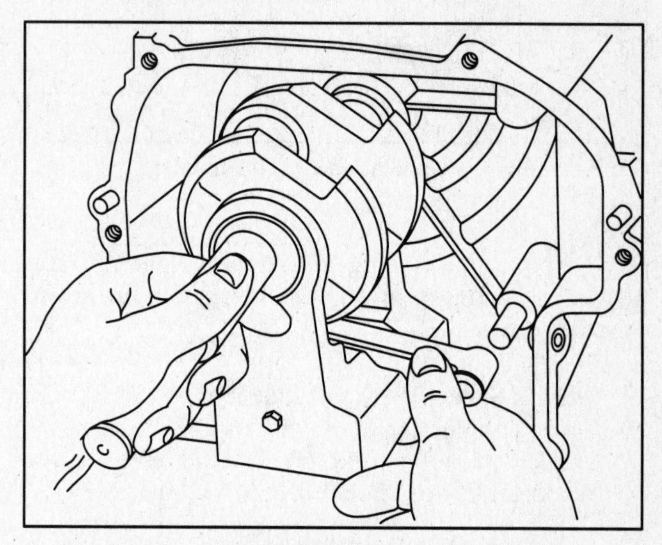

Fig. 11 – Installing Crankshaft and Counterweight Assembly

11. Install connecting rod and piston with lubrication hole in rod toward magneto side. This will expose rod assembly marks to view.

12. Assemble the cap screws and screw locks with dipper (Model Series 171700) toward cam gear side.

13. Torque screws and bend up locks. Proceed to install tappets, cam gear, etc., in usual manner, Section 10.

12

NOTE: METRIC EQUIVALENTS ARE LISTED ON PAGE 7 OF THIS SECTION.

METRIC EQUIVALENTS

DIMENSIONS, FRACTIONAL	
Inches	**Millimeters**
1/8	3
1/4	6
5-1/2	14

DIMENSIONS, DECIMAL	
1.870	47.51
1.881	47.78
2.120	53.85
2.131	54.13
2.202	55.93
2.212	56.18

TORQUE		
In. Lbs.	**Kgcm Kpcm**	**Nm**
50	58	5.6
80	92	9.0
115	130	13.0
120	140	13.6
200	230	22.6

NOTE: METRIC EQUIVALENTS ARE LISTED ON PAGE 7 OF THIS SECTION.

Section 13
TOOLS

It is assumed that Authorized Briggs & Stratton Service Centers have common hand tools to repair engines.

All Authorized Briggs & Stratton Service Centers are required to have Tool Kit #19300. All the tools listed below are part of Tool Kit #19300 and are also recommended for school shops teaching small engine repair of Single Cylinder "L" Head Engines.

TOOL NO.	DESCRIPTION	USE
19063	Valve Spring Compressor	Remove and install valve springs – All models.
19069	Flywheel Puller	Remove flywheel – Model Series 60000, 80000, 90000, 100700, 110000, 120000.
19070	Piston Ring Compressor	Compress piston rings – Model Series 60000, 80000, 90000, 100000, 110000, 120000, 130000.
19165	Flywheel Puller	Remove flywheels – Model Series 140000, 170000, 190000, 250000.
19167	Flywheel Holder	Hold flywheel while removing or installing flywheel nut or starter clutch – Model Series 60000, 80000, 90000, 100200, 100900.

BRIGGS & STRATTON REPAIR TOOLS (Cont'd.)

TOOL NO.	DESCRIPTION	USE
19200	Tachometer Range - 800 to 50,000 RPM	Set correct idle and Top No Load RPM.
19203	Flywheel Puller	Remove flywheels – Model Series 190000, 220000, 230000, 240000, 250000, 280000,300000, 320000.
19229	Tang Bender	Adjust governor tangs for Top No Load RPM and governed idle – Model Series 130000, 140000, 170000, 190000, 220000, 250000, 250000, 280000.
19230	Ring Compressor	Compress piston rings – Model Series 140000, 170000, 190000, 220000, 230000, 240000,250000, 280000, 300000, 320000.
19244	Starter Clutch Wrench	Remove and torque rewind starter clutch – All models with rewind starters.
19256	Band Brake Adjustment Gauge	To adjust band brakes on Model Series 90000, 110000, 130000 with flywheel brakes.

BRIGGS & STRATTON REPAIR TOOLS (Cont'd.)

TOOL NO.	DESCRIPTION	USE
19258 Includes 19266 19268	Valve Lapping Kit Replacement Suction Cup – 3/4" Replacement Suction Cup – 1-1/4"	Lap valve face to valve seat – All Model Series. 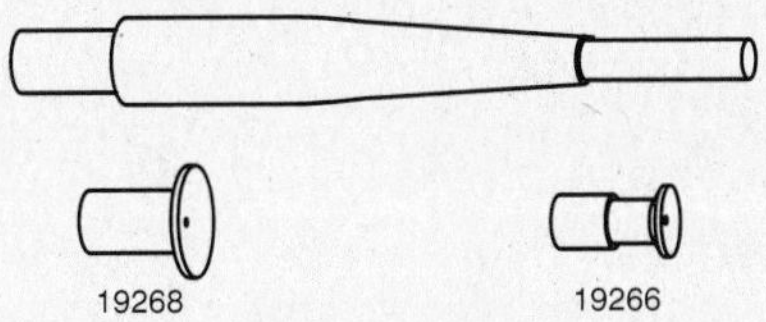 19268 19266
19263	Carburetor Adjustment	Adjust Vacu-Jet and Pulsa-Jet carburetors – Model Series 82000, 90000, 110000. 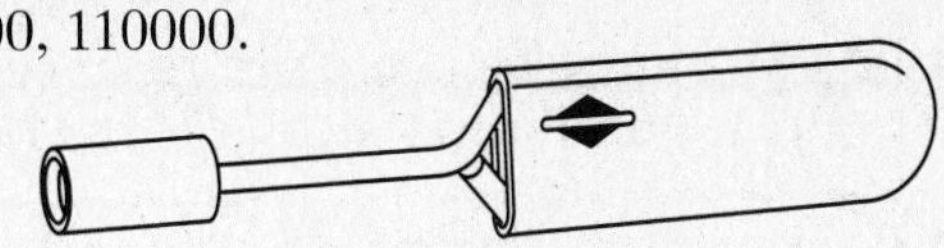
19280	Carburetor Nozzle Screwdriver	Remove and install nozzles on one and two piece Flo-Jet carburetors. 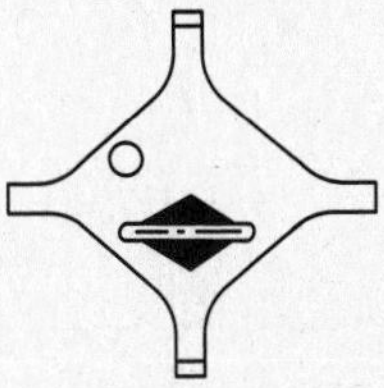
19368	Ignition Tester	Check for ignition spark – All models. 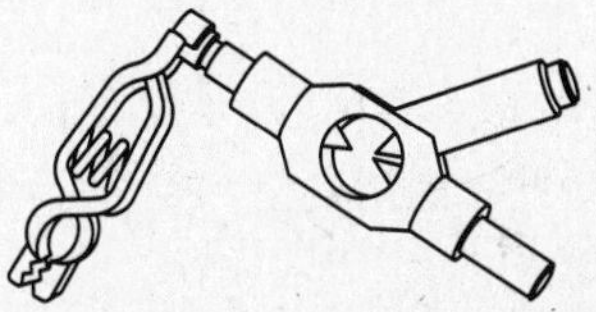
93963	Valve Guide Lubricant	Lubricate valve stems and valve guides, spark plug threads, muffler bolts and cylinder head bolts. 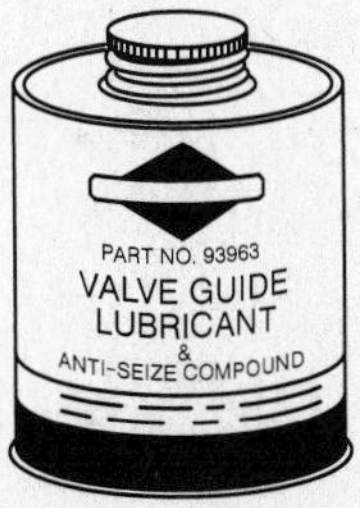 PART NO. 93963 VALVE GUIDE LUBRICANT & ANTI-SEIZE COMPOUND
94150	Valve Lapping Compound	Lap in valves to valve seats – All Model Series.  CLOVER BRAND COARSE & FINE VALVE LAPPING COMPOUND

13

BRIGGS & STRATTON REPAIR TOOLS (Cont'd.)

TOOL NO.	DESCRIPTION	USE
MS-8746	Service Tools Catalog	

The following Special Tools are required for Authorized Briggs & Stratton Service Center, in addition to Tool Kit #19300, or tools of equal or better accuracy.

TOOL NO.	DESCRIPTION	USE
19199	Dial Caliper Range – 0" to 6" Accurate to .001"	Measure engine wear. 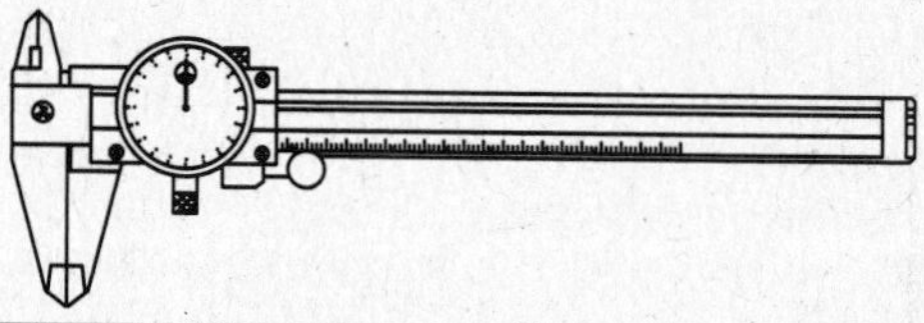
19232 Includes 19151 19204 19231 19233 19234 19238 19239 19240 19264	Valve Guide Repair Kit (5/16" Valve Guides) Plug Gauge Bushing Driver Counterbore Reamer Finish Reamer Reamer Guide Bushing Puller Screw Puller Nut Puller Washer 9mm Tap	Repair valve guides – Model Series 140000, 170000, 190000, 220000, 250000, 280000, 300000, 320000. 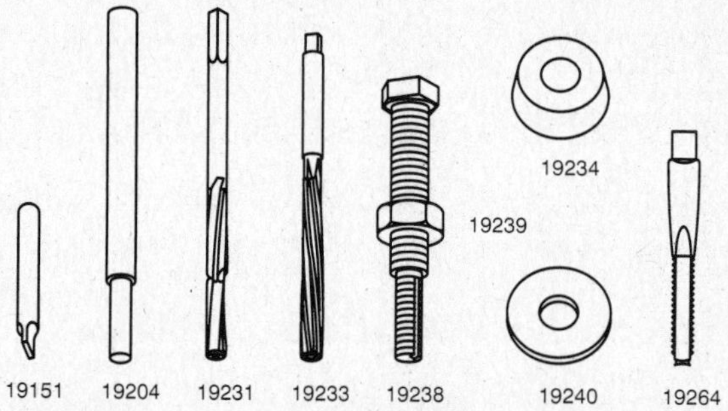 19151 19204 19231 19233 19238 19234 19239 19240 19264
19237	Valve Seat Cutter Kit 30° and 45°	Cut valve seats. 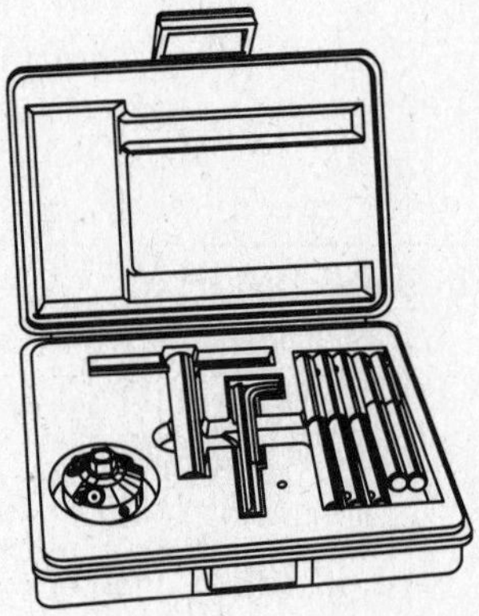

BRIGGS & STRATTON REPAIR TOOLS (Cont'd.)

TOOL NO.	DESCRIPTION	USE
19269	Valve Guide Repair Kit (1/4" Valve Guides)	Repair valve guides – Model Series 60000, 80000, 90000, 100000, 110000, 120000, 130000. 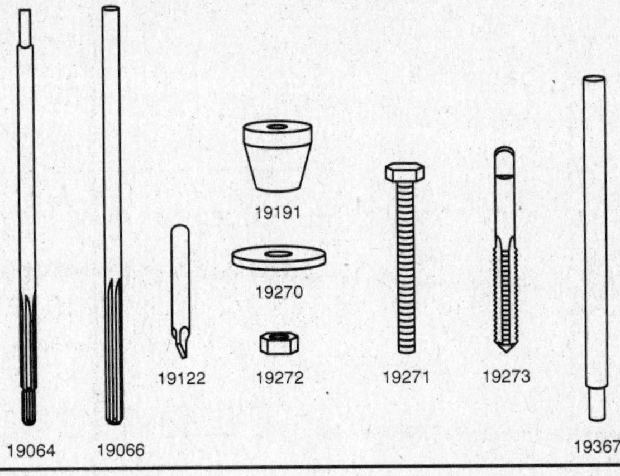
Includes		
19064	Counterbore Reamer	
19066	Finish Reamer	
19122	Plug Gauge	
19191	Reamer Guide Bushing	
19270	Puller Washer	
19271	Puller Screw	
19272	Hex Nut	
19273	Tap 7 mm	
19367	Bushing Driver	
19393	Torque Wrench - 0 to 300 in. lbs.	Accurately torque connecting rod, cylinder head, sump and crankcase screws. 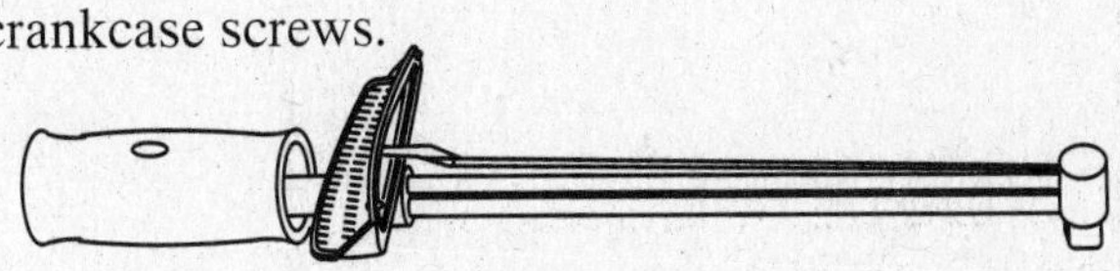
19404	Telescoping Gauge Range - 2" to 3-1/2"	Measure cylinder bores, crankshaft for wear. 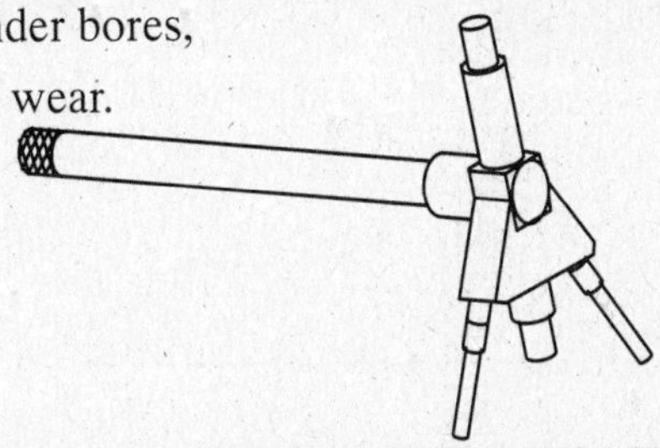

The following tools, while not required, are recommended for complete engine repair.

TOOL NO.	DESCRIPTION	USE
19055	Plug Gauge	Reject gauge for breaker point plunger hole – Model Series 60000, 80000, 90000, 100200,100900, 110000, 130000, 140000, 170000, 190000, 220000, 250000. 
19056	Counterbore Reamer	Ream worn breaker point plunger hole – Model Series 60000, 80000, 90000, 100200,100900, 110000, 130000, 140000, 170000, 190000,220000, 250000. 

13

BRIGGS & STRATTON REPAIR TOOLS (Cont'd.)

TOOL NO.	DESCRIPTION	USE
19057	Bushing Driver	Install breaker point plunger bushing – Model Series 60000, 80000, 90000, 100200,100900, 110000, 130000, 140000, 170000, 190000, 220000, 250000.
19058	Finish Reamer	Ream breaker point plunger bushing – Model Series 60000, 80000, 90000, 100200,100900, 110000, 130000, 140000, 170000, 190000, 220000, 250000.
19061	Screwdriver	Remove main nozzle on two-piece Flo-Jet carburetors.
19062	Screwdriver	Remove main nozzle on two-piece Flo-Jet carburetors.
19067	Plunger Hole Gauge	Check worn plunger hole, Model Series 60000, 80000, 90000, 100200, 100900, 110000, 130000, 140000, 170000, 190000, 220000, 250000.
19126	Expansion Pilot	Guides cutter shank #19129, counterbore cutters #19131, #19132, #19133 Guides valve seat driver #19136 – All Model Series.
19127	Expansion Pilot	Guides cutter shank #19129, counterbore cutters #19131, #19132, #19133 – 230000, 240000 – Guides valve seat driver #19136 – All Model Series.

13

BRIGGS & STRATTON REPAIR TOOLS (Cont'd.)

TOOL NO.	DESCRIPTION	USE
19129	Cutter Shank	Holds counterbore cutters #19131, #19132, #19133 for counterboring worn valve seats on Cast Iron Model Series 230000, 240000.
19130	T-Handle	Turns cutter shank #19129 and counterbore cutters #19131, #19132, #19133 – Cast Iron Model Series 230000, 240000.
19131	Counterbore Cutter	Counterbore worn intake seats – Cast Iron Model Series 230000, 240000.
19132	Counterbore Cutter	Counterbore worn intake seats – Cast Iron Model Series 8, 9.
19133	Counterbore Cutter	Counterbore worn intake seats – Cast Iron Model Series N, 5, 6.
19135	Knockout Pin	Remove cutter shank #19129 from counterbore cutters #19131, #19132, #19133.

BRIGGS & STRATTON REPAIR TOOLS (Cont'd.)

TOOL NO.	DESCRIPTION	USE
19136	Valve Seat Driver	Drive in valve seats – All Model Series. 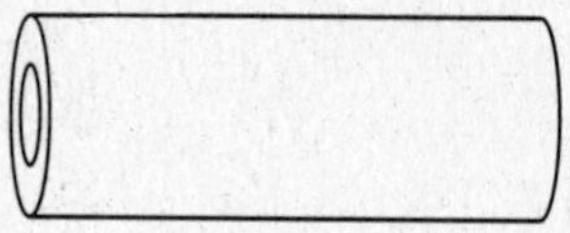
19137	T-Handle	Install and remove expansion pilots #19126, #19127.
19137	T-Handle	Install and remove expansion pilots #19126, #19127. 
19138	Valve Seat Puller Kit	Remove valve seats. 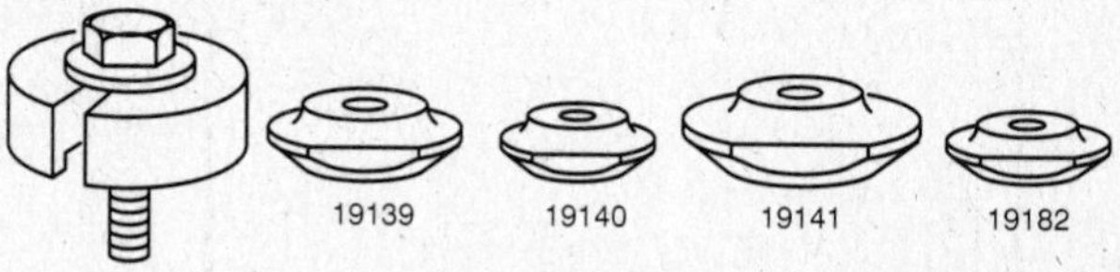
Includes		
19139	Puller Nut	
19140	Puller Nut	
19141	Puller Nut	
19182	Puller Nut	
19158	Main Bearing Tool Kit	Repair worn main bearings Model Series 60000, 80000, 90000, 100200, 100900, 100700, 110000, 120000, 130000. 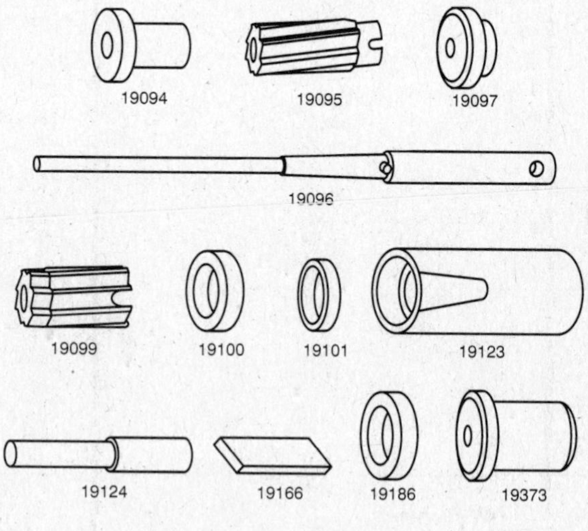
Includes		
19094	Pilot Guide Bushing	
19095	Finish Reamer	
19096	Pilot	
19097	Pilot Guide Bushing	
19099	Counterbore Reamer	
19100	Reamer Guide Bushing	
19101	Reamer Guide Bushing	
19123	Cylinder Support	
19124	Bushing Driver	
19166	Plug Gauge	
19186	Reamer Guide Bushing	
19373	Pilot Guide Bushing	
19164	Plug Gauge	Check cam gear bearings on most aluminum cylinders. 

BRIGGS & STRATTON REPAIR TOOLS (Cont'd.)

TOOL NO.	DESCRIPTION	USE
19184	Main Bearing Tool Kit	Repair worn main bearings – Model Series 140000, 170000, 190000. 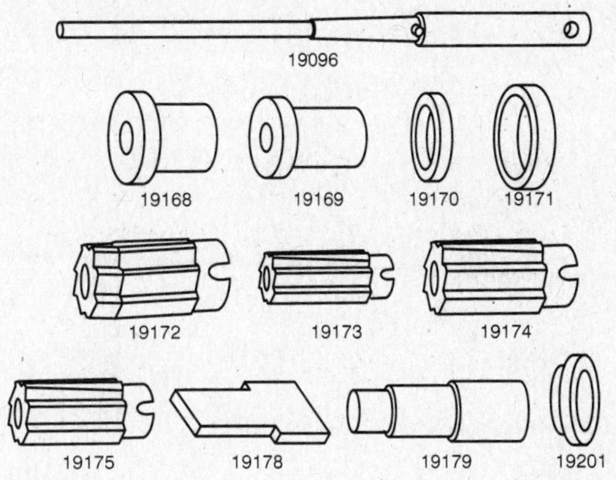
Includes		
19096	Pilot	
19168	Pilot Guide Bushing	
19169	Pilot Guide Bushing	
19170	Reamer Guide Bushing	
19171	Reamer Guide Bushing	
19172	Counterbore Reamer	
19173	Finish Reamer	
19174	Counterbore Reamer	
19175	Finish Reamer	
19178	Plug Gauge	
19179	Bushing Driver	
19201	Reamer Guide Bushing	
19205	Hone Set, Aluminum Cylinder Bores	Resize cylinder bores – All aluminum bore Model Series. 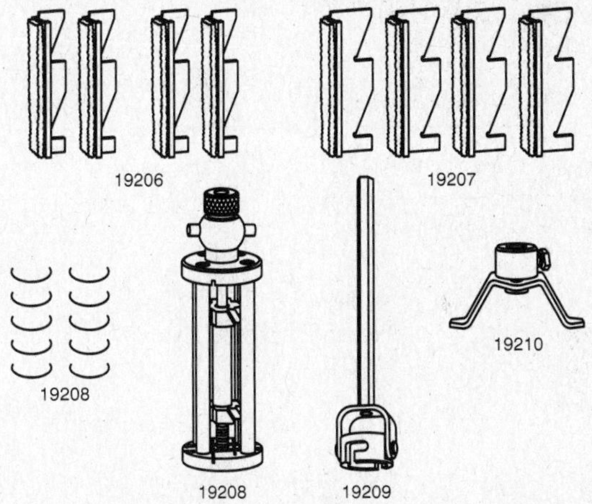
Includes		
19206	Stone Set – Range 1-7/8" to 2-3/4"	
19207	Stone Set – Range 2-3/4" to 3-5/8"	
19208	Stone Retainer Set	
19209	Drive Shank	
19210	Drive Shank Stop	
19211	Hone Set, Cast Iron Sleeves and Bores	Resize cast iron sleeves and bores. 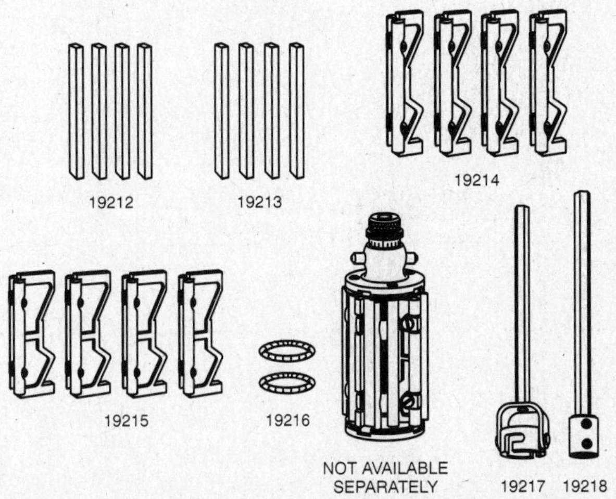
Includes		
19212	Stone Set – 60 Grit	
19213	Stone Set – 200 Grit	
19214	Stone Carriers Range – 2-1/2" to 3-5/16"	
19215	Stone Carrier Range – 3-5/16" to 4-1/8"	
19216	Stone Retainer Spring Set	
19217	Drive Shank	
19218	Drive Shank Extension	

13

BRIGGS & STRATTON REPAIR TOOLS (Cont'd.)

TOOL NO.	DESCRIPTION	USE
19228	Main Bearing Tool Kit	Repair worn main bearings – Model Series 220000, 250000, 280000. 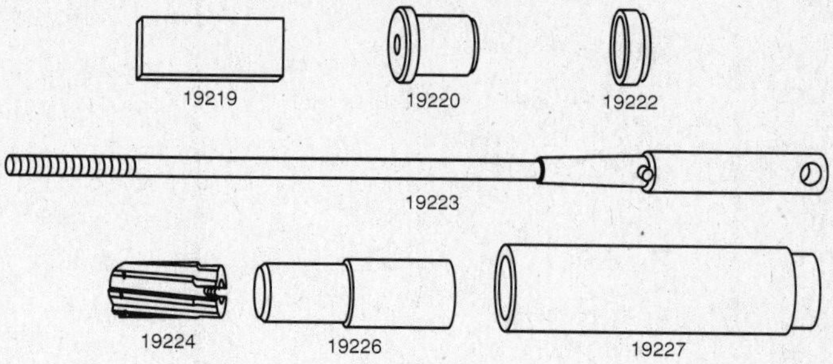
Includes		
19219	Plug Gauge	
19220	Pilot Guide Bushing	
19222	Reamer Guide Bushing	
19223	Pilot	
19224	Counterbore Reamer	
19226	Bushing Driver	
19227	Cylinder Support	
19245	Tap Set	To restore damaged nozzle threads on two piece Flo-Jet carburetor bodies. 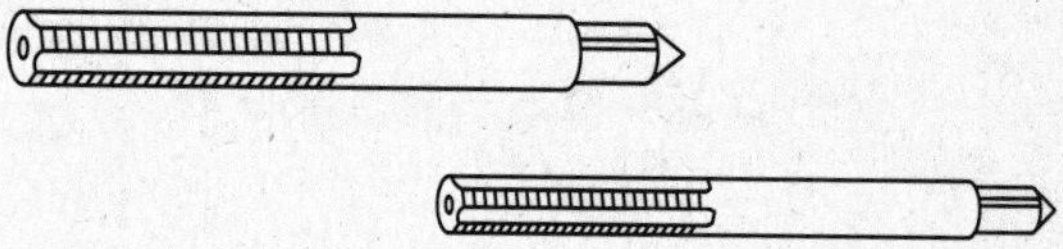
No Longer Available	Blade Monitor®	Test engines for cranking RPM, Idle RPM, Top No Load RPM, blade tip speed, engine stopping time for engine with band brakes or blade brake clutches. 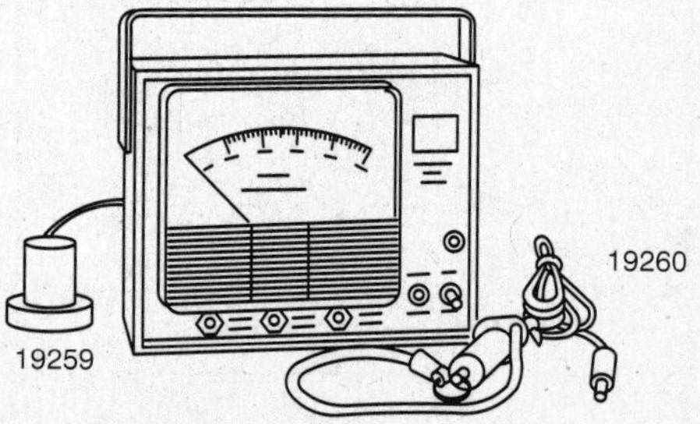
19259	Magnetic Pickup	
19260	Trip Cord and Socket	
19281	Counterbore Reamer	Repair worn main bearings – Model Series 140000, 170000, 190000. 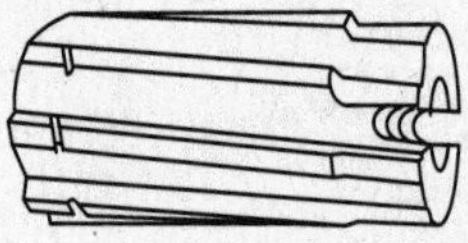
19282	Reamer Guide Bushing	Repair worn main bearings – Model Series 170000, 190000. 

BRIGGS & STRATTON REPAIR TOOLS (Cont'd.)

TOOL NO.	DESCRIPTION	USE
19301	Reamer Guide Bushing	Repair worn main bearings – Model Series 170000, 190000.
19302	Valve Seat Cutter Repair Kit	Replace damaged or dull cutters on #19237 valve seat cutter kit.
19303	Stone Set – 60 Grit	Used with #19205 hone set for resizing cast iron sleeves on Model Series 80000, 110000.
19304	Stone Set – 220 Grit	Used with 19205 hone set for resizing cast iron sleeves on Model Series 80000, 110000.
19305	Carburetor Screwdriver	Remove and install Pulsa-Jet carburetors and fuel tanks - Horizontal Crankshaft Models.
19310	Flywheel Holder	Hold flywheel while removing or installing flywheel nut Model Series 100700.
19321	Flywheel Holder	Hold flywheel while removing or installing flywheel nut or rewind starter clutch – Model Series 280000.

BRIGGS & STRATTON REPAIR TOOLS (Cont'd.)

TOOL NO.	DESCRIPTION	USE
19333	Finish Reamer	Ream governor shaft bushings – Model Series 170000, 190000, 200000, 230000, 240000, 250000, 280000, 300000, 320000. 
19356	Oil Seal Protector Kit White, .787" Red, .875" Blue, .984" Orange, 1.000" Brown, 1.062" Green, 1.181" Purple, 1.317" Yellow, 1.378" Black, 1/503"	Protect magneto and PTO oil seals – All Model Series.
19340	Piston Ring Expander	Remove and install piston rings on pistons - All Model Series. 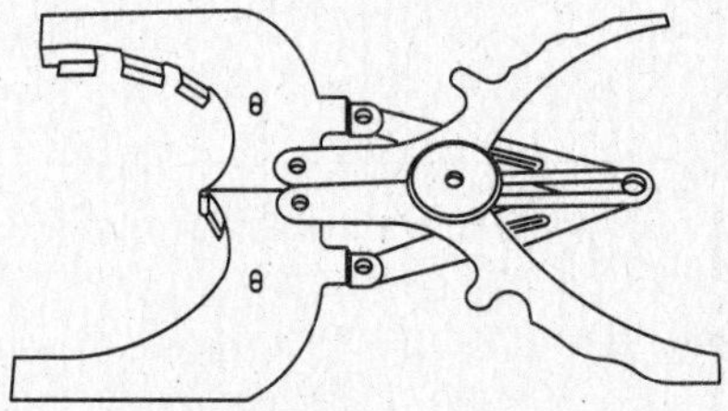
19343	Valve Seat Cutter	Resurface valve seats, Model Series 100700, 120000. 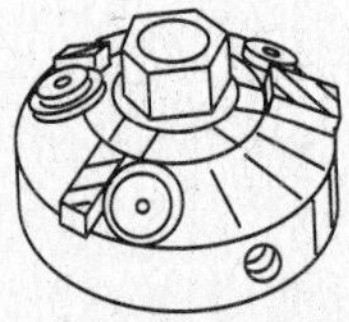
19358	AC Shunt	Measure AC current draw of 120 volt AC electric starters using 19357 or 19390 Digital Multimeter. 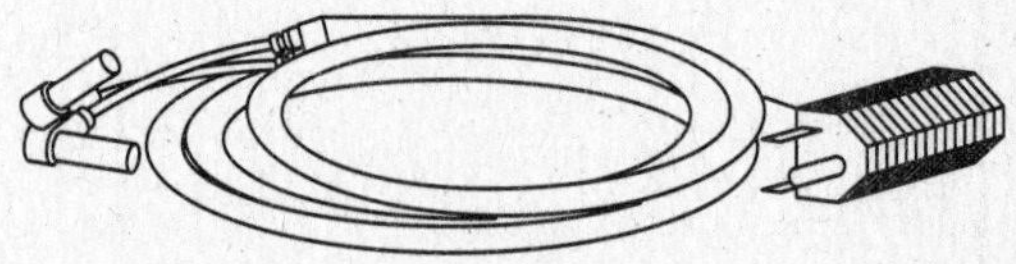
19359	DC Shunt	Measure DC Current draw of electric starters, current output of 10 & 16 Amp alternators using 19357 or 19390Digital Multimeter. 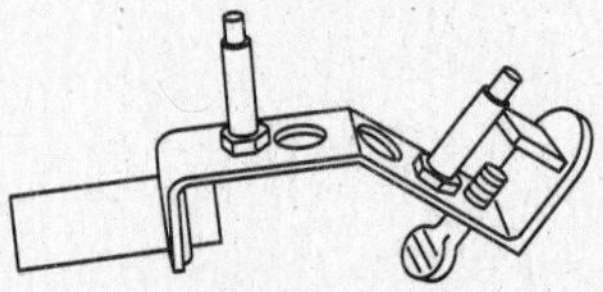

13

BRIGGS & STRATTON REPAIR TOOLS (Cont'd.)

TOOL NO.	DESCRIPTION	USE
19372	Flywheel Strap Wrench	Hold Flywheel, All Model Series.
19373	Pilot Guide Bushing	Sump Pilot Guide for reamer pilot, Model Series 100700, 120000.
19374	Spark Plug Wrench	For removing 5/8" hex head spark plugs on Vanguard engine models.
19375	Plug Gauge	Check worn sump bearing, Model Series 92000, 100700, 120000.
19390	Digital Multimeter Ranges AC Volts, 0 to 750 DC Volts, 0 to 1000 Ohms, 0 to 32,000,000 AC & DC Amps, 0 to 10 Continuous 0 to 20 for 30 seconds	Measure Electrical Equipment, All Model Series.
89838	Spark Plug Wrench	For removing both 13/16" and 3/4" hex head spark plugs.

BRIGGS & STRATTON REPAIR TOOLS (Cont'd.)

TOOL NO.	DESCRIPTION	USE
271400	Spray Paint, 13 oz.	Gloss Black 
271401	Spray Paint, 13 oz.	Pearl White
271402	Spray Paint, 13 oz.	Ice White
271403	Spray Paint, 13 oz.	Satin Black
271404	Spray Paint, 13 oz.	Industrial Gray
271675	Spray Paint, 13 oz.	American Red
5041	Gasoline Additive – 4.2 oz.	Increase storage life of gasoline, All Model Series. 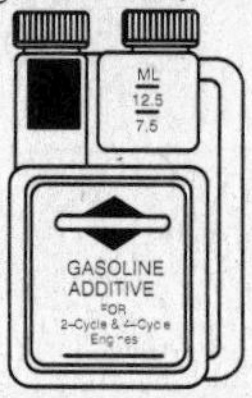
100000	Heavy Duty Towels	
100005	SAE 30 Weight Oil (20 oz.)	All Model Series "L" Head Engines. 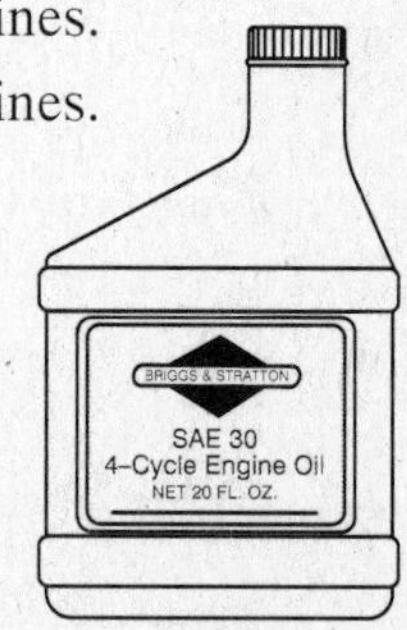
100028	SAE 30 Weight Oil (48 oz.)	All Model Series "L" Head Engines.
100006	Gasoline Additive – 32 oz.	Increase Storage Life of Gasoline, All Model Series. 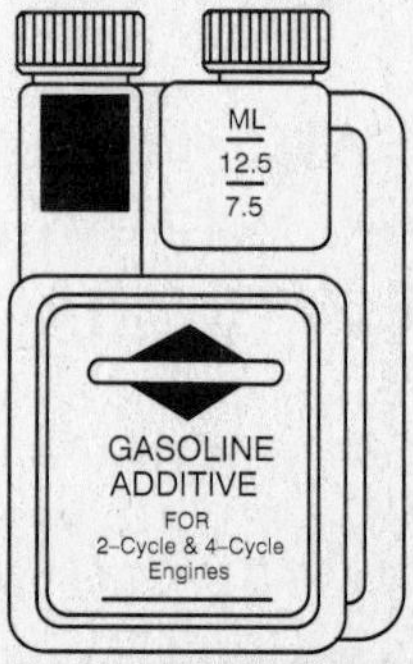

BRIGGS & STRATTON REPAIR TOOLS (Cont'd.)

TOOL NO.	DESCRIPTION	USE
100007	10-32 UNF Kit	Thread Repair, All Model Series.
100014	10-32 UNF Inserts	Insert Refill, All Model Series.
100008	1/4-20 UNC Kit	Thread Repair, All Model Series.
100015	1/4-20 UNC Inserts	Insert Refill, All Model Series.
100009	5/16-18 UNC Kit	Thread Repair, All Model Series.
100016	5/16-18 UNC Inserts	Insert Refill, All Model Series.
100013	M14X1.25 Metric Kit	Spark Plug Thread Repair, All Model Series.
100020	M14X1.25X3/8 Metric Inserts	Spark Plug Insert Refill, All Model Series.
100021	M14X1.25X3/4 Metric Inserts	Spark Plug Insert Refill, All Model Series.
100024	Thread Repair Kit–Master	For repairing damaged and stripped threads.
390619	Bulk Rope, Size #4	Vertical Pull Starters, Model Series 90000, 110000.
390620	Bulk Rope, Size #4-1/2	Rewind Starters, Model Series 60000 to 120000.
390621	Bulk Rope, Size #5-1/2	Rewind Starters, Model Series 130000 to 320000.

13

Section 14
THEORIES OF OPERATION

COMPRESSION

The general subject of compression is a familiar one to most mechanics. It has been discussed in detail by valve manufacturers, ring manufacturers, piston manufacturers, and by makers of valve grinding equipment. The home mechanics, or handyman, thinks nothing of getting out his grinding compound, lapping in the valves and putting a new set of rings on the piston - all without knowledge of proper fit or tolerance. Whether he does the job right or not, he thinks it is easy. And, it is easy. There is nothing difficult or mysterious about compression, and the nice part is that a good job that will create lasting customer satisfaction is about as easy to do as a poor job.

We must keep in mind, however, that the Briggs & Stratton engine is an air-cooled, single cylinder engine. The rules that hold true on liquid-cooled, multi-cylinder engines do not always apply to Briggs & Stratton engines. For example:

The operating temperature of a liquid-cooled engine is quite constant. The operating temperature of an air-cooled engine, however, may vary greatly with changes in air temperature, the load, and the speed. This necessitates differences in tolerances and clearances of parts like pistons, which must be fitted to Briggs & Stratton's established clearances. These can differ from those used in most automotive engines.

The advantages of an air-cooled engine are many. There is no need for a complicated cooling system. The engine is lighter in weight and occupies less space than its liquid-cooled counterpart, and is comparatively easy to repair.

Before we get into the mechanics of the subject, let us clarify some of the terms in common use.

On single cylinder engines we think of good compression, not in terms of pounds of pressure per square inch, but in terms of horsepower output. If the engine produces the power for which it was designed, we believe the compression must be good. It is extremely difficult to make an accurate compression test on a small, one cylinder engine without expensive machinery. The reasons for this are the lack of a starter to crank the engine at a constant speed and the small displacement of the cylinder. Therefore, we do not publish any compression pressure figures. As a simple compression test, give the flywheel a quick spin counterclockwise. If the flywheel rebounds on the compression stroke, the compression is at least good enough to start the engine.

We talk about "compression" stroke and "power stroke". What are they? The Briggs & Stratton engine is a four stroke cycle engine, or as it is commonly called, a four cycle engine. It operates on the same principle as an automobile engine. The crankshaft makes two complete revolutions to each power stroke of the piston.

FOUR STROKE CYCLE

First is the intake stroke. With the exhaust valve closed and the intake valve open, the piston moves downward and the air-fuel mixture is drawn into the cylinder, Fig. 1.

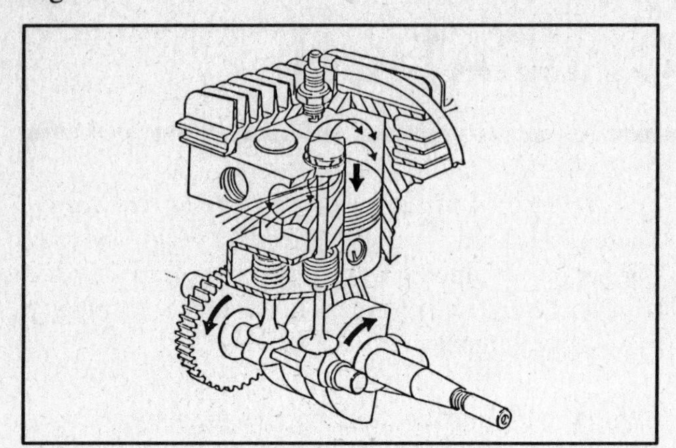

Fig. 1 - Intake Stroke

Fig. 2 - Compression Stroke

Then, the intake valve closes, and the piston moves upward on the compression stroke. The air-fuel mixture becomes greatly compressed in the small space between the top of the piston and the cylinder head, Fig. 2.

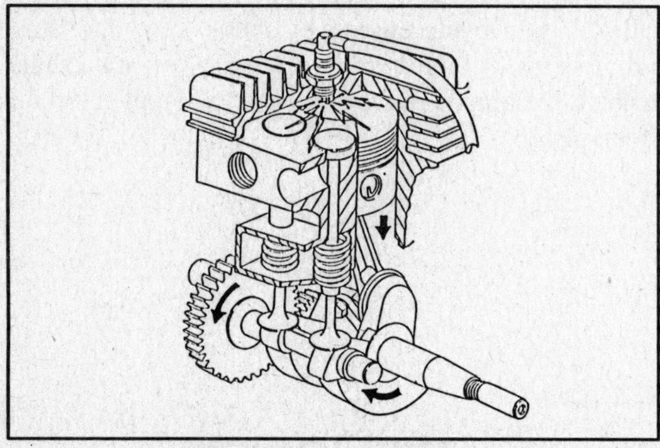

Fig. 3 - Power Stroke

The spark occurs, igniting the mixture, and the force of the expanding gases push the piston down. This is the power stroke, Fig. 3.

The exhaust valve opens, and the upward movement of the piston on the exhaust stroke forces the burnt gases out of the cylinder, Fig. 4. Then the exhaust valve closes, the intake valve opens, and the engine is ready to repeat the cycle just described. Thus, four strokes complete the cycle.

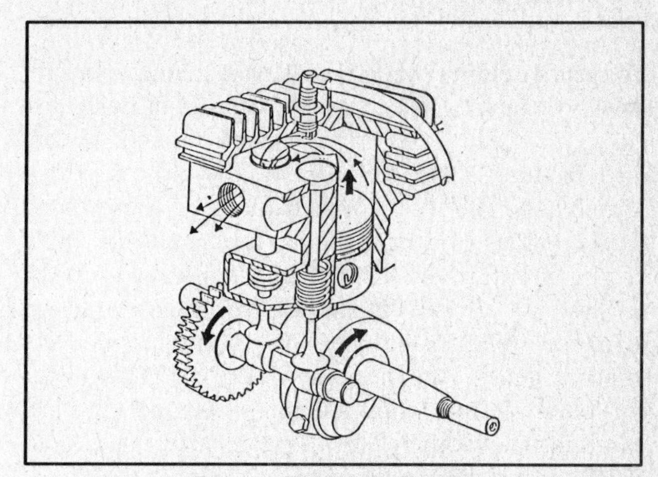

Fig. 4 - Exhaust Stroke

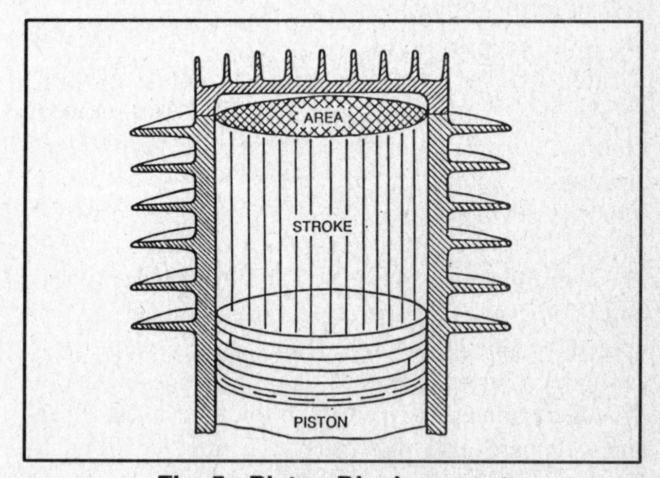

Fig. 5 - Piston Displacement

What is "piston displacement"? It is the space displaced by the piston in its up and down movement or the volume shown above the piston in Figure 5. The bigger the bore and the longer the stroke, the greater the piston displacement. Displacement is computed by the following formula:

$$\text{Displacement} = \frac{(\text{Bore})^2}{4} \times \pi \times \text{Stroke}$$

Let us compute the displacement of a Model 6 engine which has a 2" bore and a 2" stroke. Using the above formula:

$$\text{Displacement} = \frac{2 \times 2}{4} \times 3.1416 \times 2$$

Displacement = 6.2832 cubic inches

Our specification sheets show 6.28 cubic inches as the displacement for the Model 6 engine.

The model numbers of the current engines indicate the approximate piston displacement. Model 60000 has 6.65 cubic inches; Model 14 has 14.21 cubic inches, etc.

Piston displacement indicates the relative size of the engine, and usually horsepower is in direct proportion to size.

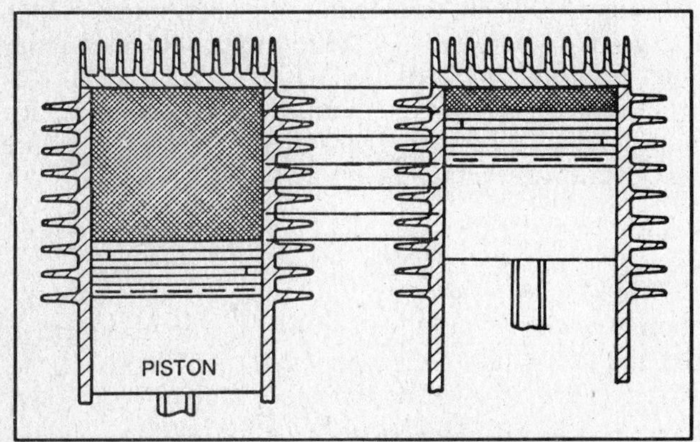

Fig . 6 - Compression Ratio 1 to 6

What do we mean when we say an engine has a 6 to 1 compression ratio? We mean that the space in the cylinder when the piston is at the top of the stroke is only one-sixth as great as when the piston is at the bottom of the stroke.

Compression ratios do not tell us the horsepower of an engine. They do have a meaning as regards the efficiency of an engine.

Generally, the higher the compression ratio, the greater the efficiency. However, as compression ratios are increased, the loads and stresses upon engine parts become more severe. Premium fuels may be required with high compression ratios. Experience has proven that compression ratios in the range of 5-1 to 6-1, currently used in Briggs & Stratton "L" head engines, are the best for the work and the conditions under which these engines must operate. Therefore premium fuel is not needed and "regular" is recommended.

It is generally conceded that the valves are the most important factor in good compression. They operate under more severe conditions than any other parts of the engine. This is particularly true of the exhaust valve.

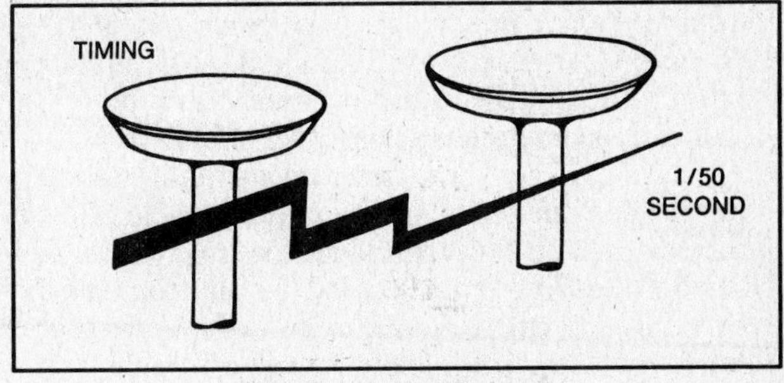

Fig. 7 - Valve Timing

The valves open and close in a little less than one revolution. When the engine is operating at 3000 RPM, each valve opens and closes in about 1/50 of a second.

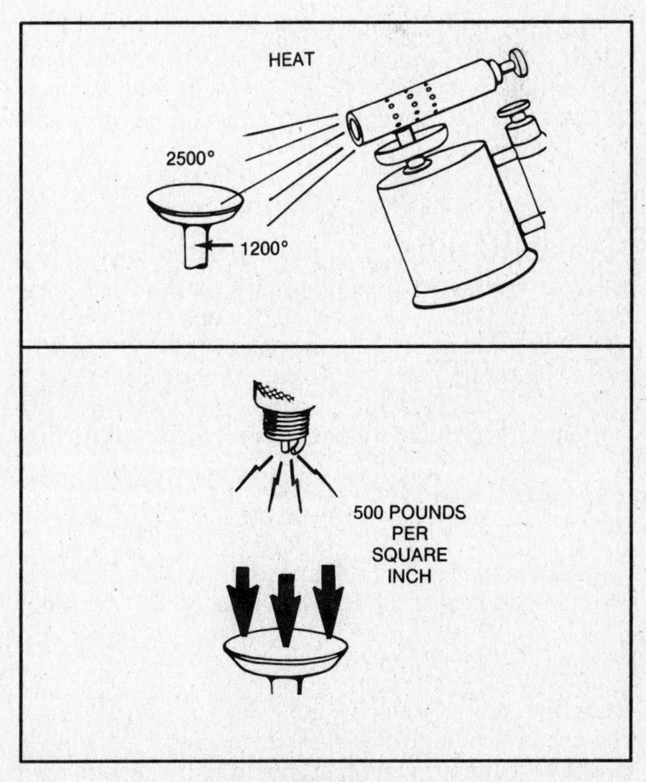

Fig. 8

Valves have to seal well enough to stand pressures up to 500 pounds per square inch. Under full load, the exhaust valve is exposed to temperatures high enough to cause it to operate at a red heat. The temperature of the exhaust valve under these conditions may be 1200° F or more. The intake valve is cooled by the incoming mixture. The exhaust valve is subjected to high temperature exhaust gases passing over it on their way out of the cylinder. It is, therefore, very difficult to cool the head of the exhaust valve. The cylinder head, the cylinder, and the top of the piston are exposed to this same heat, but these parts are cooled by air from the flywheel fan and oil from the crankcase. Very special steel is required in the exhaust valve to enable it to withstand the corrosive action of the high temperature exhaust gases.

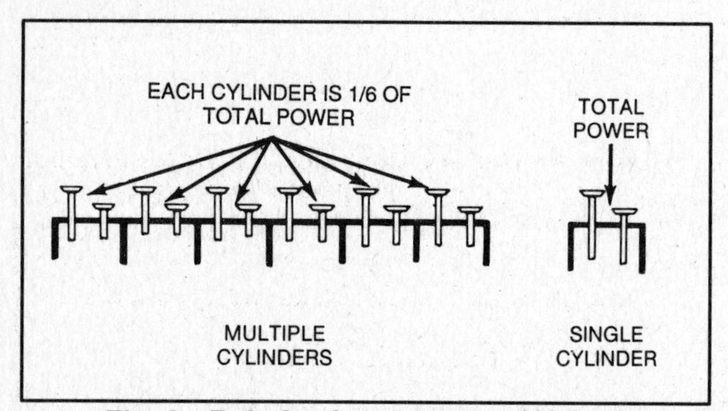

Fig. 9 - Relative Importance of Valves

Remember again that the Briggs & Stratton engine is a single cylinder engine with two (2) valves as compared to the customary 12 or 16 valves in an automotive engine. The fewer the valves, the more important they become.

In a one cylinder engine, one bad valve can cause a great drop in horsepower or cause the engine to stop entirely. In a multi-cylinder engine, one valve may fail and only 1/6th or 1/8th or the power is affected as the bad cylinder may be motorized by the other good cylinders. Hence, good valve condition is even more important in 1 cylinder engines than it is in multi-cylinder engines.

Now if the valves and seats are so important, how do we do a good valve job on a Briggs & Stratton engine?

The first requirement is good equipment. A valve refacer and valve seat grinders are necessary. If you do not have them, arrangement should be made with your local Briggs & Stratton dealer.

After the valves are removed, they should be thoroughly cleaned on a wire brush wheel to remove all carbon deposits. You will find sometimes it is easier to polish carbon than to remove it, but it must come off. Also, remove carbon from valve guides. When the valves are clean, they should be visually inspected.

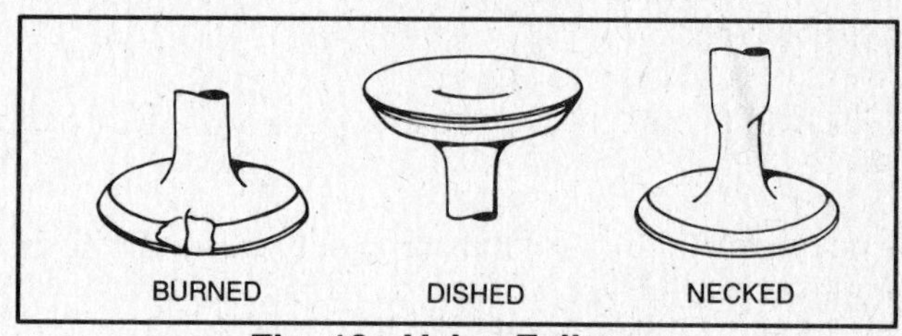

Fig. 10 - Valve Failures

As mentioned above, when a valve becomes defective in a multi-cylinder engine, the bad cylinder is motorized by the other cylinders. This may cause serious damage to the valve and seat. Briggs & Stratton engine valves are seldom subjected to the extremes of abuse that automotive valves are. While valves may burn to some extent, it is very seldom that a valve seat or face is very badly burned. Dished or necked valves are almost never found.

Valve seat burning is usually caused by an accumulation of carbon or fuel lead either on the valve stem or on the valve face, or from insufficient tappet clearance. These deposits on the valve stem or on the face will hold the valve open, allowing the hot flames of the burning fuel to eat away the valve face and seat. A dished valve is one that has a sunken head. This is caused by operating at too high a temperature with too strong a spring, or the head can be eroded away by highly leaded fuels. A necked valve is one that has the stem directly beneath the head eaten away badly by heat or where the stem has been stretched.

Valve sticking is caused by fuel lead, gum or varnish forming on the valve stem and in the valve guide. We believe that most of the deposits formed are caused by carbon, fuel lead, or gum. Since the amount of lead in different fuels varies, the rate of deposit build-up naturally will vary. When an exhaust valve no longer closes properly, due to excess deposits, the hot gases escaping from the combustion chamber heat up the valve stem and guide excessively. This causes the oil on the valve stem to oxidize into varnish which holds the valve partially open and causes burning. Intake valve sticking may be caused by the use of fuels having an excessively high gum content. Fuels that are stored for too long a period of time may contain high amount of gum.

If burning occurs in a rather limited area on the valve face, it indicates that something may have caused the valve to tip. This could be due to a bent valve stem or a deposit on one side of the valve seat or stem.

Such a condition would leave an opening for the passage of hot exhaust gases which could burn the valve so badly that it could not be refaced. These valves must be discarded.

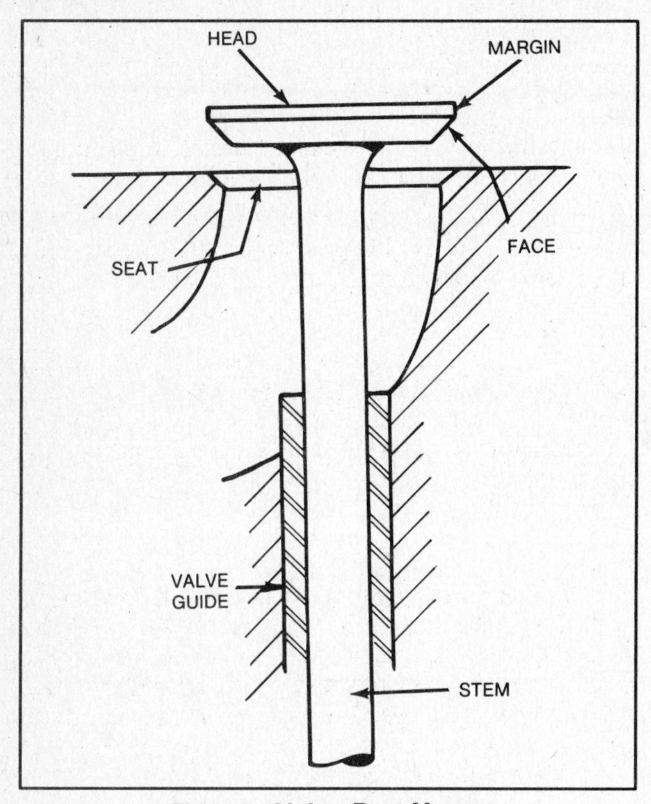

Fig. 11 - Valve Part Names

The important parts of a valve are the head, the margin, face, and stem. They make contact with the seat and the valve guide in the cylinder. The margin is the edge of the valve head. As a general rule, the valve should be discarded when the margin becomes less than one-half of the original thickness.

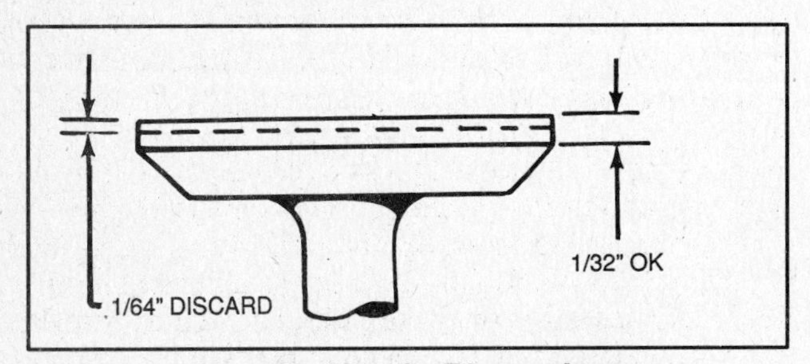

Fig. 12 - Margin Dimensions

The margin on a new Briggs & Stratton valve is 1/32 of an inch, so that when it becomes less than 1/64 of an inch the valve should be discarded. Remember, this is after all pit marks and burn marks have been removed from the valve face. If the valve is bent, the face will be ground unevenly, and if the margin becomes too thin on one side the valve should also be discarded. A valve with too thin a margin will not be able to withstand the heat and will quickly crack and burn. After facing the valves and the valve seats to a 35° or 45° angle, place a little fine grinding compound on the valve face, and very lightly lap the valve to the seat. Use of fine grinding compound removes any grinding marks and gives a clear picture of the valve seat width. Be sure to remove all grinding compound from seat and valve.

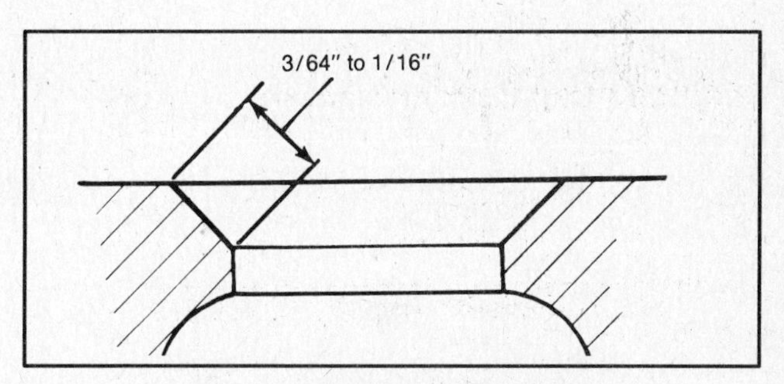

Fig. 13 - Margin Dimensions

The valve seat width is usable up to 5/64 of an inch, but a new seat should be between 3/64 and 1/16 of an inch, and it should be in the center of the valve face. After the valve seat and faces are ground, the valve should be installed in the guide, the cam gear turned to the proper position, and the tappet clearance checked. Refer to Repair instructions for tappet clearance. Usually the clearance will be too small, and the end of the valve stem will have to be ground off to obtain the proper clearance. Care should be taken not to overheat the end of the valve stem while this grinding is taking place; be sure the end is square with the stem. It is recommended that the valve springs and retainers be assembled immediately after setting the tappet clearance to prevent chances of dirt getting under the valve seat.

CARBURETION

The basic purpose of a carburetor is to produce a mixture of fuel and air on which an engine will operate; to do so is relatively easy. However, producing economical fuel consumption and smooth engine operation over a wide range of speeds creates the need for a more complicated mechanism than a mere mixing valve. There is an additional problem in that the price of such a carburetor must be held in proportion to the price of the engine. The price of a Briggs & Stratton engine is not much greater than the price of the carburetor on an automobile.

Atmospheric Pressure

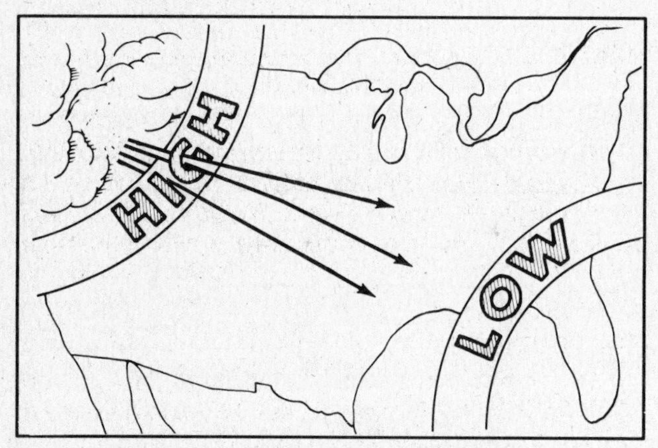

Fig. 14 - Atmospheric Pressure

Keeping this in mind, we must utilize the force of atmospheric pressure and the principles of the venturi and the airfoil.

Atmospheric pressure, while it may vary slightly due to altitude or temperature, is a constant potent force which tends to equalize itself in any given area. It is the weight of the air in the atmosphere pushing down and outward in all directions and is commonly figured as between 13 to 15 pounds per square inch. We know that air moves from a high pressure area to a low pressure area.

To use this force of atmospheric pressure in a carburetor, we artificially create low pressure areas and thus obtain movement either of air or of intervening fuel. We will show you how a little later.

The greater the difference in pressure between the two areas the greater the velocity or the greater the distance we can raise the fuel.

In the interest of brevity we often use the terms vacuum or suction when we actually mean the difference in pressures.

Venturi

What is a venturi? Have you ever noticed that the wind blowing through a narrow space between two buildings always seems to be much stronger than in the open? In other words, the velocity is greater. The same thing can be seen in a river. The current is always faster in a narrow, shallow place than in the deep wide pools.

In a fashion, these narrow places are venturis. The great bulk of air or water suddenly forced through a constricted space has to accelerate in order to maintain the volume of flow.

This is the way a venturi is placed in a carburetor, Fig. 15. The shape is carefully designed to produce certain air flow patterns.

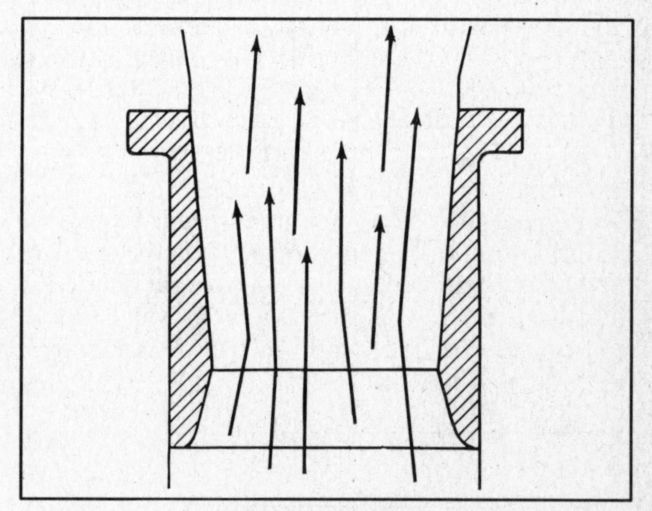

Fig. 15 - Venturi

Airfoil

Now, what is an airfoil? Here is a picture of a tube in an air stream. When still, the pressure is equal on all sides. Under movement, an air pattern is formed, Fig. 16, so that we have a high pressure area and a very low pressure area.

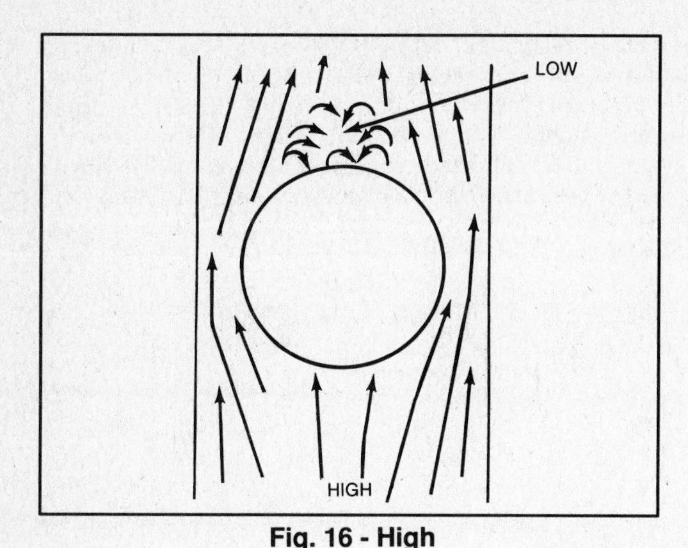

Fig. 16 - High

Now how does all this apply to Briggs & Stratton engines that employ three types of carburetors, the Flo-Jet (gravity feed or float type), the Vacu-Jet (suction feed) and the newer Pulsa-Jet (fuel pump) type?

FLO-JET CARBURETORS OR GRAVITY FEED

First, let us consider the gravity feed system. The tank is above the carburetor and fuel flows by gravity. Notice an air vent hole in the tank cap so that air can flow in as fuel flows out and a vent hole air the carburetor bowl so that air can flow out as fuel flows in. If one or both of these holes were plugged, the flow of fuel would cease and stop the engine, Fig. 17 and 18.

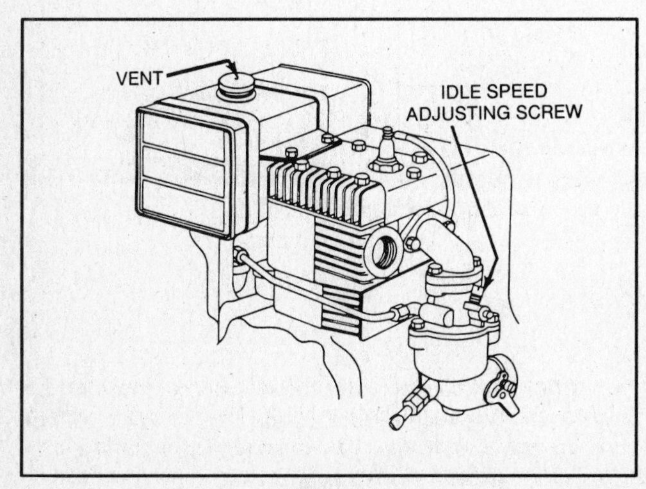

Fig. 17

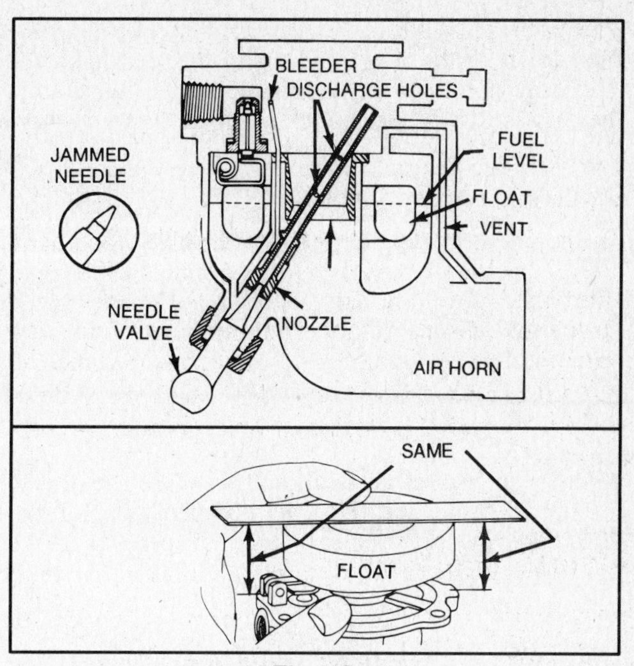

Fig. 18

As the fuel enters the bowl, it raises the float. The float in turn raises the needle in the float valve. When the needle touches the seat, it shuts off the fuel flow, and the position of the float at this time is called the float level.

Float Level

The float level in general should be high enough to afford an ample supply of fuel at full throttle and low enough to prevent flooding or leaking.

To set the level on the carburetor, invert the upper body as shown, Fig. 18. The float and the body cover should be parallel. If not, bend the tang on the float to obtain this position. The actual distance on the small carburetors is 5/16 of an inch between the float and the gasket. On the larger models it is 3/16 of an inch. The float level is not as critical as on some carburetors. Remember, however, that there should be one gasket between the float valve seat and the carburetor.

Now, the fuel is down into the bowl but how does it get into the cylinder?

Fig. 18 shows the position of the nozzle and the fuel level. The fuel in the bowl seeks its own level, which is well below the discharge holes. Notice that the discharge holes are in the venturi, the place of greatest air velocity. As the piston in the cylinder moves down with the intake valve open, it creates a low pressure area that extends down into the carburetor throat and venturi. Two things start to happen.

The air pressure above the fuel in the bowl pushes the fuel down in the bowl and up in the nozzle to the discharge holes. At the same time the air rushes into the carburetor air horn and through the venturi where its velocity is greatly increased.

The nozzle extending through this air stream acts as an air foil, creating a still lower pressure area on the upper side. This allows the fuel to stream out of the nozzle through the discharge holes into the venturi where it mixes with the air and becomes a combustible mixture ready for firing in the cylinder.

A small amount of air is allowed to enter the nozzle through the bleeder. This air compensates for the difference in engine speed and prevents too rich a mixture at high speed.

The story of carburetion could end right here if the engine were to run at only one speed and under ideal conditions. However, since smooth economical operation is desired at varying speeds, some additions must be made to the carburetor.

The ideal combustion mixture is about 14 or 15 pounds of air, in weight, to one (1) pound of gasoline. Remember that an engine operating under heavy load requires a richer mixture than under light load. In order to regulate the mixture, we place in the carburetor a threaded needle valve with a tapered point which projects into the end of the nozzle, Fig. 18.

To adjust the carburetor for maximum power, run the engine at the desired operating speed, then turn in the needle valve until the engine slows down, which indicates a lean mixture. Note the position of the needle valve, then turn the needle valve out until the engine speeds up and then slows down, which indicates a rich mixture, Note the position of the needle valve, then turn the needle valve to midway between the lean and rich position. Adjust the mixture to the requirement for each engine. Remember that too lean a mixture is not economical. It causes overheating, detonation, and short valve life. Also, since there is no accelerator pump, the mixture must be rich enough so that the engine will not stop when the throttle is suddenly opened. Engines which run at constant speeds can be slightly leaner than those whose use requires changes in speed.

The inset of Fig. 18 shows what happens when the needle valve is turned too far. A square shoulder is produced on the taper. It is possible, of course, to adjust the carburetor with the needle valve in this condition, but it is quite difficult, because a small movement of the needle makes a big difference in the amount of fuel that can enter the nozzle. And, if you do get it adjusted, vibration can soon throw it off.

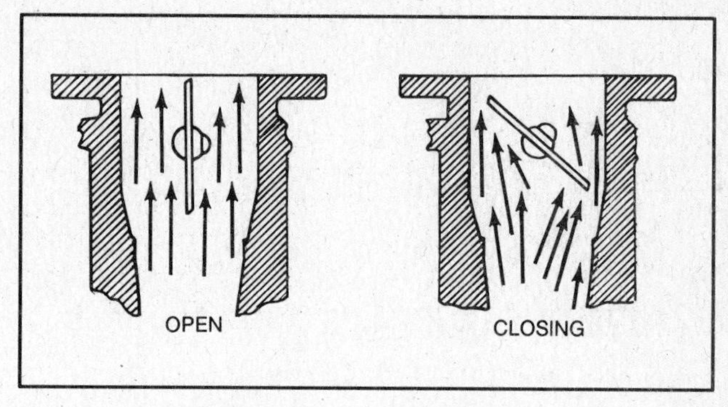

Fig. 19 - Throttle

To allow for different speeds, a flat disc called a butterfly, mounted on a shaft, is placed in the carburetor throat above the venturi. This is called the throttle, Fig. 19.

The throttle in the wide open position does not affect the air flow to any extent. However, as the throttle starts to close, it restricts the flow of air to the cylinder and this decreases the power and speed of the engine. At the same time it allows the pressure in the area below the butterfly to increase. This means that the difference between the air pressure in the carburetor bowl and the air pressure in the venturi is decreased, the movement of the fuel through the nozzle is slowed down; thus the proportion of fuel and air remain approximately the same. As the engine speed slows down to idle, this situation changes, Fig. 16.

At idle speed the throttle is practically closed, very little air is passing through the venturi and the pressure in the venturi and in the float bowl are about the same. The fuel is not forced through the discharge holes, and the mixture tends to become too lean.

Idle Valve

To supply fuel for the idle, the nozzle is extended up into the idle valve chamber. It fits snugly in the upper body to prevent leaks. Because of this tight fit, the nozzle must be removed before upper and lower bodies are separated, or the nozzle will be bent.

The idle valve chamber leads into the carburetor throat above the throttle. Here the pressure is low, and the fuel rises in the nozzle past the idle valve and into the carburetor throat through the discharge slot. The amount of fuel is metered by turning the idle valve in or out until the proper mixture is obtained. Here again we see what happens if the needle is screwed in too far. A damaged idle valve can result.

Adjustment of the idle valve is similar to that of the needle valve but should be made after the needle valve has been adjusted. The idle speed is not the slowest speed at which the engine will run. On small engines it is 1750 RPM. On larger engines the idle speed may be as low as 1200 RPM. Use a tachometer to set the speed.

Turn the idle speed adjusting screw (located on throttle shaft) until the desired idle speed is obtained and hold throttle closed. Turn the idle valve in until speed decreases, then out until speed increases and again decreases. Then turn the idle valve to a point midway between these two settings. Usually the idle speed adjusting screw will have to be reset to the desired idle speed.

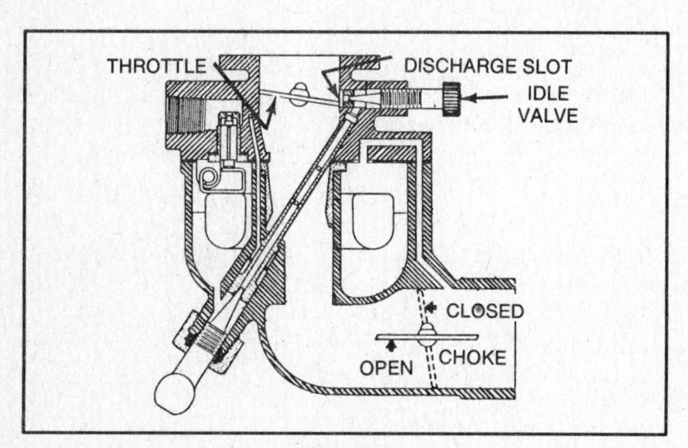

Fig. 20

The next problem is starting the engine in different temperatures and with different fuels. A butterfly, mounted on a shaft, is placed in the air horn. With this choke we can close, or almost close, the air horn and get a low pressure area in the venturi and throat, Fig. 20.

Thus, a rush of fuel is obtained from the nozzle with a relatively small amount of air. Even with low vaporization this extra rich mixture will give easy starting. Only a portion of the fuel will be consumed while choking, and a large portion will remain in the cylinder. This raw gasoline will dilute the crankcase oil and may even cause scuffing due to washing away of the oil film from between the piston rings and the cylinder wall. For this reason, prolonged choking should be avoided.

This now is our complete carburetor.

VACU-JET CARBURETORS

Now let us take a look at the Vacu-Jet system. Here the fuel tank is below the carburetor, so obviously the fuel will not flow by means of gravity. Therefore, the force of atmospheric pressure must be employed.

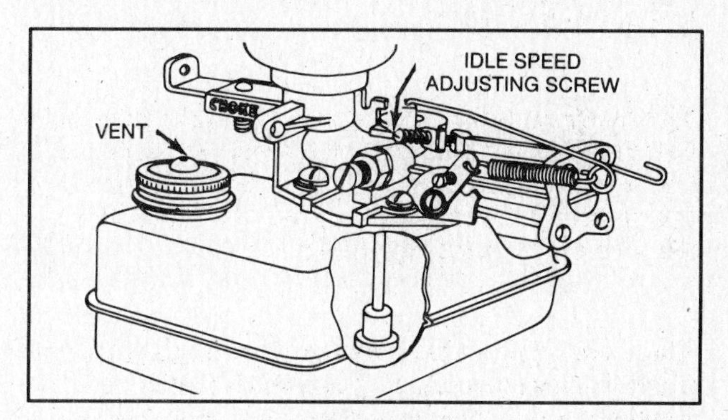

Fig. 21

Again we have a vent hole in the fuel tank cap to allow the pressure in the tank to remain constant. Now here is something important. Before adjusting the carburetor, pour in enough fuel to HALF fill the tank. The distance the fuel has to be lifted will affect the adjustment. At half full we have an average operating condition, and the adjustment will be satisfactory if the engine is run with the tank full or nearly empty.

As the piston goes down in the cylinder with both the intake valve and the throttle open, a low pressure area is created in the carburetor throat. A slight restriction is placed between the air horn and the carburetor throat at the choke. This helps to maintain the low pressure.

The difference in pressure between the tank and the carburetor throat forces the fuel up the fuel pipe, past the needle valve, through the two discharge holes. The throttle is relatively thick, so we have, in effect, a venturi at this point, thus aiding vaporization. A spiral is placed in the throat to help acceleration and also to help keep the engine from dying when the throttle is opened suddenly.

The amount of fuel at operating speed is metered by the needle valve and seat. Turning the needle valve in or out changes the setting until the proper mixture is obtained. This adjustment must always be done while the engine is running at operating speed, not at idle speed. While the needle valve may look like an idle valve due to its position, it is a true high speed mixture adjusting valve.

Since no accelerator pump is used on this carburetor and since many of these engines are used on lawn mowers where rapid acceleration is needed, the mixture should be rich. Turn the needle valve in until the engine begins to lose speed, indicating a lean mixture. Then, open the needle valve past the point of smooth operation until the engine just begins to run unevenly. Since this setting is made without load, the mixture should operate the engine satisfactorily under load.

These carburetors do not have an idle valve, but the mixture at idle speed is controlled in a different way. As the throttle closes to idle, the leading edge takes a position between the two discharge holes. The larger of the discharge holes is now in the high pressure area, and the flow of fuel through it will cease. The small hole will continue to discharge fuel but the amount will be metered by the hole size and will be in proportion to the reduced air flow. For this reason it is important that the small discharge hole be of the proper size. The needle valve will allow much more fuel to pass than should go through the small discharge hole. A number 68 drill can be used as a plug gauge to check the small hole. A number 56 drill can be used to check the larger hole. This can be done with the needle valve and seat removed, Fig. 22.

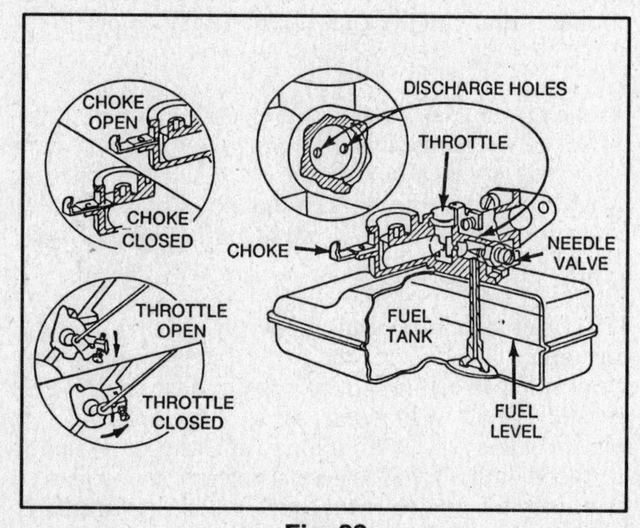

Fig. 22

You will notice a small section is milled out of the throttle where it meets the discharge hole. This concentrates the flow of air past the hole and assures good vaporization.

The idle speed adjusting screw should be set to obtain an idle speed of 1750 RPM. This may seem fast to people accustomed to auto engines, but it is necessary in order to have fast acceleration. It also helps cooling and lubrication. A slight unevenness may be noticed at idle speed, but this is normal and no readjustments of the needle valve should be made.

The choke is the sliding plate mounted at the outer end of the carburetor, Fig. 22 and 23. The choke is pushed in to close the air intake for starting but should be pulled out as soon as the engine starts. The use of this choke could be understood clearly. Many complaints of engine trouble, upon investigation prove to be nothing more than failure to properly use the choke, especially where the choke is operated by remote control. The choke must close fully.

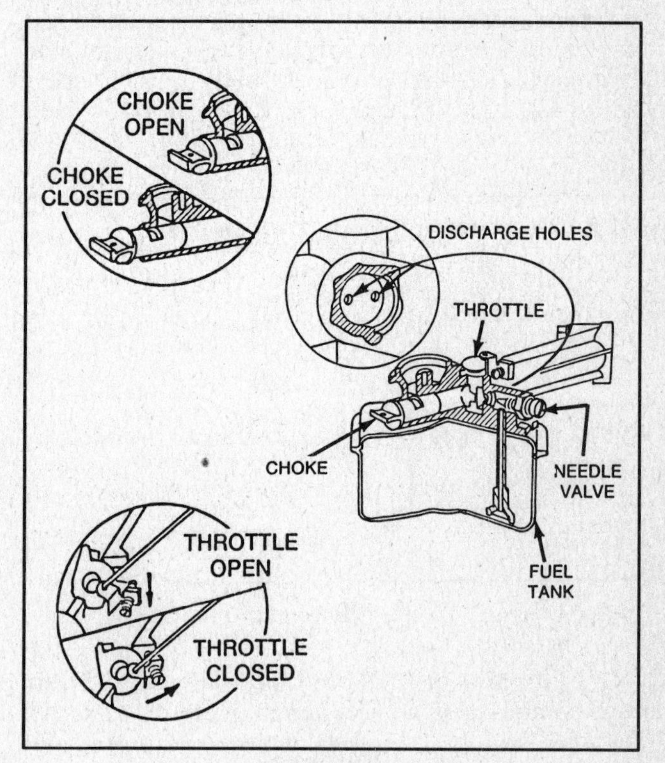

Fig. 23

The latest engines with Vacu-Jet carburetors incorporate a ball check in the fuel pipe which assures a steady flow of fuel to the needle valve and discharge holes.

PULSA-JET CARBURETORS

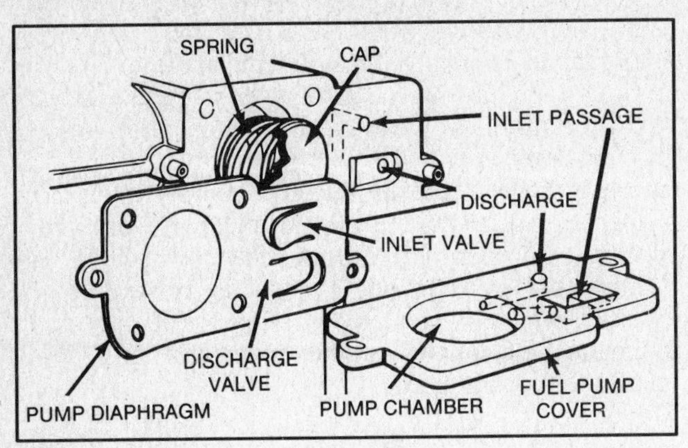

Fig. 24

The Pulsa-Jet is a full carburetor incorporating a diaphragm type fuel pump and a constant level fuel chamber.

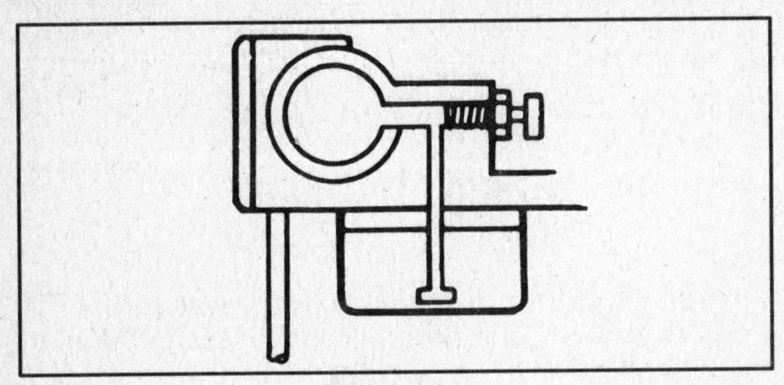

Fig. 25

The fuel tank, the fuel pump and the constant level fuel chamber serve the same functions as the gravity feed tank, the float and the float chamber of conventional "float type" carburetors.

This new design makes it possible to obtain just as much horsepower from the Pulsa-Jet carburetor as is obtained from more complex "float type" carburetors. This is due to the fact that the Pulsa-Jet provides a constant fuel level directly below the venturi as illustrated in Fig. 25 thru 28. With this design, very little fuel "lift" is required to draw gasoline into the venturi. The venturi can be made larger, permitting a greater volume of fuel-air mixture to flow into the engine with a consequent increase in horsepower.

Vacuum created in the carburetor elbow by the intake stroke of the piston pulls cap A and pump diaphragm B inward and compresses spring C, Fig. 26.

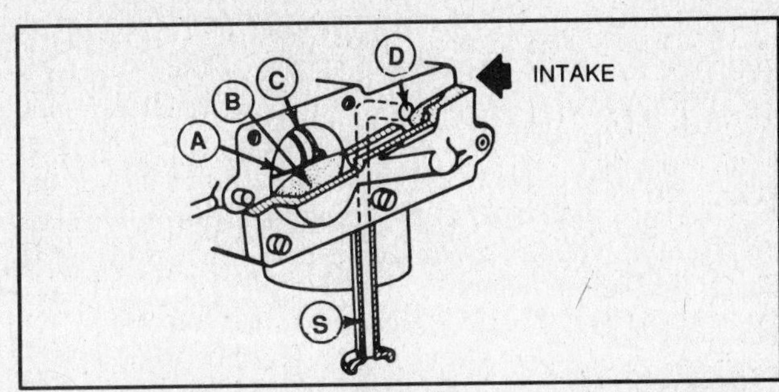

Fig. 26

The vacuum thus created on the "cover side" of the diaphragm pulls gasoline up suction pipe S and under intake valve D into the pocket created by the diaphragm moving inward, Fig. 26.

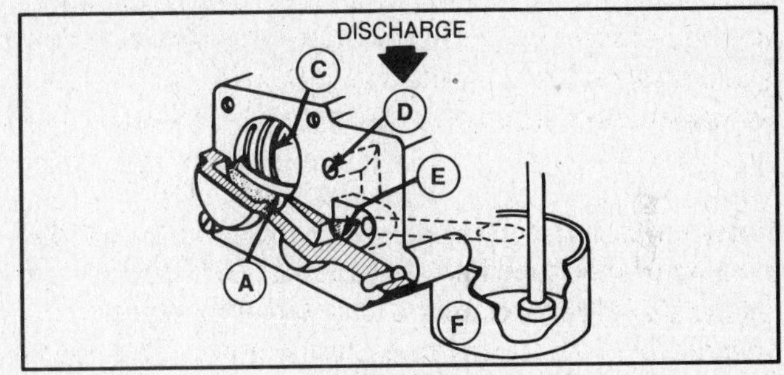

Fig. 27

When engine intake stroke is completed, spring C pushes plunger A outward. This causes gasoline in the pocket above the diaphragm to close inlet valve D and open discharge Valve E. The fuel is then pumped into fuel cup F, Fig. 27.

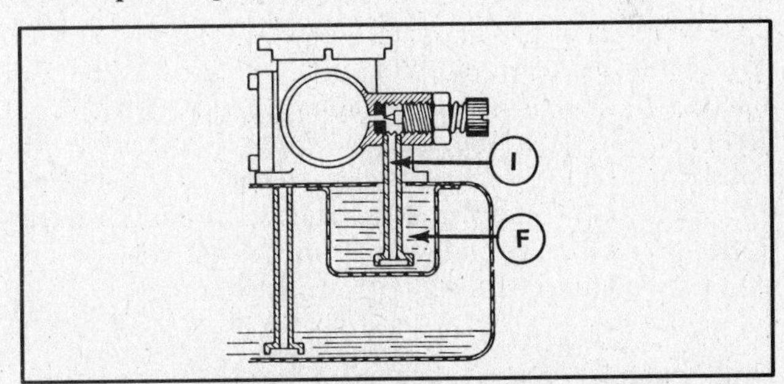

Fig. 28

On the next intake stroke the cycle is repeated and this pulsation of the diaphragm keeps the fuel cup full. Excess fuel flows back into the tank.

The venturi of the carburetor is connected to intake pipe I which draws gasoline from the fuel cup F, Fig. 28.

Since a constant level is maintained in the fuel cup, the engine gets a constant air-fuel ratio no matter what fuel level exists in the main tank.

From this point on, the carburetor operates and is adjusted in the same manner as is the Vacu-Jet carburetor except that the fuel tank does not have to be half full as in the Vacu-Jet. It can be full or almost empty and the adjustment will be the same since the fuel level in the small cup is always the same. There are no valve checks in the fuel pipes. The flaps on the diaphragm serve as valves.

Gas and Oil

This engine will operate satisfactorily on any gasoline intended for automotive use. A minimum of 77 octane is recommended. DO NOT MIX OIL WITH GASOLINE.

Use clean, fresh, lead-free gasoline. We recommend the use of Briggs & Stratton Gasoline Additive, part no. 5041. Purchase fuel in quantity that can be used within 30 days. This will assure fuel freshness and volatility tailored to the season. Leaded gasoline may be used if lead-free is not available. Use of lead-free gasoline results in fewer combustion deposits and longer valve life.

NOTE: We DO NOT recommend the use of gasoline which contains alcohol, such as gasohol. However, if gasoline with alcohol is used, it MUST NOT contain more than 10 percent Ethanol and MUST be removed from the engine during storage. DO NOT use gasoline containing Methanol.

We recommend the use of a high quality detergent oil classified "For Service SF, SE, SD, SC," such as Briggs & Stratton high quality detergent oil f10W/30 (part no. 272001) or 30 weight (part no. 100005). Detergent oils keep the engine cleaner and retard the formation of gum and varnish deposits. No special additives should be used with recommended oils.

AIR CLEANERS

The air entering the engine is important in engine performance and engine life. Power will decrease 3-1/2% for every 1,000 feet above sea level.

Power will also decrease 1% for every 10 degrees Fahrenheit above the standard temperature of 60 degrees Fahrenheit. In addition the ambient temperature is important in the cooling of the engine. (Ambient temperature is the temperature of the air immediately surrounding the engine.)

One of the reasons for engine wear is dirt that gets into the engine. When you consider that one of these 3 HP engines operating at 3600 RPM uses about 390 cubic feet of air an hour entering at the rate of about 24 miles an hour and that many such engines operate in very dusty conditions you can visualize the amount of dust and dirt that can enter an engine if it does not have an air cleaner or if the air cleaner is not functioning properly. If dirt gets past the air cleaner it enters the combustion chamber. Some may be blown out through the muffler but some may adhere to the cylinder where it creates ring wear or it may work down the walls into the crankcase where it causes wear on all the moving parts.

While speaking of the air cleaner we should remember to stress regular and proper maintenance of this important device.

Dirt that enters the engine through the breather also can wear out any engine. It is very important to see that the breather tube is in place on all engines.

Oil Foam No Spill Air Cleaners

For many years the oil bath air cleaner was considered the best, but Briggs & Stratton developed the Oil Foam "No Spill" Air Cleaner, Fig. 29. This cleaner employs a polyurethane element. The important patented feature is that it is sealed. Other cleaners are made with a polyurethane element but some are merely blocks of material with no seals of any kind thus allowing the air and dirt to bypass the element. The Briggs & Stratton cleaner uses the edges of the element as gaskets so that the air must pass through the element.

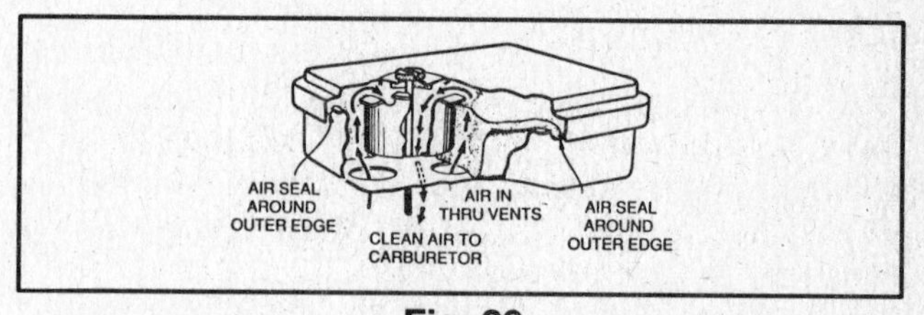

Fig. 29

There are two other important features of the "No Spill" cleaner. Oil will not spill if the engine is tilted. If the element becomes loaded with dirt, the air supply will be shut off so the engine will lose power or stop entirely. Then the element can be cleaned, re-oiled and reinstalled as good as new. The element must be re-oiled after cleaning.

IGNITION

A magneto in a sense consists of two simple circuits, one called a primary circuit and the other the secondary circuit. Both circuits have windings which surround the same iron core and the magnets in the flywheel or rotor act on both circuits. Current can be induced in each by changing the magnetism in or around the coils of the circuit.

The primary circuit has relatively few turns of heavy wire and the circuit includes a set of breaker points and a condenser, or an electronic switch.

The secondary circuit has a coil with many turns of lighter wire which are wound around the outside of the primary winding, and includes a spark plug. There are about 60 turns in the secondary to each turn in the primary.

A permanent magnet is mounted in the flywheel or rotor. As the flywheel rotates, the magnet is brought into proximity with the coil and core.

The Briggs & Stratton new ignition magneto system differs from ordinary magnetos in that the voltage produced is tailored to the needs of the engine, Fig. 30. The magnet used in this new type is a ceramic which develops a very high magnetic strength in a very short distance. The length of this magnet is 3/8" as compared with Alnico magnet length of 7/8".

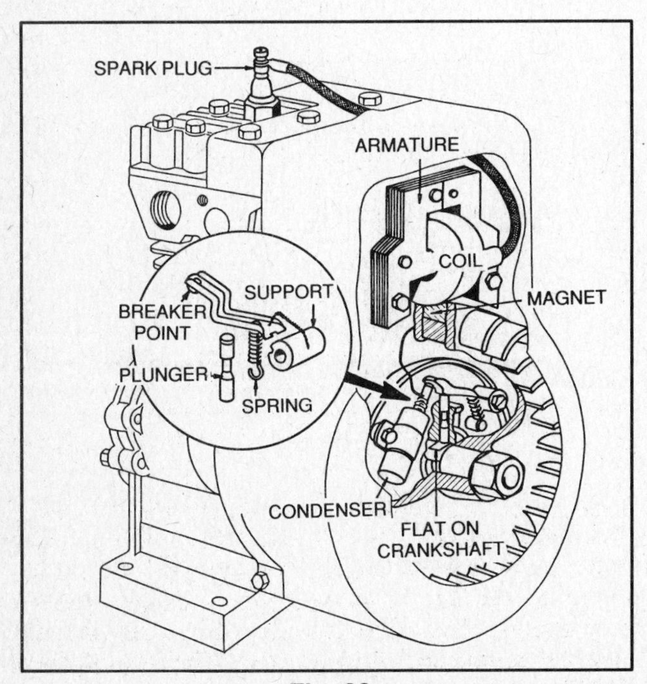

Fig. 30

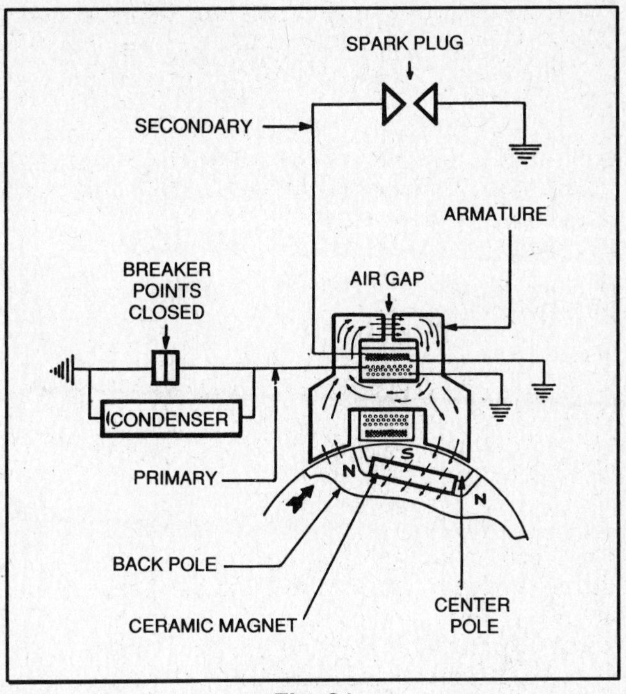

Fig. 31

Fig. 31 shows the flow of magnetism through the iron core of the coil as the magnet in the flywheel approaches the armature. The arrows indicate the direction of flow of the magnetic field. You will notice that there is no (or very little) magnetism flowing through the upper part of the core. This is because of the air gap at the top which causes a resistance. In this position our breaker points close.

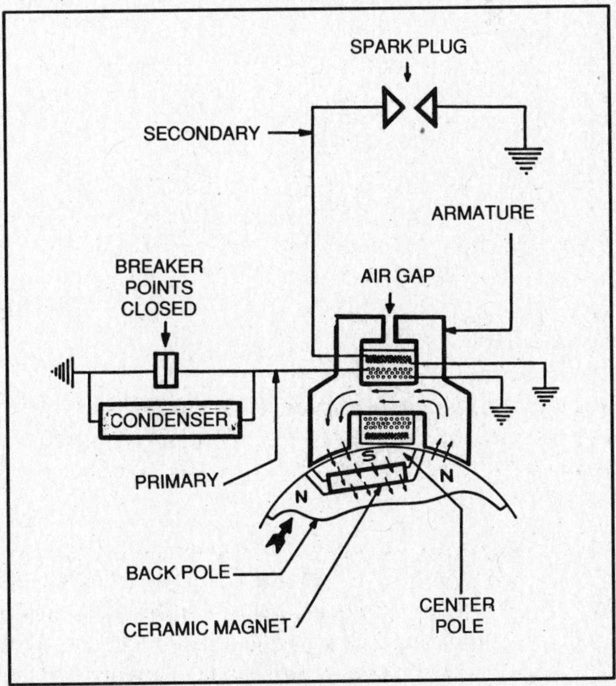

Fig. 32

The flywheel continues to rotate to the position shown in Fig. 32. The magnetism continues to flow in the same direction and magnitude through the center of the core because of primary current. However, the magnetism flows in an opposite direction through the outer portion of the core and through the top air gap because of the change of flywheel position. Since the shunt air gap provides a path for the flux from the armature legs and the core, the required current flow through the primary circuit is low, assuring long breaker point life.

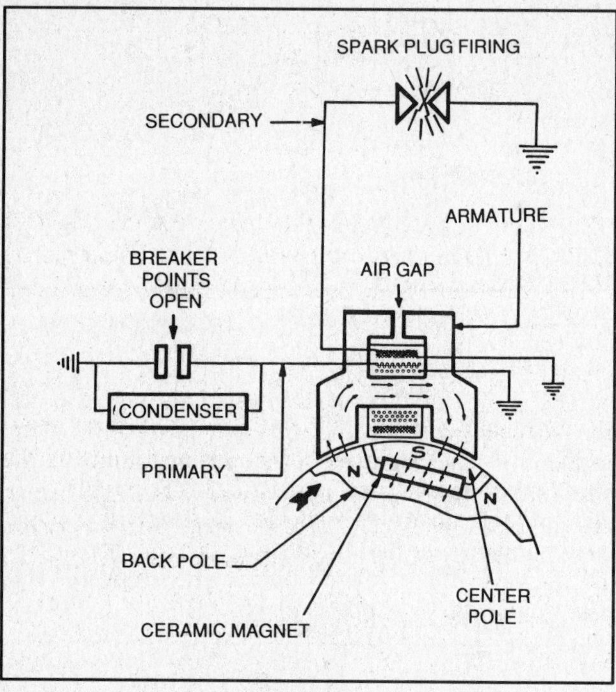

Fig. 33

At this position our breaker points open, the current stops flowing in the primary circuit and therefore the electromagnetic effect ceases. The magnetism instantaneously changes from the flow shown in Fig. 32 to that shown in Fig. 33. Note the opposite direction of the arrows indicating a complete reversal of magnetism which has happened so fast that the flywheel magnet has not had a chance to move any noticeable amount.

The rapid change in magnetism produces 170 volts in the primary winding. A voltage is also induced in the secondary but it is in proportion to the turns ratio, i.e., 60 to 1 or 10,000 volts. This voltage is more than ample to fire across the spark plug electrodes. This rapid magnetism change is very short and therefore the flow of current across the spark plug gap is as long as necessary, but short enough to afford long electrode life. Thus we achieve our aims of full power plus long life dependability.

Now, we haven't said much about one thing, the condenser. The condenser is a sort of safety valve on the primary circuit. It is connected across the breaker points to prevent the circuit from jumping the breaker point gap, arcing, as it is called.

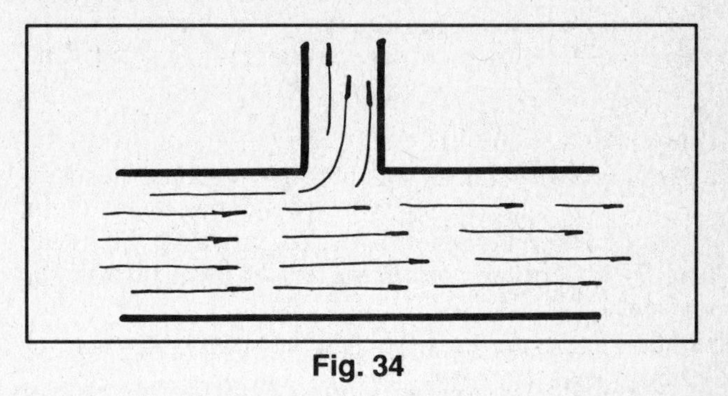

Fig. 34

Let us explain it this way. Suppose we had a large pipe through which we forced water at a high rate of speed, Fig. 34. This corresponds to our primary circuit. Coming out of the large pipe is a much smaller pipe. This is our secondary circuit. As long as the large pipe is unobstructed, the water is free to flow and very little will flow out through the small pipe.

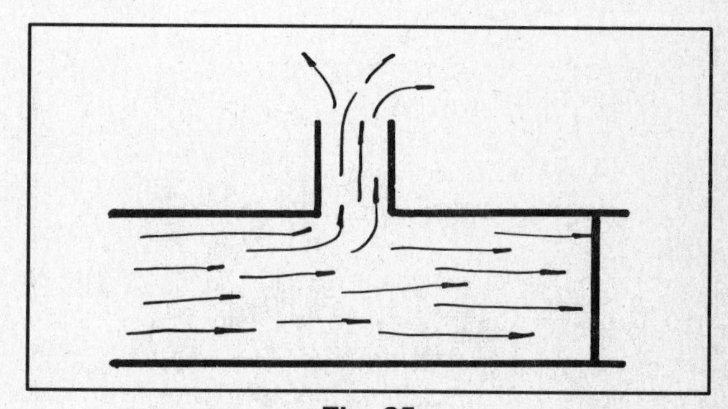

Fig. 35

Now suppose we could suddenly shut off the large pipe, Fig. 35. The water will stop flowing through the large pipe, but the inertia of the water back in the large pipe will force the water out through the small pipe at a tremendous velocity until the pressure is dissipated. This corresponds to the high voltage in our secondary circuit.

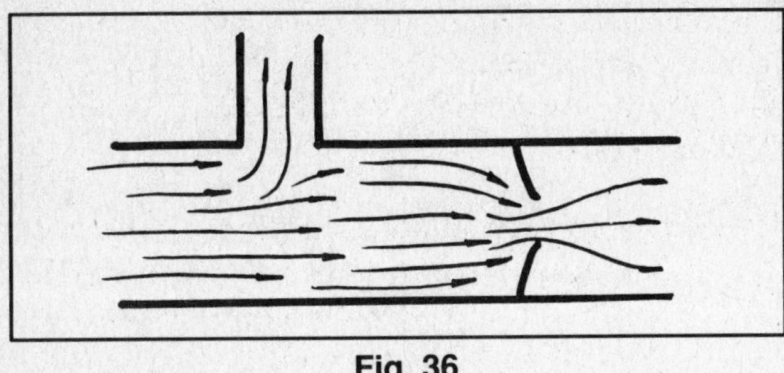

Fig. 36

However, suppose our valve could not stand the pressure and would break, Fig. 36. This would correspond to arcing across the breaker points. The flow would continue through the large pipe, and very little would flow through the small pipe.

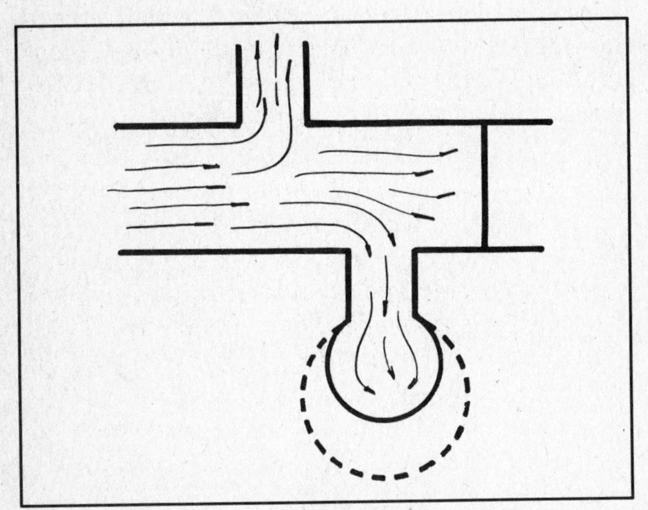

Fig. 37

If we put another small pipe near the valve, Fig. 37, and over the end place a strong rubber bag, we have the equivalent to our condenser. Thus, when we close our valve, the pressure on the valve would be partially absorbed by the rubber bag, the valve would not break and water would stream out the small pipe where we want it to go.

The rubber bag must be of the proper size and strength. If it is too small, it will not take up enough of the pressure and the valve will break anyway. If it is too large, it will hold too much water, and there will not be enough pressure to force the water out through the small pipe.

The same thing applies to the condenser. The proper capacity should be about .2 microfarads or .16 to .24. This is just right to prevent arcing at the points and still cause the primary current to stop flowing.

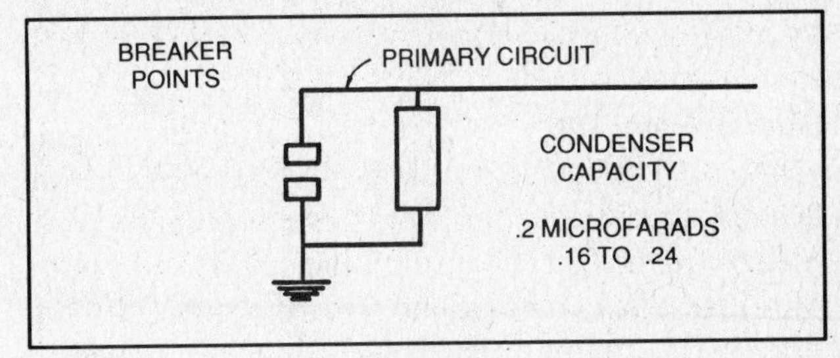

Fig. 38

Spark plug cables are molded into the coil so that moisture cannot short out the spark as could happen on older coils that had an open connection between coil and spark plug cable.

We would like to point out that at one time some mechanics would try to judge the condition of the magneto system by the brightness and the noise or "snap" of the spark. This is not a good criterion as you can quickly demonstrate by using a resistor type spark plug and a regular type spark plug. Lay them on top of the cylinder head and connect the spark plug cable to first one and then the other. Spin the flywheel and notice the spark across the electrodes. You will see that the spark across the resistor plug will be much thinner and makes less noise and yet we know that engines run very well on these plugs and spark plug cable.

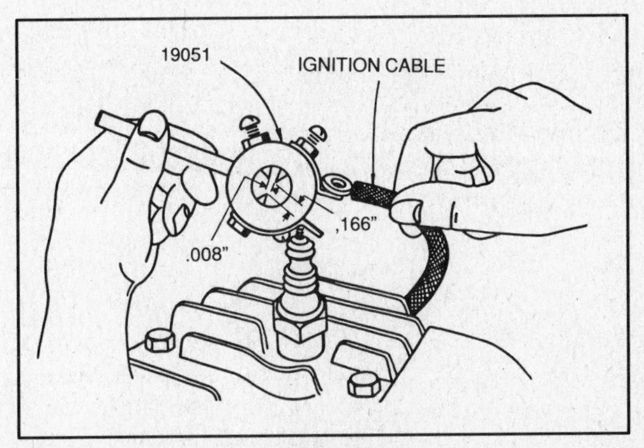

Fig. 39

14

The magneto can be tested by placing the spark tester, #19051, between the ignition cable and the spark plug as shown in Fig. 39. Then spin the flywheel vigorously. The spark should jump the .166" gap.

This test can also be performed with the engine running but the cable should be shifted quickly from spark plug to tester or from tester to spark plug. Damage to the coil can result if the engine spins more than just a few revolutions with the cable disconnected. This running test should not be performed on the Models 9, 14, 19, 23 with the Magnamatic ignition system.

Through the years the magneto systems on the various Briggs & Stratton engines have differed somewhat in the design of the parts. However, the basic principle of a primary and a secondary circuit is used in all models.

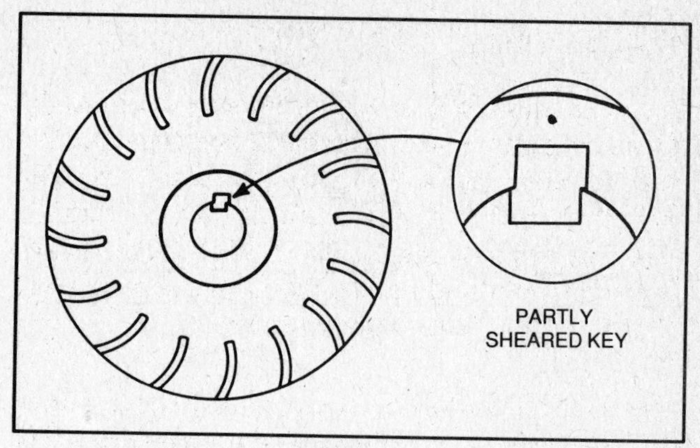

Fig. 40

On small engines, be sure that the flywheel key is not partially sheared as this can cause the timing to be off enough to result in hard starting. Do not, however, use a steel key. The soft metal key is used so that if the flywheel should become loose the key will be sheared, allowing the flywheel to shift and stop the engine before any further damage occurs. Remember that the flywheel key is a locator and not a driver.

"EASY-SPIN®" STARTING

Good compression is necessary in order to obtain the full horsepower of the engine but at the same time this makes it more difficult to turn the engine over fast enough to start it. The resistance of compression is most noticeable during the first few revolutions after which the momentum of the flywheel and crankshaft help until firing starts in the cylinder.

In order to reduce this resistance during starting time, various types of compression releases have been used. However, none proved entirely satisfactory until Briggs & Stratton developed the "Easy Spin®" starting system. This is so simple one wonders why it was never thought of before.

The intake lobe on the cam gear is ground with a small ramp which holds the intake valve open 1/100 of an inch for a tiny fraction of the compression stroke. At slow starting speed the interval of time that the valve is open is relatively long and therefore enough air escapes to noticeably reduce the compression. However, at operating speeds the interval of time is so short that there is practically no escape and therefore horsepower is unimpaired. Actually at 3600 RPM the valve is opened for a mere 1/200 of a second. In all other respects, the valves operate as in any other four stroke cycle engine.

The force required to start an engine is reduced by 50% with "Easy Spin®" and would be noticed most by a person who has difficulty starting the ordinary engine.

One thing we must remember. When testing the compression of "Easy Spin®" engines one must spin the flywheel "backward", in the opposite direction to normal rotation. This will bring the compression stroke on the opposite side of the cam lobe and allow you to feel the compression.

GOVERNING

While some people think that a governor on an engine is to prevent overspeeding, the real purpose in the small engine field is to maintain a desired speed regardless of load. With a fixed throttle position, the engine could speed up if the load was lightened; if the load is increased the engine would slow down or even stop.

A governor on the other hand will close the throttle if the load is lightened or open the throttle to obtain more power if the load is increased.

Basically, governors consist of two types - the pneumatic or air vane type, Fig. 41 and the mechanical or flyball weight type, Fig. 42.

The pneumatic governor as illustrated in Fig. 41 is operated by the force of the air from the flywheel fins. When the engine is running, the air from the fins pushes against the air vane. The air vane is connected to the carburetor throttle by means of a link. The force and movement of these parts tends to close the carburetor and thus slow down the engine speed.

Opposed to this is the governor spring which tends to pull the opposite way, opening the throttle. This spring is usually connected to an adjustable control of some kind so that the tension on the spring can be changed at the will of the operator. Increasing the tension of the spring will increase the engine speed. Decreasing the tension will lower the engine speed. The point at which the pull of the spring equals the force of the air vane is called the “governed speed”.

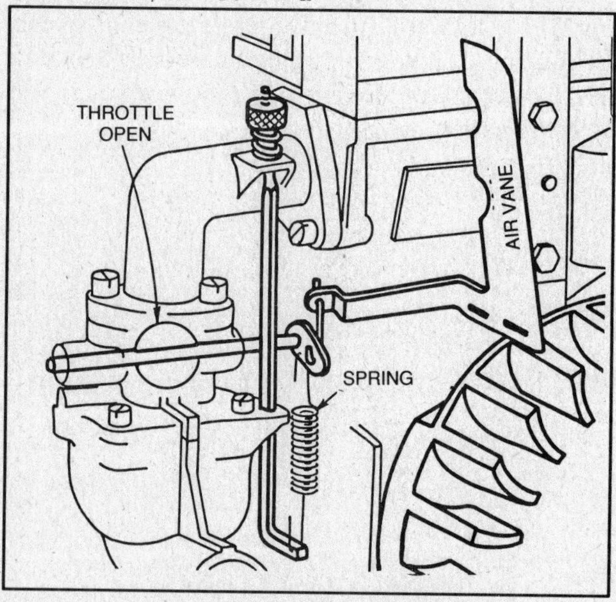

ENGINE NOT RUNNING

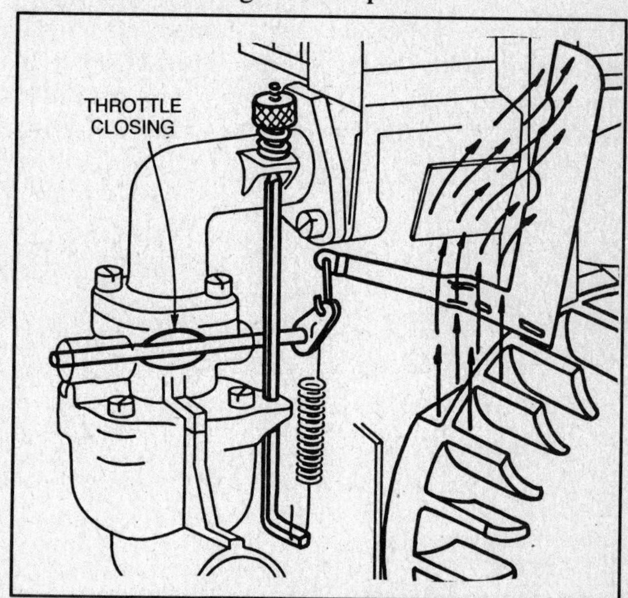

ENGINE RUNNING

Fig. 41

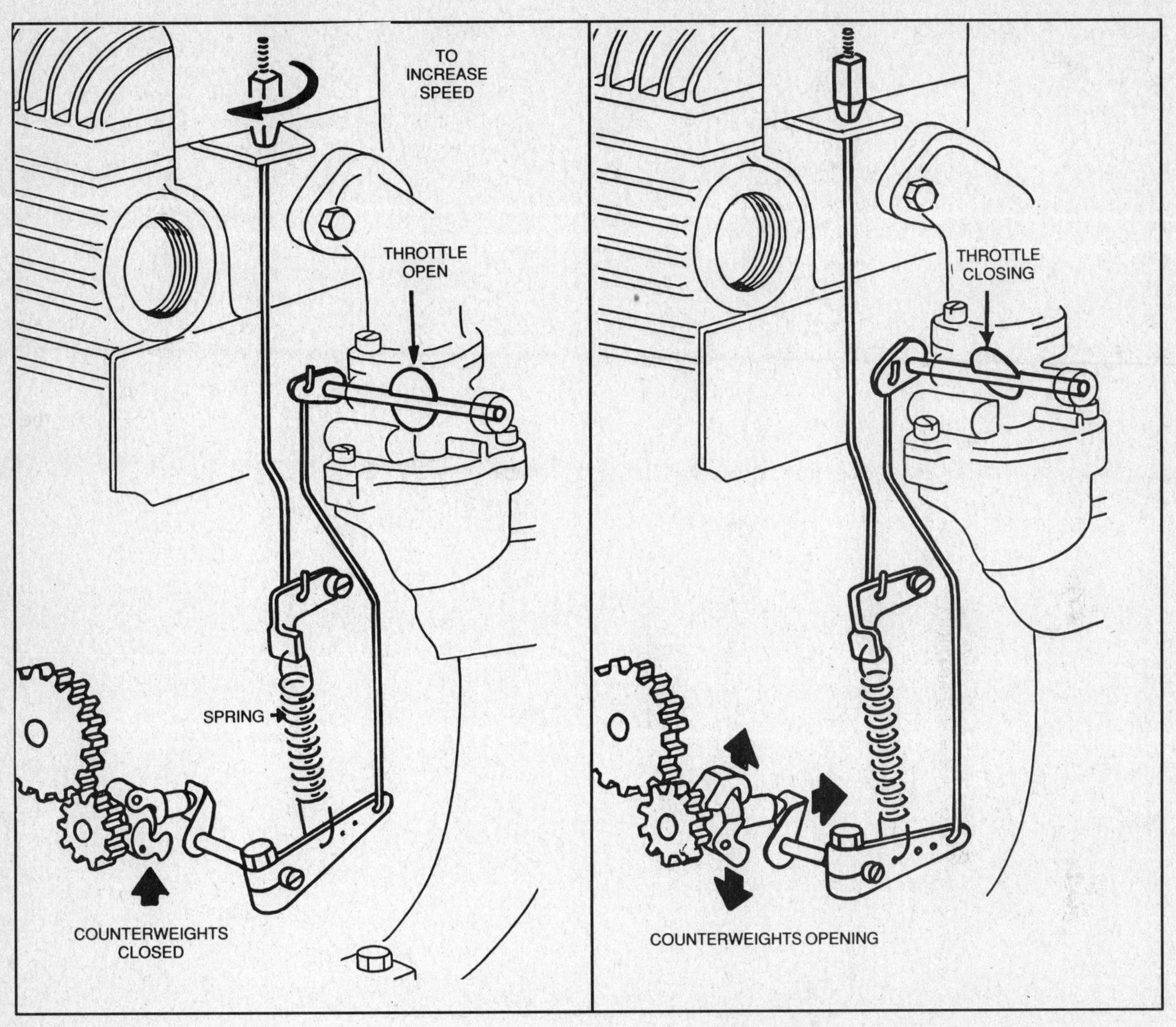

Fig. 42

The mechanical governor, Fig. 42, works in a similar manner except that instead of the force of the air blowing against the vane, we have the centrifugal force of flyball weights opposing the governor spring.

In either case, operation is the same. As the load on the engine increases, the engine will start to slow down. As soon as this happens, the centrifugal force of the flyball weights lessens. This allows the governor spring to pull the throttle open wider increasing the horsepower to compensate for the increased load and thus maintain the desired governed speed.

If the load on the engine lessens, the engine starts to speed up.This will increase the pressure of the centrifugal force and the spring will be stretched a little farther thus closing the throttle and reducing the engine power. A properly functioning governor will maintain this desired governed speed within fairly close limits.

In general, an engine that has good compression, carburetion, and ignition will operate efficiently. However, dirt or neglect can ruin an engine quickly. It should be the duty, therefore, of every salesman or repairman to instruct the customer in the proper operation and care of the engine so that he will obtain the long service life that is built into the engine at the factory.